4/E 72373

2650 San Francisco

GRAPHICS FOR ENGINEERS

WARREN J. LUZADDER, P.E.

Professor of Engineering Graphics, Purdue University.
Member, American Society for Engineering Education,
National Society of Professional Engineers, Society of
American Military Engineers, etc.

PRENTICE-HALL, INC. *Englewood Cliffs, N.J.* 1957

PRINTED IN THE UNITED STATES OF AMERICA

36345

Preface

This book has been written to fulfill the needs of a new era in engineering education, which began with the phenomenal upsurge of technological advancement in the early years of World War II. At that time professional engineers found themselves working side by side with theoretical scientists, adapting newly discovered scientific principles to the development of atomic energy, radar, and so forth. Since the war, some engineers have continued to work closely with theoretical scientists, but now their efforts are usually devoted to the creation and development of devices and structures that are useful to the civilian population in peace time.

Competition between industrial organizations has been keen, as each organization has striven for supremacy in its field. Realizing that the survival of an industrial organization often depends upon technological improvement in products and production methods, administrators are calling upon their engineers to use their creative ability and scientific knowledge to the utmost to develop new ideas for useful mechanisms and to improve existing ones. In order to make the best use of the short supply of engineering manpower, much of their detail work has been placed in the hands of technical assistants.

Engineering educators recognize that conditions have changed, and have revised curricula to meet the needs of the profession in the future. The Report on Evaluation of Engineering Education prepared by the Committee on Evaluation of Engineering Education of the ASEE in 1955 states, concerning engineering graphics:

> Graphical expression is both a form of communication and a means for analysis and synthesis. The extent to which it is successful for these purposes is a measure of its professional usefulness. Its value as a skill alone does not justify its inclusion in a curriculum. The emphasis should be on spatial visualization, experience in creative thinking, and the ability to convey ideas, especially by freehand sketching, which is the normal mode of expression in the initial stages of creative work. Though the engineer may only supervise the preparation of the drawings required to execute his designs, he can hardly be expected to do this effectively unless he himself is thoroughly familiar with graphical communication.

This report recognizes the change of emphasis that has taken place already in the basic engineering graphics courses in our more progressive schools of engineering. The art of making engineering drawings has been almost ignored for some time, and more attention has been given to developing the ability to visualize spatial conditions, to solve problems by graphical methods, and to use graphical forms of representation, prepared by freehand sketching, as a means of communication.

In this book, emphasis has been placed upon engineering geometry, multiview representation, basic descriptive geometry, and freehand sketching, with particular attention being given to perspective pictorials, and graphical methods for solving engineering problems. Also important is the presentation of the basic material needed to understand communication drawings in the different fields of engineering.

The various chapters covering multiview drawing (orthographic projection) will be found to cover fully all of the fundamentals of projection. With a full knowledge of these basic principles, the student should be able to understand completely the graphical methods of representing shapes and to solve problems by using projection. Descriptive geometry is presented along with multiview projection, of which it is logically a part. The material as presented will satisfy the needs of most design engineers. Aeronautical engineers and others who plan to enter specialized fields of design should expect to take a formal course in descriptive geometry.

Since the engineering profession has at last recognized the importance of freehand pictorial sketching, full coverage has been given to the methods and aids that can be used for preparing satisfactory pictorial representations. Some of these aids can be abandoned as the sketcher becomes proficient, for it must be remembered that sketching must be done rapidly when one is doing creative work. Sketches follow one after another in quick succession as ideas are developed or changed.

The chapter on communication drawings helps to explain them as they are used in the various fields of engineering. Additional material can be found in the chapters covering dimensioning and fasteners. These latter chapters are complete enough to enable a student to prepare a satisfactory working drawing, either detail or assembly, as may be assigned. Although charts and graphs can also be considered forms of communication drawings, it was considered desirable to place the information about them in a special chapter.

So the student can appreciate the usefulness of graphics in solving problems that arise in engineering, some coverage of vector geometry, graphical calculus, and simple alignment charts has been included. Since this material is new to most engineering drawing courses, the beginning student was kept in mind. The written material and illustrations should be within the beginners comprehension and the problems as they are presented should be understood by any who have had a high school physics course. Problems that might require some training in one or more of the engineering sciences have been avoided.

Every teacher should offer his students some experience in creative thinking. For this purpose some problems have been given at the end of the chapter covering pictorial sketching. Additional problems may be created by requiring the redesign of some existing part of a mechanism as given in the problem sections of other chapters of the text.

Drafting practices as they have developed in some fields have been purposely omitted. Those persons who are interested in preparing structural drawings, architectural plans, and maps should consult the author's text, *Fundamentals of Engineering Drawing*, 3rd edition.

The reading material, illustrations, and problems have been made to conform to the latest ASA (American Standards Association) and SAE (Society of Automotive Engineers) standards that were available at the time of going to press. Some attention has been given to other standards, and where there appeared to be a definite trend towards the use of a particular practice, it has been recognized in this text. For instance, since the aeronautical and automotive industries have adopted the decimal-inch system for dimensioning, many of the illustrations and some of the problems have been dimensioned using this system.

Acknowledgment must be made for the assistance of Professors C. J. Rogers and R. C. Carpenter of Purdue University, Department of Engineering Graphics. Professor Rogers prepared problems for the chapter covering basic descriptive geometry, and Professor Carpenter prepared some of the illustrations for pictorial sketching.

The author wishes to express his appreciation for the helpful criticism and sound suggestions made by his close friend, Major Robert H. Hammond of the United States Military Academy, who read portions of the manuscript and checked many of the problems.

Finally, special acknowledgment must be made here for the kindness of Professor Frank J. Burns of the Newark College of Engineering, who took time from his work to read the entire manuscript. Many of Professor Burns' suggestions have been incorporated in this text.

W. J. LUZADDER

Purdue University
West Lafayette, Indiana.

Contents

Appendix Contents

1

Introduction

An engineer of professional caliber must be dedicated to creating structures and products for the benefit of his fellow men. This requires that he bring together knowledge of the arts of production and an understanding of the sciences, and that he add his own original thinking. For most improvements in the design and operation of machines and structures are produced by imaginations sparked with desire to change and improve existing ways of producing something for which there is a need. The imagination, freely exercised, can ultimately create entirely new products.

The rapid advance of scientific knowledge and the shortage of professionally trained men has brought about changes in the place and the work expected of the engineer in an industrial organization. He has become a decidedly more creative person, who must be able to visualize and strengthen the space relationship and movement of dim images of ideas.

Since an engineer may frequently have to prepare preliminary design drawings and to direct the making of the working (shop) drawings which follow, he should have a complete understanding of the principles of orthographic projection and a knowledge of conventional practices and dimensioning. Without this knowledge he is in no position to assume the professional responsibilities that may be placed upon him by his superiors and by the laws of his state.

For a full and complete exchange of ideas with others, the engineer must be proficient in the three means of communication that are at his disposal; (1) English; both written and oral, (2) symbols; as used in the basic sciences, and, (3) engineering graphics.

In past years emphasis has been placed upon the communication forms of graphics, such as working drawings for the fabrication and erection of structures and graphical representations for conveying semi-technical information to associates. The engineers of today and of the

1

future must all be given more training in the art of sketching so they will be fully capable of "thinking with a pencil."

At first ideas may be presented with sketches in either orthographic or pictorial form. Orthographic and pictorial sketches follow one after another as problems are encountered and possible solutions are considered. Sketch making continues into the preliminary design stages, for the engineer must usually serve as both planner and director. In so doing, he uses sketches to exchange ideas around the conference table and to present instructions to others. One need not have an artist's training to produce satisfactory engineering sketches, for the technical sketcher need only be able to draw fairly straight lines and judge proportions reasonably well.

Proficiency in applying the principles of orthographic projection leads to easy graphical methods of solving space problems such as the determination of the clearance distance between members of a structure, the distance from a point to a plane, or the true angle between plane surfaces.

Since there are many problems arising in engineering design where a graphical method for solution is faster and much less laborious than its mathematical counterpart, engineering students as well as professional men should have some knowledge of both vector geometry and graphical calculus. Noncoplanar or three dimensional force problems are solved by applying the principles of orthographic drawing. Graphical integration and differentiation are particularly desirable for problems where only empirical data are available or where values are shown by mechanically produced curves.

A study of engineering graphics offers an insight into the engineer's methods of attacking his problems. Its lessons teach the importance of accuracy, exactness, and positiveness both in representation and in the solution of problems. Finally, it tends to develop ability to visualize space conditions as they arise in the creation of nonexisting structures and to analyze situations and recognize relationships when solving problems.

2

Drawing Equipment and
Use of Instruments

2.1. The instruments and materials needed for making ordinary engineering drawings are shown in Fig. 2.1. The instruments in the plush-lined case should be particularly well made and easy to service, for with cheap, inferior ones, it is often difficult to produce accurate drawings of professional quality.

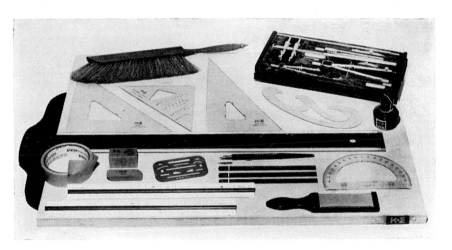

Fig. 2.1.   Essential drafting equipment.

2.2. List of equipment and materials. The following list is a practical selection of equipment and materials necessary for making pencil drawings and ink tracings.

3

(1) Case of drawing instruments.
(2) Drawing board.
(3) T-square.
*(4) 45° triangle.
(5) 10″ 30°–60° triangle.
(6) French curve.
(7) Scales (see Sec. 2.15).
(8) Drawing pencils.
(9) Pencil pointer (file or sandpaper pad).
(10) Thumb tacks, brad machine, or Scotch tape
(11) Pencil eraser.
(12) Cleaning eraser.
(13) Erasing shield.
(14) Dusting brush.
(15) Bottle of black waterproof drawing ink.

(16) Pen wiper.
(17) Penholder.
(18) Lettering pens.
(19) Protractor.
(20) Pad of sketching paper (plain or ruled).
(21) Drawing paper.
(22) Tracing paper.
(23) Tracing cloth.

To these may be added the following useful items:

(24) Piece of soapstone.
(25) Ink-bottle holder.
(26) Tack lifter.
(27) Slide rule.

2.3. The set of instruments. A standard set of drawing instruments in a velvet-lined case and an alternative set, which is capable of fulfilling the needs of most engineers, are shown in Figs. 2.1 and 2.2 respectively.

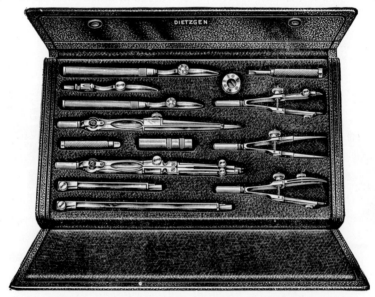

Fig. 2.2. A standard set of drawing instruments.

2.4. Pencils. The student and professional man should be equipped with a selection of good, well-sharpened pencils with leads of various

---

* A 6″ 45° Braddock Lettering Triangle, which may be used as either a triangle or a lettering instrument, may be substituted for this item.

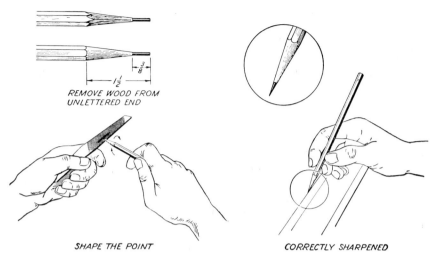

SHAPE THE POINT   CORRECTLY SHARPENED

Fig. 2.3.   Conical point.

degrees of hardness such as: 9*H*, 8*H*,
7*H*, and 6*H* (hard); 5*H* and 4*H* (medium
hard); 3*H* and 2*H* (medium); and *H* and
F (medium soft).

The grade of pencil to be used for
various purposes depends upon the type
of line desired, the kind of paper employed, and the humidity, which affects
the surface of the paper. Standards for
line quality usually will govern. As a
minimum, however, the student should
have available a 6*H* pencil for the light
construction lines in layout work where
accuracy is required, a 4*H* for repencil-
ing light finished lines (dimension lines,
center lines and invisible object lines), a
2*H* for visible object lines, and an *F* or *H*
for all lettering and freehand work.

2.5. Pointing the pencil. Many
persons prefer the conical point for general
use (Fig. 2.3), while others find the wedge
point more suitable for straight-line work,
as it requires less sharpening and makes a
denser line (Fig. 2.4).

When sharpening a pencil, the wood
should be cut away (on the unlettered
end) with a knife or a pencil sharpener equipped with draftsman's

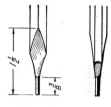

REMOVE WOOD FROM
UNLETTERED END

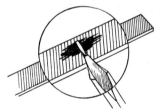

SHAPE THE POINT

CORRECTLY SHARPENED

Fig. 2.4.   Wedge point.

cutters. About $\frac{3}{8}$ inch of the lead should be exposed and should form a cut, including the wood, about $1\frac{1}{2}$ inches long. The lead then should be shaped to a conical point on the pointer (file or sandpaper pad). This is done by holding the file stationary in the left hand and drawing

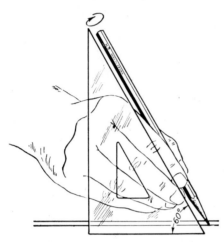

the lead toward the handle while rotating the pencil against the movement (Fig. 2.3). All strokes should be made in the same manner, a new grip being taken each time so that each stroke starts with the pencil in the same rotated position as at the end of the preceding stroke.

2.6. Drawing pencil lines. Pencil lines should be sharp and uniform along their entire length, and sufficiently distinct to fulfill their ultimate purposes. Construction lines (preliminary lines) should be drawn *very* lightly so that they may be easily erased.

Fig. 2.5. Using the pencil.

Finished lines should be made boldly and distinctly, so that there will be definite contrast between visible and invisible object lines and auxiliary lines, such as dimension lines, center lines, and section lines. To give this contrast, which is necessary for clearness and ease in reading, object lines should be of medium width and very black, invisible lines black and not so wide, and auxiliary lines dark and thin.

When drawing a line, the pencil should be inclined slightly (about

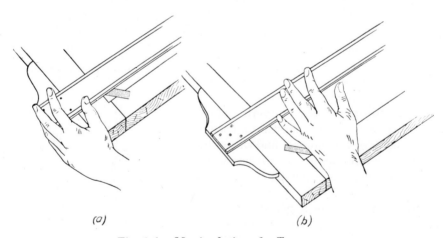

(a)   (b)

Fig. 2.6.   Manipulating the T-square.

60 degrees) in the direction in which the line is being drawn (Fig. 2.5). The pencil should be "pulled" (never pushed) at the same inclination for the full length of the line. If it is rotated (twirled) slowly between the fingers as the line is drawn, a symmetrical point will be maintained and a straight uniform line will be insured.

2.7. Placing and fastening the paper. For accuracy and ease in manipulating the T-square, the drawing paper should be located well up on the board and near the left-hand edge. The lower edge of the sheet (if plain) or the lower border line (if printed) should be aligned along the working edge of the T-square before the sheet is fastened down at all four corners with thumb tacks, Scotch tape, or staples.

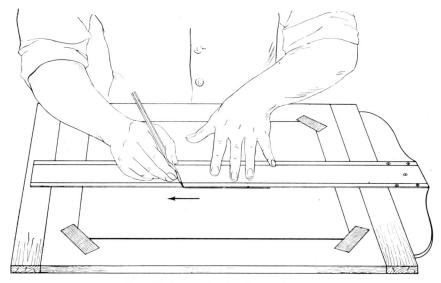

*Fig. 2.7.   **Drawing horizontal lines.***

2.8. The T-square. The T-square is used primarily for drawing horizontal lines and for guiding the triangles when drawing vertical and inclined lines. It is manipulated by sliding the working edge (inner face) of the head along the left edge of the board until the blade is in the required position. The left hand then should be shifted to a position near the center of the blade to hold it in place and to prevent its deflection while drawing the line. Experienced draftsmen hold the T-square, as shown in Fig. 2.6(*b*), with the fingers pressing on the blade and the thumb on the paper. Small adjustments may be made with the hand in this position by sliding the blade with the fingers.

Horizontal lines are drawn from left to right along the upper edge of the T-square (Fig. 2.7). (*Exception:* left-handed persons should use the T-square head at the right side of the board and draw from right to left.)

While drawing the line, the ruling hand should slide along the blade on the little finger.

2.9. The triangles.   The 45° and the 30° × 60° triangles are the ones commonly used for ordinary work (Fig. 2.8).

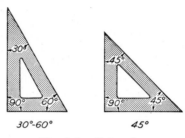

30°-60°   45°

Fig. 2.8.   Triangles.

2.10. Vertical lines.   Vertical lines are drawn upward along the vertical leg of a triangle whose other (horizontal) leg is supported and guided by the T-square blade.   The blade is held in position with the palm and thumb of the left hand, and the triangle is adjusted and held

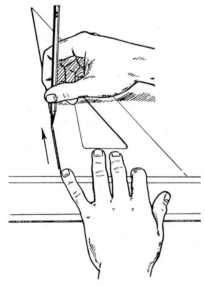

Fig. 2.9.   Drawing vertical lines.

by the fingers as shown in Fig. 2.9. In the case of a right-handed person, the triangle should be to the right of the line to be drawn.

Either the 30° × 60° or the 45° triangle may be used since both triangles have a right angle. However, the 30° × 60° is generally preferred because it usually has a longer perpendicular leg.

2.11. Inclined lines.   Triangles also are used for drawing inclined lines.   Lines that make angles of 30°, 45°, or 60° with the horizontal may be drawn with the 30° × 60° or the 45° triangle in combination with the T-square, as shown in Fig. 2.10.   If the two triangles are combined, lines that make 15° or a multiple of 15° may be drawn with the horizontal.

Several possible arrangements and the angles that result are shown in Fig. 2.11.

The triangles used singly or in combination offer a useful method for dividing a circle into four, six, eight, twelve, or twenty-four equal parts. For angles other than those divisible by 15, a protractor must be used.

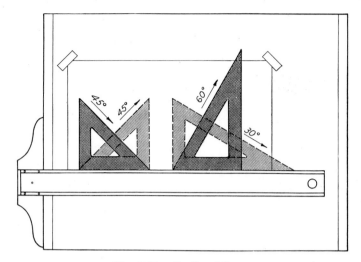

Fig. 2.10.   Inclined lines.

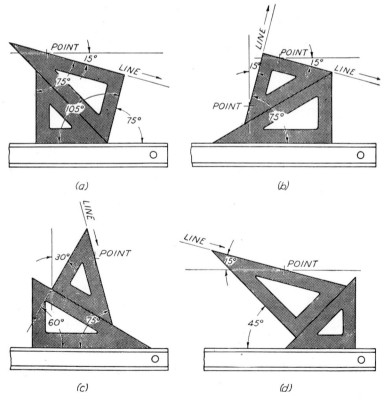

Fig. 2.11.   Drawing inclined lines with triangles.

2.12. Parallel lines. The triangles are used in combination to draw a line parallel to a given line. To draw such a line, place a ruling edge of a triangle, supported by a T-square or another triangle, along the given line; then slip the triangle, as shown in Fig. 2.12, to the required position and draw the parallel line along the same ruling edge that previously coincided with the given line.

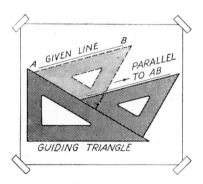

2.13. Perpendicular lines. Either the sliding triangle method (Fig. 2.13a) or the revolved triangle method (Fig. 2.13b) may be used to draw a line perpendicular to a given line. When using the sliding triangle method, adjust to the given line a side of a triangle that is adjacent to the right angle.

Fig. 2.12. To draw a line parallel to a given line.

Guide the side opposite the right angle with a second triangle as shown in Fig. 2.13(a); then slide the first triangle along the guiding triangle until it is in the required position for drawing the perpendicular along the other edge adjacent to the right angle.

Although the revolved triangle method is not so quickly done, it is widely used (Fig. 2.13b). To draw a perpendicular using this method,

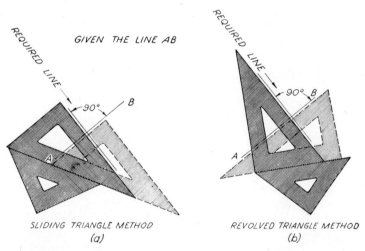

Fig. 2.13.   To draw a line perpendicular to another line.

align along the given line the hypotenuse of a triangle, one leg of which is guided by the T-square or another triangle, then hold the guiding member in position and revolve the triangle about the right angle until the other leg is against the guiding edge. The new position of the hypotenuse will be perpendicular to its previous location along the given line and, when moved to the required position, may be used as a ruling edge for the desired perpendicular.

2.14. Inclined lines making 15°, 30°, 45°, 60°, or 75° with an oblique line. A line making with an oblique line an angle equal to any angle of a triangle may be drawn with the triangles. The two methods previously discussed for drawing perpendicular lines are applicable with slight modifications. To draw an oblique line using the revolved triangle method (Fig. 2.14a), adjust along the given line the edge that is opposite the required angle, then revolve the triangle about the required angle, slide it into position, and draw the required line along the side opposite the required angle.

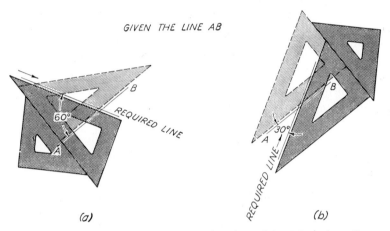

GIVEN THE LINE AB

60°
REQUIRED LINE
A
B

30°
A
B
REQUIRED LINE

(a)　　　　　(b)

Fig. 2.14. *To draw lines making 30°, 45°, or 60° with a given line.*

To use the sliding triangle method (Fig. 2.14b), adjust to the given line one of the edges adjacent to the required angle, and guide the side opposite the required angle with a straight edge; then slide the triangle into position and draw the required line along the other adjacent side.

To draw a line making 75° with a given line, place the triangles together so that the sum of a pair of adjacent angles equals 75°, and adjust one side of the angle thus formed to the given line; then slide the triangle, whose leg forms the other side of the angle, across the given line into position, and draw the required line, as shown in Fig. 2.15(a).

To draw a line making 15° with a given line, select any two angles whose difference is 15°. Adjust to the given line a side adjacent to one of these angles, and guide the side adjacent with a straight edge. Remove the first triangle and substitute the other so that one adjacent side of the angle to be subtracted is along the guiding edge, as shown in Fig. 2.15(b); then slide it into position and draw along the other adjacent side.

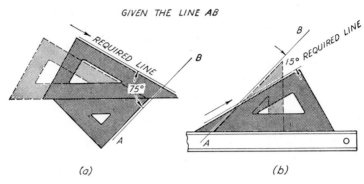

Fig. 2.15.   *To draw lines making 15° or 75° with a given line.*

2.15. Scales.   A number of kinds of scales are available for varied types of engineering design.   For convenience, however, all scales may be classified according to their use as mechanical engineers' scales (both fractional and decimal), civil engineers' scales, architects' scales, or metric scales.

The mechanical engineers' scales are generally of the full-divided type, graduated proportionally to give reductions based on inches.   On one form the principal units are divided into the common fractions of an inch; 4, 8, 16, 32 parts (Fig. 2.16).   The scales are indicated on the stick as eighth-size $(1\frac{1}{2}'' = 1')$, quarter-size $(3'' = 1')$, half size $(6'' = 1')$, and full size.

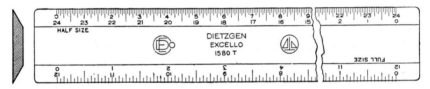

Fig. 2.16.   *Mechanical engineers' scale.   Full divided.*

Since the decimal system, employed in automotive design for more than twenty years and in aircraft design since World War II, has been rapidly spreading into other fields in recent years, decimals of an inch may soon replace the use of fractions in most of the divisions of American industry.   In any case, the use of decimal scales has become so wide-spread that the American Standards Association found it desirable to establish the standard ASA Z75.1–1955 for markings on scales used with decimal-inch dimensioning.   The full size scale, which has the principal units (inches) divided into fiftieths, is particularly suited for use with the two place decimal system (Fig. 2.17).   The half-size, three-eighths size, and quarter-size scales have the principal units divided into tenths (Fig. 2.20).

Fig. 2.17. Engineers' decimal scale.

The civil engineers' (chain) scales are full-divided, and are graduated in decimal parts, usually 10, 20, 30, 40, 50, 60, 80, and 100 divisions to the inch (Fig. 2.18).

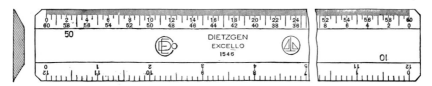

Fig. 2.18. Civil engineers' scale.

Architects' scales differ from mechanical engineers' scales in that the divisions represent a foot, and the end units are divided into inches, half inches, quarter inches, and so forth (6, 12, 24, 48, or 96 parts). The usual scales are $\frac{1}{8}'' = 1'$, $\frac{1}{4}'' = 1'$, $\frac{3}{8}'' = 1'$, $\frac{1}{2}'' = 1'$, $1'' = 1'$, $1\frac{1}{2}'' = 1'$, and $3'' = 1'$ (Fig. 2.19).

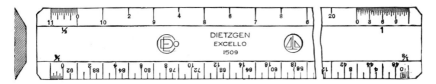

Fig. 2.19. Architects' scale. Open-divided.

The sole purpose of the scale is to reproduce the dimensions of an object full size on a drawing or to reduce or enlarge them to some regular proportion such as eighth size, quarter size, half size, or double size.

It is essential that a draftsman always think and speak of each dimension as full size when scaling measurements, because the dimension figures given on the finished drawing indicate full-size measurements of the finished piece, regardless of the scale used.

The reading of an open-divided scale is illustrated in Fig. 2.21 with the eighth-size ($1\frac{1}{2}'' = 1'$) scale shown. The dimension can be read directly as 21 inches, the 9 inches being read in the divided division to the left of the cipher. Each long open division represents twelve inches (one foot).

To lay off a measurement, using a scale starting at the left of the stick, align the scale in the direction of the measurement with the zero of the scale being used toward the left. After it has been adjusted to the correct location, make short marks opposite the divisions on the scale that establish the desired distance (Fig. 2.22).   For ordinary work most men use the same pencil used for the layout.   When extreme accuracy is necessary, however, it is better practice to use a pricker and make slight

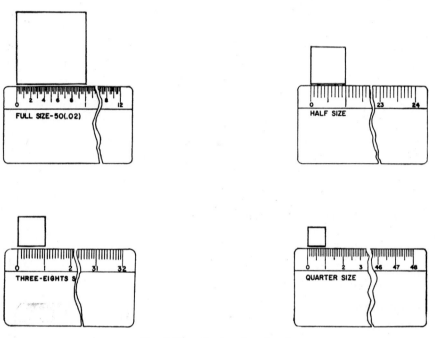

Fig. 2.20.   *Decimal scales.**

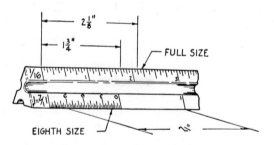

Fig. 2.21.   *Reading a scale.*

indentations (not holes) at the required points.   If a regular pricker is not available, the dividers may be opened to approximately 60° and the point of one leg used as a substitute.

To insure accuracy, place the eye directly over the division to be marked, hold the marking instrument perpendicularly to the paper

* ASA Z75.1–1955.

directly in front of the scale division, and mark the point. Always check the location of the point before removing the scale. If a slight indentation is made, it will be covered by the finished line; if a short mark is made, and it is *very* light, it will be unnoticeable on the finished drawing.

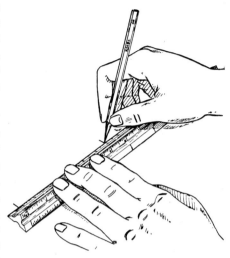

To set off a measurement (say 2'-9'') to half scale, the scale indicated either as $\frac{1}{2}$ (Fig. 2.23) or $\frac{1}{2}'' = 1'$ should be used. If the measurement is to be made from left to right, place the 9-inch fractional division mark (counted toward the left from the cipher) on the given line, and make an indentation (or mark) opposite the 2-foot division point (Fig.

Fig. 2.22. To lay off a measurement.

2.23*a*). The distance from the line to the point represents 2'-9'', although it is actually $1\frac{3}{8}$ inches. To set off the same measurement from right to left, place the 2-foot mark on the given line, and make an indentation opposite the 9-inch fractional division mark (Fig. 2.23*b*).

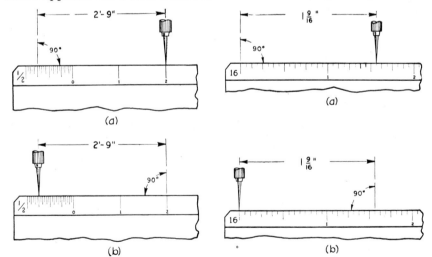

Fig. 2.23. To lay off a measurement.   *Fig. 2.24. To lay off a measurement (full size).*

The procedure for setting off a distance to full size is illustrated in Fig. 2.24. The scale that is full divided into inches and sixteenths is best suited for this purpose.

To set off a measurement (say $1\frac{9}{16}$ inches) from left to right, place the initial mark at the start of the scale on the given line, and make an indentation opposite the $1\frac{9}{16}$-inch mark (Fig. 2.24a).   To set off the same measurement from right to left, place the $1\frac{9}{16}$-inch mark on the given line, and make an indentation opposite the initial division mark at the start of the scale (Fig. 2.24b).

The use of the decimal scale is illustrated in Fig. 2.25.

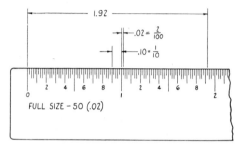

Fig. 2.25.   *Reading the decimal scale.*

2.16. The compass or large bow.   The compass or large bow is used for drawing circles and circle arcs.   For drawing pencil circles, the style of point illustrated in Fig. 2.26(c) should be used because it gives more accurate results and is easier to maintain than most other styles. This style of point is formed by first sharpening the outside of the lead on a file or sandpad to a long flat bevel approximately $\frac{1}{4}$ of an inch long

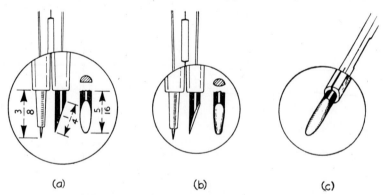

(a)   (b)   (c)

Fig. 2.26.   *Shaping the compass lead.*

(Fig. 2.26a), and then finishing it (Fig. 2.26b) with a slight rocking motion to reduce the width of the point.   Although a hard lead (4H to 6H) will maintain a point longer without resharpening, it gives a finished object line that is too light in color.   Soft lead (F or H) gives a darker line but quickly loses its edge and, on larger circles, gives a thicker line at the end than at the beginning.   Some draftsmen have found that a medium grade (2H–3H) lead is a satisfactory compromise for ordinary working drawings. For design drawings, layout work, and graphical solutions, however, a harder lead will give better results.

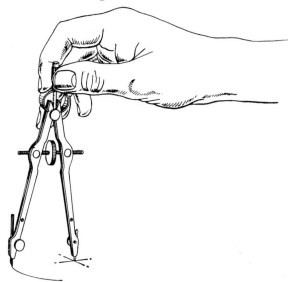

Fig. 2.27. Using the large bow (Vemco).

The needle point should have the shouldered end out, and should be adjusted approximately ⅜ of an inch beyond the end of the split sleeve.

2.17. Using the compass or large bow. To draw a circle, it is first necessary to draw two intersecting center lines at right angles and mark off the radius as previously explained. The pivot point should be guided accurately into position at the center. After the pencil point has been adjusted to the radius mark, the circle is drawn in a clockwise direction as shown in Fig. 2.27. While drawing the circle, the instrument should be inclined slightly forward. If the pencil line is not dark enough, it may be drawn around again.

When using a compass for a radius larger than 2 inches, the legs should be bent at the knee joints to stand approximately perpendicular to the paper (Fig. 2.28). It is particularly important that this adjustment

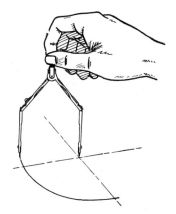

Fig. 2.28. Using the compass (legs bent).

be made when drawing ink circles, otherwise both nibs will not touch the paper. For circles whose radii exceed 5 inches, the lengthening bar should be used to increase the capacity.

The beam compass is manipulated by steadying the instrument at the pivot leg with one hand while rotating the marking leg with the other (Fig. 2.29).

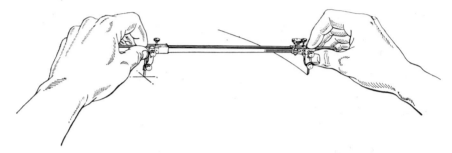

Fig. 2.29.   Drawing large circles (Vemco beam compass).

2.18. The dividers.   The dividers are used principally for dividing curved and straight lines into any number of equal parts, and for transferring measurements.   If the instrument is held with one leg between the forefinger and second finger, and the other leg between the thumb and third finger, as illustrated in Fig. 2.30, an adjustment may be made quickly and easily with one hand.   The second and third fingers are used to "open out" the legs, and the thumb and forefinger to close them.   This method of adjusting may seem awkward to the beginner at first, but with practice absolute control can be developed.

Fig. 2.30.   To adjust the large dividers.

2.19. Use of the dividers.   The trial method is used to divide a line into a given number of equal parts (Fig. 2.31).   To divide a line into a desired number of equal parts, open the dividers until the distance between the points is estimated to be equal to the length of a division, and step off the line *lightly*.   If the last prick mark misses the end point, increase or decrease the setting by an amount estimated to be equal to the error divided by the number of divisions, before lifting the dividers from the paper.   Step off the line again.   Repeat this procedure until the dividers are correctly set, then space the line again and indent the division points.   When stepping off a line, the dividers are rotated alternately in an opposite direction on either side of the line, each half revolution, as shown in Fig. 2.31.

Although the dividers are used to transfer a distance on a drawing, they should never be used to transfer a measurement from the scale, as the method is slow and inaccurate and results in serious damage to the graduation · marks. Care should be taken to avoid pricking large unsightly holes with the divider points. It is the common practice of many expert draftsmen to draw a small free-hand circle around a very light indentation to establish its location.

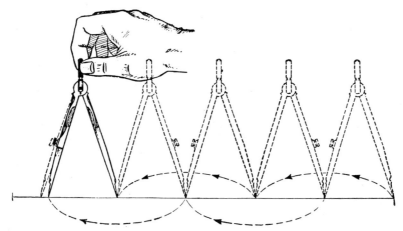

Fig. 2.31. Use of the dividers.

2.20. Use of the bow instruments. The bow pen and bow pencil are convenient for drawing circles having a radius of 1 inch or less (Fig. 2.32). The needle points should be adjusted slightly longer than the marking points, as in the case of the compass.

Small adjustments are made by the fingers of the hand holding the instrument, with the pivot point in position at the center of the required circle or arc.

2.21. Use of the French curve. A French curve is used for drawing irregular curves that are not circle arcs. After sufficient points have been located, the French curve is applied so that a portion of its ruling edge passes through at least three points, as shown in Fig. 2.33. It should be so placed that the increasing curvature of the section of the ruling edge being used

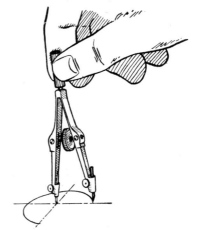

Fig. 2.32. Use of the bow pencil.

follows the direction of that part of the curve that is changing most rapidly. To insure that the finished curve will be free of humps and sharp breaks, the first line drawn should start and stop short of the first and last points to which the French curve has been fitted. Then the curve is adjusted in a new position with the ruling edge coinciding with a section of the line previously drawn. Each successive segment should stop short of the last point matched by the curve. In Fig. 2.33, the curve fits the three points, *A*, 1, and 2.

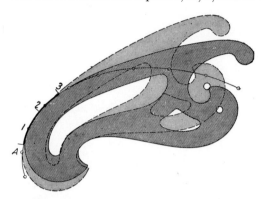

Fig. 2.33.   Using the irregular curve.

A line is drawn from between point *A* and point 1 to between point 1 and point 2. Then, the curve is shifted, as shown, to again fit points 1 and 2 with an additional point 3, and the line is extended to between point 2 and point 3.

Some people sketch a smooth continuous curve through the points in pencil before drawing the mechanical line. This procedure makes the task of drawing the curve less difficult, since it is easier to adjust the ruling edge to segments of the free-hand curve than to the points.

2.22. Use of the erasing shield and eraser. An erasure is made on a drawing by placing an opening in the erasing shield over the work to be erased and rubbing with a pencil eraser (never an ink eraser) until it is removed (Fig. 2.34). Excessive pressure should not be applied to the eraser, because, although the lines will disappear more quickly, the surface of the paper is likely to be permanently damaged. The fingers holding the erasing shield should rest partly on

Fig. 2.34.   Using the erasing shield.

the drawing paper to prevent the shield from slipping.

2.23. Use of the ruling pen. The ruling pen is used to ink mechanical lines. It is always guided by the working edge of a T-square, triangle, or French curve, and is never used freehand.

When ruling a line, the pen should be in a vertical plane and inclined slightly (approximately 60°) in the direction of the movement. It is held by the thumb and forefinger, as illustrated in Fig. 2.35, with the blade against the second finger and the adjusting screw on the outside away from the ruling edge. The third and fourth fingers slide along the T-square blade and help control the pen. Short lines are drawn with a hand movement; long lines with a free arm movement that finishes with a finger movement. While drawing, the angle of inclination and speed must remain constant to obtain a line of uniform width and straightness. Particular attention should be given to the position of the pen, as prac-

tically all faulty lines are due to incorrect inclination or to leaning the pen so that the point is too close to the straightedge or too far away from it. The correct position of the pen for drawing a satisfactory line is illustrated in Fig. 2.35.

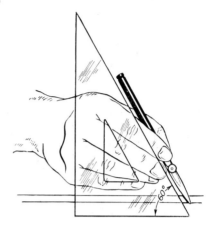

If the pen is held so that it leans outward, as shown in Fig. 2.36(*a*), the point will be against the straightedge, and ink will run under and cause a blot; or, if it leans inward, as in Fig. 2.36(*b*), the outer nib will not touch the paper and the line will be ragged.

Fig. 2.35.   Holding the pen.

Unnecessary pressure against the straightedge changes the distance between the nibs, which in turn may either reduce the width of the line along its entire length or cause its width to vary as in Fig. 2.36(*d*).

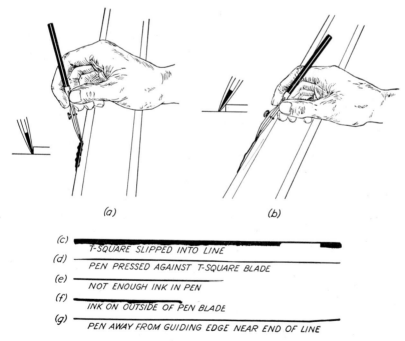

(*a*)   (*b*)

(*c*) ——— T-SQUARE SLIPPED INTO LINE

(*d*) ——— PEN PRESSED AGAINST T-SQUARE BLADE

(*e*) ——— NOT ENOUGH INK IN PEN

(*f*) ——— INK ON OUTSIDE OF PEN BLADE

(*g*) ——— PEN AWAY FROM GUIDING EDGE NEAR END OF LINE

Fig. 2.36.   Common faults in handling a ruling pen.

It will not take any beginner long to discover that care must be taken when removing a T-square or triangle away from a wet ink line.

The ruling pen is filled by inserting the quill or dropper device of the stopper between the nibs.   Care must be taken, while filling, to see that there is enough ink to finish the line and that none of the ink from the filler gets on the outside of the blades.   No more than $\frac{1}{4}$ inch should ever be put in; there is a danger of blotting if the pen is used with a greater amount.

The width of a line is determined by the distance between the nibs, which is regulated by the adjusting screw.   When setting the pen, a series of test lines should be drawn with a straightedge on a small piece of the same kind of paper or cloth to establish the setting for the desired width of the line.   The American Standards Association conventional symbols for ink lines for different purposes are shown in Fig. 8.15.   They have been reproduced full width so that they appear as required for a well-executed ink tracing.

If the ink refuses to flow when the pen is touched to the paper, either the ink has thickened or the opening between the nibs has become clogged. To start it flowing, draftsmen often touch the point to the back of a finger or pinch the blades together.   Whenever this fails to produce an immediate flow, the pen should be cleaned and refilled.

A dirty pen in which the ink has been allowed to thicken will not draw any better than a dull one.   To avoid changing the setting of the pen when cleaning it, fold the pen wiper twice at 90° and draw the corner of the fold between the ends of the blades.

2.24. Tracing.   Often, when it is necessary to make duplicate copies (blueprints) of important drawings for a machine or structure, the original pencil drawings are traced in ink on a tracing medium, usually tracing cloth.   Contrary to the practice of old-time draftsmen and the intention of the early manufacturers of this medium, the dull side is now almost universally used for the inking surface instead of the slick side because it produces less light glare, will take both pencil and ink lines better, and will withstand more erasing.   The fact that the dull side will take pencil lines is important because, on some occasions, in order to save time, drawings are made directly on the cloth and then traced.   Upon completion of the tracing, all pencil lines including the guide lines and slope lines for the lettering may be removed by wiping the surface of the cloth with a rag moistened with a small amount of gasoline, benzine, or cleaning fluid.

When the tracing cloth has been fastened down over the drawing, a small quantity of tracing cloth powder may be sprinkled over the surface to make it take the ink evenly and smoothly.   After it has been well rubbed in, the excess must be thoroughly removed by wiping with a clean cloth, for even a small amount of loose powder left on the surface can cause clogging of the pen.   Powder is also used by some persons over a spot where an erasure has been made; but a better practice is to use a piece of soapstone, which will put a smooth, slick finish over the damaged area. In applying the soapstone, rub the spot and then wipe a finger over it a few times. Following this treatment, the erased area will take ink almost as well as the original surface.

Since ink lines are made much wider than pencil lines, in order to get a good contrast on a blueprint, they should be carefully centered over the pencil lines when tracing. The center of an ink line should fall directly on the pencil line as shown in Fig. 2.37. For ink work it might be said that ink lines are tangent when their center lines touch. In this same illustration, note the poor junctures obtained when ink lines are not centered so that their center lines are tangent.

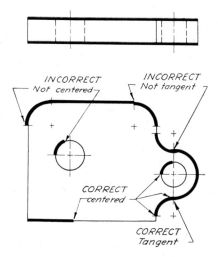

Fig. 2.37. Inking over pencil lines.

When a working drawing is traced in ink on either paper or cloth, the lines should be "inked" in a definite order. Otherwise, the necessity of waiting for the ink to dry after every few lines not only wastes time, but often results in a line here and there being left out. Furthermore, hit-and-miss inking may produce lines of unequal width. It is therefore recommended that the student make a conscientious attempt to follow the order of inking suggested in this chapter.

After the paper or cloth has been fastened down over the drawing, and before the inking is begun, each tangent point should be marked and all centers should be indented.

ORDER OF INKING

I. Curved Lines:
  1. Circles and circle arcs (small circles first) in the order of (a), (b), and (c).
    (a) Visible.
    (b) Invisible.
    (c) Circular center lines and dimension lines.
  2. Irregular curves.
    (a) Visible.
    (b) Invisible.
II. Straight Lines:
  1. Visible.
    (a) Horizontal, from the top of the sheet down.
    (b) Vertical, from the left side of the sheet to the right.
    (c) Inclined, from the left to the right.

  2. Invisible.
    (*a*) Horizontal.
    (*b*) Vertical.
    (*c*) Inclined.
  3. Auxiliary (center, extension, and dimension lines, etc.).
    (*a*) Horizontal.
    (*b*) Vertical.
    (*c*) Inclined.
    (*d*) Section lines.
III. Arrowheads and Dimension Figures.
IV. Notes and Titles.
 V. Border.

2.25. The protractor.   The protractor is used for measuring and laying off angles (Fig. 2.38).

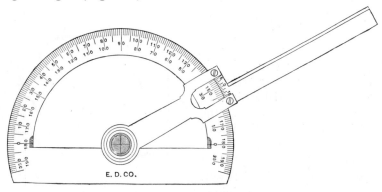

Fig. 2.38.   Protractor.

2.26. Mechanical lettering devices and templates.   Although mechanical lettering devices produce letters that may appear stiff to an expert, they are used in many drafting rooms for the simple reason that they enable even the unskilled to do satisfactory lettering. The average draftsman rightly prefers stiff uniformity to wavy lines and irregular shapes.

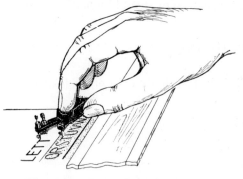

Fig. 2.39.   Leroy lettering device.

2.27. Special instruments and templates.   A few of the many special instruments and templates that are convenient for drawing are shown in Figs. 2.40 to 2.45.

The flexible curves shown in Fig. 2.40, because of their limitless variations, are extremely convenient.   The type shown in (*a*) is a lead bar enclosed in rubber.   The more

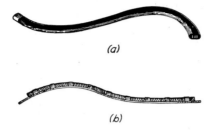

(a)

(b)

Fig. 2.40.   Flexible curves.

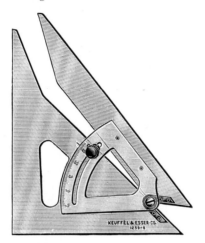

Fig. 2.41.   Protractor angle.

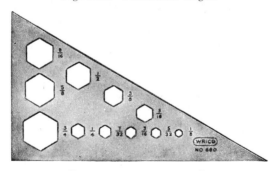

Fig. 2.42.   Wrico triangle.

desirable one shown in (*b*) has a steel ruling edge attached to a spring with a lead core.

Although it is not widely used, the protractor angle (Fig. 2.41) is a useful device.   It is hinged in such a manner that it may be substituted for a protractor and a set of triangles.

The Wrico triangle is one of several types of special triangles that may be used also for drawing the end views of standard bolt heads and nuts.

Electro Symbol Template

Chemistry Template

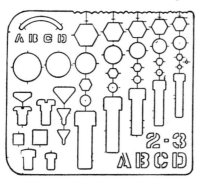

Tooling Template

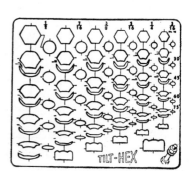

Tilt-Hex Drafting Template

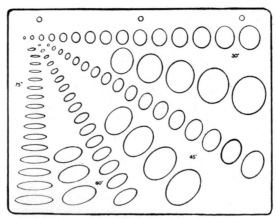

Ellipses

Courtesy Frederick Post Co.

Fig. 2.43.   Special templates.

The use of templates can save valuable time in the drawing of standard figures and symbols on plans and drawings (Fig. 2.43).

Proportional dividers are used to reproduce distances to a reduced or an enlarged scale (Fig. 2.44).

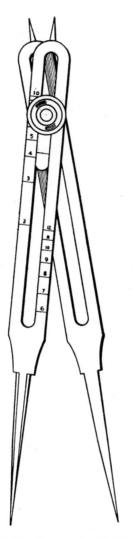

Fig. 2.44.   Proportional dividers.

The drafting machine (Fig. 2.45) is designed to combine the functions of the T-square, triangles, scale, and protractor.   Drafting machines are used extensively in commercial drafting rooms because it has been estimated that their use leads to a 25 to 50 per cent saving in time.

Fig. 2.45.   Drafting machine.

2.28. Tracing paper.   White light-weight tracing paper, on which pencil drawings can be made and from which blueprints can be produced, is used in most commercial drafting rooms in order to keep labor costs at a minimum.

2.29. Tracing cloth.   The two general types of cloth available are ink cloth and pencil cloth.   The cloth used for ink is clear and transparent, dull on one side, and glossy on the other.   Pencil cloth is a white cloth with a surface specially prepared to take pencil marks readily.

2.30. Exercises in instrumental drawing.   The following elementary exercises have been designed to offer experience in the use of the drafting instruments.   The designs should be drawn *lightly* with a hard pencil.   After making certain that all constructions shown on a drawing are correct, the lines forming the designs should be heavied with a medium hard pencil.   The light construction lines need not be erased if the drawing has been kept relatively clean.   All dimensions and letters should be omitted except in problem 5.

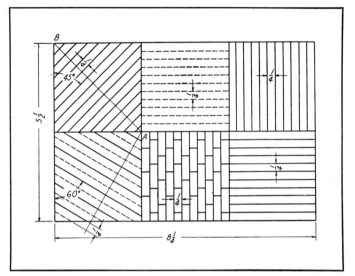

Fig. 2.46.

1. (Fig. 2.46).   On a sheet of drawing paper reproduce the line formations shown.   If the principal border lines have not been printed on the sheet, they may be drawn first so that the large $5\frac{1}{2}''\times 8\frac{1}{4}''$ rectangle can be balanced horizontally and vertically within the border.   To draw the inclined lines, first draw the indicated measuring lines through the lettered points at the correct angle, and mark off $\frac{1}{4}''$ distances.   These division points establish the locations of the required lines of the formation.   The six squares of the formation are equal in size.

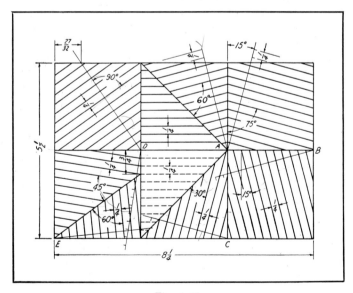

Fig. 2.47.

2. (Fig. 2.47.)   Reproduce the line formations shown, following the instructions given for problem 1.

3. (Fig. 2.48.)   This exercise is designed to give the student practice with the bow pencil and compass by drawing some simple geometrical figures.   The line

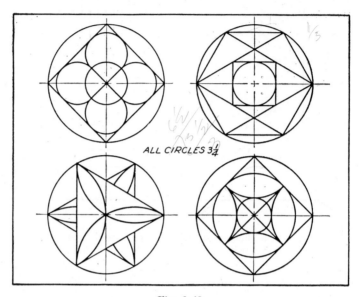

ALL CIRCLES 3¼

Fig. 2.48.

work within each large circle may be reproduced with the knowledge only that the diameter is $3\frac{1}{4}''$.   All circles and circle arcs are to be made finished weight when they are first drawn, since retracing often produces a double line.   Do not "overrun" the straight lines or stop them too short.

4. (Fig. 2.49.)   Reproduce the contour view of the stamping.

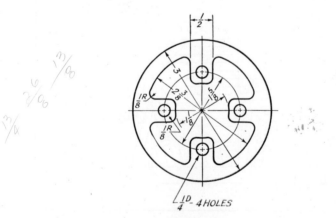

Fig. 2.49.

5. (Fig. 2.50.)   Select a suitable scale and reproduce the design of the highway intersection shown.   Using $\frac{3}{16}''$ capital letters, letter the words HIGHWAY INTERSECTION.   Using $\frac{1}{8}''$ letters and numerals, letter the dimensions. Draw the arrows indicating the direction of traffic flow.

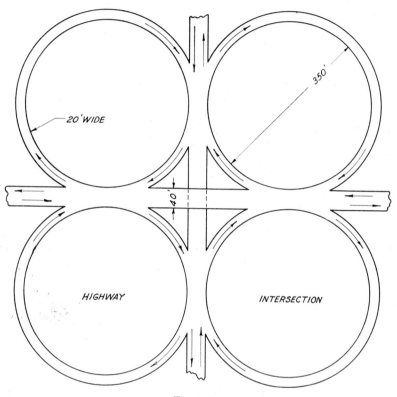

Fig. 2.50.

6–9. (Figs. 2.51–2.54.)   Reproduce the geometrical shapes.

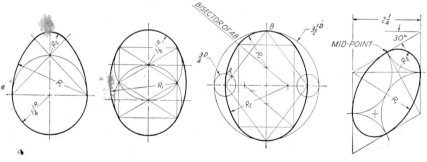

Fig. 2.51. **Oval.**   *Fig. 2.52.* **Ellipse (approximate).**   *Fig. 2.53.* **Ellipse (approximate).**   *Fig. 2.54.* **Ellipse (pictorial).**

3

Freehand Technical Lettering

3.1. To impart all the necessary information for the complete construction of a machine or structure, the shape description, conveyed graphically by the views, must be accompanied by size descriptions and instructive specifications in the form of figured dimensions and notes.

All dimensions and notes should be lettered freehand in a plain legible style that can be rapidly executed.

3.2. Single-stroke Gothic letters (Reinhardt). The simplified single-stroke Gothic letters developed by Charles W. Reinhardt are now used universally for technical drawings. This style is suitable for most purposes because it possesses the qualifications necessary for legibility and speed. On commercial drawings it appears in slightly modified forms, however, as each person finally develops a style that reflects his own individuality.

The expression "single-stroke" means that the width of the straight and curved lines that form the letters are the same width as the stroke of the pen or pencil.

3.3. The general proportions of letters. Although there is no fixed standard for the proportions of the letters, certain definite rules in their design must be observed if one wishes to have his lettering appear neat and pleasing to the eye. The recognized characteristics of each letter should be carefully studied, and then thoroughly learned through practice.

NORMAL LETTERS

COMPRESSED LETTERS

EXTENDED LETTERS

Fig. 3.1. Compressed and extended letters.

It is advisable for the beginner, instead of relying on his untrained eye for proportions, to follow the fixed proportions given in this chapter. Otherwise, his lettering most likely will be displeasing to the trained eye of the professional man. Later, after he has thoroughly mastered the art of lettering, his individuality will be revealed naturally by slight variations in the shapes and proportions of some of the letters.

It is often desirable to increase or decrease the width of letters in order to make a word or group of words fill a certain space.   Letters narrower than normal letters of the same height are called *compressed letters;* those that are wider are called *extended letters* (Fig. 3.1).

3.4. Lettering pencils and pens.   Pencil lettering is usually done with a medium-soft pencil.   Since the degree of hardness of the lead required to produce a dark opaque line will vary with the type of paper used, a pencil should be selected only after drawing a few trial lines.   In order to obtain satisfactory lines, the pencil should be sharpened to a long conical point and then rounded slightly on a piece of scratch paper. To keep the point symmetrical while lettering, the pencil should be rotated a partial revolution before each new letter is started.

The choice of a type of pen point for lettering depends largely upon the personal preference and characteristics of the individual.   The beginner can learn only from experience which of the many types available are best suited to him.

A pen that makes a heavy stroke should be used for bold letters in titles and so forth, while a light-stroke pen is required for the lighter letters in figures and notes.

A very flexible point never should be used for lettering.   Such a point is apt to shade the downward stem strokes as well as the downward portions of curved strokes.   A good point has enough resistance to normal pressure to permit the drawing of curved and stem strokes of uniform width.

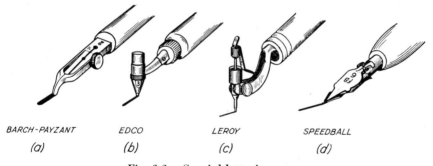

BARCH-PAYZANT   EDCO   LEROY   SPEEDBALL

(a)   *(b)*   *(c)*   *(d)*

Fig. 3.2.   Special lettering pens.

Four of the many special pens designed for single-stroke letters are illustrated in Fig. 3.2.   The *Barch-Payzant* pen (*a*) is available in graded sizes from No. 000 (very coarse) to No. 8 (very fine).   The very fine size is suitable for lettering $\frac{1}{8}$ inch to $\frac{3}{16}$ inch high on technical drawings. The *Edco* (*b*) has a patented holder into which any one of a graded set of lettering nibs (ranging in sizes from No. 0 to No. 6) may be screwed.

The tubular construction of the point makes it possible to draw uniform lines regardless of the direction of the stroke.   Also of tubular construction is the *Leroy* (*c*).   The *Speedball* (*d*) may be obtained in many graded sizes.

3.5. Devices for drawing guide lines and slope lines.   Devices for drawing guide lines are available in a variety of forms.   The two most

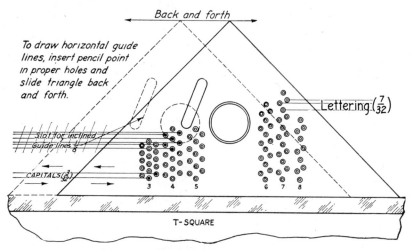

Fig. 3.3.   Braddock lettering triangle.

popular are the *Braddock Lettering Triangle* (Fig. 3.3), and the *Ames Lettering Instrument* (Fig. 3.4).

The Braddock Lettering Triangle is provided with sets of grouped countersunk holes that may be used to draw guide lines by inserting a sharp-pointed pencil (4*H* or 6*H*) into the holes and sliding the triangle back and forth along the guiding edge of a T-square or a triangle supported by a T-square.   The holes are grouped to give guide lines for capitals and lower-case letters.   The numbers below each set indicate the

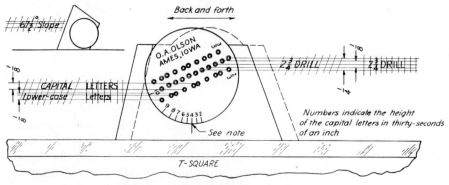

Fig. 3.4.   Ames lettering instrument.

height of the capitals in thirty-seconds of an inch. For example, the No. 3 set is for capitals $\frac{3}{32}''$ high, the No. 4 set is for capitals $\frac{1}{8}''$ high, the No. 5 is for capitals $\frac{5}{32}''$ high, and so on.

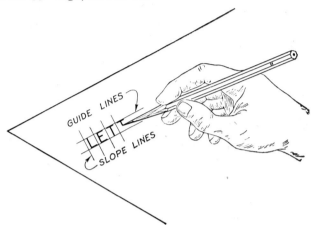

Fig. 3.5. *Guide lines and slope lines.*

3.6. Uniformity in lettering. Uniformity in height, inclination, spacing, and strength of line is essential for good lettering (Fig. 3.6). Professional appearance depends as much upon uniformity as upon the correctness of the proportion and shape of the individual letters. Uniformity in height and inclination is assured by the use of guide lines and slope lines; uniformity in weight and color, by the skillful use of the pencil and proper control of the pressure of its point on the paper. The ability to space letters correctly becomes easy after continued thoughtful practice.

UNIFORMITY IN HEIGHT, INCLINATION, AND STRENGTH OF LINE IS ESSENTIAL FOR GOOD LETTERING.

Fig. 3.6. *Uniformity in lettering.*

3.7. Composition. In combining letters into words, the spaces for the various combinations of letters are arranged so that the areas appear to be equal (Fig. 3.7). For standard lettering, this area should be about equal to one-half the area of the letter M. If the adjacent sides be stems, this area is obtained by making the distance between the letters slightly greater than one-half the height of a letter, and a smaller amount depending on the contours, for other combinations. Examples of good and poor composition are shown in Fig. 3.7.

The space between words should be equal to or greater than the height of a letter, but not more than twice the height. The space between sentences should be somewhat greater. The distance between lines of lettering may vary from one-half the height of the capitals to one and one-half times their height.

Fig. 3.7. Letter areas.

3.8. Stability. If the areas of the upper and lower portions of certain letters are made equal, an optical illusion will cause them to appear to be unstable and top heavy. To overcome this effect, the upper portions of the letters *B, E, F, H, K, S, X,* and *Z* and the figures *2, 3,* and *8* must be reduced slightly in size.

An associated form of illusion is the phenomenon that a horizontal line drawn across a rectangle at the vertical center will appear to be below the center. Since the letters *B, E, F,* and *H* are particularly subject to this illusion, their central horizontal strokes must be drawn slightly above the vertical center in order to give them a more balanced and pleasing appearance.

The letters *K, X, S, Z* and the figures *2, 3,* and *8* are stabilized by making the width of the upper portion less than the width of the lower portion.

3.9. The technique of freehand lettering. Any prospective engineer can learn to letter if he practices intelligently and is persistent in his desire to improve. The necessary muscular control, which must accompany the knowledge of lettering, can be developed only through constant repetition.

Pencil letters should be formed with strokes that are dark and sharp; never with strokes that are gray and indistinct. Beginners should avoid the tendency to form letters by sketching, as strokes made in this manner vary in color and width.

When lettering with ink, the results obtained depend largely upon the manner in which the pen is used. Many complain that the execution of good freehand lettering is impossible with an ordinary pen point although their own incorrect habits may have resulted in the inability to make strokes of uniform width. This lack of uniformity may be due to one of four causes: (1) excessive pressure on the pen point; (2) an accumulation of lint, dirt, or dried ink on the point; (3) tilting the point while forming a stroke; or (4) fresh ink on the point. The latter cause requires some explanation, since very few persons know the proper method of "inking" the pen.   The pen should be wiped thoroughly clean, and the ink should be deposited on the under side over the slot, well above the point.   When the pen is filled in this manner, the ink feeds down the slit in an even flow, making possible the drawing of uniform curved and straight lines.   If ink is placed on the point or allowed to run to the point, an excessive amount of ink will be deposited on the first letters made, and the width of the strokes will be somewhat wider than the strokes of, say, the sixth or seventh letter (Fig. 3.8).

When lettering, the pen is held as

INK ON POINT

Fig. 3.8.   **Fig. 3.9.   Holding the pen.**

shown in Fig. 3.9.   It should rest so loosely between the fingers that it can be slid up and down with the other hand.

The thin film of oil on a new point must be removed by wiping before it is used.

3.10. Inclined and vertical capital letters.   The letters shown in Figs. 3.10 and 3.11 have been arranged in related groups.   In laying out the characters, the number of widths has been reduced to the smallest number consistent with good appearance; similarities of shape have been emphasized and minute differences have been eliminated.   Each letter is drawn to a large size on a cross-section grid that is two units wider, to facilitate the study of its characteristic shape and proportions.   Arrows with numbers indicate the order and direction of the strokes.   The curves of the inclined capital letters are portions of ellipses while the curves of the vertical letters are parts of circles.

The I, T, L, E, and F.   The letter *I* is the basic or stem stroke.   The horizontal stroke of the *T* is drawn first, and the stem starts at the exact center of the bar.   The *L* is 5 units wide, but it is often desirable to reduce this width when an *L* is used in combination with such letters as *A* and *T*. It should be observed that the letter *L* consists of the first two strokes of the *E*.   The middle bar of the *E* is $3\frac{1}{2}$ units long and is placed slightly above the center for stability.   The top bar is one-half unit shorter than the bottom bar.   The letter *F* is the *E* with the bottom bar omitted.

The H and N.   Stroke 3 of the *H* should be slightly above the center, for stability.   The outside parallel strokes of the *N* are drawn first to permit an accurate estimate of its width.   The inclined stroke should intersect these accurately at their extremities.

The Z and X.   The top of the *Z* should be one unit narrower than the bottom, for stability.   In the smaller sizes, this letter may be formed

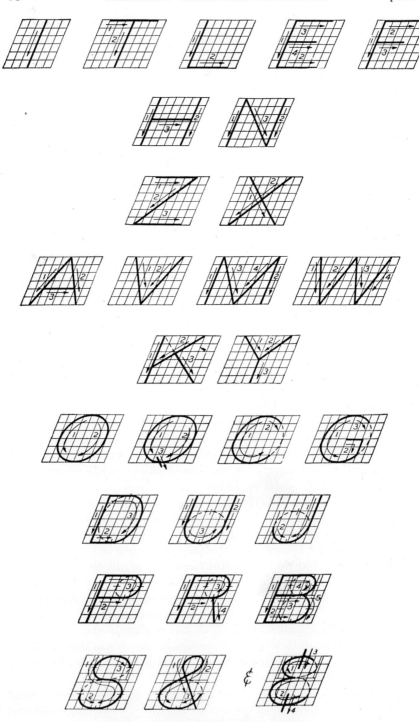

Fig. 3.10.   *Inclined capital letters.*

Fig. 3.11. *Vertical capital letters.*

without lifting the pen.   The X is similar to the Z in that the top is made one unit narrower than the bottom.   The inclined strokes cross slightly above center.

The A, V, M, and W.   The horizontal bar of the A is located up from the bottom a distance equal to one-third of the height of the letter. The V is the letter A inverted without the crossbar, and is the same width.   The letters M and W are the widest letters of the alphabet.   The outside strokes of the M are drawn first, so that its width may be judged accurately.   The inside strokes of this letter meet at the center of the base.   The W is formed by two modified V's.   Alternate strokes are parallel.

The K and Y.   The top of the letter K should be made one unit narrower than the bottom, for stability.   Stroke 2 intersects the stem one-third up from the bottom.   Stroke 3 is approximately perpendicular to stroke 2, and, if extended, would touch the stem at the top.   The strokes of the Y meet at the center of the enclosing parallelogram or square.

The O, Q, C, and G.   Stroke 1 of the letter O starts just to the right of the top and continues to the left around the side to a point beyond the bottom.   Thus stroke 1 forms more than half of the ellipse or circle.   The Q is the letter O with the added kern, which is a straight line located near the bottom tangent point.   The C is based on the O, but since it is not a complete ellipse or circle, it is narrower than either the O or Q.   The top extends one unit down and the bottom one unit up on the right side. G is similar to C.   The horizontal portion of stroke 2 starts at the center.

The D, U, and J.   The first two strokes of the D form an incomplete letter L.   Stroke 3 starts as a horizontal line.   The bottom third of the U is one-half of an ellipse or circle. J is similar to the letter U.

The P, R, and B.   The middle horizontal bar of the P is located at the center of stroke 1.   The curved portion of stroke 3 is one-half of a perfect ellipse or circle.   The R is constructed similarly to the P.   The tail joins at the point of tangency of the curve and middle bar.   To stabilize the letter B, the top is made one-half unit narrower than the bottom and the middle bar is placed slightly above the center.   The curves are halves of ellipses or circles.

The S and &.   The upper and lower portions of the S are perfect ellipses with one-quarter removed.   The top ellipse should be made one-half unit narrower than the lower one, for stability.   In the smaller sizes this letter may be made with one or two strokes, depending upon its size.   The true ampersand is made with three strokes.   Professional men, however, usually represent an ampersand with a character formed by using portions of the upper and lower ellipses of the numeral 8 with the addition of two short bars.

Although many favor the inclined letters, recent surveys indicate that vertical letters are being more generally used.

3.11. Inclined and vertical numerals. The numerals shown in Figs. 3.12 and 3.13 have been arranged in related groups in accordance with the common characteristics that can be recognized in their construction.

The 1, 7, and 4. The stem stroke of the *4* is located one unit in from the right side. The bar is one and one-half units above the base. The stem of the *7* terminates at the center of the base.

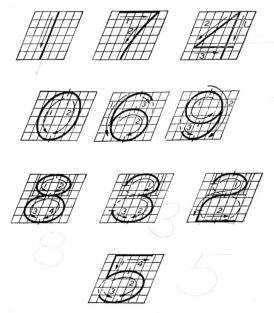

Fig. 3.12.   Inclined numerals.

The 0, 6, and 9. The cipher, which is one unit narrower than the letter *O*, is the basic form for this group. In the figure *6*, the right side of the large ellipse ends one unit down from the top, and the left side ends at the center of the base. The small loop is slightly more than three-fourths of an ellipse. The *9* is the *6* inverted.

The 8, 3, and 2. Each of these figures is related to the letter *S*, and the same rule of stability should be observed in their construction. The top portion of the figure *8* is shorter and one-half unit narrower than the lower portion. Each loop is a perfect ellipse. The figure *3* is the *8* with the lower left quarter of the upper loop and the upper left quarter of the lower loop omitted. The *2* is simply three-quarters of the upper loop of the *8* and the upper left quarter of the lower loop of the *8* with straight lines added.

The 5. This figure is a modification of the related groups previously described. The top is one-half unit narrower than the bottom, for stability. The curve is a segment of a perfect ellipse, ending one unit up from the bottom.

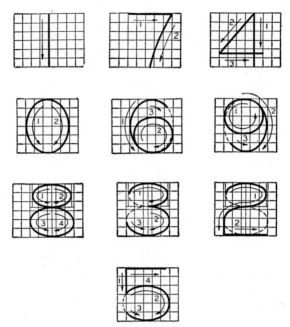

Fig. 3.13.   Vertical numerals.

3.12. Single-stroke lower-case letters. Single-stroke lower-case letters, either vertical or inclined, are commonly used on map drawings, topographic drawings, structural drawings, and in survey field books. They are particularly suitable for long notes and statements because, first, they can be executed much faster than capitals and, second, words and statements formed with them can be read more easily.

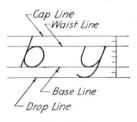

Fig. 3.14.

The construction of inclined lower-case letters is based upon the straight line and the ellipse (Fig. 3.15). This basic principle of forming letters is followed more closely for lower-case letters than for capitals. The body portions are two-thirds the height of the related capitals. As shown in Fig. 3.14, ascenders extend to the cap line, and descenders descend to the drop line. For lower-case letters based on a capital letter six units high, the waistline is two units down from the top and the drop line two units below the base line.

The order of stroke, direction of stroke, and formation of the letters follow the same principles as for the capitals. The letters are presented in family groups having related characteristics, to enable the beginner to understand their construction. The vertical lower-case letters, illustrated in Fig. 3.16, are constructed in the same manner as inclined letters.

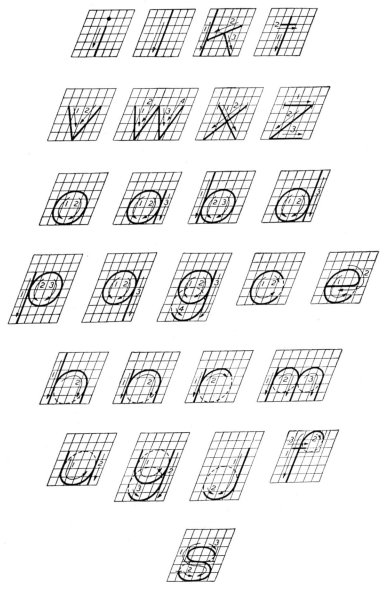

Fig. 3.15.　Inclined lower-case letters.

The i, l, k, and t.　All letters of this group are formed by straight lines of standard slope.　The *i* is drawn four units high, and the dot is placed halfway between the waistline and cap line.　Stroke 2 of the *k* starts at the waistline and intersects stroke 1 two units above the base. Stroke 3, extended, should intersect stroke 1 at the top.　The *t* is five units high, and the crossbar is on the waistline.

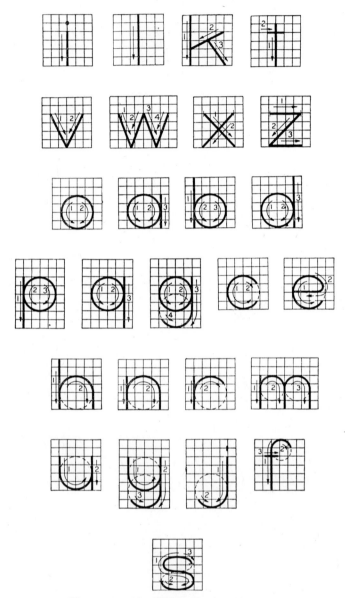

Fig. 3.16. Vertical lower-case letters.

The v, w, x, and z. All of these letters are similar to the capitals. Alternate strokes of the *w* are parallel. The width of the top of both the *x* and the *z* is made one-half unit less than the width across the bottom, for stability.

The o, a, b, d, p, and q. The bodies of the letters in this group are formed by the letter *o*, and they differ only in the position and length of the stem stroke. The *o* is made with two strokes, and the first stroke should form more than half of the character.

The g. The *g* is related to the letters *o* and *y*. Stroke 3 starts at the waistline and ends slightly beyond the point of tangency of the curve with the drop line.

The c and e. The *c* is a modified letter *o*. It is not a complete form. Therefore, its width is less than its height. Stroke 1 ends one unit up on the right side, stroke 2 one unit down. The *e* is similarly constructed, except for the fact that stroke 2 continues as a curve and finishes as a horizontal line that terminates at the middle of the back.

The h, n, r, and m. The curve of the *h* is the upper portion of the letter *o*. Stroke 2 starts 2 units above the bottom of the stem and finishes parallel to stroke 1. The *n* differs from the *h* in that the stem stroke extends only from the waistline to the base line. The *r* is a portion of the letter *n*, stroke 2 ending one unit down from the top. The *m* consists of two modified letter *n*'s. The straight portions of strokes 2 and 3 are parallel to stroke 1.

The u and y. The letter *u* is an inverted *n*, and the curve is a portion of the letter *o*. It should be noted that stroke 2 extends to the base line. The *y* is a partial combination of the letters *u* and *g*.

The j and f. The portion of the *j* above the base line is the letter *i*. The curve is the same as that which forms the tail of the *g*. The *f* is two and one-half units wide, stroke 1 starting slightly to the right of the point of tangency with the cap line.

The s. The lower-case *s* is almost identical to the capital *S*.

3.13. Fractions. The height of the figures in the numerator and denominator is equal to three-fourths the height of the whole number, and the total height of the fraction is twice the height of the whole number. The division bar should be horizontal and centered between the fraction numerals as shown in Fig. 3.17. It should be noted that the sloping center line of the fraction bisects both the numerator and denominator and is parallel to the sloping center line of the whole number.

Fig. 3.17.

3.14. Titles. Every drawing, sketch, graph, chart, or diagram has some form of descriptive title to impart certain necessary information and to identify it. On machine drawings, where speed and legibility are prime requirements, titles are usually singlestroke Gothic. On display drawings, maps, architectural designs, and so on, which call for an artistic effect, the titles are usually composed of "built-up" ornate letters.

To be pleasing in appearance, a title should be symmetrical about a vertical center line and should have some simple geometrical form.

An easy way to insure the symmetry of a title is first to count the letter and word spaces, then, working to the left and right from the middle

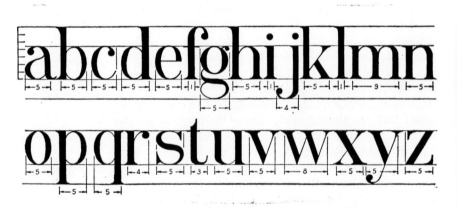

Fig. 3.18. *Modern Roman letters.*

space or letter on the vertical center line, to sketch the title lightly in pencil, before lettering it in finished form. An alternate method is to letter a trial line along the edge of a piece of scrap paper and place it in a balanced position just above the location of the line to be lettered.

3.15. Modern Roman. The Modern Roman letters shown in Fig. 3.18 are used extensively by engineers for names and titles on maps. Students should be familiar with this alphabet, for it appears in all modern publications. As is the case with some other styles, these letters must be drawn first in outline, in skeleton form, and then be filled in with a ball-pointed or wide-line pen. The straight lines are usually drawn with a ruling pen. The curved lines, except for the serifs, may be formed either mechanically or freehand. When attempting to construct this type of letter it is wise to bear in mind the following facts: (1) All vertical strokes are heavy except those forming the letters M, N, and U. (2) All horizontal strokes are light. (3) The serif extends about one unit on either side of the body of the stem. (4) The width of the heavy strokes may vary from one-eighth to one-sixth of the height of the letter.

Roman letters may be drawn either extended or compressed, depending upon the area to be covered or the space restrictions determined by other lettering, such as on maps. If a draftsman using the Roman-style letter would have his work look professional, he must pay particular attention to detail. Care must be taken to keep the proportions of a letter appearing more than once in a name or title identical. Most persons experienced at drawing should have little difficulty with these letters, if they follow carefully the details and proportions given in Fig. 3.18.

3.16. Problems. It should be noted that while these exercises are offered to give the student practice in letter forms and word composition, they also contain statements of important principles of drawing, shop notes, and titles with which every engineer should be familiar. Each lettering exercise should be submitted to the instructor for severe criticism before the student proceeds to the next. Sec. 3.3 should be reread before starting the first exercise.

1. Letter the statement given in Fig. 3.19 in $\frac{5}{32}''$ capital letters using an appropriate pencil that is suited to the type of paper being used and one that will produce uniform opaque lines. The necessary guide lines should be drawn with a hard pencil.

POOR LETTERING DETRACTS FROM THE
APPEARANCE OF A DRAWING

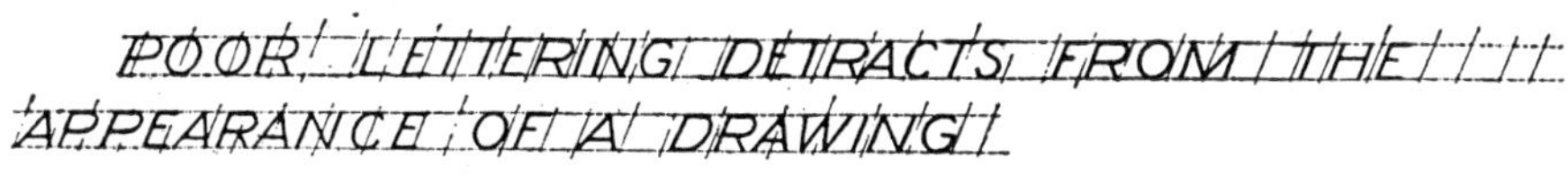

Fig. 3.19.

2–3. Letter the statements given in Figs. 3.20–3.21 in $\frac{1}{8}''$ capital letters using an appropriate pencil that is suited to the type of paper being used and one that will produce uniform opaque lines. The necessary guide lines should be drawn with a hard pencil.

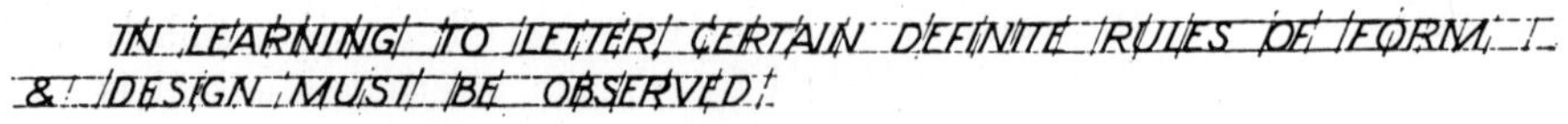

IN LEARNING TO LETTER CERTAIN DEFINITE RULES OF FORM
& DESIGN MUST BE OBSERVED.

Fig. 3.20.

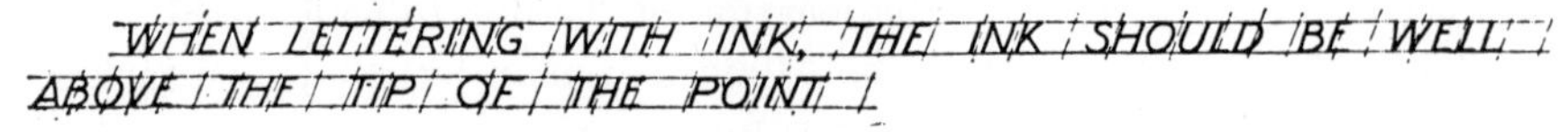

WHEN LETTERING WITH INK, THE INK SHOULD BE WELL
ABOVE THE TIP OF THE POINT.

Fig. 3.21.

4. Letter the statement given in Fig. 3.22 in $\frac{5}{32}''$ capital letters using an appropriate pencil that is suited to the type of paper being used and one that will produce uniform opaque lines. The necessary guide lines should be drawn with a hard pencil.

#26 (.1470) DRILL AND REAM FOR #1×1 TAPER PIN
WITH PC #41 IN POSITION

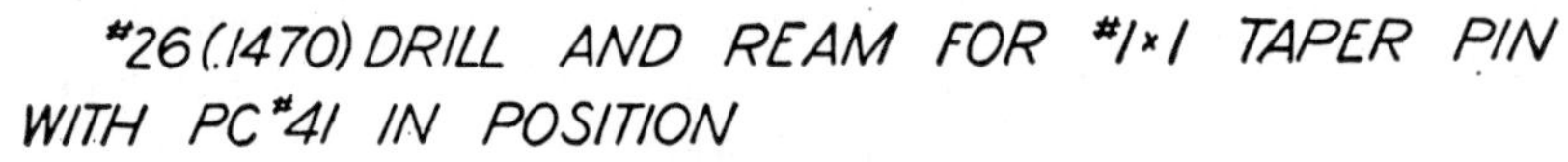

Fig. 3.22.

5–6. Letter the statements given in Figs. 3.23–3.24 in $\frac{1}{8}''$ capital letters using an appropriate pencil that is suited to the type of paper being used and one that will produce uniform opaque lines. The necessary guide lines should be drawn with a hard pencil.

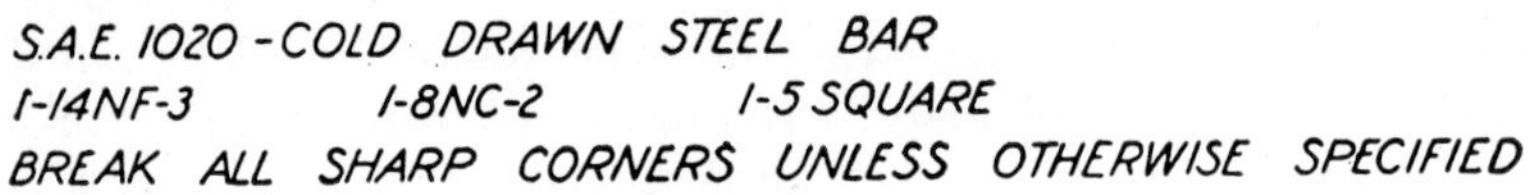

S.A.E. 1020 - COLD DRAWN STEEL BAR
1-14NF-3
1-8NC-2
1-5 SQUARE
BREAK ALL SHARP CORNERS UNLESS OTHERWISE SPECIFIED

Fig. 3.23.

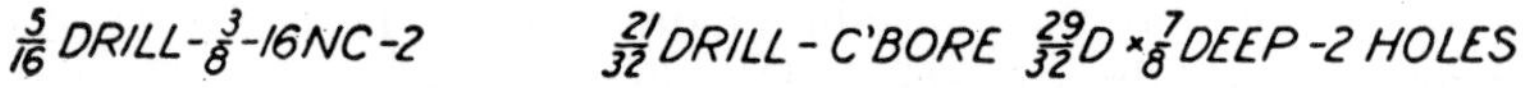

5/16 DRILL-3/8-16NC-2
21/32 DRILL - C'BORE 29/32 D × 7/8 DEEP -2 HOLES

Fig. 3.24.

7–16. Letter the following statements in $\frac{1}{8}''$ capital letters using an appropriate pencil that is suited to the type of paper being used and one that will produce uniform opaque lines. The necessary guide lines should be drawn with a hard pencil.

(7) A GOOD STUDENT REALIZES THE IMPORTANCE OF NEAT AND ATTRACTIVE LETTERING.

A GOOD STUDENT REALIZES THE
IMPORTANCE OF NEAT AND ATTRACTIVE
LETTERING.
DOE, J. X.

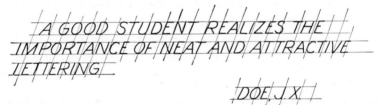

Fig. 3.25.

(8) THE CIRCUMFERENCE OF A CIRCLE MAY BE DIVIDED INTO TWENTY-FOUR EQUAL ARCS USING ONLY A T-SQUARE IN COMBINATION WITH THE 30°–60° AND 45° TRIANGLES.

(9) A TRUE ELLIPSE MAY BE CONSTRUCTED BY THE TRAMMEL METHOD.

(10) THE POSITION OF THE VIEWS OF AN ORTHOGRAPHIC

DRAWING MUST BE IN STRICT ACCORDANCE WITH THE UNIVERSALLY RECOGNIZED ARRANGEMENT ILLUSTRATED IN FIG. 6.6.

(11) THE VIEWS OF AN ORTHOGRAPHIC DRAWING SHOULD SHOW THE THREE DIMENSIONS, LENGTH, BREADTH, AND THICKNESS.

(12) AN INVISIBLE LINE SHOULD START WITH A SPACE WHEN IT FORMS AN EXTENSION OF A SOLID LINE.

(13) THE FRONT VIEW OF AN ORTHOGRAPHIC DRAWING SHOULD BE THE VIEW THAT SHOWS THE CHARACTERISTIC SHAPE OF THE OBJECT.

(14) AN AUXILIARY VIEW SHOWS THE TRUE SIZE AND SHAPE OF AN INCLINED SURFACE.

(15) A SECTIONAL VIEW SHOWS THE INTERIOR CONSTRUCTION OF AN OBJECT.

(16) #404 WOODRUFF KEY.

DRILL AND REAM FOR #2 TAPER PIN WITH PC#10 IN POSITION.

17–21. Using a hard pencil, draw two or more sets of horizontal and inclined guide lines for $\frac{5}{32}''$ letters, then execute directly with India ink the following exercises in lower-case letters:

(17) The front and top views are always in line vertically.

(18) The front and side views are in line horizontally.

(19) The depth of the top view is the same as the depth of the side view.

(20) If a line is perpendicular to a plane of projection, its projection will be a point.

(21) If a line is parallel to a plane of projection, its projection on the plane is exactly the same length as the true length of the line.

22–26. Draw two or more sets of both horizontal and inclined guide lines, and letter the following series of words, whole numbers, and fractions, once in pencil and once in India ink.

(22) $1\frac{1}{2}$, $3\frac{3}{4}$, $2\frac{7}{8}$, $1\frac{9}{16}$, $9\frac{17}{32}$, $4\frac{5}{8}$, $9\frac{13}{32}$, $7\frac{13}{64}$, $8\frac{1}{2}$, $\frac{11}{16}$, $5\frac{3}{8}$.

(23) $\frac{1}{2}'' \times 2\frac{3}{4}''$ HEX. HD. CAP SCREW, $\frac{3}{8} \times 1\frac{1}{4}$ UNC HEX. HD. BOLT & HEX. NUT.

(24) $\frac{3}{16}$ DRILL—$\frac{3}{8}$ DEEP, $\frac{1}{4}$ DRILL—4 HOLES, $\frac{1}{8} \times 45°$ CHAMFER.

(25) $\frac{1}{8}$ AM. STD. PIPE TAP, $\frac{1}{2}$—13 UNC—2B.

(26) $2\angle s\ 2\frac{1}{2} \times 2\frac{1}{2} \times \frac{1}{4} \times 8'$-$4''$, $10''$ I $30\#$, $24''$ W⁻$74\#$.

27. Draw horizontal and inclined guide lines and letter the following detail titles. Use $\frac{5}{32}''$ capitals for the part names and $\frac{1}{8}''$ capitals for the remainder of the titles.

BASE	BUSHING	SPINDLE
C.I. 1 REQ'D	BRO. 1 REQ'D	C.R.S. 1 REQ'D

28. Letter the following map title in Modern Roman. The letters of the first and third lines are to be $\frac{1}{2}''$ high, and those of the second line, which give the name of the county, are to be $\frac{3}{4}''$ high. Draw all necessary guide lines.

MAP OF

TIPPECANOE COUNTY

INDIANA

4

Engineering Geometry

4.1. Introduction. The simplified geometrical constructions presented in this chapter are those with which an engineer should be familiar, for they frequently occur in engineering drawing. The methods are applications of the principles found in textbooks on plane geometry. The constructions have been modified to take advantage of time-saving methods made possible by the use of drawing instruments.

Since a study of the subject of plane geometry should be a prerequisite for a course in engineering drawing, the mathematical proofs have been omitted intentionally. Geometrical terms applying to lines, surfaces, and solids, however, are given in Figs. 4.53 and 4.54 for the purpose of review.

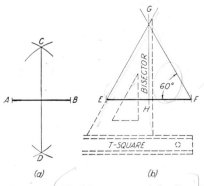

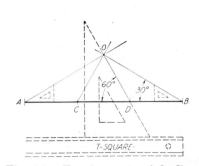

Fig. 4.1. *To bisect a straight line.*   **Fig. 4.2.** *To trisect a straight line.*

4.2. To bisect a straight line (Fig. 4.1).

(*a*) With *A* and *B* as centers, strike the intersecting arcs as shown using any radius greater than one-half of *AB*. A straight line through points *C* and *D* bisects *AB*.

(*b*) Draw either 60° or 45° lines through *E* and *F*. Through their intersection draw the perpendicular *GH* that will bisect *EF*.

The use of the dividers to divide or bisect a line by the trial method is explained in Sec. 2.19.

4.3. To trisect a straight line (Fig. 4.2). Given the line AB. Draw the lines AO and OB making 30° with AB. Similarly, draw CO and OD making 60° with AB. AC equals CD equals DB.

4.4. To bisect an angle (Fig. 4.3).

(a) Given the angle BAC. Use any radius with the vertex A as a center, and strike an arc that intersects the sides of the angle at D and E.

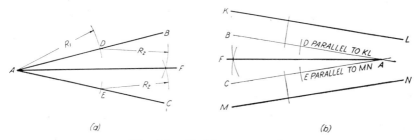

Fig. 4.3.　To bisect an angle.

With D and E as centers and a radius larger than one-half of DE, draw intersecting arcs. Draw AF. Angle BAF equals angle FAC.

(b) Given an angle formed by the lines KL and MN having an inaccessible point of intersection. Draw BA parallel to KL and CA parallel to MN at the same distance from MN as BA is from KL. Bisect angle BAC using the method explained in (a). The bisector FA of angle BAC bisects the angle between the lines KL and MN.

4.5. To draw parallel curved lines about a curved center line (Fig. 4.4). Draw a series of arcs having centers located at random along the given center line AB. Using the French curve, draw the required curved lines tangent to these arcs.

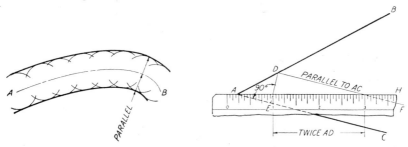

Fig. 4.4.　To draw parallel curved lines.　　　**Fig. 4.5.　To trisect an angle.**

4.6. To trisect an angle (Fig. 4.5). Given the angle BAC. Lay off along AB any convenient distance AD. Draw DE perpendicular to AC and DF parallel to AC. Place the scale so that it passes through A with a distance equal to twice AD intercepted between the lines DE with DF. Angle HAC equals one-third of the angle BAC.

4.7. To divide a straight line into a given number of equal parts
(Fig. 4.6). Given the line LM which is to be divided into five equal parts.

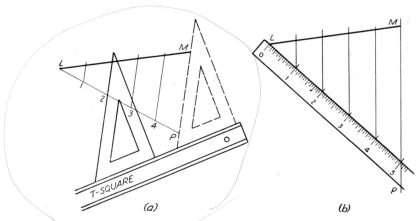

Fig. 4.6. *To divide a straight line into a number of equal parts.*

(*a*) Step off, with the dividers, five equal divisions along a line making
any convenient angle with LM. Connect the last point P with M, and
through the remaining points draw lines parallel to MP intersecting the
given line. These lines divide LM into five equal parts.

(*b*) Some commercial draftsmen prefer a modification of this construction known as the scale method. For the first step, draw a vertical PM
through point M. Place the scale so that
the first mark of five equal divisions is at L
and the last mark falls on PM. Locate the
four intervening division points, and through
these draw verticals intersecting the given
line. The verticals will divide LM into five
equal parts.

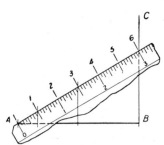

Fig. 4.7. *To divide a line
proportionally.*

4.8. To divide a line proportionally
(Fig. 4.7). Given the line AB. Draw BC
perpendicular to AB. Place the scale across
A and BC so that the number of divisions
intercepted is equal to the sum of the num-
bers representing the proportions. Mark off these proportions and
draw lines parallel to BC to divide AB as required. The proportions in
Fig. 4.7 are $1:2:3$.

4.9. To construct an angle equal to a given angle (Fig. 4.8).
Given the angle BAC and the line $A'C'$ that forms one side of the transferred angle. Use any convenient radius with the vertex A as a center,
and strike the arc that intersects the sides of the angle at D and E. With
A' as a center, strike the arc intersecting $A'C'$ at E'. With E' as a center

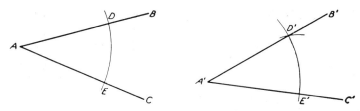

Fig. 4.8.   To construct an angle equal to a given angle.

and the chord distance DE as a radius, strike a short intersecting arc to locate D'. A'B' drawn through D' makes angle B'A'C' equal angle BAC.

4.10. To draw a line through a given point and the inaccessible intersection of two given lines (Fig. 4.9). Given the lines KL and MN, and the point P. Construct any triangle such as PQR having its vertices falling on the given lines and the given point. At some convenient location construct triangle STU similar to PQR, by drawing SU parallel to PR, TU parallel to QR, and ST parallel to PQ. PS is the required line.

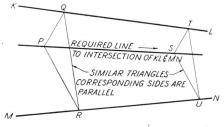

Fig. 4.9. To draw a line through a given point and the inaccessible intersection of two given lines.

4.11. To construct an angle, tangent method (Fig. 4.10). Draftsmen often find it necessary to draw long lines having an angle between them that is not equal to an angle of a triangle. Such an angle may be laid off with a protractor, but it should be remembered that as the lines are extended any error is multiplied. To avoid this situation, the tangent method may be used. The tangent method involves trigonometry but, since it is frequently used, a discussion of it here is pertinent. (See Table XX of the Appendix.)

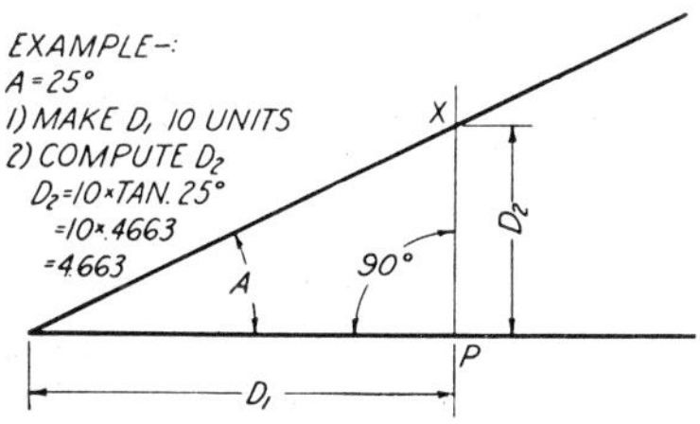

Fig. 4.10.   To construct an angle, tangent method.

In this method, a distance D_1 is laid off along a line that is to form one side of the angle, and a distance D_2, equal to D_1 times the natural tangent of the angle, is marked off along a perpendicular through point P. A line through point X is the required line, and angle A is the required angle. In laying off the distance D_1, unnecessary multiplication will be eliminated if the distance is arbitrarily made 10″. When the use of 10″ for D_1 makes P fall off the drawing, a temporary auxiliary sheet will furnish space needed to carry out the construction.

This method is also used for angles formed by short lines whenever a protractor is not available.

4.12. To construct a triangle having its three sides given (Fig. 4.11). Given the three sides *AB*, *AC*, and *BC*. Draw the side *AB* in its correct location. Using its end points *A* and *B* as centers and radii equal to *AC* and *BC*, respectively, strike the two intersecting arcs locating point *C*. *ABC* is the required triangle. This construction is particularly useful for developing the surface of a transition piece by triangulation.

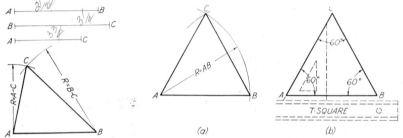

Fig. 4.11. To construct a triangle with three sides given.

Fig. 4.12. To construct an equilateral triangle.

4.13. To construct an equilateral triangle (Fig. 4.12). Given the side *AB*.

(*a*) Using the end points *A* and *B* as centers and a radius equal to the length of *AB*, strike two intersecting arcs to locate *C*. Draw lines from *A* to *C* and *C* to *B* to complete the required equilateral triangle.

(*b*) Using a 30°–60° triangle, draw through *A* and *B* lines that make 60° with the given line. If the line *AB* is inclined, the 60° lines should be drawn as shown in Fig. 2.14.

4.14. To transfer a polygon (Fig. 4.13). Given the polygon *ABCDE*.

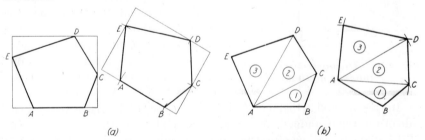

Fig. 4.13. To transfer a polygon.

(*a*) Enclose the polygon in a rectangle. Draw the "enclosing rectangle" in the new position and locate points *A*, *B*, *C*, *D*, and *E* along the sides by measuring from the corners of the rectangle. A compass may be used for transferring the necessary measurements.

(b) To transfer a polygon by the triangle method, divide the polygon into triangles and, using the construction explained in Sec. 4.12, reconstruct each triangle in its transferred position.

4.15. To construct a square (Fig. 4.14).

(a) Given the side *AB*. Using a T-square and a 45° triangle, draw perpendiculars to line *AB* through points *A* and *B*. Locate point *D* at the intersection of a 45° construction line through *A* and the perpendicular from *B*. Draw *CD* parallel to *AB* through *D* to complete the square. To eliminate unnecessary movements the lines should be drawn in the order indicated.

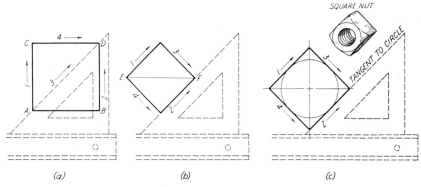

Fig. 4.14.   *To construct a square.*

(b) Given the diagonal length *EF*. Using a T-square and a 45° triangle, construct the square by drawing lines through *E* and *F* at an angle of 45° with *EF* in the order indicated.

(c) The construction of an inscribed circle is the first step in one method for drawing a square when the location of the center and the length of one side are given.

Using a T-square and a 45° triangle, draw the sides of the square tangent to the circle. This construction is used in drawing square bolt heads and nuts.

4.16. To construct a regular pentagon (Fig. 4.15). Given the circumscribing circle. Draw the perpendicular diameters *AB* and *CD*. Bisect *OB* and, with its mid-point *E* as a center and *EC* as a radius, draw the arc *CF*. Using *C* as a center and *CF* as a radius, draw the arc *FG*. The line *CG* is one of the equal sides of the

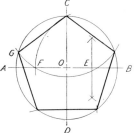

Fig. 4.15. To construct a regular pentagon.

required pentagon. Locate the remaining vertices by striking off this distance around the circumference.

If the length of one side of a pentagon is given, the construction described in Sec. 4.19 should be used.

4.17. To construct a regular hexagon (Fig. 4.16).

(*a*) Given the distance *AB* across corners. Draw a circle having *AB* as a diameter. Using the same radius and with points *A* and *B* as centers, strike arcs intersecting the circumference. Join these points to complete the construction.

(*b*) Given the distance *AB* across corners. Using a 30°–60° triangle and a T-square, draw the lines in the order indicated by the numbers on the figure.

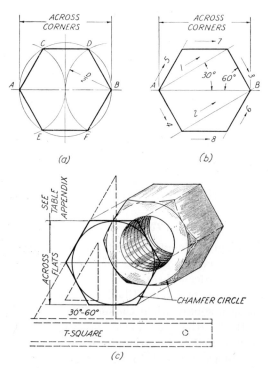

(a)   *(b)*

(c)

Fig. 4.16.   To construct a regular hexagon.

(*c*) Given the distance across flats. Draw a circle whose diameter equals the distance across flats. Using a 30°–60° triangle and a T-square, as shown, draw the tangents that establish the sides and vertices of the required hexagon.

This construction is used in drawing hexagonal bolt heads and nuts.

4.18. To construct a regular octagon (Fig. 4.17).

(*a*) Given the distance across flats. Draw the circumscribed square and its diagonals. Using the corners as centers and one-half the diagonal as a radius, strike arcs across the sides of the square. Join these points to complete the required octagon.

(*b*) Given the distance across flats. Draw the inscribed circle; then,

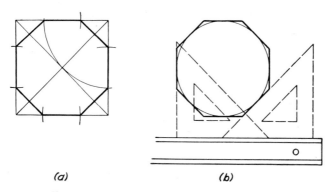

(a)   *(b)*

Fig. 4.17. To construct a regular octagon.

using a 45° triangle and T-square, draw the tangents that establish the sides and vertices of the required octagon.

4.19. To construct any regular polygon having one side given (Fig. 4.18). Given the side LM. With LM as a radius, draw a semicircle and divide it into the same number of equal parts as the number of sides needed for the polygon. Suppose the polygon is to be seven-sided. Draw radial lines through points 2, 3, and so forth. Point 2 (the second division point) is always one of the vertices of the polygon, and line $L2$ is a side. Using point M as a center and LM as a radius, strike an arc across the radial line $L6$ to locate point N. Using the same radius with N as a center, strike another arc across $L5$ to establish O on $L5$. Although this

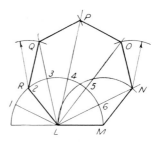

Fig. 4.18. To construct any regular polygon, having one side given.

procedure may be continued with point O as the next center, more accurate results will be obtained if point R is used as a center for the arc to locate Q, and Q as a center for P.

4.20. To divide the area of a triangle or trapezoid into a given number of equal parts (Fig. 4.19).

(a) Given the triangle ABC. Divide the side AC into (say five) equal parts, and draw a semicircle having AC the diameter. Through the division points (1, 2, 3, and 4) draw perpendicular lines to points of intersection with the semicircle (5, 6, 7, and 8). Using C as a center, strike arcs through these points (5, 6, 7, and 8) that will cut AC. To complete the construction, draw lines parallel to AB through the points (9, 10, 11, and 12) at which the arcs intersect the side AC.

(b) Given the trapezoid $DEBA$. Extend the sides of the trapezoid to form the triangle ABC and draw a semicircle on AC with AC as a diameter. Using C as a center and CD as a radius, strike an arc cutting the semi-

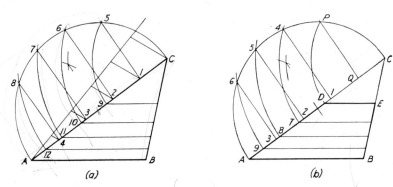

Fig. 4.19.   To divide the area of a trapezoid into a given number of equal parts.

circle at point P.   Through P draw a perpendicular to AC to locate point Q.   Divide QA into the same number of equal parts as the number of equal areas required (in this case four), and proceed using the construction

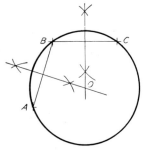

Fig. 4.20.   To find the center of a circle through three points.

explained in (*a*) for dividing the area of a triangle into a given number of equal parts.

4.21. To find the center for a circle through three given points not in a straight line (Fig. 4.20).   Given the three points A, B, and C.   Join the points with straight lines (which will be chords of the required circle), and draw the perpendicular bisectors.   The point of intersection O of the bisectors is the center of the required circle, and OA, OB, or OC is its radius.

4.22. Tangent circles and arcs.   Fig. 4.21 illustrates the geometry of tangent circles.   In (*a*) it can be noted that the locus of centers for circles of radius R tangent to AB is a line that is parallel to AB at a distance R from AB.   The locus of centers for circles of the same radius

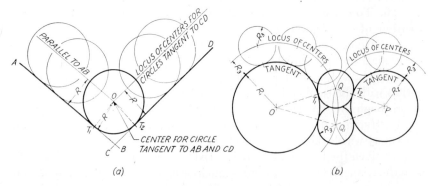

Fig. 4.21.   Tangent circles.

tangent to CD is a line that is parallel to CD at R (radius) distance from CD. Since point O at which these lines intersect is R distance from both AB and CD, a circle of radius R with center at O must be tangent to both AB and CD.

In (b) the locus of centers for circles of radius R_3 that will be tangent to the circle with a center at O and having a radius R_1 is a circle that is concentric with the given circle at R_3 distance. The radius of the locus of centers will be $R_1 + R_3$. In the case of the circle with center at point P, the radius of the locus of centers will be $R_2 + R_3$. Points Q and Q_1 where these arcs intersect are points that are R_3 distance from both circles. Therefore, circles of R_3 radius that are centered at Q and Q_1 will be tangent to both circles with centers at O and P.

4.23. To draw a circular arc of radius R tangent to two lines (Fig. 4.22).

(a) Given the two lines AB and CD at right angles to each other, and the radius of the required arc R. Using their point of intersection X as a

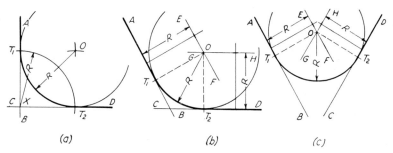

Fig. 4.22.   To draw a circular arc tangent to two lines.

center and R as a radius, strike an arc cutting the given lines at T_1 and T_2 (tangent points). With T_1 and T_2 as centers and the same radius, strike the intersecting arcs locating the center O of the required arc.

(b) and (c) Given the two lines AB and CD, not at right angles, and the radius R. Draw lines EF and GH parallel to the given lines at a distance R. Since the point of intersection of these lines is distance R from both given lines, it will be the center O of the required arc. Mark the tangent points T_1 and T_2 that lie along perpendiculars to the given lines through O.

These constructions are useful for drawing fillets and rounds on views of machine parts.

4.24. To draw a circular arc of radius R_1 tangent to a given circular arc and a given straight line (Fig. 4.23). Given the line AB and the circular arc with center O.

(a) and (b) Let R_1 be the radius of the required arc. Draw line CD parallel to AB at a distance R_1. Using the center O of the given arc and a radius equal to its radius plus or minus the radius of the required arc

(R_2 plus or minus R_1), swing a parallel arc intersecting CD. Since the line CD and the intersecting arc will be the loci of centers for all circles of radius R_1, tangent respectively to the given line AB and the given arc, their point of intersection P will be the center of the required arc. Mark the points of tangency T_1 and T_2. T_1 lies along a perpendicular to AB

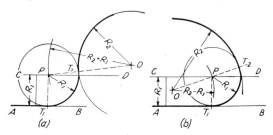

Fig. 4.23. *To draw a circular arc tangent to a given circular arc and a line.*

through the center P, and T_2 along a line joining the centers of the two arcs.

This construction is also useful for drawing fillets and rounds on views of machine parts.

4.25. To draw a circular arc of a given radius R_1 tangent to two given circular arcs (Fig. 4.24). Given the circular arcs AB and CD with centers O and P, and radii R_2 and R_3, respectively. Let R_1 be the radius of the required arc.

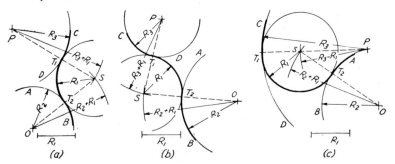

Fig. 4.24. *To draw a circular arc tangent to two given arcs.*

(a) and (b) Using O as a center and R_2 plus R_1 as a radius, strike an arc parallel to AB. Using P as a center and R_3 plus R_1 as a radius, strike an intersecting arc parallel to CD. Since each of these intersecting arcs is the locus of centers for all circular arcs of radius R_1 tangent to the given arc to which it is parallel, their point of intersection S will be the center for the required arc that is tangent to both. Mark the points of tangency T_1 and T_2 that lie on the lines of centers PS and OS.

(c) Using O as a center and R_2 plus R_1 as a radius, strike an arc parallel to AB. Using P as a center and R_3 minus R_1 as a radius, strike an intersecting arc parallel to CD.   The point of intersection of these arcs is the center for the required arc.

4.26. To draw a reverse (ogee) curve (Fig. 4.25).   Given the two parallel lines AB and CD.   At points B and C, the termini and tangent points of the reverse curve, erect perpendiculars.   Join BC with a straight line and assume a point E that will be the point at which the curves will be tangent to each other.   Draw the perpendicular bisectors of BE and EC.   Since an arc tangent to AB at B must have its center on the perpendicu-lar BP, point of intersection P of the bisector and the perpendicular is the center for the required arc that is to be tangent to the line at B and the other required arc at point E.   For the same reason, point Q is the center for the other required arc.

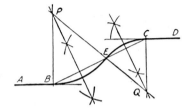

Fig. 4.25.   To draw a reverse curve.

This construction is useful to engi-neers in laying out center lines for railroad tracks, pipe lines, and so forth.

4.27. To draw a line tangent to a circle at a given point on the circumference (Fig. 4.26).   Given a circle with center O and point P on its circumference.   Place a triangle supported by a T-square or another triangle in such a position that one side passes through the center O and point P.   When using the method illustrated in (a), align the hypotenuse

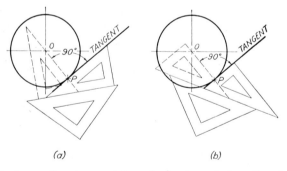

(a)   (b)

Fig. 4.26.   To draw a line tangent to a circle at a point on the circumference.

of one triangle to the center of the circle and the point of tangency; then, with a guiding triangle held in position, revolve the triangle about the 90° angle and slide into position for drawing the required tangent line.

Another procedure is shown in (b).   To draw the tangent by this method, align one leg of a triangle, which is adjacent to the 90° angle, through the center of the circle and the point of tangency; then, slide it along the edge of a guiding triangle into position.

This construction satisfies the geometrical requirement that a tangent must be perpendicular to a radial line drawn to the point of tangency.

4.28. To draw a line tangent to a circle through a given point outside the circle (Fig. 4.27).   Given a circle with center O, and an external point P.

Join the point P and the center O with a straight line, and bisect it to locate point S.   Using S as a center and SO (one-half PO) as a radius, strike an arc intersecting the circle at point T (point of tangency).   Line PT is the required tangent.

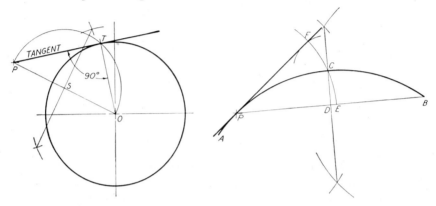

Fig. 4.27.   To draw a line tangent to a circle through a given point outside.

Fig. 4.28.   To draw a tangent to a circular arc having an inaccessible center.

4.29. To draw a tangent through a point P on a circular arc having an inaccessible center (Fig. 4.28).   Draw the chord PB; then, erect a perpendicular bisector.   With point P as a center swing an arc through point C where the perpendicular bisector cuts the given arc.

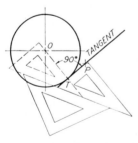

Fig. 4.29.   To draw a line tangent to a circle through a given point outside.

With C as a center and a radius equal to the chord distance CE, draw an arc to establish the location of point F.   A line drawn through points P and F is the required tangent.

4.30. To draw a line tangent to a circle through a given point outside the circle (Fig. 4.29).   Place a triangle supported by a T-square or another triangle in such a position that one leg passes through point P tangent to the circle, and draw the tangent.   Slide the triangle along the guiding edge until the other leg coincides with the center O, and mark the point of tangency.   Although this method is not as accurate as the geometrical one explained in Sec. 4.28, it is frequently employed by commercial draftsmen.

4.31. To draw a line tangent to two given circle arcs (circles) (Fig. 4.30). Given two circle arcs with centers O and Q, respectively.

Let R and R_1 be the radii of the circle arcs. Using O as a center and

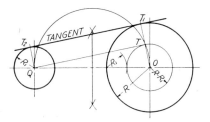

a radius equal to R minus R_1, draw an arc. Through Q draw a tangent to this arc and mark the point of tangency T. Project the radius OT to locate T_1, and draw QT_2 parallel to OT_1. The line from T_1 to T_2 is the required tangent to the given circle arcs (circles).

Fig. 4.30. To draw a line tangent to two given circles.

4.32. To approximate a curve with tangent circular arcs (Fig. 4.31). Draftsmen often find it desirable to approximate a noncircular curve with a series of tangent arcs. If the curve consists of a number of points, a pleasing curve should be sketched lightly through points before starting to draw the arcs. The cen-

ters and radii are selected by trial but it must be remembered after the first arc has been drawn as far as it coincides with the sketched curve that when arcs are tangent the centers are on a common normal through their point of tangency. Sometimes draftsmen use this method to draw curves in ink instead of using a French curve.

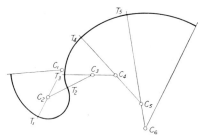

Fig. 4.31. To approximate a curve with tangent circular arcs.

4.33. To lay off the approximate length of the circumference of a circle (Fig. 4.32). Draw a line through point A tangent to the circle and lay off along it a distance AB equal to three times the diameter ($3D$).

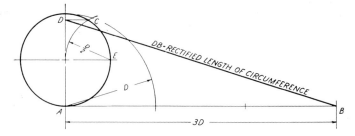

Fig. 4.32. To lay off the approximate length of the circumference of a circle.

Using point E on the circumference as a center and a radius equal to the radius of the circle strike an arc to establish the location of point C. Draw CD perpendicular to the vertical center line through point A. DB is the rectified length of the circumference; however, it is slightly longer than the true circumference by a negligible amount (approximate error 1/21,800).

4.34. To lay off the approximate length of a circular arc on its tangent (Fig. 4.33).   Given the arc AB.

(a) Draw the tangent through A, and extend the chord BA.   Locate point C by laying off AC equal to one-half the length of the chord AB. With C as a center and a radius equal to CB, strike an arc intersecting the tangent at D.   The length AD along the tangent is slightly shorter than the true length of the arc AB by an amount that may be disregarded, for, when the angle between the chord and the tangent is less than 60°, the length of AD differs from the true length of the arc AB by less than 6' in one mile; when 30°, the error is $4\frac{1}{2}''$ in one mile.

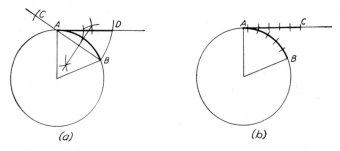

(a)   (b)

Fig. 4.33.   To lay off the approximate length of a circular arc on its tangent.

(b) Draw the tangent through A.   Using the small dividers, start at B and step off equal chord distances around the arc until the point nearest A is reached.   From this point (without raising the dividers) step off along the tangent an equal number of distances to locate point C.   If the point nearest A is indented into the tangent instead of the arc, the almost negligible error in the length of AC will be still less.

Since the small distances stepped off are in reality the chords of small arcs, the length AC will be slightly less than the true length of the arc. For most practical purposes the difference may be disregarded.

4.35. Conic sections (Fig. 4.34).   When a right circular cone of revolution is cut by planes at different angles four curves of intersection are obtained that are called conic sections.

When the intersecting plane is perpendicular to the axis the resulting curve of intersection is a circle.

If the plane makes a greater angle with the axis than do the elements the intersection is an ellipse.

If the plane makes the same angle with the axis as the elements the resulting curve is a parabola.

Finally, if the plane makes a smaller angle with the axis than do the elements or is parallel to the axis the curve of intersection is a hyperbola.

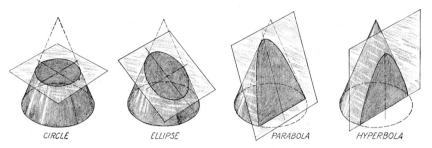

Fig. 4.34. Conic Sections.

The geometric methods for constructing the ellipse, parabola, and hyperbola are discussed in succeeding sections.

4.36. The ellipse. Mathematically the ellipse is a curve generated by a point moving so that at any position the sum of its distances from two fixed points (foci) is a constant (equal to the major diameter). It is encountered very frequently in orthographic drawing when holes and circular forms are viewed obliquely. Ordinarily, the major and minor diameters are known.

4.37. To construct an ellipse, trammel method (Fig. 4.35). Given the major axis AB and the minor axis CD. Along the straight edge of a strip of paper or cardboard, locate the points O, C, and A, so that the distance OA is equal to one-half the length of the major axis and the distance OC is equal to one-half the length of the minor axis. Place the marked edge across the axes so that point A is on the minor axis and point C is on the major axis. *Point O will fall on the circumference of the ellipse.* Move the strip, keeping A on the minor axis and C on the major axis, and mark at least five other positions

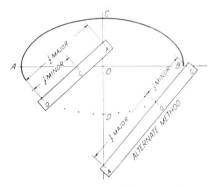

Fig. 4.35. To construct an ellipse, trammel method.

of O on the ellipse in each quadrant. Using a French curve, complete the ellipse by drawing a smooth curve through the points. The ellipsograph, which draws ellipses mechanically, is based on this same principle. The trammel method is an accurate method.

An alternate method for marking off the location of points A, O, and C is given in Fig. 4.35.

4.38. To construct an ellipse, concentric circle method (Fig. 4.36). Given the major axis AB and the minor axis CD. Using the center of the ellipse (point O) as a center, describe circles having the major and minor axes as diameters. Divide the circles into equal central angles and draw diametrical lines such as P_1P_2. From point P_1 on the circum-

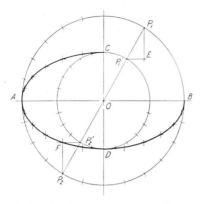

ference of the larger circle, draw a line parallel to CD, the minor axis, and from point P_1' at which the diameter P_1P_2 intersects the inner circle, draw a line parallel to AB, the major axis. The point of intersection of these lines, point E, is on the required ellipse. At points P_2 and P_2' repeat the same procedure and locate point F. Thus, two points are established by the line P_1P_2. Locate at least five points in each of the four quadrants. The ellipse is completed by drawing a smooth curve through the points.

Fig. 4.36. To construct an ellipse, concentric circle method.

This is one of the most accurate methods used to form ellipses.

4.39. To construct an ellipse, four-center method (Fig. 4.37). Given the major axis AB and the minor axis CD. Draw the line AC. Using the center of the ellipse O as a center and OC as a radius, strike an arc intersecting OA at point E. Using C as a center and EA as a radius, strike an arc intersecting the line AC at F. Draw the perpendicular bisector of the line AF. The points G and H, at which the perpendicular bisector intersects the axes AB and CD (extended) are the centers of two of the arcs forming the ellipse. Locate the other two centers, J and K, by laying off OJ equal to OH and OK equal to OG. To determine the junction points (tangent points), T, T_1, T_2, and T_3, for the arcs, draw lines through the centers of the tangent arcs.

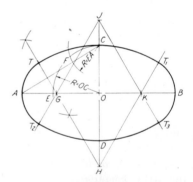

Fig. 4.37. To construct an ellipse, center method.

The figure thus formed by the four circle arcs approximates a true ellipse.

4.40. To construct an ellipse, parallelogram method (Fig. 4.38). Given the major axis AB and the minor axis CD. Construct the circumscribing parallelogram. Divide AO and AE into the same number of equal parts (say four) and number the division points from A. From C draw a line through point 3 on line AE, and from D draw a line through point 3 on line AO. The point of intersection of these lines is on the required ellipse. Similarly, the intersections of lines from C and D through points numbered 1 and 2 are on the ellipse. A similar construction will locate points in the other three quadrants of the ellipse. Use of a French curve will permit a smooth curve to be drawn through the points.

Had the circumscribing parallelogram not been a rectangle as in Fig. 4.38, the completed construction would appear as in Fig. 4.39, and AB and CD would be conjugate axes. To establish the major and minor axes, draw a semicircle on CD as a diameter, intersecting the ellipse at E. FG, running parallel to CE through the center of the ellipse, will be the required minor axis. HK, running through the

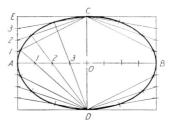

Fig. 4.38. To construct an ellipse, parallelogram method.

center of the ellipse parallel to DE and perpendicular to FG, will be the major axis.

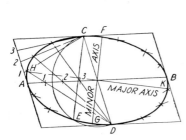

Fig. 4.39. To draw the major and minor axes of an ellipse, given the conjugate diameters.

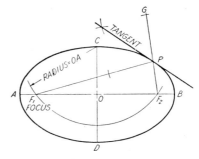

Fig. 4.40. To draw a tangent to an ellipse.

4.41. To draw a tangent to an ellipse at any given point (Fig. 4.40). Given any point, such as P, on the perimeter of the ellipse $ABCD$. Using C as a center and a radius equal to OA (one-half the major diameter),

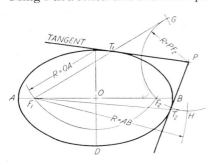

Fig. 4.41. To draw a tangent to an ellipse through a point outside of the ellipse.

strike arcs across the major axis at F_1 and F_2. From these points, which are foci of the ellipse, draw F_1P and F_2G. The bisector of the angle GPF_1 is the required tangent to the ellipse.

In practice it will often be convenient to use the chord method explained in Sec. 19.4 for constructing tangents. See Fig. 19.8.

4.42. To draw a tangent to an ellipse from a given point P outside of the ellipse (Fig. 4.41). With the end of the minor axis as a center and a radius R equal to one-half of the length of the major axis, strike an arc to find the foci F_1 and F_2. With point P as a center and the distance PF_2 as a radius, draw an arc. Using F_1 as a center and the length AB as a radius strike arcs cutting the arc with center of P at points G and H. Draw lines GF_1 and HF_1 to establish the location of the tangent points T_1 and T_2. Draw the required tangent.

4.43. The parabola. Mathematically the parabola is a curve generated by a point moving so that at any position its distance from a fixed point (the focus) is always exactly equal to its distance to a fixed line (the directrix). The construction shown in Fig. 4.42 is based on this definition.

In engineering design, the parabola is used for parabolic sound and light reflectors, for vertical curves on highways, and for bridge arches.

4.44. To construct a parabola (Fig. 4.42). Given the focus F and the directrix AB. Draw the axis of the parabola perpendicular to the directrix. Through any point on the axis, for example point C, draw a line parallel to the directrix AB. Using F as a center and the distance OC as a radius, strike arcs intersecting the line at points P_4 and P_4'. Repeat this procedure until a sufficient number of additional points have been located to determine a smooth curve. The vertex V is located at a point midway between O and F.

To construct a tangent to a parabola, say at point P_6, draw the line P_6D parallel to the axis; then, bisect the angle DP_6F. The bisector of the angle is the required tangent. Read Sec. 19.4 and study Fig. 19.8.

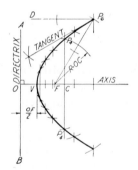

Fig. 4.42. To construct a parabola.

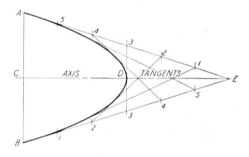

Fig. 4.43. To construct a parabola, tangent method.

4.45. To construct a parabola, tangent method (Fig. 4.43). Given the points A and B and the distance CD from AB to the vertex. Extend the axis CD, and set off DE equal to CD. EA and EB are tangents to the parabola at A and B respectively.

Divide EA and EB into the same number of equal parts (say six), and number the division points as shown. Connect the corresponding points 1 and 1, 2 and 2, 3 and 3, and so forth. These lines, as tangents of the required parabola, form its envelope. Draw the tangent curve.

4.46. To construct a parabola, offset method (Fig. 4.44). Given the enclosing rectangle $A'ABB'$. Divide DA' into any number of equal parts (say four), and draw from the division points the perpendiculars parallel to DC, along which the offset distances are to be measured off. The offsets vary as the square of their distances from D. For example, since $D1$ is one-fourth of the distance from A' to D, $1–1'$ will be $(\frac{1}{4})^2$, or one-sixteenth of $A'A$. Similarly, $2–2'$ will be $(\frac{1}{2})^2$, or $\frac{1}{4}$ of $A'A$; and $3–3'$ will be $\frac{9}{16}$ of $A'A$. To complete the parabola, lay off the computed offset values along the perpendiculars and form the figure with a French curve.

This method is preferred by civil engineers for laying out parabolic arches and computing vertical curves for highways.

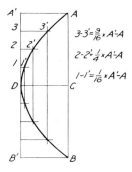

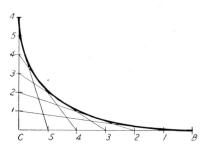

Fig. 4.44. To construct a parabola, offset method.

Fig. 4.45. To construct a curve of parabolic form.

4.47. To construct a curve of parabolic form through two given points (Fig. 4.45). Given the points A and B. Assume a point C. Draw the tangents CA and CB, and construct the parabolic curve using the tangent method shown in Fig. 4.43. This method is frequently used in machine design to draw curves that are more pleasing than circular arcs.

4.48. The hyperbola. Mathematically, the hyperbola can be described as a curve generated by a point moving so that at any position the difference of its distances from two fixed points (foci) is a constant (equal to the transverse axis of the hyperbola). This definition is the basis for the construction shown in Fig. 4.46.

4.49. To construct a hyperbola (Fig. 4.46). Given the foci F_1 and F_2, and the transverse axis AB. Using F_1

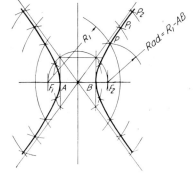

Fig. 4.46. To construct a hyperbola.

and F_2 as centers and any radius R_1 greater than F_1B, strike arcs. With these same centers and a radius equal to $R_1–AB$, strike arcs intersecting the first arcs at point P. Point P is on the required hyperbola. Repeat this procedure and locate as many additional points, such as P_1, P_2, and so forth, as are required to form the hyperbola accurately with a French curve.

The tangent to the hyperbola at any point, such as P, is the bisector of the angle between the focal radii F_1P and F_2P. Read Sec. 19.4 and study Fig. 19.8.

4.50. An involute. The spiral curve traced by a point on a chord as it unwinds from around a circle or a polygon is an involute curve. Fig. 4.47(a) shows an involute of a circle, while (b) shows that of a square. The involute of a polygon is obtained by extending the sides and drawing arcs using the corners, in order, as centers. The circle in (a) may be considered to be a polygon having an infinite number of sides.

4.51. To draw an involute of a circle (Fig. 4.47a). Divide the circumference into a number of equal parts. Draw tangents through the division points. Then, along each tangent, lay off the rectified length of the corresponding circular arc, from the starting point to the point of tangency. The involute curve is a smooth curve through these points. The involute of a circle is used in the development of tooth profiles in gearing.

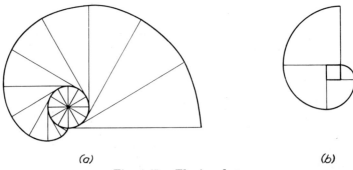

(a)   *(b)*

Fig. 4.47.   The involute.

4.52. To draw the involute of a polygon (Fig. 4.47b). Extend the sides of the polygon as shown in (b). With the corners as centers, in order around the polygon, draw arcs terminating on the extended sides. The first radius is equal to the length of one side of the polygon. The radius of each successive arc is the distance from the center to the terminating point of the previous arc.

4.53. A cycloid. A cycloid is the curve generated by a point on the circumference of a moving circle when the circle rolls in a plane along a straight line, as shown in Fig. 4.48.

4.54. To draw a cycloid (Fig. 4.48). Draw the generating circle and the line AB tangent to it. The length AB should be made equal to the circumference of the circle. Divide the circle and the line AB into the same number of equal parts. With this much of the construction completed, the next step is to draw the line of centers CD through point O and project the division points along AB to CD by drawing perpendiculars. Using these points as centers for the various positions of the moving circle, draw circle arcs. For the purpose of illustration, assume the circle is moving to the left. When the circle has moved along CD to x, point P

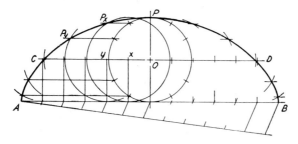

Fig. 4.48. A cycloid.

will have moved to point P_x. Similarly, when the center is at y, P will be at P_y. To locate positions of P along the cycloidal curve, project the division points of the divided circle in their proper order, across to the position circles. A smooth curve through these points will be the required cycloid.

4.55. An epicycloid (Fig. 4.49). An epicycloid is the curve generated by a point on the circumference of a circle that rolls in a plane on the outside of another circle. The method used in drawing an epicycloid is similar to the one used in drawing the cycloid.

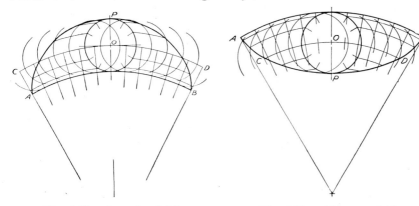

Fig. 4.49. An epicycloid.　　　　Fig. 4.50. A hypocycloid.

4.56. A hypocycloid (Fig. 4.50). A hypocycloid is the curve generated by a point on the circumference of a circle that rolls in a plane on the inside of another circle. The method used to draw a hypocycloid is similar to the method used to draw the cycloid.

Practical examples of the use of cycloidal curves to form the outlines of cycloidal gear teeth are shown in the chapter on gears in this text.

4.57. Spiral of Archimedes. Archimedes spiral is a plane curve generated by a point moving uniformly around and away from a fixed point. In order to define this curve more specifically, it can be said that it is generated by a point moving uniformly along a straight line while the line revolves with uniform angular velocity about a fixed point.

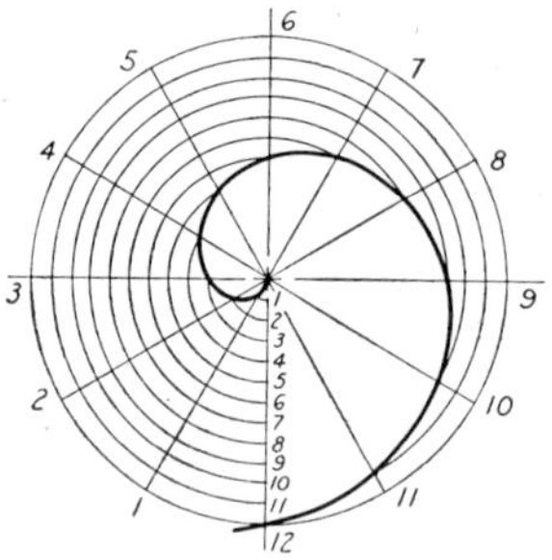

The definition of the Spiral of Archimedes is applied in drawing this curve as illustrated in Fig. 4.51. To find a sufficient number of points to allow the use of an irregular curve for drawing the spiral it is the practice to divide the given circle into a number of equal parts (say twelve) and draw radial lines to the division points. Next, divide a radial line into the same number of equal parts as the circle and number the division points on the circumference of the circle beginning with the radial line adjacent to the divided one. With the center of the circle as a center draw concentric arcs that in each case will start at a numbered division point on the divided radial line and will end at an intersection with the radial line that is numbered correspondingly. The arc starting at point *1* gives a point on the curve at its intersection with radial line *1*; the arc starting at *2* gives an intersection point on radial line *2*; etc. The spiral is a smooth curve drawn through these intersection points.

Fig. 4.51. Spiral of Archimedes.

4.58. The helix (Fig. 4.52). The cylindrical helix is a space curve that is generated by a point moving uniformly on the surface of a cylinder. The point must travel parallel to the axis with uniform linear velocity

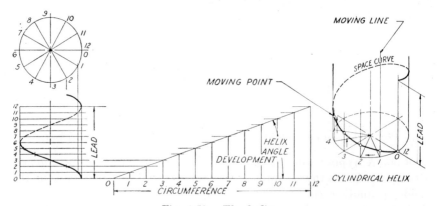

Fig. 4.52.   The helix.

while at the same time it is moving with uniform angular velocity around the axis. The curve can be thought of as being generated by a point moving uniformly along a straight line while the line is revolving with uniform angular velocity around the axis of the given cylinder. Study the pictorial drawing, Fig. 4.52.

The first step in drawing a cylindrical helix is to lay out the two views of the cylinder. Next, the lead should be measured along a contour element and divided into a number of equal parts (say twelve). Divide the

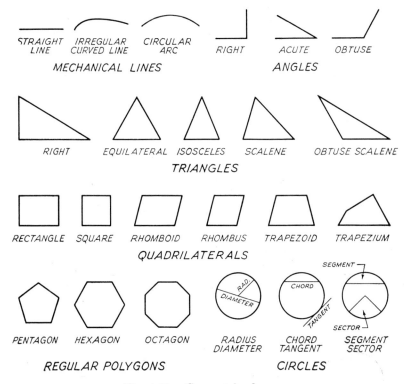

MECHANICAL LINES

STRAIGHT LINE · IRREGULAR CURVED LINE · CIRCULAR ARC

ANGLES

RIGHT · ACUTE · OBTUSE

TRIANGLES

RIGHT · EQUILATERAL · ISOSCELES · SCALENE · OBTUSE SCALENE

QUADRILATERALS

RECTANGLE · SQUARE · RHOMBOID · RHOMBUS · TRAPEZOID · TRAPEZIUM

REGULAR POLYGONS

PENTAGON · HEXAGON · OCTAGON

CIRCLES

RADIUS DIAMETER · CHORD TANGENT · SEGMENT SECTOR

Fig. 4.53.   Geometric shapes.

circular view of the cylinder into the same number of parts and number the division points.

The division lines of the lead represent the various positions of the moving point as it travels in a direction parallel to the axis of the cylinder along the moving line. The division points on the circular view are the related position of the moving line. For example, when the line has moved from the *0* to the *1* position, the point has traveled along the line a distance equal to one-twelfth of the lead; when the line is in the *2* position, the point has traveled one-sixth of the lead. (See pictorial drawing, Fig. 4.52.) In constructing the curve the necessary points are found by projecting from a numbered point on the circular view to the division line of the lead that is numbered similarly.

A helix may be either right-hand or left-hand.   The one shown in Fig. 4.52 is a left-hand helix.

When the cylinder is developed, the helix becomes a straight line on the development as shown.   It is inclined to the base line at an angle known as the "helix angle."

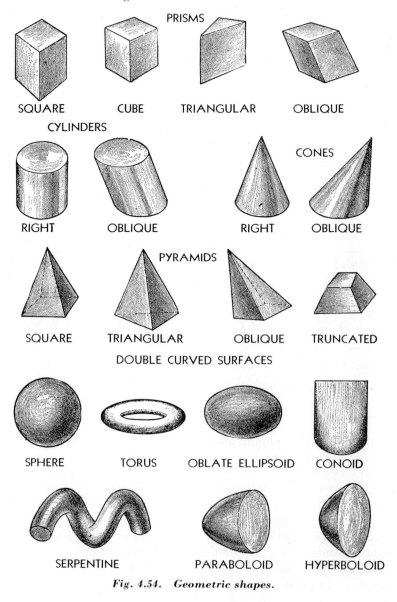

Fig. 4.54.   *Geometric shapes.*

A screw thread is an example of a practical application of the cylindrical helix.

4.59. Problems. The following exercises not only require the student to study and use certain common geometrical constructions, but also furnish additional practice in applying good line technique to the drawing of instrumental figures and practical designs. All work should be very accurately done. Tangent points should be indicated by a light short dash across the line.

1. Draw a horizontal line $4\frac{3}{8}''$ long. Bisect it by the method shown in Fig. 4.1(*b*).

2. Draw a line $3\frac{3}{4}''$ long, inclined at 30° to the horizontal. Divide it into five equal parts. Use the method illustrated in Fig. 4.6(*a*).

3. Draw a line $3\frac{1}{4}''$ long. Divide it into three equal parts. Use the method shown in Fig. 4.2.

4. Draw a line $3\frac{1}{8}''$ long. Divide it proportionally in the ratio 1:2:3. Use the method shown in Fig. 4.7.

5. Using a line $3\frac{1}{4}''$ long as the base line, construct a triangle having sides $2\frac{1}{2}''$, $3\frac{1}{4}''$, and $3\frac{3}{4}''$ long, respectively. Study the method that is illustrated in Fig. 4.11.

6. Construct a regular hexagon having a $2\frac{1}{2}''$ distance across flats. Select the most practical procedure.

7. Construct a regular hexagon having a $3\frac{1}{4}''$ distance across corners. Select the most practical method.

8. Construct a regular pentagon having $1\frac{1}{4}''$ sides. Use the method illustrated in Fig. 4.18.

9. Divide the area of the triangle in problem 5 into four equal parts. Use the method shown in Fig. 4.19(*a*).

10. Trisect the angle between the $3\frac{1}{4}''$ and $3\frac{3}{4}''$ sides of the triangle in problem 5. Use the method illustrated in Fig. 4.5.

11. Draw two horizontal lines $2''$ apart. Locate two points $3''$ apart horizontally, one on each line. Draw an ogee curve tangent to these lines. Study the procedure illustrated in Fig. 4.25.

12. Draw a $2\frac{1}{2}''$ circle. Select a point $2''$ from the center and draw a line tangent to it, using the method illustrated in Fig. 4.27.

13. Draw a $2\frac{3}{4}''$ circle, and draw tangent to it a line that makes 15° with the horizontal. Draw a $1\frac{1}{2}''$ circle tangent to the line and the $2\frac{3}{4}''$ circle. Use the method illustrated in Fig. 4.23.

14. Draw a $3''$ circle. Inside this circle, and tangent to it, draw a $1\frac{1}{4}''$ circle. See that the centers of both circles are on the same vertical center line. Draw two $1''$ circles tangent to the $3''$ and the $1\frac{3}{4}''$ circle. Use the method illustrated in Fig. 4.24.

15. Construct an ellipse having a major diameter of $4\frac{1}{4}''$ and a minor diameter of $2\frac{3}{4}''$. Use the trammel method illustrated in Fig. 4.35.

16. Construct an ellipse having a major diameter of $4''$ and a minor diameter of $2\frac{3}{4}''$. Use the concentric circle method illustrated in Fig. 4.36. Find a sufficient number of points to obtain a smooth curve.

17. Construct the ellipse required in problem 16, using the four-center method. Study Sec. 4.39 and Fig. 4.37.

18. Construct an ellipse having conjugate axes $3\frac{3}{4}''$ and $2\frac{1}{2}''$ long inclined one to the other at 75°. Determine the major and minor axes (Fig. 4.39).

19. Construct a parabola with vertical axis. Make the focus $\frac{3}{4}''$ from the directrix. Select a point on the curve and draw a line tangent to the parabola. Study Sec. 4.44 and Fig. 4.42.

20. Construct a hyperbola having a transverse axis of $1''$ and foci $1\frac{5}{8}''$ apart. Study Sec. 4.49 and Fig 4.46.

21. Construct the involute of an equilateral triangle with $1''$ sides. Study Sec. 4.52.

22. Construct the involute of a circle $\frac{7}{8}''$ in diameter. Study Sec. 4.51 and Fig. 4.47(a).

23. Construct the cycloid generated by a $1\frac{1}{2}''$ circle. Study Sec. 4.54 and Fig. 4.48.

24. Construct the epicycloid generated by a $1\frac{1}{2}''$ circle rolling on a $5''$ circle. Study Sec. 4.55 and Fig. 4.49.

25. Construct the hypocycloid generated by a $1\frac{1}{2}''$ circle rolling on a $4\frac{1}{2}''$ circle. Study Sec. 4.56 and Fig. 4.50.

26. Reconstruct the view of the gasket shown in Fig. 4.55 to full scale. Mark all of the tangent points with short lines. Study Fig. 4.24. Do not place dimensions on the finished drawing.

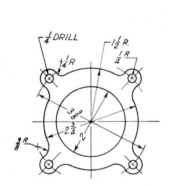

Fig. 4.55.   Gasket.

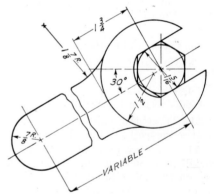

Fig. 4.56.   Wrench.

27. Reconstruct the view of the wrench shown in Fig. 4.56. Mark all tangent points with short lines.

28. Reconstruct the view of the gasket shown in Fig. 4.57. Mark all tangent points with short marks across tangent lines.

29. Reconstruct the view of the guide shown in Fig. 4.58.

30. Reconstruct the view of the cam shown in Fig. 4.59. Mark all tangent points.

31. Construct the shape of the slotted guide shown in Fig. 4.60. Show all construction for locating centers and mark points of tangency.

32. Construct the adjustable Y-clamp shown in Fig. 4.61. Show all construction for locating centers and mark points of tangency.

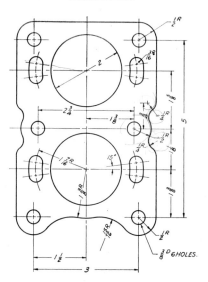

Fig. 4.57. Gasket.

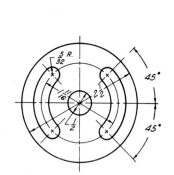

Fig. 4.58. Guide.

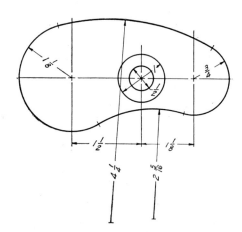

Fig. 4.59. Cam.

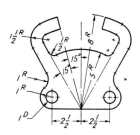

Fig. 4.60. Slotted guide.

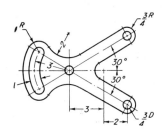

Fig. 4.61. Adjustable Y-clamp.

33. Reconstruct the geometrical design shown in Fig. 4.62. Mark all tangent points with short marks across tangent lines, as shown in the given view.

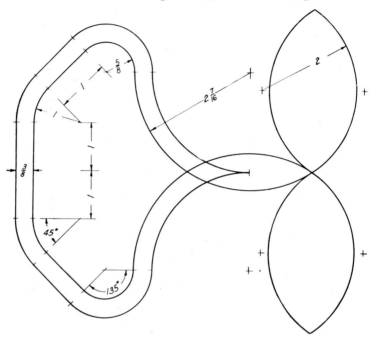

Fig. 4.62. Geometrical design.

34. Reconstruct the view of the cover gasket shown in Fig. 4.63.

35. Reconstruct the view of the C-ring shown in Fig. 4.64.

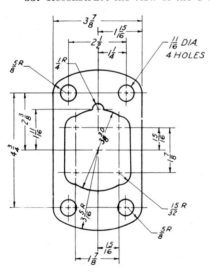

Fig. 4.63. Cover gasket.

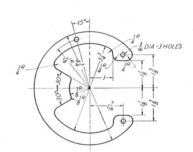

Fig. 4.64. C-ring.

36. (Fig. 4.65.) Using an eighth size scale, make a one-view drawing of the housing gasket. Use approved geometrical constructions and mark all tangent points with $\frac{1}{8}''$ dash across the line. Be prepared to explain to your instructor the procedure for determining the locations for centers and tangent points and demonstrate the manipulation of the triangles for the 15° angles. Study Sec. 4.11.

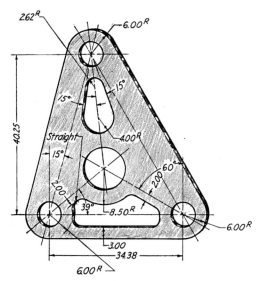

Fig. 4.65. Housing gasket.

Supplementary information: (1) the three small circular holes are to be 6″ in diameter, (2) the large hole in the center of the gasket must have a $10\frac{1}{2}''$ diameter, (3) all small radii are 2″, (4) the gasket is to be cut from $\frac{1}{16}''$ fiber stock.

37. Reconstruct the end view of the dolly block shown in Fig. 4.66.

38. Reconstruct the view of the electrode shown in Fig. 4.67.

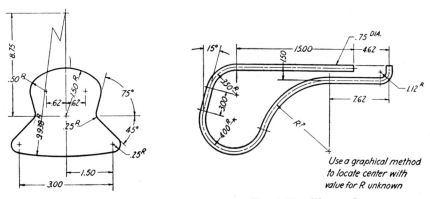

*Fig. 4.66. End view—
dolly block.*

Fig. 4.67. Electrode.

39. Reconstruct the plat of a land survey shown in Fig. 4.68. Use the tangent method, as explained in Sec. 4.11, to determine the direction of the

center line of state road 26.   The triangles used in combination will produce the
other angles.

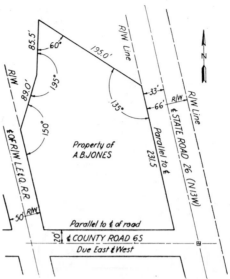

Fig. 4.68.   A plat of a land survey.

40. (Fig. 4.69.)   Part A is free to pivot about a shaft.   If this part should
be revolved in a counterclockwise direction as indicated by the arrows, it would
contact surface C.   Reproduce the drawing as given and show part A revolved
until it is in contact with surface C.   Use the symbolic line for showing an alternate position for part A in this new position.   Show all geometrical constructions
clearly and do not erase construction lines.

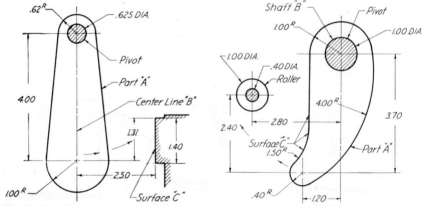

Fig. 4.69.   Geometrical construction.   **Fig. 4.70.   Geometrical construction.**

41. (Fig. 4.70.)   Part A revolves about shaft B in a clockwise direction from
the position shown until surface C comes into contact with the cylindrical surface
of the roller.   Reproduce the drawing as given and show part A in its revolved
position using the symbolic alternate position line for this new position.   Show
all geometrical constructions clearly and do not erase construction lines.

5

The Theory of Projection

5.1. Since engineers are confronted with the task of recording the shapes and sizes of three-dimensional objects on the plane of a sheet of drawing paper, it is obvious that recognized procedures must be followed if their drawings and sketches are to be easily understood. Size description and shape description are equally important, but, in order to simplify the presentation of the fundamentals of making drawings and sketches, this chapter is concerned entirely with the methods commonly employed in describing shape. A later chapter will discuss size description.

Each of the different methods, axonometric, oblique, and orthographic, is based on some form of projection. The theory governing a method should be understood thoroughly before it is used.

5.2. Perspective (scenographic) projection. In perspective projection, the projecting lines (visual rays) converge to a point, as shown in Fig. 5.1. The representation upon the transparent picture plane may be

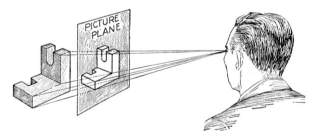

Fig. 5.1. Perspective projection.

considered the view that would be seen by one eye located at a definite point in space. The picture is established on the imaginary plane by the piercing points of the projecting lines from the eye to the object. The size of the view depends upon the distance from the observer to the plane and the distance from the plane to the object.

Perspective projection is not suitable for working drawings because a perspective view does not reveal exact size and shape.   It is used to some extent by engineers in preparing preliminary sketches.

5.3. Orthographic projection (parallel projection). If the observer in Fig. 5.1 moves straight back from the picture plane until he is an infinite distance from it, the projecting lines (projectors) from the eye to the object become parallel to each other and perpendicular to the picture plane.   The resulting projection (Fig. 5.2) will then be the same shape and size as the front surface of the object.   From a practical viewpoint, the projection may be thought of as being formed by perpendicular

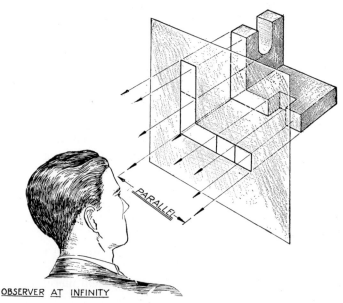

Fig. 5.2.   Orthographic projection.

projectors extended from the object to the plane.   The view is called an orthographic projection.

Since the view shown in Fig. 5.2 does not reveal the thickness of the object, one or more additional projections (Fig. 5.3) are necessary to complete the description.   Two projections are usually sufficient to describe simple objects, but three or more are necessary for complicated ones.

The picture planes are customarily called the principal or co-ordinate planes of projection, and the perpendiculars, projectors.   In engineering drawing, the planes are usually arranged as shown in Fig. 5.4.   Since all three are mutually perpendicular, they are called the horizontal, frontal, and profile co-ordinate planes.   To maintain this mutual relationship when laying out views, it is the usual practice to consider the frontal plane as lying in the plane of the paper and the horizontal and profile planes as being revolved into position (Fig. 5.6).   Note in Fig. 5.5 the manner

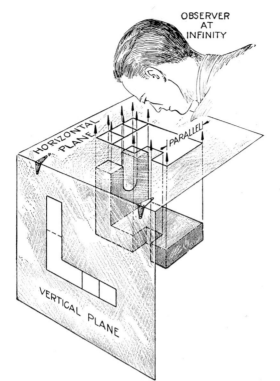

Fig. 5.3. Planes of projection.

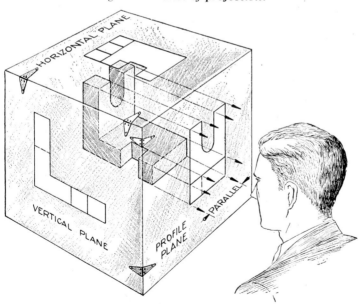

Fig. 5.4. Planes of projection.

in which the planes are revolved. This theoretical treatment of the co-ordinate planes establishes an absolute relationship between the views. Visualizing an object would be considerably more difficult than it is, if it were not for this fixed relationship, for it would be impossible to determine quickly the direction of sight for a particular view.

5.4. One-plane projection. If the object is turned and then tilted so that three faces are inclined to the plane of projection, the resulting projection is a special type of orthographic projection known as axonometric projection. Fig. 5.7 illustrates an axonometric projection of a

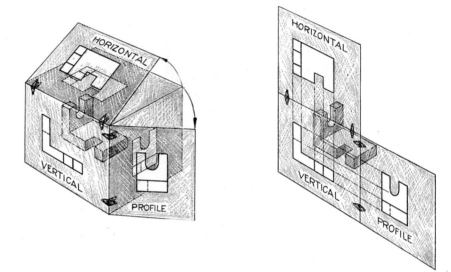

*Fig. 5.5.   The revolution of the planes
of projection.*

*Fig. 5.6.   The planes resolved into
the plane of the paper.*

cube. Note that the projectors from the object to the plane are perpendicular to the plane. The three recognized subdivisions of axonometric projection, namely, isometric, dimetric, and trimetric, are explained in Chapter 11.

Another form of one-plane projection is known as oblique projection. This form differs from orthographic projection in that, although one face is imagined to be parallel to the plane of projection, the projectors make an angle other than 90° with it (Fig. 5.8). Obviously an infinite number of different views are possible, depending upon the angle the parallel projectors make with the plane of projection (picture plane). The various subdivisions are cavalier projection, cabinet projection, and clinographic projection (Chapter 11).

Axonometric projection, oblique projection, and perspective projection may all be classed together as one-plane pictorial projection.

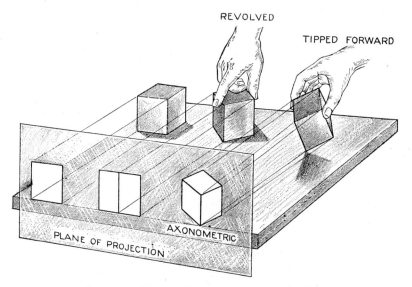

Fig. 5.7.   Theory of axonometric projection.

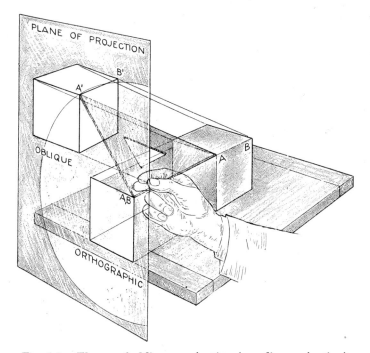

Fig. 5.8.   Theory of oblique projection (cavalier projection).

5.5. First- and third-angle projection. If the horizontal and frontal planes are assumed to extend indefinitely on one side of the profile plane, four dihedral angles are formed and are designated as the *first, second, third,* and *fourth* angles (Fig. 5.9).   The lines of intersection of these planes are called co-ordinate axes.   Their point of intersection is called the origin.   In this discussion of first- and third-angle projection, it should be remembered that no matter in which angle the object is placed, the observer views it from in front of the frontal plane and from above the horizontal plane.   To avoid misunderstandings, the directions

Fig. 5.9.   Planes of projection.

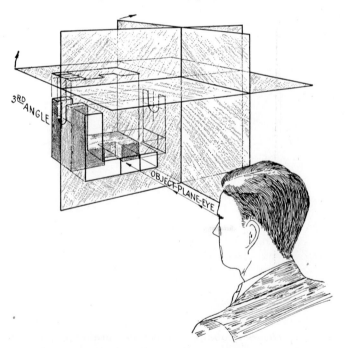

Fig. 5.10.   Third-angle projection.

for revolving the horizontal and profile planes into the frontal plane are illustrated in Fig. 5.10. Note that the first and third quadrants are "opened" and the second and fourth are "closed" in revolving the horizontal plane into the frontal plane.

If an object, such as the one shown in Fig. 5.10, is placed so that its main faces are parallel to the principal planes, the respective projection on each plane will show the true size and shape of all surfaces that are parallel to that principal plane. Theoretically, the object could have been shown in any one of the four quadrants. It has been placed in the third quadrant simply because engineering custom in the United States dictates the

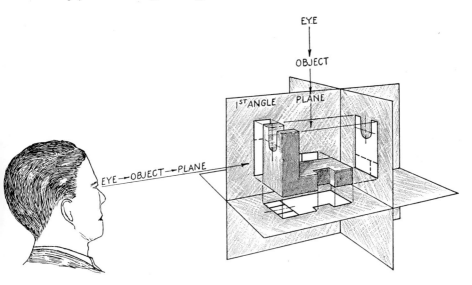

Fig. 5.11. First-angle projection.

use of the third. This quadrant is used because the views, when revolved into the frontal plane, are in their natural positions. That is: the top view appears *above* the front view, as is expected, and the profile view, showing the *right side*, falls on the *right* of the front view.

In most foreign countries, "first-angle projection" is used for working drawings. (Study Fig. 5.11.) Observe that the top view is projected upon the horizontal plane and the front view upon the frontal plane. For this reason, the top view falls below the front view when the co-ordinate planes are revolved.

In this country, the use of first-angle projection for working drawings was abandoned by engineering draftsmen some fifty years ago, although it is still used by architects and structural designers.

5.6. Systems of projection. The different systems of projection may be conveniently classified as follows:

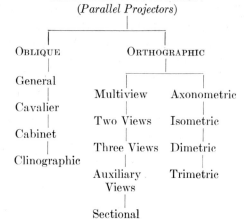

CONVERGENT PROJECTION
(Converging Projectors)

LINEAR   AERIAL

PARALLEL
(One Point)

ANGULAR
(Two Point)

OBLIQUE
(Three Point)

PARALLEL PROJECTION
(Parallel Projectors)

OBLIQUE   ORTHOGRAPHIC

General   Multiview   Axonometric

Cavalier   Two Views   Isometric

Cabinet   Three Views   Dimetric

Clinographic   Auxiliary   Trimetric
                      Views

                     Sectional
                     Views

Multiview Representation

PRINCIPAL VIEWS

6.1. Engineers use the orthographic system of projection for describing the shape of machine parts and structures. Practical application of this method of describing an object results in a drawing consisting of a number of systematically arranged views that reproduce the object's exact shape. It was explained in the preceding chapter, Sec. 5.3, that a set of views showing the object from different positions is always taken.

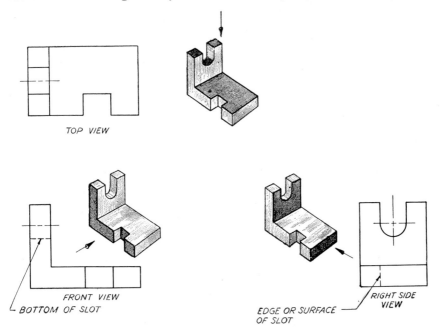

TOP VIEW

FRONT VIEW

BOTTOM OF SLOT

EDGE OR SURFACE OF SLOT

RIGHT SIDE VIEW

Fig. 6.1. Three views of an object.

The position of these views, in strict accordance with a universally recognized arrangement, must show the three dimensions, length, height, and depth.   Although three views (Fig. 6.1) are usually required to describe an ordinary object, only two may be needed for a particularly simple one. A very complicated object may require four or more views.   A view projected upon an auxiliary plane also may be desirable (see Figs. 6.24 and 6.25).   Such a view often makes possible the elimination of one of the principal views.   Therefore, it is up to the individual to determine the number and type of views needed to produce a satisfactory drawing.   He will soon develop a knack for this, if he bears in mind that the number of views required depends entirely upon the complexity of the shape to be described.

6.2. Definition.   Multiview (multiplaner) projection is a method by means of which the exact shape of an object can be represented by two or more separate views produced upon projection planes that are usually at right angles to each other.

6.3. Methods of obtaining the views.   The views of an object may be obtained by either of two methods:

(1) The natural method.

(2) The glass box method.

Since the resulting views will be the same in either case, the beginner should adopt the method he finds the easiest to understand.   Both methods are explained here in detail.

6.4. The natural method.   In using this method, each of the necessary views is obtained looking directly at the particular side of the object the view is to represent.

Fig. 6.2 shows three of the principal views of an object, the front, top, and side views.   They were obtained by looking directly at the front, top, and right side, respectively.   In the application of this method, some consider the position of the object as fixed and the position of the observer as shifted for each view; others find it easier to consider the observer's position as fixed and the position of the object as changed (Fig. 6.2) for each view.   Regardless of which procedure is followed, the top and side views must be arranged in their natural positions relative to the front view.

Fig. 6.3 illustrates the natural relationship of views.   Note that the top view is *vertically above* the front view, and the side view is *horizontally in line with* the front view.   In both of these views the *front of the block is toward the front view.*

6.5. The "glass box" method.   An imaginary "glass box" is used widely by instructors to explain the arrangement of orthographic views. An explanation of this scheme can be best made by reviewing the use of planes of projection (Chapter 5).   It may be considered that planes of projection placed parallel to the six faces of an object form an enclosing "glass box" (see Fig. 6.4).   The observer views the enclosed object from the outside.   The views are obtained by running projectors from points on the object to the planes.   This procedure is in accordance with the theory of orthographic projection explained in Sec. 5.3, as well as the

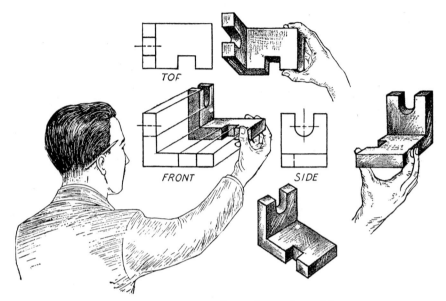

Fig. 6.2.   Obtaining three views of an object.

definition in Sec. 6.2.   The front, top, and right side of the box represent the H (horizontal), F (frontal), and P (profile) projection planes.

Since the projections on the sides of the three-dimensional transparent box are to appear on a sheet of drawing paper, it must be assumed that the box is hinged (see Fig. 6.5) so that, when it is opened outward into the plane of the paper, the planes assume the positions illustrated in Figs. 6.5 and 6.6.   Note that all of the planes, except the back one, are hinged to the frontal plane.   In accordance with this universally recognized assumption, the top projection must take a position directly above the front projection, and the right side projection must lie horizontally to

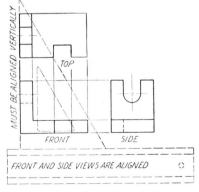

Fig. 6.3.   Position of views.

the right of the front projection.   To identify the separate projections, engineers call the one on the frontal plane the *front view* or *front elevation*,

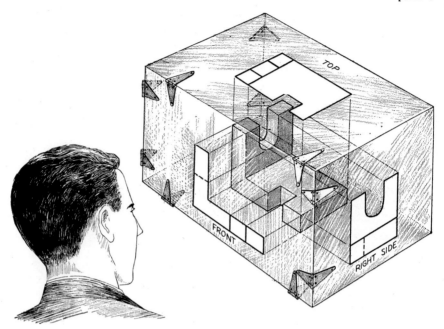

Fig. 6.4.   The glass box.

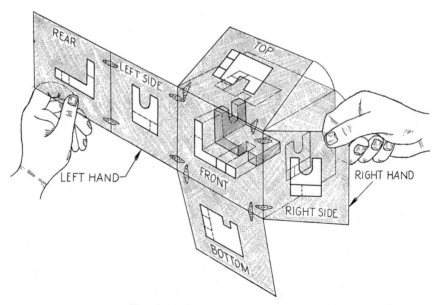

Fig. 6.5.   Opening the glass box.

the one on the horizontal plane the *top view* or *plan,* and the one on the side or profile plane the *side view, side elevation,* or *end view.*   Fig. 6.6 shows the six views of the same object as they would appear on a sheet of drawing paper.   Ordinarily, only three of these views are necessary

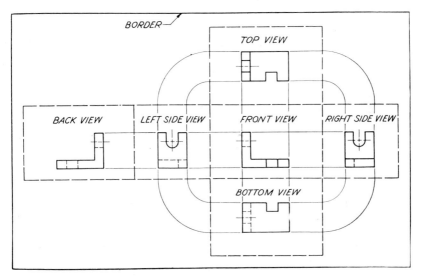

Fig. 6.6.   *Six views of an object on a sheet of drawing paper.*

(front, top, and right side).   A bottom or rear view will be required in comparatively few cases.

6.6. The "second position."   Sometimes, especially in the case of a broad flat object, it is desirable to hinge the sides of the box to the horizontal plane so that the side view will fall to the right of the top view, as illustrated in Fig. 6.7.   This arrangement conserves space on the paper and gives the views better balance.

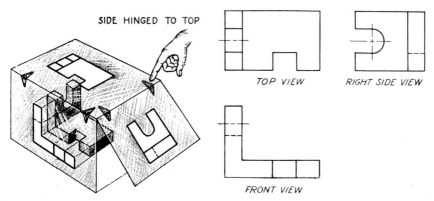

Fig. 6.7.   *The "second position" for the side view.*

6.7. The principles of multiview drawing. The following principles should be studied carefully and understood thoroughly before any attempt is made to prepare an orthographic drawing.

1. The front and top views are *always* in line vertically.

2. The front and side views are in line horizontally, except when the second position is used.

3. The front of the object in the top view faces the front view.

4. The front of the object in the side view faces the front view.

5. The depth of the top view is the same as the depth of the side view (or views).

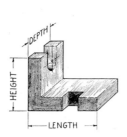
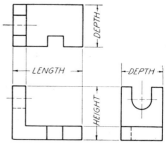

Fig. 6.8.   View terminology.

6. The length of the top view is the same as the length of the front view.

7. The height of the side view is the same as the height of the front view.

8. If a line is parallel to a plane of projection, its projection on the plane is exactly the same length as the true length of the line (Fig. 6.9*a*, *b*, *c*).

9. If a line is inclined to a plane of projection, its projection on the plane will be shorter than the true length of the line (Fig. 6.9*d*).

10. If a line is perpendicular to a plane of projection, its projection will be a point.

11. If a surface is parallel to a plane of projection, its projection on the plane will show its true size and shape.

12. If a surface is inclined to a plane of projection, its projection on the plane will be foreshortened.

13. If a surface is perpendicular to a plane of projection, its projection on the plane will be a line.

The student should study Fig. 6.9 and attempt to visualize the space position of each of the given lines.   It is very necessary both in preparing and reading graphical representations to recognize the position of a point, line, or plane and to know whether the projection of a line is true length or foreshortened or whether the projection of a plane shows the true size and shape.   The indicated reference lines may be thought of as representing the edges of the glass boxes shown. The projections of a line are identified as being on either a frontal, horizontal, or profile plane by the use of the letters F, H, or P with the lower-case letters that identify the end points of the line. For example, in Fig. 6.9(a), $a^H b^H$ is the horizontal projection of line AB, $a^F b^F$ is the frontal projection, and $a^P b^P$ is the profile projection.

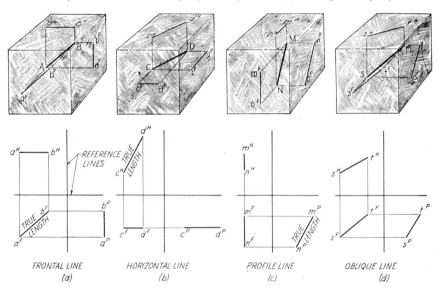

FRONTAL LINE $\qquad$ HORIZONTAL LINE $\qquad$ PROFILE LINE $\qquad$ OBLIQUE LINE
(a) $\qquad\qquad$ (b) $\qquad\qquad$ (c) $\qquad\qquad$ (d)

Fig. 6.9. Some typical line positions.

6.8. Relationship of views. The following principles of the relationship of views should be carefully read and understood (Fig. 6.6).

1. A view taken from above is a top view and *must* be drawn above the front view and in line with it vertically.

2. A view taken from the right, in relation to the selected front, is a right-side view and *must* be drawn to the right of the front view and in line with it horizontally.

3. A view taken from the left is a left-side view and *must* be drawn to the left of the front view.

4. A view taken from below is a bottom view and *must* appear below the front view.

6.9. The selection of views. Careful study should be given to the outline of an object before the views are selected (Fig. 6.10). Otherwise there is no assurance that the object will be described completely from the reader's viewpoint (Fig. 6.11). Only those views that are necessary for a clear and complete description should be selected. Since the repetition of information only tends to confuse the reader, superfluous views should be avoided. In Fig. 6.6, note that three views (front, top, and right side) describe the object fully. The other three views are unnecessary.

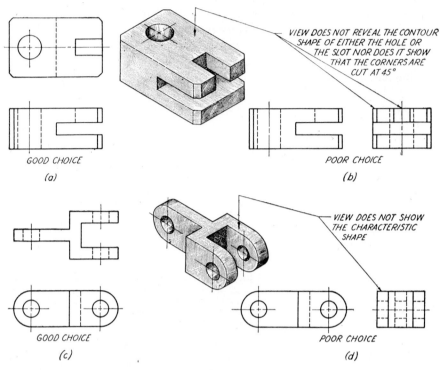

Fig. 6.10.   *Choice of views.*

Although some objects, such as cylinders, bushings, bolts, and so forth, require only two views (front and side), more complicated pieces may require an auxiliary or sectional view in addition to the ordinary three views.

The space available for arranging the views often governs the choice

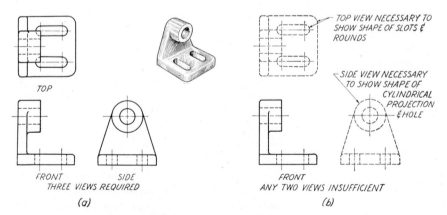

Fig. 6.11.   *Choice of views.*

between the use of a top or side view. The difference between the descriptive values of the two frequently is not great. For example, a draftsman often finds that the views of a long object will have better balance if a top view is used (see Fig. 6.12a); while, in the case of a short object (see b), the use of a side view may make possible a more pleasing arrangement.

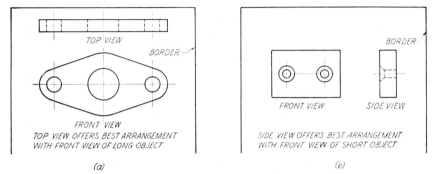

Fig. 6.12. Selection of views.

It should be remembered that the choice of views for many objects is definitely fixed by the contour alone, and no choice is offered as far as spacing is concerned. It is more important to have a set of views that describes an object clearly than one that is artistically balanced.

Often there is a choice between two equally important views, such as between a right-side and left-side view (Fig. 6.13) or between a top and

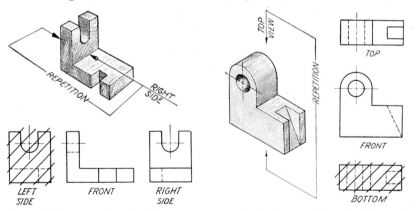

Fig. 6.13. The preferred side view.   Fig. 6.14. The preferred choice of a top view.

bottom view (Fig. 6.14). In such cases, one should adhere to the following rule: *A right-side view should be used in preference to a left-side view, and a top view in preference to a bottom view.* When this rule is applied to irregular objects, the front (contour) view should be drawn so that the most irregular outline is toward the top and right side.

Another rule, one that must be considered in selecting the front view, is as follows: *Place the object so as to obtain the smallest number of hidden lines.*

6.10. The principal (front) view. The principal view is the one that shows the characteristic contour of the object. See Fig. 6.15(a) and (b). Good practice dictates that this be used as the front view on a drawing. It should be clearly understood that the view of the natural front of an object is not always the principal view, because frequently it fails to show the object's characteristic shape. Therefore, another rule to be

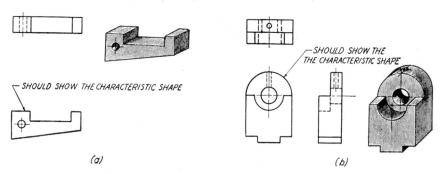

Fig. 6.15. The principal view of an object.

followed is: *Ordinarily, select the view showing the characteristic contour shape as the front view, regardless of the normal or natural front of the object.*

When an object does have a definite normal position, however, the front view should be in agreement with it. In the case of most machine parts, the front view can assume any convenient position that is consistent with good balance.

6.11. Invisible lines. Dotted lines are used on an external view of an object to represent surfaces and intersections invisible at the point from which the view is taken. In Fig. 6.16(a), one invisible line represents a line of intersection or edge line while the other invisible line may be considered to represent either the surface or lines of intersection. On the

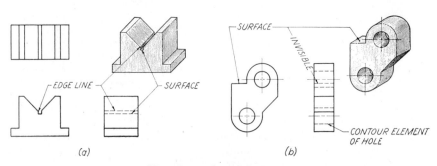

Fig. 6.16. Invisible lines.

side view in (*b*) there are invisible lines which represent the contour elements of the cylindrical holes.

6.12. Treatment of invisible lines. The short dashes that form an invisible line should be drawn carefully in accordance with the recommendations in Sec. 6.14. An invisible line always starts with a dash in contact with the object line from which it starts, unless it forms a continuation of a visible line. In the latter case, it should start with a space, in order to establish at a glance the exact location of the end point of the visible line. (See Fig. 6.17*C*.) Note that the effect of definite corners is secured at points *A*, *B*, *E*, and *F*, where, in each case, the end dash touches the intersecting line. When the point of intersection of an invisible line and

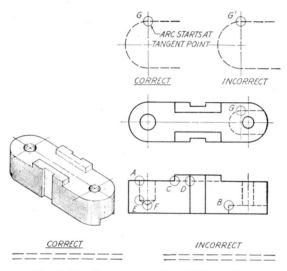

Fig. 6.17. Junctures of invisible outlines.

another object line does not represent an actual intersection on the object, the intersection should be open as at points *C* and *D*. An open intersection tends to make the lines appear to be at different distances from the observer.

Parallel invisible lines should have the breaks staggered.

The correct and incorrect treatment for starting invisible arcs is illustrated at *G* and *G'*. Note that an arc should start with a dash at the point of tangency. This treatment enables the reader to determine the exact end points of the curvature.

6.13. Omission of invisible lines. Although it is common practice for commercial draftsmen to omit hidden lines when their use tends to further confuse an already overburdened view or when the shape description of a feature is sufficiently clear in another view, it is not advisable for a beginning student to do so. The beginner, until he has developed the discrimination that comes with experience, will be wise to show all hidden lines.

6.14. To make an orthographic drawing. The location of all views should be determined before a drawing is begun. This will insure balance in the appearance of the finished drawing. The contour view is usually started first. After the initial start, the draftsman should construct his views simultaneously by projecting back and forth from one to the other. It is poor practice to complete one view before starting the others, as much more time will be required to complete the drawing.

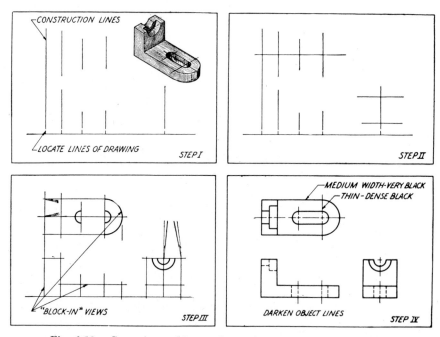

Fig. 6.18. Steps in making a three-view drawing of an object.

Fig. 6.18 shows the procedure for laying out a three-view drawing. The general outline of the views first should be drawn in lightly with a hard pencil and then heavied with a medium grade pencil. Although experienced persons sometimes deviate from this procedure by drawing in the lines of known length and location in finished weight while constructing the views, it is not recommended that beginners do so.

The dividers are used to transfer depth distances between the top view and the side view. See Fig. 6.18, step III.

When making an orthographic drawing in pencil, the beginner should endeavor to use the line weights recommended in Sec. 8.11. The object lines should be made very dark and bright, to give snap to the drawing as well as to create the contrast necessary to cause the shape of the object to stand out. Special care should be taken to gauge the dashes and spaces in invisible object lines. On ordinary drawings, $\frac{1}{8}''$ dashes and $\frac{1}{32}''$ spaces are recommended (Fig. 6.19).

Center lines consist of alternate long and short dashes. The long dashes are from $\frac{3}{4}''$ to $1\frac{1}{2}''$ long, the short dashes $\frac{1}{8}''$, and the spaces $\frac{1}{32}''$ (Fig. 6.19). The following technique is recommended in drawing center lines.

1. Where center lines cross, the short dashes should intersect symmetrically (see Fig. 6.19). (In the case of very small circles the breaks may be omitted.)

2. The breaks should be so located that they will stand out and still allow the center line to be recognized as such.

3. Center lines should extend approximately $\frac{1}{8}''$ beyond the outline of the part whose symmetry they indicate (Fig. 6.19).

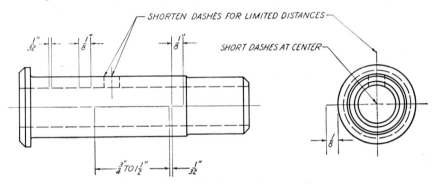

Fig. 6.19. Invisible lines and center lines.

4. Center lines should not end at object lines.

5. Center lines which are aligned with object lines should have not less than a $\frac{1}{16}''$ space between the end of the center line and the object line.

For a finished drawing to be pleasing in appearance, all lines of the same type must be uniform, and each type must have proper contrast with other symbolic types. The contrast between the types of pencil lines is similar to that of ink lines (Fig. 8.15), except that pencil lines are never as wide as ink lines. Read Sec. 8.11. On commercial drawings, the usual practice is to "burn in" the object lines by applying heavy pressure.

If reasonable care is taken not to soil a drawing, it will not be necessary to clean any part of it with an eraser. Since the practice in most commercial drawing rooms is not to erase construction lines if they have been drawn lightly, the student, at the very beginning of his first course, should try to acquire habits that insure cleanliness.

When constructing a two-view drawing of a circular object, the pencil work must start with the drawing of the center lines, as shown in Fig. 6.20. This is necessarily the first step because the construction of the circular (contour) view is based upon a horizontal and a vertical center line. The horizontal object lines of the rectangular view are projected from the circles.

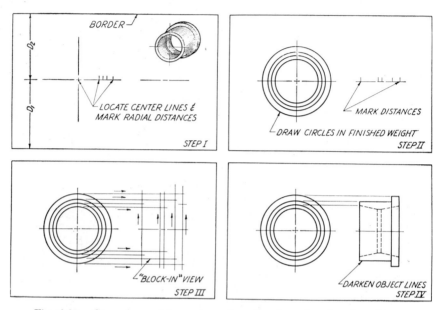

Fig. 6.20.   Steps in making a two-view drawing of a circular object.

6.15. Visualizing an object from given views.   Most students in elementary drawing courses find it difficult to visualize an object from two or more views. This trouble is largely due to the lack of systematic procedure for analyzing complex shapes.

The simplest method of determining shape is illustrated pictorially in Fig. 6.21. This method of "breaking down" may be applied to any object, since all objects may be thought of as consisting of elemental geometrical forms, such as prisms, cylinders, cones, and so on. These

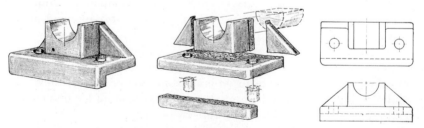

Fig. 6.21.   "Breaking down" method.

imaginary component parts may be additions in the form of projections or subtractions in the form of cavities. Following such a detailed geometric analysis, a clear picture of an entire object can be obtained by mentally assembling a few easily visualized forms.

It should be realized, when analyzing component parts, that it is impossible ordinarily to determine whether a form is an addition or a subtraction by looking at one view. For example, the small circles in the top view in Fig. 6.21 indicate a cylindrical form, but they do not reveal whether the form is a hole or a projection. By consulting the front view, however, the form is shown to be a hole (subtracted cylinder).

The graphic language is similar to the written language in that neither can be read at a glance. A drawing must be read patiently by referring systematically back and forth from one view to another. The reader at the same time must imagine a three-dimensional object and not a two-dimensional flat projection.

A student usually will find that a pictorial sketch will clarify the shape of a part that is difficult to visualize. The method for preparing quick sketches in isometric is explained in Secs. 10.3 and 10.4.

6.16. Analysis of surfaces, lines, and points in three principal views. An analysis of the representation of the surfaces of a mutilated block is given pictorially in Fig. 6.22. It can be noted that each of the surfaces *A*, *B*, and *C* appears in true size and shape in one view, and as a

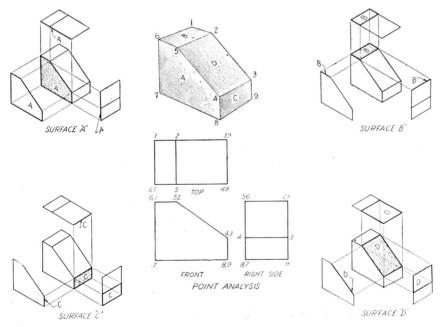

Fig. 6.22. *Analysis of surfaces, lines, and points.*

line in each of the other two related views. Surface D, which is inclined, appears with foreshortened length in the top and side views, and as an inclined line in the front view.

Three views of each of the visible points are shown on the multiview drawing. At the very beginning of an elementary course in drawing, a student will often find it helpful to number the corners of an object in all views.

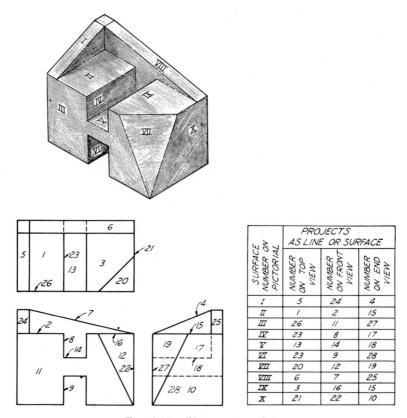

SURFACE NUMBER ON PICTORIAL	PROJECTS AS LINE OR SURFACE		
	NUMBER ON TOP VIEW	NUMBER ON FRONT VIEW	NUMBER ON END VIEW
I	5	24	4
II	1	2	15
III	26	11	27
IV	23	8	17
V	13	14	18
VI	23	9	28
VII	20	12	19
VIII	6	7	25
IX	3	16	15
X	21	22	10

Fig. 6.23. Lines and surfaces.

Fig. 6.23 shows a pictorial drawing and a three-view orthographic drawing of a mutilated block. The accompanying table gives an orderly analysis of the reading of the three views of the object. A table similar to this one may be prepared by a student to facilitate study of a particular drawing.

All lines and surfaces are numbered at random on the orthographic drawing so that the student may take each surface designated on the pictorial drawing and identify it by a different number on each of the three views. For example, surface I on the pictorial view appears as a surface in the top view and is identified by the number 5.   The same surface appears as surface 24 in the front view, and as line 4 in the end view.

AUXILIARY VIEWS

6.17.   When it is desirable to show the true size and shape of an irregular surface, which is inclined to two or more of the co-ordinate planes of projection, a view of the surface must be projected on a plane parallel to it.   This imaginary projection plane is called an auxiliary plane, and the view obtained is called an auxiliary view (Fig. 6.24).

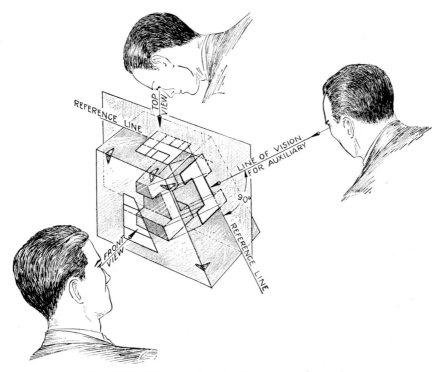

Fig. 6.24.   Theory of projecting an auxiliary view.

The theory underlying the method of projecting principal views applies also to auxiliary views.   In other words, an auxiliary view shows an inclined surface of an object as it would appear to an observer stationed an infinite distance away (Fig. 6.24).

6.18. The use of auxiliary views.   An auxiliary view ordinarily is a partial view showing only an inclined surface.   The reason for this is that a projection showing the entire object adds very little to the shape description.   For example, a complete drawing of the casting in Fig. 6.26 must include an auxiliary view of the inclined surface in order to show the true shape of the surface and the location of the holes.   Compare the

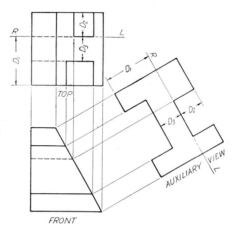

Fig. 6.25.   An auxiliary view.

views in (a) and (b) and note the confused appearance of the view in (b). In engineering schools, some instructors require that an auxiliary view show the entire object, including all invisible lines.   Such a requirement, although usually impractical, is justified in the classroom, for the construction of a complete auxiliary view furnishes excellent practice in projection.

A partial auxiliary view often is needed to complete the projection of a foreshortened feature in a principal view.   This second important function of auxiliary views is explained in Sec. 6.26.

6.19. Types of auxiliary views.   Although auxiliary views may have an infinite number of positions in relation to the three principal

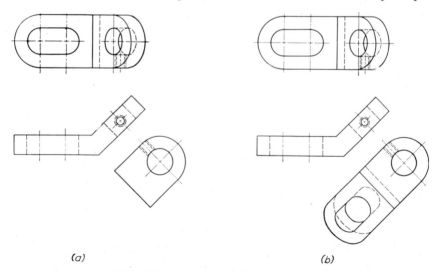

(a)   (b)

Fig. 6.26.   Partial and complete auxiliary views.

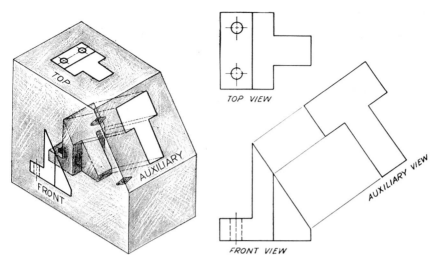

Fig. 6.27. *Auxiliary view projected from front view.*

planes of projection, primary auxiliary views may be classified into three general types in accordance with position relative to the principal planes. Fig. 6.27 shows the first type where the auxiliary plane is perpendicular to the frontal plane and inclined to the horizontal plane of projection. Here the auxiliary view and top view have one dimension that is common to both, the depth. Note that the auxiliary plane is hinged to the frontal plane, and that the auxiliary view is projected from the front view.

In Fig. 6.28 the auxiliary plane is perpendicular to the horizontal plane and inclined to the frontal and profile planes of projection. The auxiliary view is projected from the top view, and its height is the same as the height of the front view.

The third type of auxiliary view, as shown in Fig. 6.29, is projected

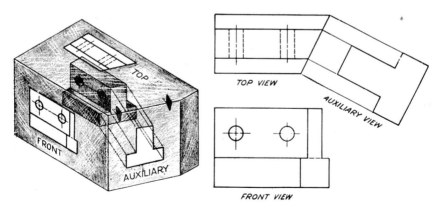

Fig. 6.28. *Auxiliary view projected from top view.*

from the side view and has a common dimension with both the front and top views. To construct it, distances may be taken from either the front or top view.

All three types of auxiliary views are constructed similarly. Each is projected from the view that shows the surface as an oblique line, and the distances for the view are taken from the other principal view that has a common dimension with the auxiliary. A careful study of the three illustrations will reveal the fact that the inclined auxiliary plane is always hinged to the principal plane to which it is perpendicular.

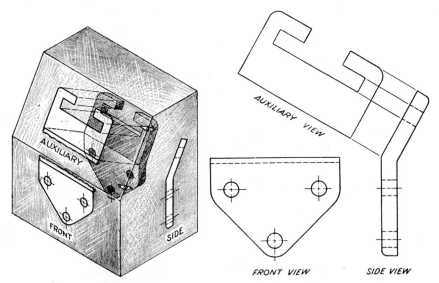

Fig. 6.29.   Auxiliary view projected from side view.

6.20. Symmetrical and unsymmetrical auxiliary views. Auxiliary views are either symmetrical or unsymmetrical about a center line or reference line. The symmetrical view is drawn symmetrically about a center line, the unsymmetrical view, either entirely on one side of a reference line or on both sides.

6.21. To draw a symmetrical auxiliary view. When an inclined surface is symmetrical, the auxiliary view is "worked" from a center line (Fig. 6.30). The first step in drawing such a view is to draw a center line parallel to the oblique line that represents an edge view of the surface. If the object is assumed to be enclosed in a glass box, this center line may be considered the line of intersection of the auxiliary plane and an imaginary vertical center plane. There are professional draftsmen who, not acquainted with the "glass" box, proceed without theoretical explanation. Their method is simply to draw a working center line for the auxiliary view and a corresponding line in one of the principal views.

Although, theoretically, this working center line may be drawn at any distance from the principal view, actually it should be so located to give the whole drawing a balanced appearance.   If not already shown, it also must be drawn in the principal view showing the true width of the inclined surface.

The next step is to draw projection lines from each point of the sloping face, remembering that the projectors make an angle of 90° with the inclined line representing the surface.   With the projectors drawn, the location of each point in the auxiliary can be established by setting the dividers to each point's distance from the center line in the principal view and transferring the distance to the auxiliary view.   For example, point X is projected to the auxiliary by drawing a projector from point X

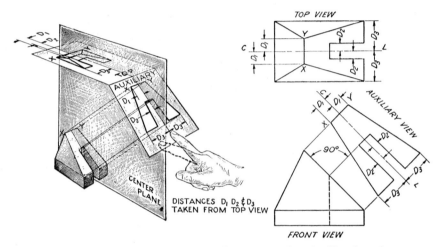

Fig. 6.30.   *A symmetrical auxiliary view of an inclined surface.*

in the front view perpendicular to the center line.   Since its distance from the center line in the top view is the same as it is from the center line in the auxiliary view, the point's location along the projector may be established by using the distance taken from the top view.   In the case of point X, the distance is set off from the center line toward the front view.   Point Y is set off from the center line away from the front view.   A careful study of Fig. 6.30 reveals the fact that if a point lies between the front view and the center line of the top view, it will lie between the front view and the center line of the auxiliary view, and, conversely, if it lies away from the front view with reference to the center line of the top view, it will lie away from the front view with reference to the center line of the auxiliary view.

Fig. 6.31 shows an auxiliary view of an entire object.   In constructing such a view, the projectors from all points of the object must be perpendicular to the working center line, since the observer views the entire

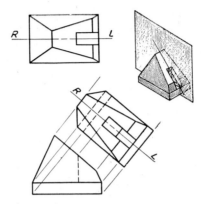

Fig. 6.31. An auxiliary view of an object.

figure by looking directly at the inclined surface. The distances perpendicular to the auxiliary center line are taken from the top view.

6.22. Unsymmetrical auxiliary views. When constructing an unsymmetrical auxiliary view, it is necessary to work from a reference line that is drawn in a manner similar to the working center line of a symmetrical view. (See Figs. 6.32 and 6.35.)

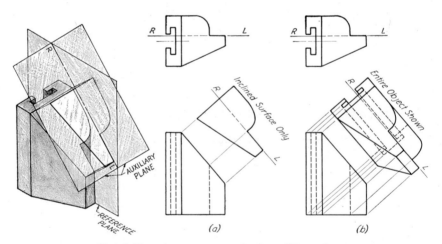

Fig. 6.32. An unsymmetrical auxiliary view.

6.23. Curved lines in auxiliary views. To draw a curve in an auxiliary view, one must plot a sufficient number of points to insure a smooth curve (Fig. 6.33). The points are projected first to the oblique line representing the surface in the front view and then to the auxiliary view. The distance of any point from the center line in the auxiliary view is the same as its distance from the center line in the end view.

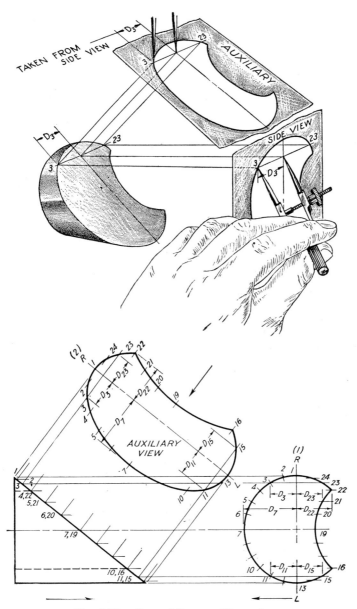

Fig. 6.33. Curved line auxiliary view.

6.24. Use of partial views. Often the use of an auxiliary view allows the elimination of one of the principal views (front, top, or side) or makes possible the use of a partial principal view. The shape description furnished by the partial views shown in Fig. 6.34 is sufficient for a complete understanding of the shape of the part. The use of partial

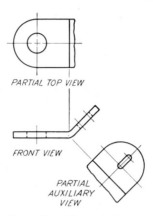

PARTIAL TOP VIEW

FRONT VIEW

PARTIAL
AUXILIARY
VIEW

Fig. 6.34.   Partial views.

views simplifies the drawing, saves valuable time, and tends to make the drawing easier to read.

A break line is used at a convenient location to indicate an imaginary break for a partial view.

6.25. To construct an auxiliary view, practical method.   The usual steps in constructing an auxiliary view are shown in Fig. 6.35.   The

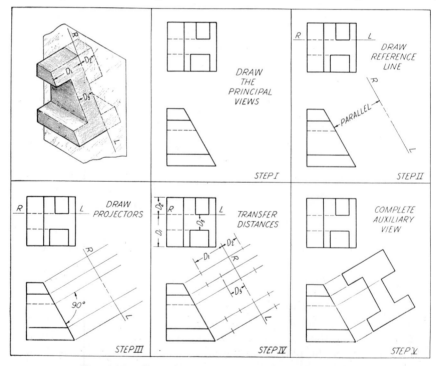

DRAW
THE
PRINCIPAL
VIEWS

STEP I

DRAW
REFERENCE
LINE

PARALLEL

STEP II

DRAW
PROJECTORS

90°

STEP III

TRANSFER
DISTANCES

STEP IV

COMPLETE
AUXILIARY
VIEW

STEP V

Fig. 6.35.   Steps in constructing an auxiliary view.

illustration should be studied carefully, as each step is explained on the drawing.

6.26. The use of an auxiliary view to complete a principal view. As previously stated, it is frequently necessary to project a foreshortened feature in one of the principal views from an auxiliary view. In the case of the object shown in Fig. 6.36, the foreshortened projection of the inclined face in the top view can be projected from the auxiliary view. The elliptical curves are plotted by projecting points from the auxiliary view to the front view and from there to the top view. The location of these points in the top view with respect to the center line is the same as their location in the auxiliary view with respect to the auxiliary center

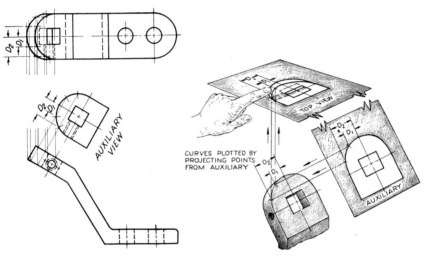

Fig. 6.36.   Use of auxiliary to complete a principal view.

line. For example, the distance D_1 from the center line in the top view is the same as the distance D_1 from the auxiliary center line in the auxiliary view.

The steps in preparing an auxiliary view and using it to complete a principal view are shown in Fig. 6.37.

6.27. Secondary (oblique) auxiliary views. Frequently an object will have an inclined face that is not perpendicular to any one of the principal planes of projection. In such cases it is necessary to draw two auxiliary views (Fig. 6.38). The primary auxiliary view is constructed by projecting the figure upon a primary auxiliary plane that is perpendicular to the inclined surface and one of the principal planes. This plane may be at any convenient location. In the illustration, the primary auxiliary plane is perpendicular to the frontal plane. Note that the inclined face appears as a straight line in the primary auxiliary view. Using this view as a regular view, the secondary auxiliary view may be projected upon a plane parallel to the inclined face.   Fig. 6.38(b) shows a practical application of the theoretical principles shown pictorially in (a).

Fig. 6.39 shows the progressive steps in preparing and using a secondary auxiliary view of an oblique face to complete a principal view.   Reference planes have been used as datum planes from which to take the necessary measurements.   Step II shows the partial construction of the primary auxiliary view in which the inclined surface appears as a line.   Step III shows the secondary auxiliary view projected from the primary view and completed, using the known measurements of the lug.   The primary

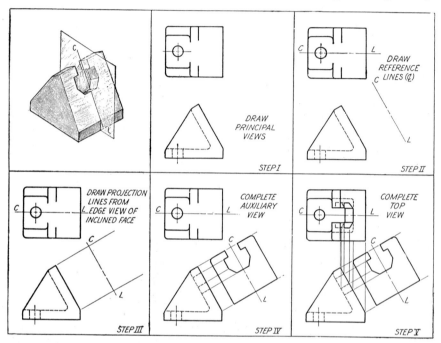

Fig. 6.37.   Steps in preparing an auxiliary view and completing a principal view.

auxiliary view is finished by projecting from the secondary auxiliary view. Step IV illustrates the procedure for projecting from the secondary auxiliary view to the top view through the primary auxiliary in order to complete the foreshortened view of the lug.   It should be noted that distance D_1 taken from reference plane R_2P_2 in the secondary auxiliary is transferred to the top view because both views show the same width distances in true length.   A sufficient number of points should be obtained to allow the use of an irregular curve.   Step V shows the projection of these points on the curve to the front view.   In this case the measurements are taken from the primary auxiliary view because the height distances from reference plane R_1P_1 are the same in both views.

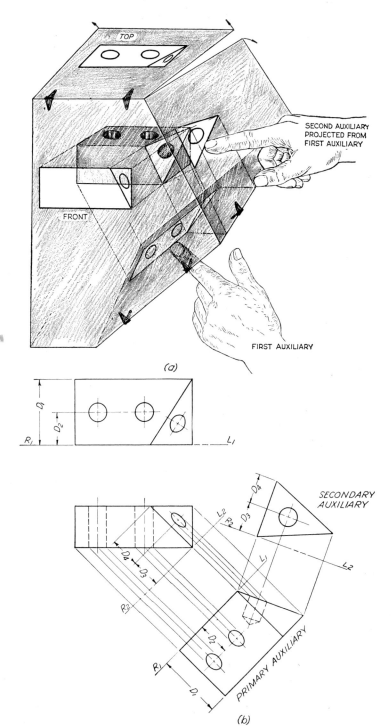

Fig. 6.38.   A secondary auxiliary view of an oblique face.

115

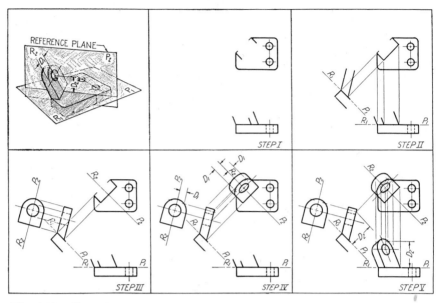

Fig. 6.39. *Steps in drawing a secondary auxiliary view and using it to complete a principal view.*

6.28. Line of intersection. It is frequently necessary to represent a line of intersection between two surfaces when making a multiview drawing involving an auxiliary view. Fig. 6.40 shows a method for drawing the line of intersection on a principal view. In this case the scheme commonly used for determining the intersection involves the use of elements drawn on the surface of the cylindrical portion of the part as shown on the pictorial drawing. These elements such as AB, are common to the cylindrical surface. Point B where the element pierces the flat sur-

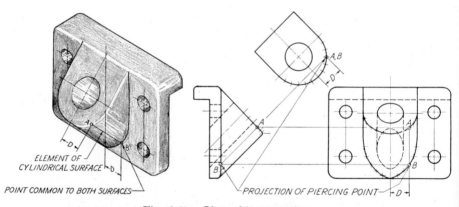

Fig. 6.40. *Line of intersection.*

face, is a point that is common to both surfaces and, therefore, lies on the line of intersection.

On the orthographic views, element AB appears as a point on the auxiliary view and as a line on the front view. The location of the projection of the piercing point on the front view is visible upon inspection. Point B is found in the other principal view by projecting from the front view and setting off the distance D taken from the auxiliary view. The distance D of point B from the center line is a true distance for both views. The center line in the auxiliary view and side view can be considered as the edge view of a reference plane or datum plane from which measurements can be made.

REVOLUTION

6.29. Revolution. Although in general the principal views of an ordinary drawing will represent satisfactorily an object in a fixed natural position, in order to improve the representation or to reveal the true size and shape of a principal surface, it sometimes is desirable to revolve an elemental part until it is parallel to a co-ordinate plane.

The distinguishing difference between this method and the method of auxiliary projection is that, in the procedure of revolution, the observer turns the object with respect to himself instead of shifting his viewing position with respect to an oblique surface of the object.

Despite the fact that the revolution of an entire object, as illustrated in Fig. 6.41, rarely has a practical application in commercial drafting, the making of such a drawing provides excellent drill in projection.

6.30. Simple (single) revolution. When the regular views are given, an object may be drawn in any oblique position by imagining it to be revolved about an axis perpendicular to one of the principal co-ordinate (frontal, horizontal, or profile) planes. A single revolution about such an axis is known as a "simple revolution." Figs. 6.41, 6.42, and 6.43 illustrate the three general cases.

6.31. Revolution about a horizontal axis perpendicular to the frontal plane. A simple revolution about an axis perpendicular to the frontal plane is illustrated in Fig. 6.41. The object is first revolved about an imaginary assumed axis, AB, until it is in the desired position. The views of it then are obtained by orthographic projection, as in the case of any ordinary multiview drawing. Because the front face revolves parallel to the frontal plane, the projection on that plane will change in position but will retain its true size and shape. For this reason, the most convenient drawing procedure is to first copy the front view, as it is shown in (a), in its new revolved position (say at 30°). Then, since the depth of the top view is unchanged by the revolution of the object, the required top view can be drawn easily by projecting each point horizontally from the top view in (a) to a projection line drawn upward through

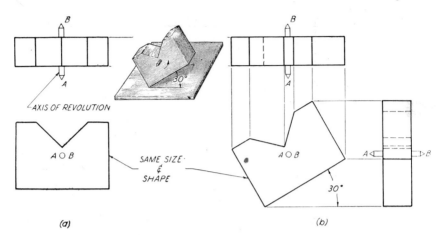

Fig. 6.41. *A single revolution about an axis perpendicular to the frontal plane.*

the corresponding point on the revolved front view in (*b*).   The side view may be constructed by regular projection.

6.32. Revolution about a vertical axis perpendicular to the horizontal plane.   If an object is revolved about an imaginary axis perpendicular to the horizontal plane, as shown in Fig. 6.42, the top view changes in position but not in size and shape.   The top view, therefore, should be drawn first in its revolved position, and the front and side views should be projected from it.   The height of the front view and the side view is the same as the height of the normal front view in (*a*) and, for this reason, vertical dimensions can be conveniently projected from the initial views.

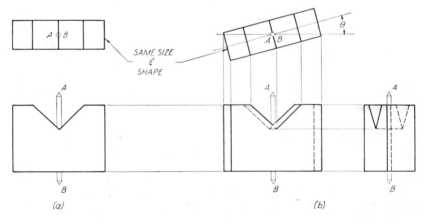

Fig. 6.42. *A single revolution about an axis perpendicular to the horizontal plane.*

6.33. Revolution about a horizontal axis perpendicular to the profile plane. A single revolution of an object about an axis perpendicular to the profile plane is illustrated in Fig. 6.43. Since in this case it is the side view that is perpendicular to the axis and that revolves parallel to a co-ordinate plane, it is the side view that remains unchanged in size and shape. The length of the top and front views is not affected by the revolution. Therefore, horizontal dimensions for these views may be set off by measurement.

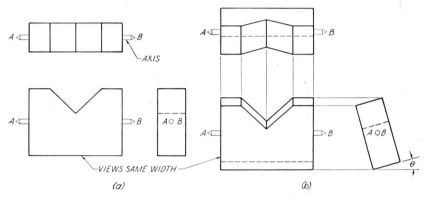

Fig. 6.43. *A single revolution about an axis perpendicular to the profile plane.*

From these general cases of simple revolution, two principles have appeared that can be stated as follows:

1. The view that is perpendicular to the axis of revolution changes only in position.

2. The lengths of the lines parallel to the axis do not change during the revolution and, therefore, may be either measured or projected from the normal views of the object.

6.34. Clockwise and counterclockwise revolution. An object may be revolved either clockwise or counterclockwise about an axis of revolution. The direction is indicated by the view to which the axis is perpendicular.

6.35. Successive (multiple) revolution. Since it is possible to draw an object in any oblique position relative to the co-ordinate planes, it is possible to show it revolved through a series of successive simple revolutions. Usually such a series is limited to three or four stages. Fig. 6.44 shows an object revolved successively about three separate axes. The normal orthographic views are shown in space I. In space II, the object has been revolved clockwise through an angle of 30 degrees about an axis perpendicular to the frontal plane. A system of numbers by which each corner is identified, as shown, is not necessary in the case of a simple object. If the object is in the least complex, however, possible confusion is avoided by the use of identification symbols of some type. In space III, the object has been revolved counterclockwise from its position in space II through an angle of 15 degrees about an axis perpendicular to the horizontal plane. From this position, represented in space III, the object is revolved clockwise through 15 degrees into the position shown in space IV. This last simple revolution completes a series of three simple revolutions involving the three general cases previously discussed.

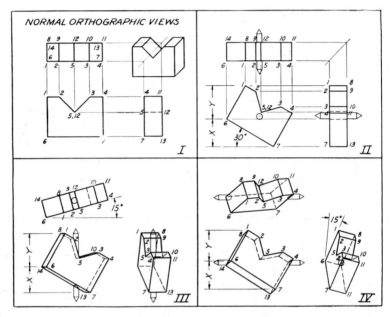

Fig. 6.44.   Successive revolution.

6.36. To find the true length of a line by revolution. In engineering layout work, it frequently is necessary to determine the true length of a line when constructing the development of a surface. The true lengths must be found of those lines that are not parallel to any co-ordinate plane and, therefore, appear foreshortened in all the principal views. A practical as well as the theoretical procedure is to revolve any such oblique line into a position parallel to a co-ordinate plane so that its projection on that particular plane will be the same length as the line. In Fig. 6.45(a), this is illustrated by the edge AB on the pyramid. AB is oblique to the co-ordinate planes and its projections are foreshortened. If this edge line is imagined to be revolved until it becomes parallel to the frontal plane, then the projection ab_r in the front view will be the same length as the true length of AB.

A practical application of this method is shown in Fig. 6.45(c). The true length of the edge AB, in Fig. 6.45(a), would be found by revolving its top projection into the position ab_r representing AB revolved parallel to the frontal plane, and then projecting the end point b_r down into its new position along a horizontal line through b.   The horizontal line represents the horizontal plane of the base in which the point B travels as the line AB is revolved.

Note in Fig. 6.45(a and b) that the true length of a line is equal to the hypotenuse of a right triangle whose altitude is equal to the difference in the elevation of the end points and whose base is equal to the top projection of the line.   With this fact in mind, many persons determine the true length of a line by constructing a true-length triangle similar to the one illustrated in Fig. 6.45(d).

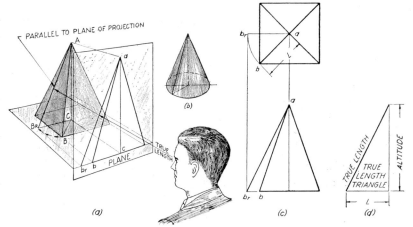

Fig. 6.45.   True length of a line, revolution method.

Students who lack a thorough understanding of the principles of projection, and find it difficult to determine whether or not a projection of a line in one of the principal views shows the true length of the line, should study carefully the following facts:

1. If the projection of a line shows the true length of a line, one of the other projections must appear as a horizontal line, a vertical line, or a point on one of the other views of the drawing.

2. If the top and front views of a line are horizontal, then both views show the true length.

3. If the top view of a line is a point, the front and side views show the true length.

4. If the front view of a line is a point, the top and side views show the true length.

5. If the top and front views of a line are vertical, the side view shows the true length.

6. If the side projection of a line is a point, the top and front views show the true length.

7. If the front view of a line is horizontal and the top view is inclined, the top inclined view shows the true length.

8. If the top view of a line is horizontal and the front view is inclined, the front inclined view shows the true length.

6.37. Problems. The problems that follow are intended primarily to furnish study in multiview projection through the preparation of either sketches or instrumental drawings. Many of the other problems in this chapter, however, may be prepared in more complete form. Their views may be dimensioned as are the views of working drawings, if the student will study carefully the beginning of the chapter covering dimensioning before attempting to record size description (Chap. 16). All dimensions should be placed in accordance with the general rules of dimensioning.

The views shown in a sketch or drawing should be spaced on the paper with aim for balance within the border lines. Ample room should be allowed between the views for the necessary dimensions. If the views are not to be dimensioned, the distance between them may be made somewhat less than would be necessary otherwise.

Before starting to draw, the student should reread Sec. 6.14 and study Fig. 6.18, which shows the steps in making a multiview drawing. The preparation of a preliminary sketch always proves helpful to the beginner.

All construction work should be done in light lines with a sharp hard pencil. A drawing should be checked by an instructor before the lines are "heavied in," unless the preliminary sketch was checked beforehand.

1–2. (Figs. 6.46–6.47.) Draw a table similar to that shown in Fig. 6.23 and fill in the required information for each of the surfaces designated on the pictorial

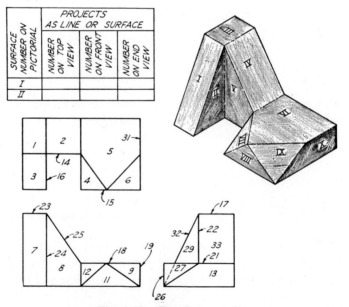

Fig. 6.46. Reading exercise.

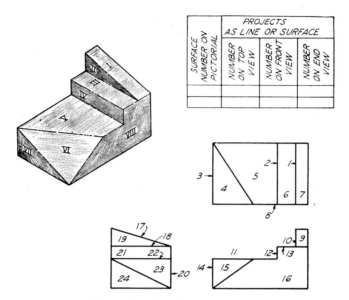

SURFACE NUMBER ON PICTORIAL	PROJECTS AS LINE OR SURFACE		
	NUMBER ON TOP VIEW	NUMBER ON FRONT VIEW	NUMBER ON END VIEW

Fig. 6.47. Reading exercise.

drawing by a Roman numeral. Draw the necessary guide lines and letter the column headings and information in $\frac{1}{8}''$ capitals.

3. (Fig. 6.48.) A line is missing from each of the three-view drawings. When the correct missing line is found, the three views of each object will be consistent with one another. *Suggestion:* A good method of visualizing these objects is to sketch them pictorially or to cut a model from a piece of modeling clay, a cake of soap, or an ordinary potato.

4. (Fig. 6.49.) Add the missing line or lines in one view of each of the three-view drawings. When the missing line or lines have been determined, the three views of each object will be consistent with one another.

5. (Fig. 6.50.) Draw or sketch the third view for each of the given objects.

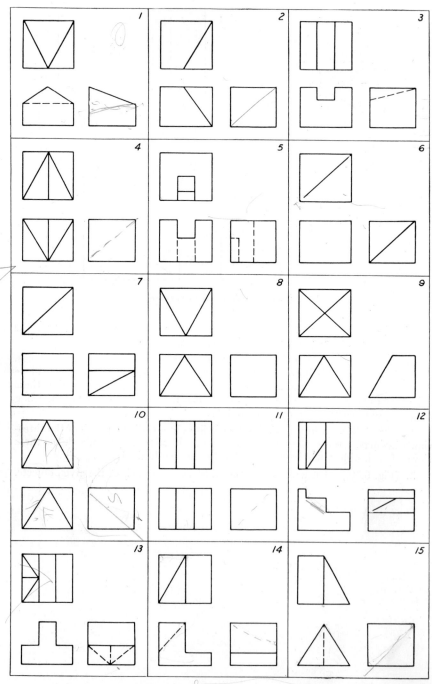

Fig. 6.48. Missing-line exercises.

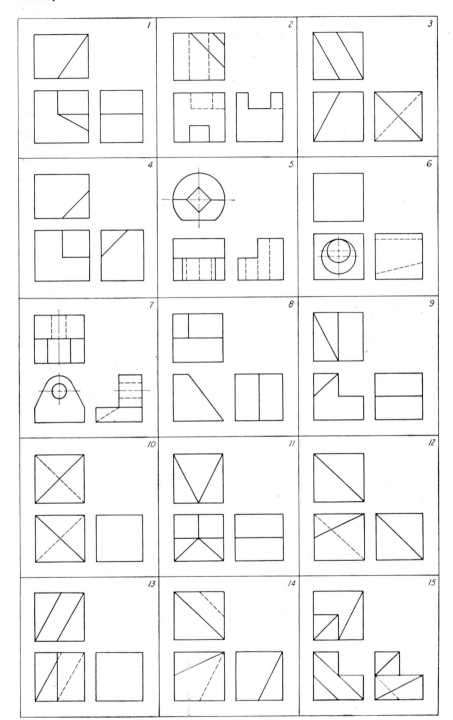

Fig. 6.49.

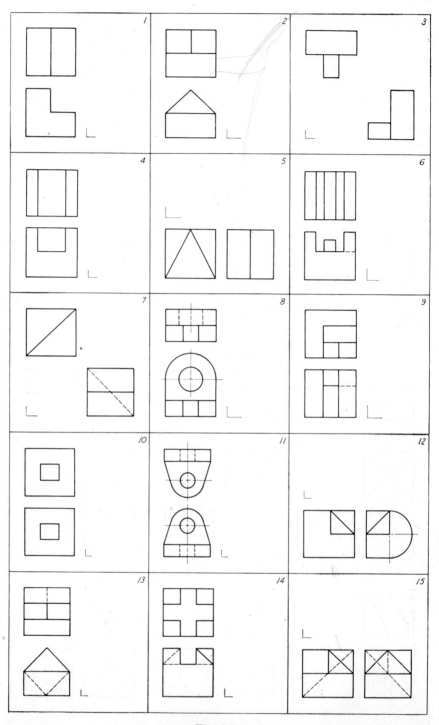

Fig. 6.50.

6–15. (Figs. 6.51–6.60.)   Reproduce the given views and draw the required view.   Show all hidden lines.

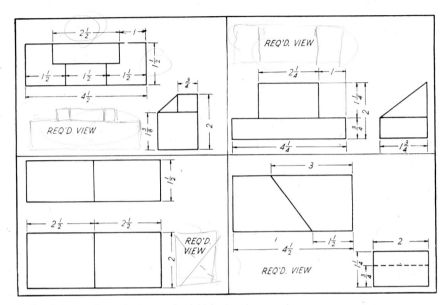

Fig. 6.51.

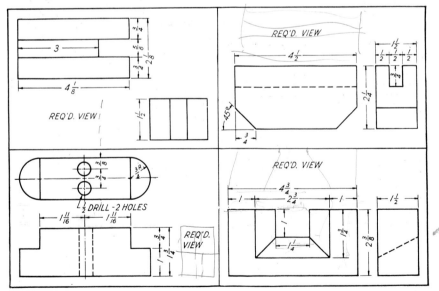

Fig. 6.52.

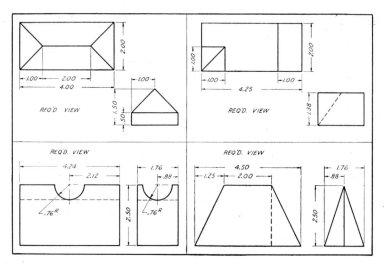

Fig. 6.53.

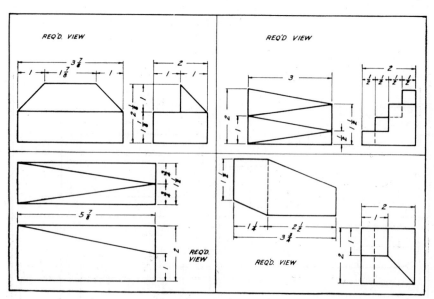

Fig. 6.54.

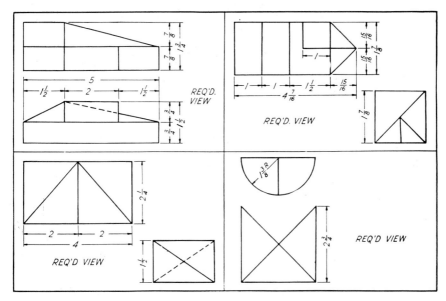

Fig. 6.55.

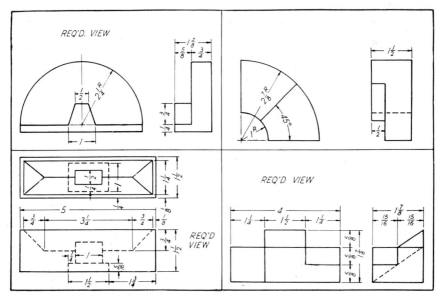

Fig. 6.56.

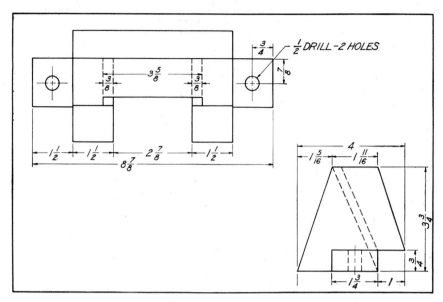

Fig. 6.57.

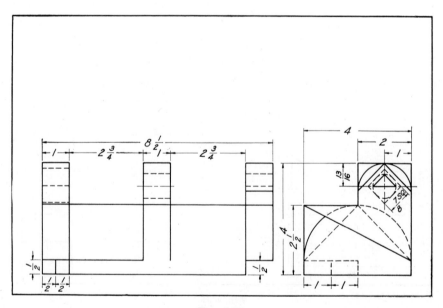

Fig. 6.58.

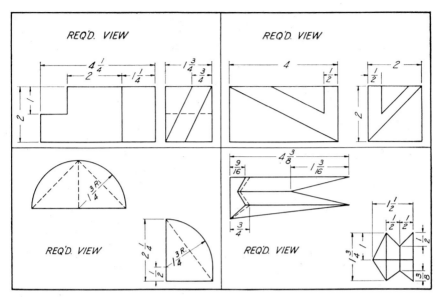

Fig. 6.59.

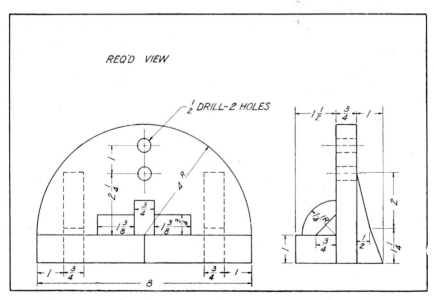

Fig. 6.60.

16–49. (Figs. 6.61–6.94.) These problems are designed to give the student further study in multiview drawing. The views of the drawings of the given objects may or may not be dimensioned. (Further instructions on page 139.)

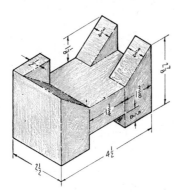

Fig. 6.61. Rest block.

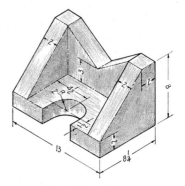

Fig. 6.62. V-rest.

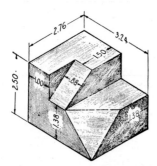

Fig. 6.63. Corner block.

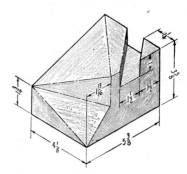

Fig. 6.64. Adjustment block.

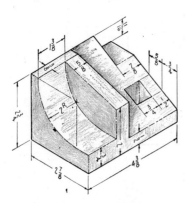

Fig. 6.65. Stop block.

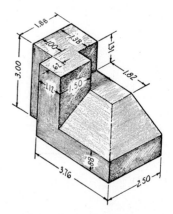

Fig. 6.66. Angle block.

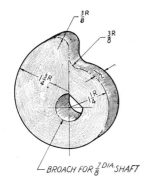

Fig. 6.67.   Cam.

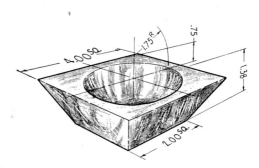

Fig. 6.68.   Ash tray.

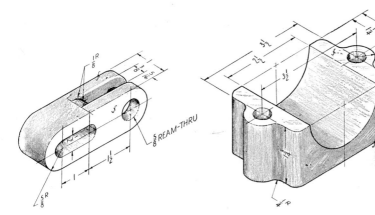

Fig. 6.69.   Connecting link.

Fig. 6.70.   Bearing block.

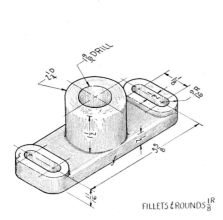

Fig. 6.71.   Support base.

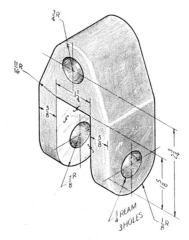

Fig. 6.72.   Hinge link.

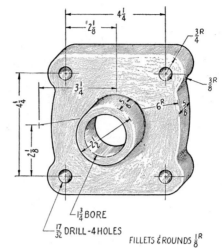

Fig. 6.73.   Regulator body cover.

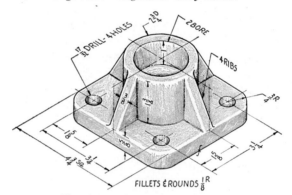

Fig. 6.74.   Stanchion support.

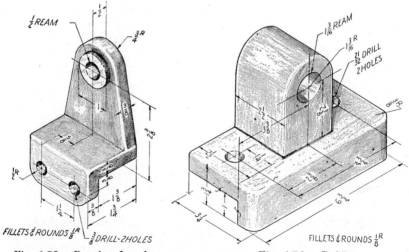

Fig. 6.75.   Bearing bracket.   **Fig. 6.76.   Guide.**

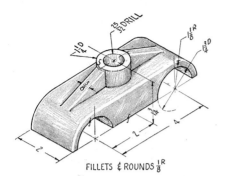

Fig. 6.77.   *Support cap.*

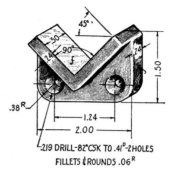

Fig. 6.78.   *Corner stop.*

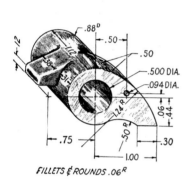

Fig. 6.79.   *Trip.*

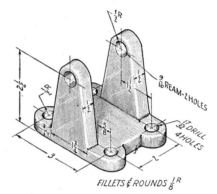

Fig. 6.80.   *Support bracket.*

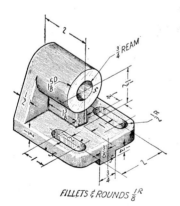

Fig. 6.81.   *Control bracket.*

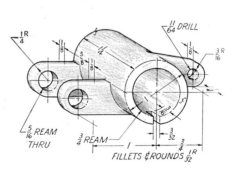

Fig. 6.82.   *Shaft guide.*

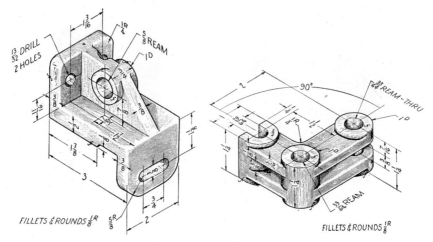

Fig. 6.83.   Support bracket.   **Fig. 6.84.   Shifter link.**

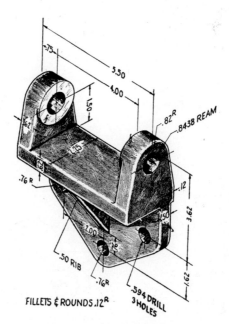

Fig. 6.85.   Guide bracket.

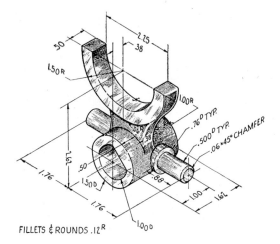

FILLETS & ROUNDS .12 R

Fig. 6.86. Shifter.

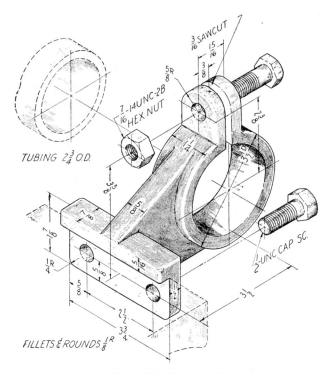

FILLETS & ROUNDS $\frac{1}{8}$ R

Fig. 6.87. Tube holder.

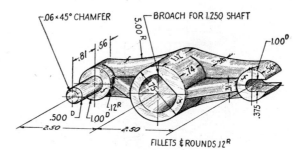

Fig. 6.88. Stud guide.

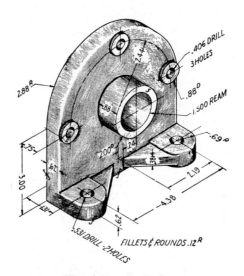

Fig. 6.89. End plate.

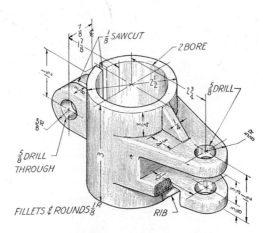

Fig. 6.90. Guide bracket.

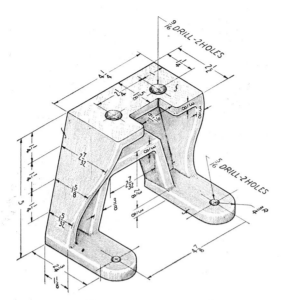

Fig. 6.91.   Lathe leg.

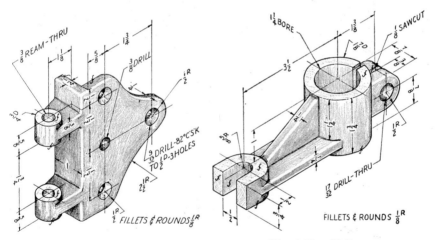

Fig. 6.92.   Corner bracket.   Fig. 6.93.   Shifter.

Only the necessary views on which all of the hidden lines are to be shown should be drawn.   It is suggested that a preliminary sketch be made on a piece of scratch paper before starting to draw.   The sketch should show the proposed arrangement of the views and the calculated location of each view in relation to the border and the other views.   The student should keep in mind the fact that the drawing is to be well balanced on the sheet and that the views are not to be crowded.   If dimensions are to be given, ample space must be allowed between the views for their placement.   It is usually wise for a student to consult his class instructor about the scale he has selected before reaching a final decision.

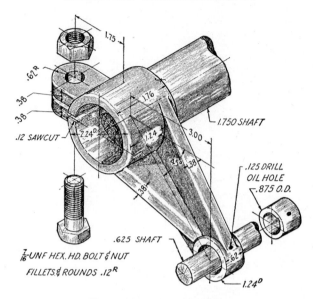

Fig. 6.94.   Shaft bracket.

50. (Fig. 6.95.)   Make a drawing of the bell crank.   The bell crank is a part of the control mechanism of a vertical single spindle boring machine.   The rod which extends downward connects with a foot-operated control.   The link carries the movement to the drive unit.   *Supplementary design data:* (1) The distance from the pivot center of the crank to the center of the connecting pin for the rod is $3\frac{1}{2}''$, and the distance from the center of the crank to the pin connecting the

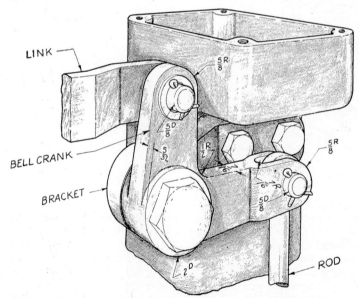

Fig. 6.95.   Bell crank.

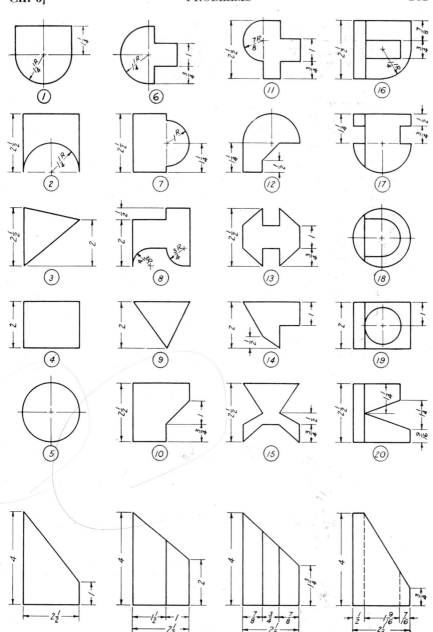

Fig. 6.96.

link is $2\frac{1}{2}''$.   (2) The limiting position for any counter-clockwise movement of
the bell crank is as shown; namely, that the line connecting the centers of the pivot
and the rod-pin is horizontal.   The crank is to be drawn to allow the rod a $1\frac{1}{2}''$
downward movement.   The upper arm of the crank is to be located so that there
will be exactly $\frac{1}{8}''$ clearance between the arm and the housing when the crank is
in the extreme clockwise position.   The horizontal distance from the pivot center
to the left face of the housing is $1\frac{5}{8}''$.   (3) The end of the rod through which the
pin passes in $1\frac{1}{2}''$ in diameter, and $\frac{3}{8}''$ thick.   Allow adequate clearance.   (4) The
crank pivots about a $1''$ diameter shoulder screw which is screwed into the
bracket.   (5) The crank is of cast iron.   Fillets and rounds $\frac{1}{8}''$ R except as noted.

The problems shown in Fig. 6.96 are designed to give the student
practice in constructing auxiliary views of the inclined surfaces of simple
objects formed mainly by straight lines.   These problems will provide
needed drill in projection if, for each of the objects, an auxiliary is drawn
showing the entire object.   Complete drawings may be made of the
objects shown in Figs. 6.97–6.111.   If the views are to be dimensioned,
the student should adhere to the rules of dimensioning given in Chapter
16 and should not take too seriously the locations for the dimensions on
the pictorial representations.

51. (Fig. 6.96.)   Using instruments, reproduce the given views of an assigned
object and draw an auxiliary view of its inclined surface.

52. (Fig. 6.97.)   Draw the views that would be necessary on a working drawing of the *boiler bracket*.

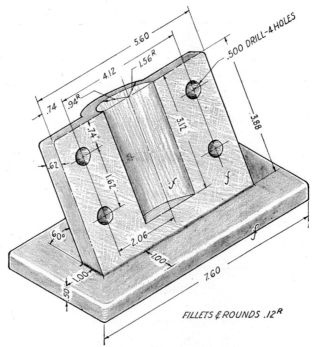

Fig. 6.97.   Boiler bracket.

53. (Fig. 6.98.) Draw the views that are necessary to describe fully the *sliding guide*. The auxiliary view should show only the inclined surface.

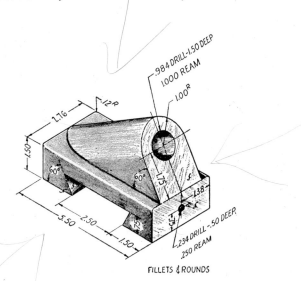

Fig. 6.98.   Sliding guide.

54. (Fig. 6.99.) Draw the views that would be necessary on a working drawing of the *feeder bracket*.

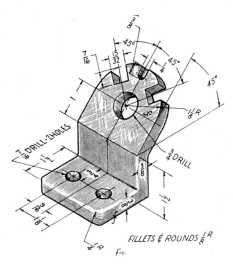

Fig. 6.99.   Feeder bracket.

55. (Fig. 6.100.) Draw the views that would be necessary on a working drawing of the *45° elbow*.

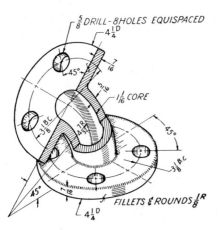

Fig. 6.100. *45° elbow.*

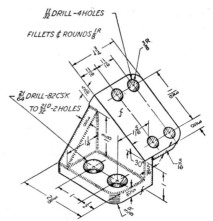

Fig. 6.101. *Offset bracket.*

56. (Fig. 6.101.) Draw the necessary views of the *offset bracket*. It is suggested that partial views be used, except in the view where the inclined surface appears as a line.

57. (Fig. 6.102.) Draw the necessary views of the *anchor bracket*. Make partial views for the top and end views.

58. (Fig. 6.103.) Draw the views that would be needed on a working drawing of the *gear cover*. The opening on the inclined face is circular. The pictorial drawing shows an unfinished casting. Show finished surfaces where necessary.

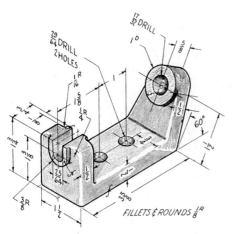

Fig. 6.102. *Anchor bracket.*

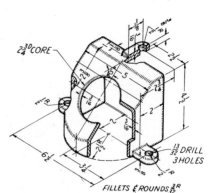

Fig. 6.103. *Gear cover.*

59. (Fig. 6.104.) Draw the views that would be necessary on a working drawing of the *instrument panel bracket*. Note that two auxiliary views will be required.

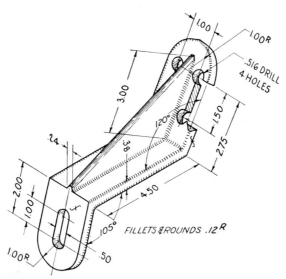

Fig. 6.104.   Instrument panel bracket.

60. (Fig. 6.105.) Draw the views that would be necessary on a working drawing of the *angle bearing*.

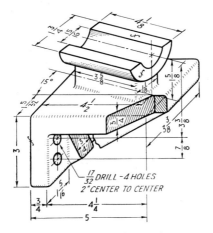

Fig. 6.105.   Angle bearing.

61. (Fig. 6.106.)   Draw the necessary views of the *hinge bracket*.

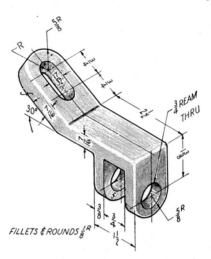

Fig. 6.106.   Hinge bracket.

62. (Fig. 6.107.)   Draw the necessary views of the *angle bracket*.

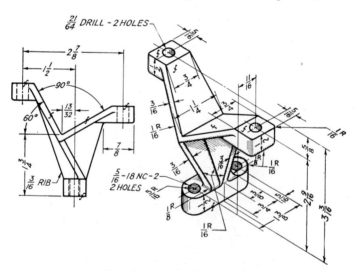

Fig. 6.107.   Angle bracket.

63. (Fig. 6.108.)   Draw the views as given.   Complete the top view.

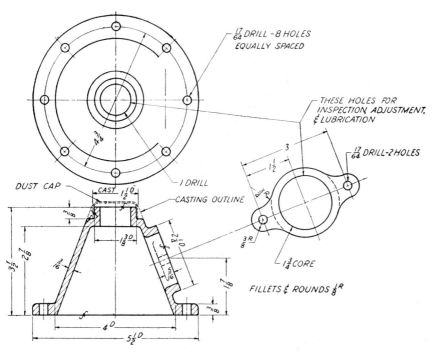

Fig. 6.108.   Housing cover.

64. (Fig. 6.109.)   Draw the views as given.   Complete the auxiliary view and the front view.

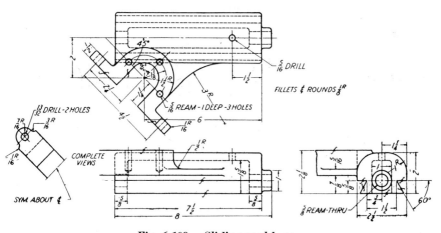

Fig. 6.109.   Sliding tool base.

65. (Fig. 6.110.)   Draw the necessary views of the adjustment block.

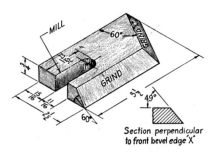

Fig. 6.110.   Adjustment block.

66. (Fig. 6.111.)   Draw the views as given and add the required primary and secondary auxiliary views.

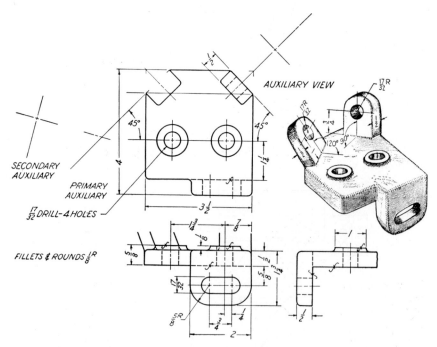

Fig. 6.111.   Cross anchor.

67. (Fig. 6.112.)   Draw the layout for the *support anchor* as given and then, using the double auxiliary view method, complete the views as required.

The plate and cylinder are to be welded.   Since the faces of the plate show as oblique surfaces in the front and top views, double auxiliary views are necessary to show the thickness and the true shape.

Start the drawing with the auxiliary views that are arranged horizontally on the paper, then complete the principal views.   The inclined face of the cylinder will show as an ellipse in top and front views; but do not show this in the auxiliary view that shows the true shape (4.00″ square) of the plate.

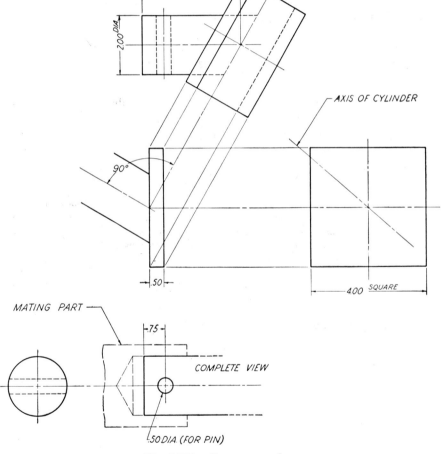

Fig. 6.112.   Support anchor.

How would you find the view that shows the true angle between the inclined face and the axis of the cylinder?

68. (Fig. 6.113.) Using instruments, reproduce the given views of an assigned object and draw a secondary auxiliary view that will show the true size and shape of the inclined surface.

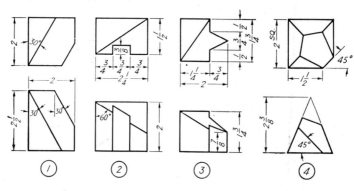

Fig. 6.113.

The following problems in revolution furnish excellent drill in projection and offer the student a chance to develop further his imagination and ability to visualize in three dimensions. It will be found worth while to number all the corners of each object used, both on the normal views and on the views of the successive stages.

69. Divide, into four equal areas, the space inside the border line of a sheet of drawing paper. In the upper left-hand space, draw the normal orthographic views of an object assigned from Fig. 6.114. In the lower left-hand space, show the object revolved through an angle of 30° about an axis perpendicular to the front plane (see Fig. 6.41). In the upper right-hand space, show a simple revolution from the normal orthographic view about an axis perpendicular to the top plane (see Fig. 6.42). Revolve the object through an angle of 30°. Complete the drawing by making a simple revolution about an axis perpendicular to the side or profile plane (see Fig. 6.43). Revolve the object from the original normal position through an angle of 30°.

70. Divide a sheet of drawing paper into four equal areas and make a series of successive revolutions of an object assigned from Fig. 6.114.   Revolve the object through the three stages shown in Fig. 6.44.   Make the revolutions in the following order: (1) in the lower left-hand space, revolve the object through an angle of 30° about an axis perpendicular to the front plane; (2) in the lower right-hand space, revolve the object from its previous position through an angle of 15° about an axis perpendicular to the top plane; (3) in the upper right-hand space, make a revolution through an angle of 15° about an axis perpendicular to the side or profile plane.

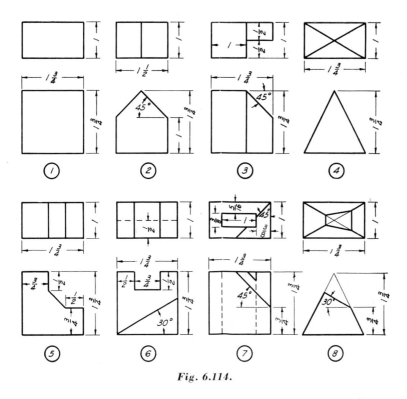

Fig. 6.114.

71. (Fig. 6.115.)   Make a complete two-view orthographic drawing of the *guide bracket* which is shown by a pictorial sketch.   The student is advised to

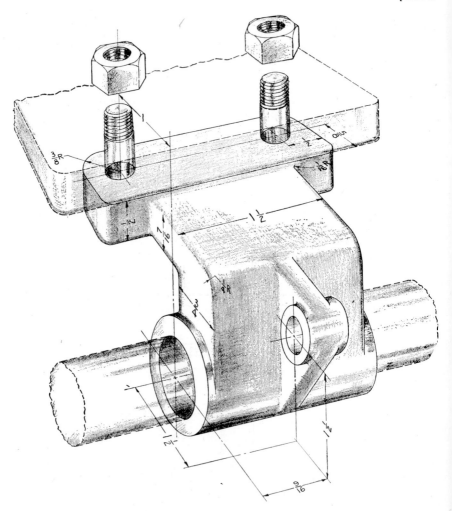

Fig. 6.115.   Guide bracket.

give careful consideration to the choice of views remembering that it is the usual practice to show the circular form of each cylindrical feature on one of the selected views.   Dimension the views completely while keeping in mind the fact that dimensions are oftentimes not placed on a pictorial drawing as they should be placed on the orthographic drawing. *Supplementary information:* (1) The centerline for the main $1''$ shaft is $2\frac{3}{8}''$ below the flat finished base surface.   The hole for this shaft is to be reamed.   (2) The length of the cylindrical portion is $1\frac{3}{4}''$ between contact faces.   The O.D. is $1\frac{1}{2}''$.   (3) The hole for the smaller shaft is to be reamed for a $\frac{5}{8}''$ shaft.   The O.D. of the cylinder is $1''$ and the distance between faces is $\frac{5}{8}''$.   The $\frac{3}{8}''$ ribs should be tangent to cylindrical surfaces. (4) The flat finished base surface is $1\frac{1}{8}'' \times 2\frac{3}{4}''$.   The holes which are to be drilled $\frac{1}{32}''$ over-size for $\frac{3}{8}''$ bolts are $1\frac{3}{4}''$ apart, and are centered in the direction parallel to the axes of the shafts.   (5) Fillets and rounds $\frac{1}{8}$ R.

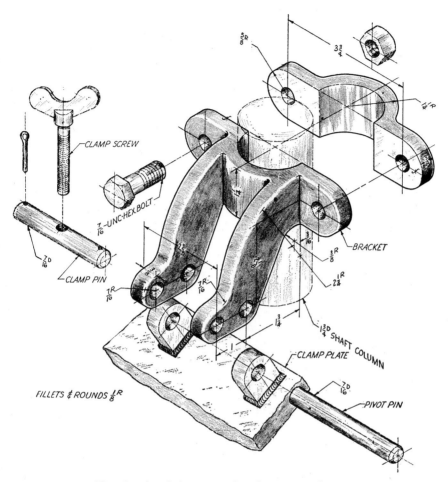

Fig. 6.116.　Adjustment bracket—core blower.

72. (Fig. 6.116.)　Make a multiview drawing of the bracket or its mating part that clamps around the $1\frac{3}{4}''$ shaft.

The given pictorial drawing shows the adjustment bracket assembly of a positioning mechanism on a cartridge type core blower.　The bracket when attached to the vertical column supports a positioning clamp that may be tilted into different positions.　The clamp screw keeps the positioning clamp in a desired position when it is tightened down against the clamp plate.

73–79. Using instruments make a multiview drawing of a part as assigned.

73. (Fig. 9.58.)　Guide bracket.

74. (Fig. 9.61.)　Link.

75. (Fig. 9.66.)　Bearing bracket.

76. (Fig. 9.67.)　Control bracket.

77. (Fig. 9.68.)　Control bracket (airplane).

78. (Fig. 9.72.) Motor bracket.

79. (Fig. 9.75.) Offset shaft bracket.

80. Make a multiview drawing of the *airplane engine mount* shown in Fig. 6.117. The engine mount is formed of three pieces of steel plate welded to a piece of steel tubing. The completed drawing is to consist of four views. It is suggested that the front view be the view obtained by looking along and parallel to the axis of the tube. The remaining views that are needed are an auxiliary view showing only the inclined lug, a side view that should be complete with all hidden lines shown, and a partial top view with the inclined lug omitted.

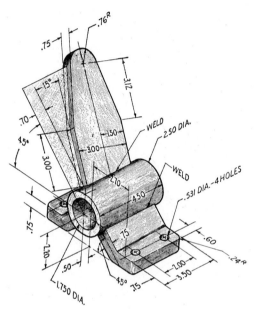

Fig. 6.117.   Airplane engine mount.

Sectional Views

7.1. Sectional views. Although the invisible features of a simple object usually may be described on an exterior view by the use of hidden lines, it is unwise to depend upon a perplexing mass of such lines to adequately describe the interior of a complicated object or an assembled

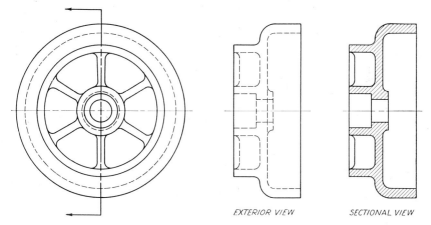

EXTERIOR VIEW   SECTIONAL VIEW

Fig. 7.1.   A sectional view.

mechanism.   Whenever a representation becomes so confused that it is difficult to read, it is customary to make one or more of the views "in section" (Fig. 7.1).   A view "in section" is one obtained by imagining the object to have been cut by a cutting plane, the front portion being removed so as to clearly reveal the interior features.   Fig. 7.2(*a*) illustrates the use of an imaginary cutting plane.   The resulting sectional (front) view, accompanied by a top view, is shown in Fig. 7.2(*c*).   At this point it should be understood that a portion is shown removed only in a sectional view, not in any of the other views.   (See Fig. 7.2(*c*).)

When the cutting plane cuts an object lengthwise, the section obtained is commonly called a longitudinal section; when crosswise, it is called a cross section.   It is designated as being either a full section, a half section, or a broken section.   If the plane cuts entirely across the object, the section represented is known as a full section.   If it cuts only halfway across a symmetrical object, the section is a half section.   A broken section is a partial one which is used when less than a half section is needed.

On a completed sectional view, fine section lines are drawn across the surface cut by the imaginary plane, to emphasize the contour of the interior (see Sec. 7.8).

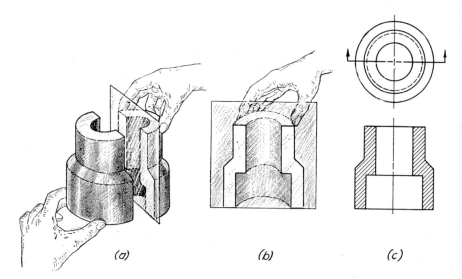

(a)   *(b)*   *(c)*

Fig. 7.2.   *The theory of the construction of a sectional view.*

7.2. A full section.   Since a cutting plane that cuts a full section passes entirely through an object, the resulting view will appear as illustrated in Fig. 7.2(*c*).   Although the plane usually passes along the main axis, it may be offset (see Fig. 7.3) to reveal important features.

A full sectional view, showing an object's characteristic shape, usually replaces an exterior front view; however, one of the other principal views, side or top, may be converted into a sectional view if some interior feature thus can be shown to better advantage or if such a view is needed in addition to a sectioned front view.

The procedure in making a full sectional view is simple, in that the sectional view is an orthographic one.   The imaginary cut face of the object simply is shown as it would appear to an observer looking directly at it from a point an infinite distance away.   In any sectional view, it is considered good practice to omit all invisible lines unless such lines are necessary to clarify the representation.   Even then they should be used sparingly.

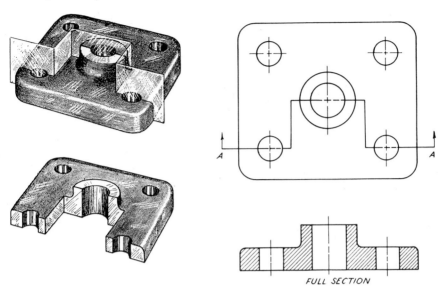

FULL SECTION

Fig. 7.3. *An offset cutting plane.*

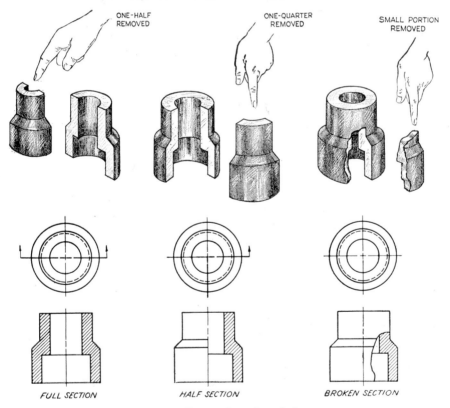

ONE-HALF REMOVED   ONE-QUARTER REMOVED   SMALL PORTION REMOVED

FULL SECTION   HALF SECTION   BROKEN SECTION

Fig. 7.4. *Types of sectional views.*

7.3. A half section. The cutting plane for a half section removes one quarter of an object. The plane cuts halfway through to the axis or center line so that half the finished sectional view appears in section and half appears as an external view (Fig. 7.4). This type of sectional view is used when a view is needed showing both the exterior and interior construction of a symmetrical object. Good practice dictates that hidden lines be omitted from both halves of the view unless they are absolutely necessary for dimensioning purposes or for explaining the construction. Although the use of a solid line object line to separate the two halves of a half section has been approved by the Society of Automotive Engineers in the new SAE Drafting Standards (Fig. 7.5a), many persons prefer to use a center line as shown in Fig. 7.5(b). They reason that the removal of a quarter of the object is theoretical and imaginary and that an actual edge, which would be implied by a solid line, does not exist. The center line is taken as denoting a theoretical edge.

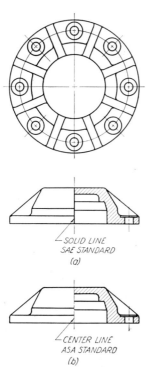

SOLID LINE
SAE STANDARD
(a)

CENTER LINE
ASA STANDARD
(b)

Fig. 7.5. A half section.

7.4. A broken section. A broken or partial section is used mainly to expose the interior of objects so constructed that less than a half section is required for a satisfactory description (Fig. 7.6). The object theoretically is cut by a cutting plane and the front portion is removed by breaking it away. The "breaking away" gives an irregular boundary line to the section.

7.5. A revolved section. A revolved section is useful for showing the true shape of the cross section of some elongated

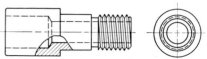

Fig. 7.6. A broken section.

object, such as a bar, or some feature of an object, such as an arm, spoke, or rib (Fig. 7.7).

To obtain such a cross section, an imaginary cutting plane is passed through the member perpendicular to its axis, and then is revolved through 90° to bring the resulting view into the plane of the paper (Fig. 7.8). When revolved, the section should show in its true shape and in its true revolved position, regardless of the location of the lines of the exterior view. If any lines of the view interfere with the revolved section, they

should be omitted (Fig. 7.9). It sometimes is advisable to provide an
open space for the section by making a break in
the object (Fig. 7.7).

7.6. Detail or removed sections. A detail
section is similar to a revolved section, except
that it does not appear on an external view but,
instead, is drawn "out of place," and appears
adjacent to it (Fig. 7.10). There are two good
reasons why detail sections frequently are
desirable. First, their use may prevent a principal view of an object, the cross section of which
is not uniform, from being cluttered with
numerous revolved sections. Second, they
may be drawn to an enlarged scale in order to
emphasize detail and allow for adequate
dimensioning.

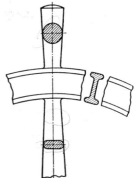

*Fig. 7.7. A revolved
section.*

Whenever a detail section is used, there must be some means of identifying it. Usually this is accomplished by showing the cutting plane on

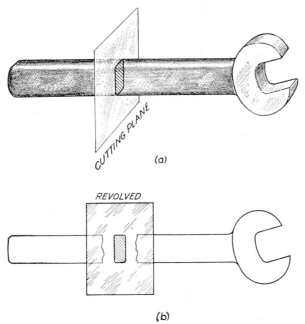

Fig. 7.8. A revolved section and cutting plane.

the principal view and then labeling both the plane and the resulting view,
as shown in Fig. 7.10.

---

* ASA Z14.1–1946.

7.7. Phantom sections. A phantom or hidden section is a regular exterior view upon which the interior construction is emphasized by crosshatching an imaginary cut surface with dotted section lines (Fig. 7.11). This type of section is used only when a regular section or a broken section would remove some important exterior detail.

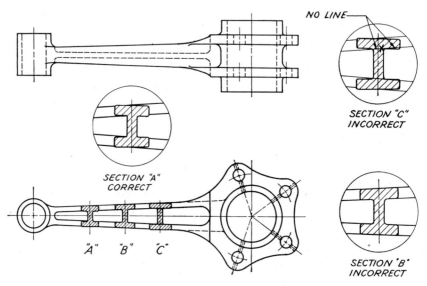

SECTION "C"
INCORRECT

SECTION "A"
CORRECT

SECTION "B"
INCORRECT

Fig. 7.9.   Revolved sections.

7.8. Section lining. Section lines are light continuous lines drawn across the imaginary cut surface of an object for the purpose of emphasizing the contour of its interior.   Usually they are drawn at an angle of 45°

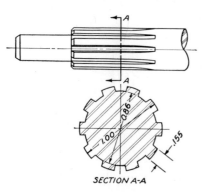

SECTION A-A

Fig. 7.10.   A detail section.

except in cases where a number of adjacent parts are shown assembled. (See Fig. 7.14.)

To be pleasing in appearance, these lines must be correctly executed. While on ordinary work they are spaced about $\frac{3}{32}''$ apart, there is no set rule governing their spacing. They simply should be spaced to suit the drawing and the size of the areas to be crosshatched. For example, on small views having small areas, the section lines may be as close as $\frac{1}{32}''$, while on large views having large areas they may be as far apart as $\frac{1}{8}''$.   In the case of very thin plates, the cross section is shown "solid black" (Fig. 7.12).

Code section lining as shown in Fig. 8.16, ordinarily is not used on a drawing of a separate part. It is considered unnecessary to indicate a material symbolically when its exact specification must also be given as a note. For this reason, and in order to save time, the easily drawn symbol for cast iron, consisting of equally spaced solid lines, is commonly used on detail drawings for all materials. (See Fig. 7.5.)

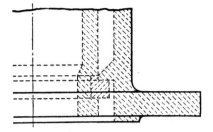

Fig. 7.11. A phantom section.

The usual mistake of the beginning student is to draw the lines too close together. This, plus the unavoidable slight variations, causes the

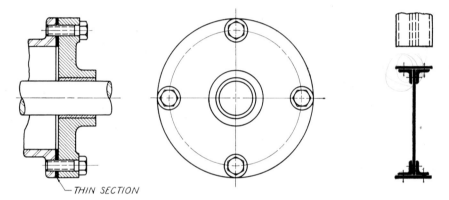

—THIN SECTION

Fig. 7.12. Thin sections.

section lining to appear streaked. Although several forms of mechanical section liners are available, most draftsmen do their spacing by eye. The

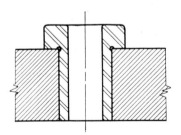

Fig. 7.13. Two adjacent pieces.

student is advised to do likewise, being careful to see that the initial pitch, as set by the first few lines, is maintained across the area. To accomplish this, he should check back from time to time to make sure there has been no slight general increase or decrease in the spacing.

As shown in Fig. 7.13, the section lines on two adjacent pieces should slope at 45 degrees in opposite directions. If a third piece adjoins the two other pieces, as in Fig. 7.14(a), it ordinarily is section-lined at 30 degrees. An alternate treatment, which might be used, would be to vary the spacing without changing the angle. On a sectional view showing an assembly of related parts, *all portions of the cut surface of any part must be section-lined in the same direction, for a change would lead the reader to consider the portions as belonging to different parts. Furthermore, to allow quick identification, each piece (and all identical pieces) in every view of the assembly drawing should be section-lined in the same direction.*

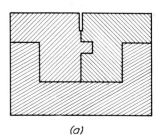
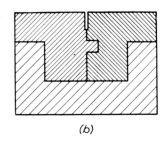

(a)   (b)

Fig. 7.14.   *Three adjacent pieces.*

POOR PRACTICE   PREFERRED   POOR PRACTICE   PREFERRED
(a)   (b)   (c)   (d)

Fig. 7.15.   *Section lining at 30°, 60°, and 75°.*

Whenever section lines drawn at 45° with the horizontal are parallel to part of the outline of the section (see Fig. 7.15), it is advisable to draw them at some other angle (say 30° or 60°). Those drawn as in (a) and (c) produce an unusual appearance that is contrary to what is expected. Note the more natural effect obtained in (b) and (d) by sloping the lines at 30° and 75°.

Shafts, bolts, pins, rivets, balls, and so on, whose axes lie in the plane of section are not treated the same as ordinary parts. Having no interior construction to be shown, they are drawn in full and thus tend to make the adjacent sectioned parts stand out to better advantage (Fig. 7.16).

7.9. Outline sectioning. Very large surfaces may be section-lined around the bounding outline only, as illustrated in Fig. 7.17.

7.10. The symbolic representation for a cutting plane. The symbolic lines that are used to represent the edge view of a cutting plane are shown in Fig. 7.18. The line is as heavy as an object line and is composed of either alternate long and short dashes or a series of dashes of equal length. The latter form is used in the automobile industry and has

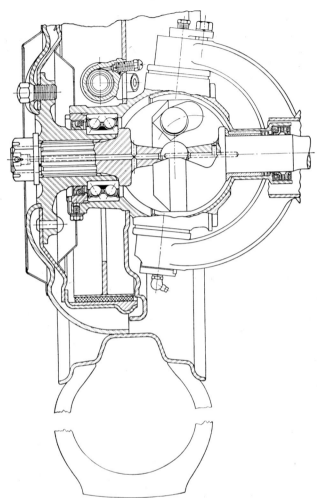

(Courtesy of New Departure, Division General Motors Sales Corporation)

Fig. 7.16. *Treatment of shafts, fasteners, ball bearings, and so forth.*

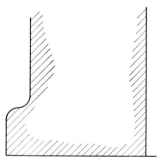

Fig. 7.17. *Outline sectioning.*

been approved by the SAE (Society of Automotive Engineers). On drawings of ordinary size, when alternate long and short dashes are used for the cutting plane line, the long dashes are $\frac{3}{4}''$ long, the short dashes $\frac{1}{8}''$ long, and the spaces $\frac{1}{32}''$ wide.

Arrowheads are used to show the direction in which the imaginary cut surface is viewed, and reference letters are added to identify it (Fig. 7.20).

Whenever the location of the cutting plane is obvious, it is common practice to omit the edge-view representation, particularly in the case of symmetrical objects. If it is shown, however, and coincides with a center line, it takes precedence over the center line.

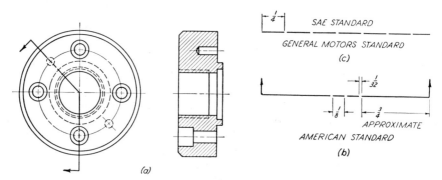

Fig. 7.18.   Cutting plane lines.

7.11. Summary of the practices of sectioning.

1. A cutting plane may be offset in order to cut the object in such a manner as to reveal an important detail that would not be shown if the cutting plane were continuous.

2. All visible lines beyond the cutting plane for the section are usually shown.

3. Invisible lines beyond the cutting plane for the section are usually not shown, unless they are absolutely necessary to clarify the construction of the piece. In a half section, they are omitted in the unsectioned half, and either a center line or a solid line is used to separate the two halves of the view (Fig. 7.5).

4. On a view showing assembled parts, the section lines on adjacent pieces are drawn in opposite directions at an angle of 45° (Fig. 7.13).

5. On an assembly drawing, the portions of the cut surface of a single piece in the same view or different views always should be section-lined in the same direction, with the same spacing (Fig. 7.16).

6. The symbolic line indicating the location of the cutting plane may be omitted if the location of the plane is obvious (Fig. 7.5).

7. On a sectioned view showing assembled pieces, an exterior view is preferred for shafts, rods, bolts, nuts, rivets, and so forth, whose axes are in the plane of section (Fig. 7.16).

7.12. Auxiliary sections. A sectional view, projected upon an auxiliary plane, is sometimes necessary to show the shape of a surface cut by a plane, or to show the cross-sectional shape of an arm, rib, and so forth, inclined to any two or all three of the principal planes of projection (Fig. 7.19). When a cutting plane cuts an object, as in Fig. 7.19, arrows should show the direction in which the cut surface is viewed. Auxiliary sections are drawn by the usual method for drawing auxiliary views. Sec. 6.25 explains in detail the method for constructing the required view. A section view of this type usually shows only the inclined cut surface.

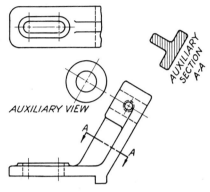

Fig. 7.19. An auxiliary section.

7.13. Conventional sections. Sometimes a less confusing sectioned representation is obtained if certain of the strict rules of projection are violated. For example, an unbalanced and confused view results when the sectioned view of the pulley shown in Fig. 7.21 is drawn in true projection, as in (*a*). It is better practice to preserve symmetry by showing the spokes as if they were aligned into one plane, as in (*c*). Such treatment of unsymmetrical features is not misleading, since their actual arrangement is revealed in the circular view. The spokes are not sectioned in the preferred view. If they were, the first impression would be that the wheel had a solid web (*b*). (See Fig. 7.22.)

The holes in a flange should be shown in a sectioned view at their true distance apart, across the bolt circle, even though their axes do not fall in the plane of section (Fig. 7.23). The unbalanced view in (*b*) conveys no impression of symmetry, nor does it reveal the true location of the holes with reference to rim. The view in (*a*), showing the upper hole as if it had been swung into the plane of section, is less misleading and is therefore to be preferred.

In Fig. 7.24 another example of conventional representation is shown. The sectional view is drawn as if the upper projecting lug had been swung until the portion of the cutting plane through it formed a continuous plane with the other portion. It should be noted that the hidden lines in the sectioned view are necessary in this case for a complete description of the construction of the lugs.

7.14. Ribs in section. When a machine part has a rib cut by a plane of section (Fig. 7.25), a "true" sectional view taken through the rib proves false and misleading, because the crosshatching on the rib causes the object to appear "solid." The preferred treatment is to omit

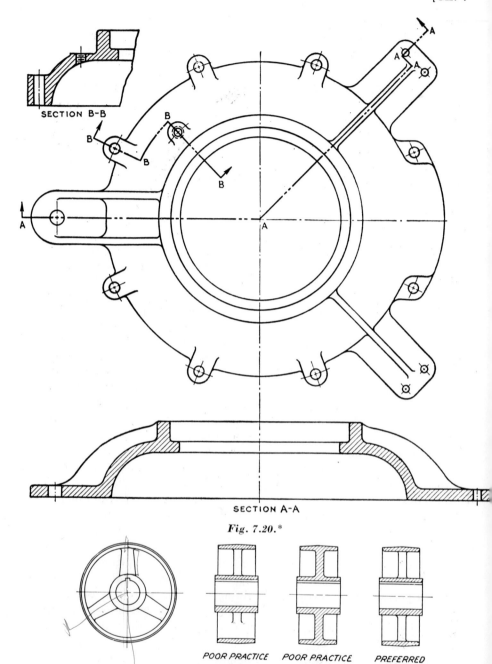

SECTION B-B

SECTION A-A

Fig. 7.20.*

POOR PRACTICE   POOR PRACTICE   PREFERRED
(a)   (b)   (c)

Fig. 7.21. Conventional treatment of spokes in section.

* ASA Z14.1–1946.

arbitrarily the section lines from the rib, as illustrated by Fig. 7.25(a). The resulting sectional view may be considered the view that would be obtained if the plane were offset to pass just in front of the rib (b).

An alternate conventional method, approved but not used as frequently as the one above, is illustrated in Fig. 7.26. This practice of

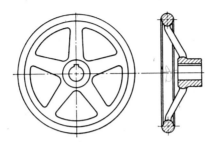

*Fig. 7.22. Spokes in section.**

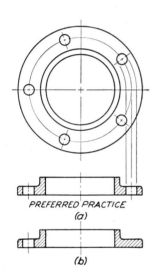

Fig. 7.23. Drilled flanges.

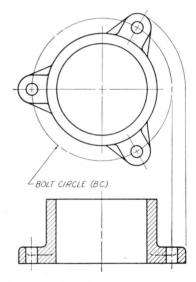

Fig. 7.24. Revolution of a portion of an object.

omitting alternate section lines sometimes is adopted when it is necessary to emphasize a rib that might otherwise be overlooked.

7.15. Problems. The following problems were designed to emphasize the principles of sectioning. It is not recommended that a great amount of time be spent on them, as more practice in applying the fundamentals of sectioning is offered the student by problems at the end of the chapter on working drawings. Those orthographic drawings that are

---

* ASA Z14.1–1946.

prepared from the pictorials of objects may be dimensioned if the elementary principles of dimensioning (Chapter 16) are carefully studied.

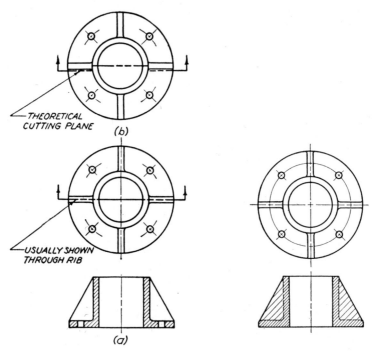

Fig. 7.25. *Conventional treatment of ribs in section.*　　Fig. 7.26. *Alternate treatment of ribs in section.*

1. (Fig. 7.27.)　Reproduce the top and side views and change the front view into a sectional view that will be in accordance with the indicated cutting plane.

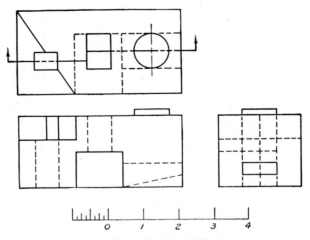

Fig. 7.27. *Mutilated block.*

2. (Fig. 7.28.) Draw a front view of the pulley (circular view) and a side view in full section.

3. (Fig. 7.29.) Reproduce the top view of the rod support and draw the front view in full section. Read Secs. 7.13 and 7.14 before starting to draw.

4. (Fig. 7.30.) Draw a front view of the "*V*" pulley (circular view) and a side view in full section.

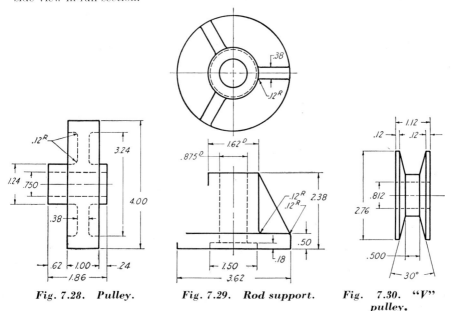

Fig. 7.28. Pulley.   **Fig. 7.29. Rod support.**   **Fig. 7.30. "*V*" pulley.**

5. (Fig. 7.31.) Make a full sectional view of the "rectangular view" of the piston head. Reproduce the circular view.

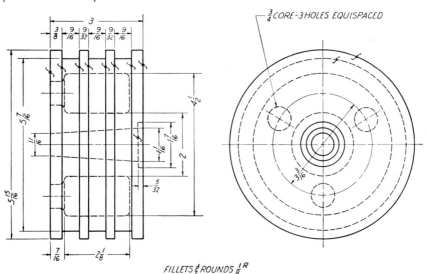

Fig. 7.31. Piston head.

6. (Fig. 7.32.)   Reproduce the circular front view of the pump cover and convert the right-side view to a full section.

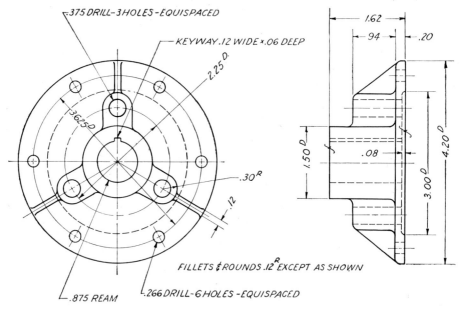

Fig. 7.32.   Pump cover.

7. (Fig. 7.33.)   Reproduce the top view of the control housing cover and convert the front view to a full section.

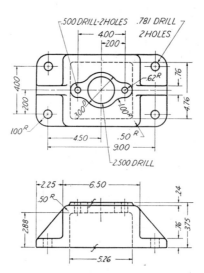

Fig. 7.33.   Control housing cover.

8. (Fig. 7.34.)   Reproduce the two views of the hand wheel and change the right-side view into a full section.

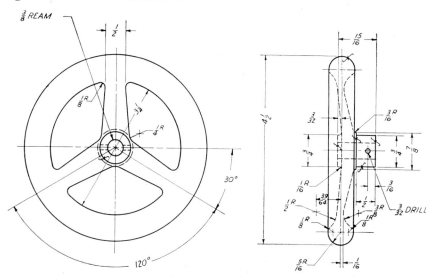

Fig. 7.34.   Hand wheel.

9. (Fig. 7.35.)   Reproduce the front and top views of the steady brace. Complete the top view and draw the required side view and auxiliary section. Since this is a structural drawing, the figure giving the value of a distance appears above on unbroken dimension line in accordance with the custom in this field of engineering.   The slope (45°) of the inclined member to which the plates are welded is indicated by a slope triangle with 12 inch legs.

This problem has been designed to make it necessary for the student to test his power of visualization if he is to determine the shape of the inclined structural

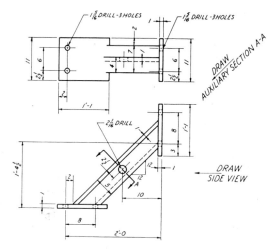

Fig. 7.35.   Steady brace.

member.   Good judgment must be exercised in determining the location of the third hole in each plate.   All hidden object lines should be shown.

10–21. (Figs. 7.36–7.47.)   These problems may be dimensioned, as are working drawings.   For each object, the student should draw all the views necessary for a working drawing of the part.   Good judgment should be exercised in deciding whether the sectional view should be a full section or a half section.   After the student has made his decision, he should consult his class instructor.

The end guide has five ribs (Fig. 7.47.)

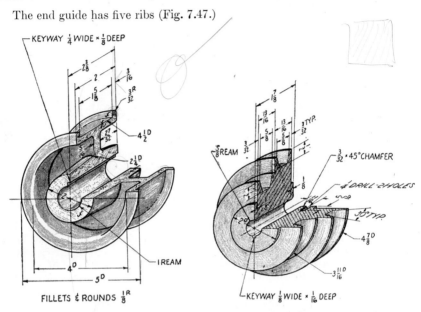

Fig. 7.36.   *Flanged pulley.*   Fig. 7.37.   *"V" motor pulley.*

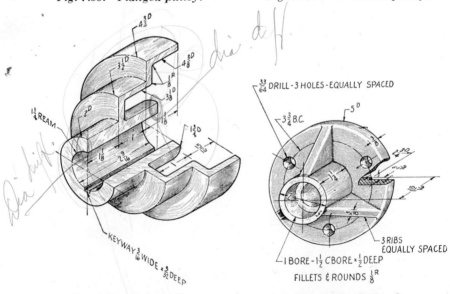

Fig. 7.38.   *Cone pulley.*   Fig. 7.39.   *Rod yoke.*

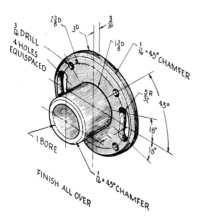

Fig. 7.40.   Attachment guide.

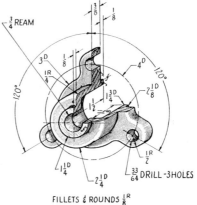

FILLETS & ROUNDS $\frac{1}{8}$R

Fig. 7.41.   End cap.

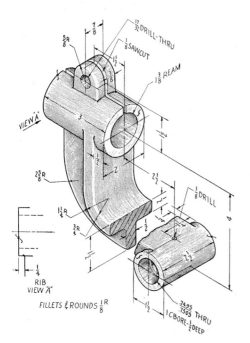

FILLETS & ROUNDS $\frac{1}{8}$R

Fig. 7.42.   Hanger bracket.

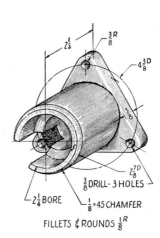

FILLETS & ROUNDS $\frac{1}{8}$R

Fig. 7.43.   Radiator outlet.

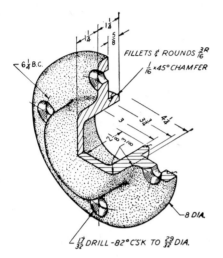

Fig. 7.44. Cover.

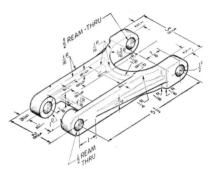

Fig. 7.45. Link.

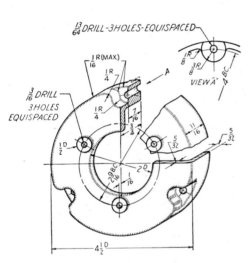

Fig. 7.46. Cover.

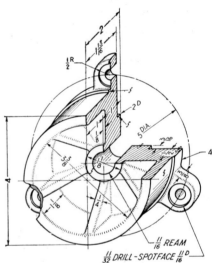

Fig. 7.47. End guide.

22. (Fig. 7.48.) Make a multiview drawing of the drum. The drum rotates when it is forced along the shaft into contact with the constantly rotating driving cone. The driving cone is fixed to the rotating shaft by a Pratt and Whitney key to insure rotary motion with the shaft, and by a taper pin to prevent longitudinal axial movement. As the drum rotates it winds or unwinds a cable. The shaft is driven by a system of gears that is not shown. The partial orthographic views show the operating mechanism for sliding the drum along the shaft into contact with the driving cone. If after studying the drawings carefully you have further questions, please consult your instructor. *Supplementary informa-*

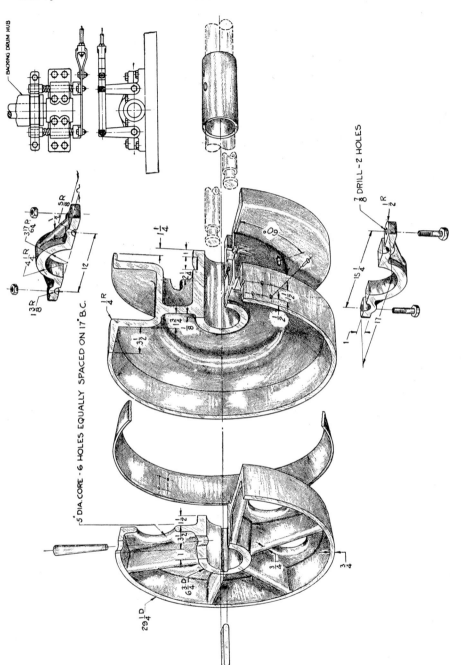

Fig. 7.48.   Hoisting machine—drum, cone, and collar.

tion: (1) The outside diameter of the drum is 30″. The diameter of the opening in the drum for the backing drum cone is $29\frac{1}{4}$″ and the taper is $2\frac{1}{2}$″ per ft. (2) The diameter of the cable section is 18″, and the width of opening for the cable is 10″. (3) The dimensions of the hub are: 8″ outside diameter (O.D.) and $12\frac{3}{8}$″ overall length. (4) The O.D. of the bushing is $4\frac{1}{4}$″. (5) There are six $\frac{5}{8}$″ thick ribs which are equally spaced. (6) The hole in the hub for an oil fitting is tapped for a $\frac{1}{4}$″ pipe thread. The hole which is to provide access to the threaded hole is drilled $\frac{3}{4}$″ in diameter. The tapped hole is $6\frac{3}{16}$″ from the face of the hub. (7) The small hole for attaching the cable is $\frac{13}{16}$″. It is located $\frac{3}{4}$″ from the face of the flange. (8) The thickness of all sections except for the ribs is $\frac{3}{4}$″. (9) There are 124 copper rivets required to fasten the brake lining to the drum. The holes in the drum are to be drilled $\frac{1}{4}$″ in diameter and are countersunk at 90°. (10) All small radii are $\frac{3}{4}$″ R.

23. (Fig. 7.48.) Make a multiview drawing of the driving cone. *Supplementary information:* (1) The surface of the driving cone which contacts the lining in the drum is tapered. The taper is $2\frac{1}{2}$″ per ft. (2) The diameter of the shaft on which the driving cone is fixed is $3\frac{3}{4}$″ dia. (3) It is suggested that a No. 34 Pratt and Whitney and No. 12 Std. taper be used for the driving cone. Taper pins have a taper of $\frac{1}{4}$″ per ft. (4) The 5″ dia. holes are to be cored in the casting.

8

Conventional Practices and Symbolic Representations

8.1. To reduce the high cost of preparing engineering drawings and at the same time to convey specific and concise information without a great expenditure of effort, some generally recognized systems of symbolic representation and conventional practices have been adopted by American industry.

A standard symbol or conventional representation can express information that might not be understood from a true line representation unless accompanied by a lettered statement. In many cases, even though a true line representation would convey exact information, very little more would be gained from the standpoint of better interpretation. Some conventional practices have been adopted for added clearness. For instance, they can eliminate awkward conditions that arise from strict adherence to the rules of projection.

These idioms of drawing have slowly developed with the graphic language until at the present time they are universally recognized and observed, and appear in the various standards of the American Standards Association.

Professional men and skilled workmen have learned to accept and respect the use of the symbols and conventional practices, for they can interpret these representations accurately and realize that their use saves valuable time in both the drawing room and the shop.

8.2. The treatment of unimportant intersections. The conventional methods of treating various unimportant intersections are shown in Fig. 8.1. To show the true line of intersection in each case would add little to the value of the drawing. Therefore, in the views designated as preferred, true projection has been ignored in the interest of simplicity. On the front views, in (a) and (b) for example, there is so little difference between the descriptive values of the true and approximate representa-

tions of the hole that the extra labor necessary to draw the true representation is unwarranted.

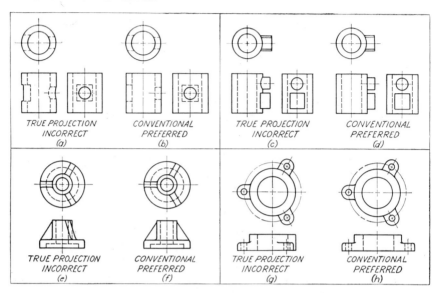

**Fig. 8.1.   *Conventional practice of representing unimportant intersections,
ribs, and lugs.***

8.3. Aligned views.   Pieces that have arms, ribs, lugs, or other parts
at an angle are often shown aligned or "straightened out" in one view, as
illustrated in Fig. 8.2.   By this method, it is possible to show the true
shape as well as the true position of such features.

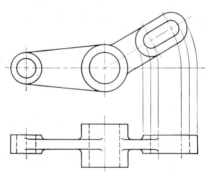

Fig. 8.2.   Aligned views.

8.4. Developed views.   Bent pieces, similar to the piece shown in
Fig. 8.3, are often drawn so that one view is a developed view of the
blank from which the piece is to be formed, and the other is a true view
showing the characteristic contour.

In laying out the developed view extra metal must be allowed for bends.

The empirical formula used for computing the bend allowance (arc length) for a bend is shown in (b).

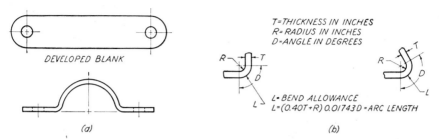

Fig. 8.3.   Developed views.

8.5. Conventional treatment of radially arranged features.

Many objects that have radially arranged features may be shown more clearly if true projection is violated as in Fig. 8.1(*f*) and (*h*).   Violation of true projection in such cases consists of intentionally showing such features swung out of position in one view so as to present the idea of symmetry and show the true relationship of the features at the same time. For example, while the radially arranged holes in a flange (Fig. 8.4) should always be shown in their true position in the circular view, they should be shown in a revolved position in the other view in order to show their true relationship with the rim.   The conventional treatment for drilled flanges in section is explained in Sec. 7.13.

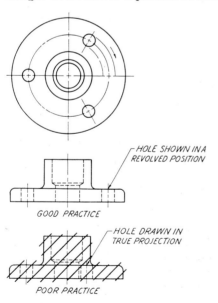

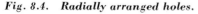

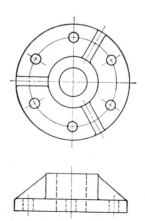

Fig. 8.4.   Radially arranged holes.

Fig. 8.5.   Conventional treatment of radially arranged ribs.

Radial ribs and radial spokes are similarly treated. The true projection of such features may create representations that are unsymmetrical and misleading. The preferred conventional method of treatment, by preserving symmetry, produces representations that are more easily understood and that at the same time are much simpler to draw. Fig. 8.5 illustrates the preferred treatment for radial ribs. The proper method for treating radial ribs and radial spokes in sectioned views is explained in Secs. 7.13 and 7.14.

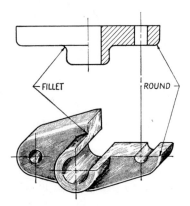

Fig. 8.6. Fillets and rounds.

8.6. Representation of fillets and rounds. Interior corners, which are formed on a casting by unfinished surfaces, always are filled in (filleted) at the intersection in order to avoid possible fracture at that point. Sharp corners are also difficult to obtain and are avoided for this reason as well (Fig. 8.6). Exterior corners are rounded for appearance and for the comfort of persons who must handle the part when assembling or repairing the machine on which the part is used. A rounded internal corner is known as a "fillet"; a rounded external corner is known as a "round."

When two intersecting surfaces are machined, however, their intersection will become a sharp corner. For this reason, all corners formed by unfinished surfaces should be shown "broken" by small rounds, and all corners formed by two finished surfaces or one finished surface and one unfinished surface should be shown "sharp." Although in the past it has been the practice to allow pattern makers to use their judgment about the size of fillets and rounds, many present-day companies require their designers and draftsmen to specify their size even though their exact size may not be important.

Since fillets and rounds eliminate the intersection lines of intersecting surfaces, they create a special problem in orthographic representation. To treat them in the same manner as they would be treated if they had large radii results in views that are misleading. For example, the true projection view in Fig. 8.7(a) confuses the reader, because at a first glance it does not convey the idea that there are abrupt changes in direction. To prevent such a probable first impression and to improve the descriptive value of the view, it is necessary to represent these theoretically nonexisting lines. These characteristic lines are projected from the approximate intersections of the surfaces, with the fillets disregarded.

Fig. 8.8 illustrates the accepted conventional method of representing the "run-out" intersection of a fillet in cases where a plane surface is

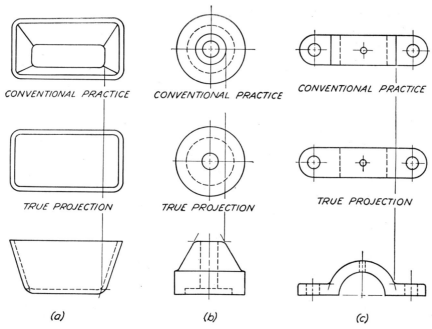

Fig. 8.7.   Conventional practice of representing nonexisting lines of inter-section.

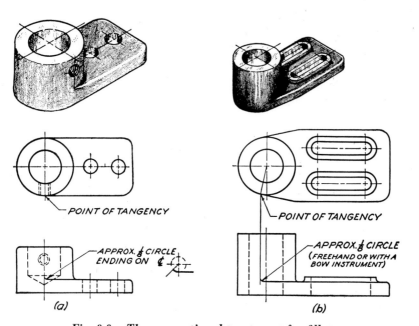

Fig. 8.8.   The conventional treatment for fillets.

tangent to a cylindrical surface.   Although run-out arcs such as these are
usually drawn freehand, a French curve or a bow instrument may be used.
If they are drawn with the latter type of instrument, a radius should be
used that is equal to the radius of the fillet, and the completed arc should
form approximately one-eighth of a circle.

The generally accepted methods of representing intersecting fillets and
rounds are illustrated in Fig. 8.9.   The treatment, in each of the cases
shown, is determined by the relationship existing between the sizes of the
intersecting fillets and rounds.   Fig. 8.9 shows several illustrations of
accepted conventional methods used to represent run-outs.

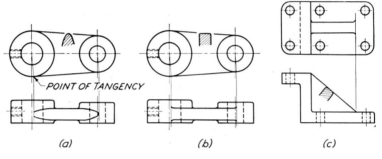

Fig. 8.9.   The approximate methods of representing intersecting fillets,
rounds.

8.7. Half views.   When the space available is insufficient to allow a
satisfactory scale to be used for the representation of a symmetrical piece,
it is considered good practice to make one view a half view, as shown in
Fig. 8.10.   The half view, however, must be the top or side view and not
the front view, which shows the characteristic contour.   When the front
view is an exterior view, the half view should be the front half of the top
or side view; when the front view is a sectional view, it should be the rear
half.

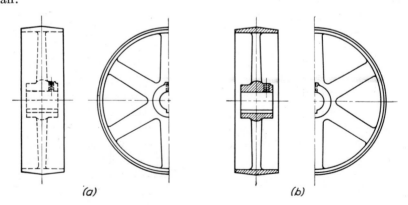

Fig. 8.10.   A half view.

8.8. Conventional breaks. A relatively long piece of uniform section may be shown to a larger scale, if a portion is broken out so that the

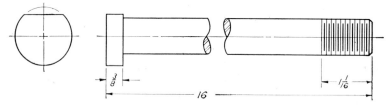

Fig. 8.11.   A broken-out view.

ends can be drawn closer together (Fig. 8.11). When such a scheme is employed, a conventional break is used to indicate that the length of the representation is not to scale. The American Standard conventional breaks, shown in Fig. 8.12, are used on either detail or assembly drawings. The break representations for indicating the broken ends of rods, shafts, tubes, and so forth, are designed to reveal the characteristic shape of the cross section in each case. Although break lines for round sections may be drawn freehand, particularly on small views, it is better practice to draw them with either an irregular curve or a bow instrument. The breaks for wood sections, however, always should be drawn freehand.

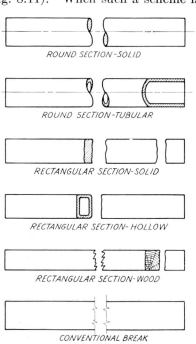

Fig. 8.12.   Conventional breaks.

8.9. Ditto lines. When it is desirable to minimize labor in order to save time, ditto lines may be used to indicate a series of identical features. For example, the threads on the shaft shown in Fig. 8.13 are just as effectively indicated by ditto lines as by a completed profile repre-

Fig. 8.13.   Ditto lines.

sentation. When ditto lines are used, a long shaft of this type may be shortened without actually showing a conventional break.

8.10. A conventional method for showing a part in alternate positions. A method frequently used for indicating an alternate position of a part or a limiting position of a moving part is shown in Fig. 8.14. The dashes forming the object lines of the view showing the alternate position should be of medium weight. The phantom line shown in Fig. 8.15 is recommended in the SAE Automotive Drafting Standards for representing an alternate position.

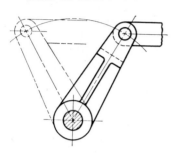

Fig. 8.14. Alternate positions.

8.11. Conventional line symbols. Symbolic lines of various weights are used in making technical drawings. The American Standards Association suggests:

Three widths of line, thick, medium, and thin are considered desirable on finished drawings in ink, both for legibility and appearance, although in rapid practice and in particular on penciled tracings from which prints are to be made this may be simplified to two weights, medium and thin. For pencil tracings the lines should be in proportion to the ink lines, *medium* for outlines, hidden, cutting plane, short breaks, adjacent part and alternate position lines; and thin for section, center, dimension, long break, and ditto lines.

The lines illustrated in Fig. 8.15 are shown full size. When symbolic lines are used on a pencil drawing they should not vary in color. For example, center lines, extension lines, dimension lines, and section lines should differ from object lines only in width. The resulting contrast makes a drawing easier to read. All lines, except construction lines, should be very dark and bright to give the drawing the "snap" that is needed for good appearance. If the drawing is on tracing paper the lead must be "packed on" so that a satisfactory print can be obtained. Construction lines should be drawn *very* fine so as to be unnoticeable on the finished drawing. The lengths of the dashes and spaces, shown in Figs. 6.19 and 7.18, are recommended for the hidden lines, center lines, and cutting plane lines on average-size drawings.

8.12. Material symbols. The section-line symbols recommended by the American Standards Association for indicating various materials are shown in Fig. 8.16.

Code section lining usually is employed on an assembly section showing the various parts of a unit in position, because a distinction between the materials causes the parts to "stand out" to better advantage. Furthermore, a knowledge of the type of material of which an individual part is composed often helps the reader to identify it more quickly and understand its function.

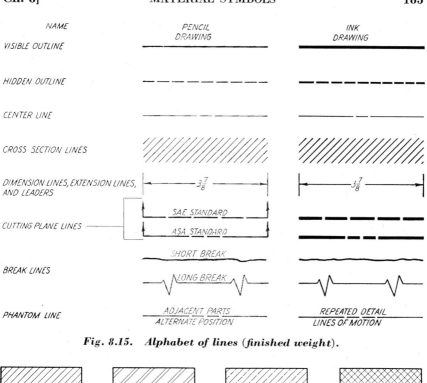

Fig. 8.15. *Alphabet of lines (finished weight).*

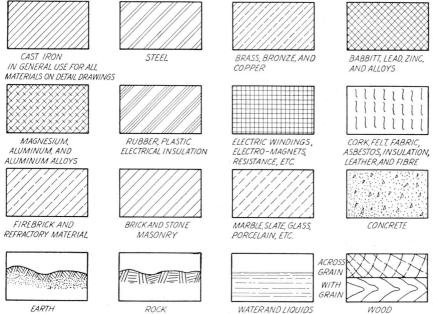

FOR OTHER SYMBOLS FOR MATERIALS IN SECTION AND ELEVATION SEE ARCHITECTURAL DRAWING CHAPTER

Fig. 8.16. *Material symbols.*

8.13. Conventional representation. Conventional representations are used by engineers of all fields to represent many of the details that occur repeatedly on their drawings. Symbols are used on topographic drawings, architectural drawings, electrical drawings, and machine drawings. No engineer serving in a professional capacity can very well escape their use.

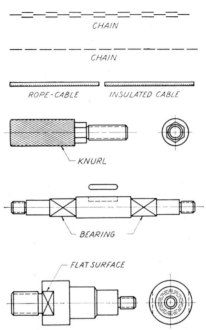

CHAIN

CHAIN

ROPE-CABLE   INSULATED CABLE

KNURL

BEARING

FLAT SURFACE

Fig. 8.17.   Conventional symbols.

Most of the illustrations that are shown in Fig. 8.17, should be easily understood. However, the crossed-lines (diagonals) symbol has two distinct and different meanings. First, this symbol may be used on a drawing of a shaft to indicate the position of a surface for a bearing or, second, it may indicate that a surface perpendicular to the line of sight is flat. These usages are illustrated with separate examples.

The conventionalized symbolic methods for representing screw threads, springs, pipe fittings, and electrical apparatus will be touched upon briefly in following sections of this chapter. More information on the representation of screw threads, welds, springs, and rivets is given in Chapter 15.

8.14. Thread representation. The American Standards Association now recognizes three conventions for depicting screw threads on drawings; the detailed, the schematic, and the simplified. The detailed representation, being a close approximation of the actual appearance of a screw thread (see Chapter 15), is used only when the drawing's purpose justifies the amount ot time needed to prepare it.   It is rarely used by engineers or draftsmen for ordinary work.   For layout and design drawings and for sketches the engineer rightly prefers to use either the schematic or simplified form of representation.

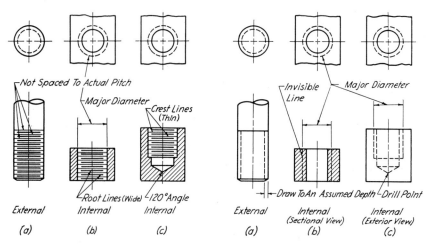

Fig. 8.18.   **Threads—schematic representation.**   Fig. 8.19.   **Threads—simplified representation.**

Only a few examples of schematic and simplified representation are given in Figures 8.18 and 8.19.   It is the usual practice to make no attempt to space the lines of a schematic representation equal to the actual distance between threads.   If the representation looks reasonably good, it will prove to be satisfactory.

In Fig. 8.18 the thin lines represent the crests of the thread on the illustration showing the external thread.   The thick lines represent the roots of the thread.   In Fig. 8.19, the invisible lines that are parallel to the axis represent the root of the thread.

Fig. 8.20.   **Single line representation of springs.***

8.15. Conventional representation of springs.
Coil springs of small size, that are made of wire of less than $\frac{1}{16}$ inch in diameter are usually represented by single line symbols as shown in Fig. 8.20.

---

* ASA Z14.1–1946.

8.16. Pipe diagrams and conventional representation of pipe fittings. Since standard pipe and fittings can be purchased for almost any purpose, a piping drawing usually shows only the arrangement of a system in some conventional form, and gives the size and location of fittings. The drawing or sketch may be either a single-line diagram or pictorial diagram.

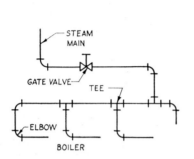

Fig. 8.21.   Single-line drawing.

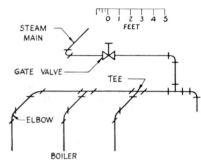

Fig. 8.22.   Pictorial line diagram.

Single-line drawings or sketches are made in orthographic projection or are drawn as if the entire system were swung into one plane (Fig. 8.21). On these drawings, single lines represent the runs of pipe, regardless of variations in diameters; conventional symbols are used for the fittings. A developed single-line sketch is frequently used for repair work, small jobs, and for making studies and calculations. For more complicated small-scale layouts, a single-line diagram drawn in orthographic projection is more suitable.

A conventional pictorial diagram (Fig. 8.22), showing a piping layout in space, reveals the changes in direction and the difference in levels more clearly than does any other type of line diagram. Pictorial diagrams are often used for preliminary layouts. Conventional symbols for fittings that have been approved by the American Standards Association may be found in the Appendix.

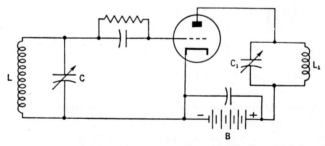

From Marcus and Marcus, Elements of Radio, *3rd Ed., Prentice-Hall, Inc.*

Fig. 8.23.   An electrical diagram.

8.17. Conventional symbols on electrical diagrams (Fig. 8.23). Graphical symbols are used freely in electrical work to represent all of the usual electrical units. The American Standards Association has approved symbols for power control and measurement units for telephone, telegraph, and radio; and for architectural plans. Conventional symbols for electric power and wiring may be found in the Appendix.

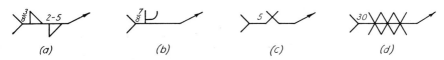

Fig. 8.24.   Examples of welding symbols.

8.18. Conventional representation of welds. A system of welding symbols for use on drawings of welded parts has been developed by the American Welding Society. These symbols show both the size and type of weld desired. The arrow is the basic portion of the symbol and it always points to the joint where the weld is to be made. The symbol, attached above or below the body of the arrow, shows the type of weld. The size or strength of the weld appears at the side of the symbol. See Fig. 8.24.

9

Freehand Drafting

9.1. Value of freehand drafting. Freehand technical drafting is primarily the language of those in responsible charge of the development of technical designs and plans. Chief engineers, chief draftsmen, designers, and squad bosses have found that the best way to present their

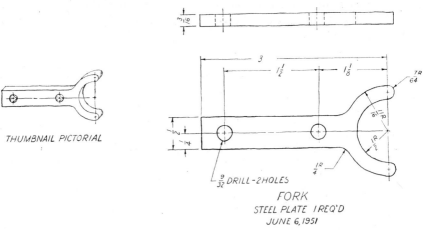

THUMBNAIL PICTORIAL

FORK
STEEL PLATE I REQ'D
JUNE 6,1951

Fig. 9.1.   Working sketch.

ideas for either a simple or complex design is through the medium of sketches. Sketches may be schematic, as are those that are original expressions of new ideas, or they may be instructional, their purpose being to convey ideas to draftsmen or shopmen. Some sketches, especially those prepared for the manufacture of parts that are to replace worn or broken parts on existing machines, may resemble complete working drawings.

Since the importance of freehand drafting very often is underestimated, the purpose of this discussion is to amplify training in this phase. The young prospective engineer should understand, when beginning his studies, that sketching and not mechanical drafting will be his ultimate form of expression and that he must be able to prepare complete sketches that will present his ideas and decisions to subordinates in an understandable manner. Fig. 9.1 is an example of a working sketch.

9.2. Sketching materials. For the type of sketching discussed here, the required materials are an F pencil, a soft eraser, and some paper. In the industrial field, men who have been improperly trained in sketching often use straight-edges and cheap pocket compasses that they could well dispense with if they would adopt the correct technique. Preparing sketches with instruments consumes much unnecessary time.

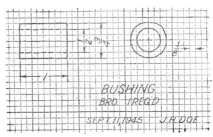

Fig. 9.2. Sketches on cross-section paper.

For the person who cannot produce a satisfactory sketch without guide lines, cross-section paper is helpful. Ordinarily, the ruling on this paper forms one-inch squares which are subdivided into one-eighth or one-tenth inch squares. Such paper is especially useful when sketching to scale is desirable (Fig. 9.2).

9.3. Projections. Although freehand drafting lacks the refinement given by mechanical instruments, it is based upon the same principles of projection and conventional practices that apply to multiview, pictorial, and the other divisions of mechanical drawing. For this reason, one must be thoroughly familiar with projection, in all of its many forms, before he is adequately trained to prepare sketches.

9.4. Technique of lines. Freehand lines quite naturally will differ in their appearance from mechanical ones. A well executed freehand line will never be perfectly straight and absolutely uniform in weight, but an effort should be made to approach *exacting uniformity*. As in the case of mechanical lines, they should be black and clear and not broad and fuzzy. (See Fig. 9.3.)

9.5. Sharpening the sketching pencil. A sketching pencil should be sharpened, on a file or piece of sandpaper, to a conical point. The point then should be rounded slightly, on the back of the sketch pad or on another sheet of paper, to the correct degree of dullness. When rounding the point, the pencil should be rotated to prevent the formation of sharp edges.

9.6. Straight lines. The pencil should rest on the second finger and be held loosely by the thumb and index finger about 1 to $1\frac{1}{2}$ inches above the point.

Horizontal lines are sketched from left to right with an easy arm motion that is pivoted about the muscle of the forearm. The straight line thus becomes an arc of infinite radius.

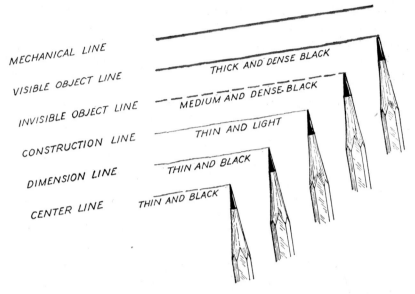

MECHANICAL LINE — THICK AND DENSE BLACK

VISIBLE OBJECT LINE

INVISIBLE OBJECT LINE — MEDIUM AND DENSE BLACK

CONSTRUCTION LINE — THIN AND LIGHT

DIMENSION LINE — THIN AND BLACK

CENTER LINE — THIN AND BLACK

Fig. 9.3. Sketch lines.

When sketching a straight line, it is advisable to first mark the end points with light dots or small crosses (Fig. 9.4). The complete procedure for sketching a straight line is as follows:

1. Mark the end points.

2. Make a few trial motions between the marked points to adjust the eye and hand to the contemplated line.

3. Sketch a *very* light line between the points by moving the pencil in two or three sweeps. When sketching the trial line, the eye should be on

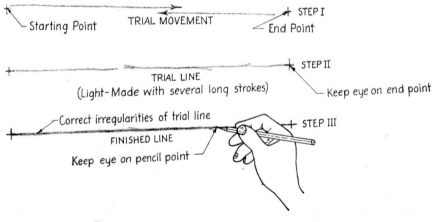

Starting Point   TRIAL MOVEMENT   STEP I   End Point

TRIAL LINE
(Light-Made with several long strokes)   STEP II   Keep eye on end point

Correct irregularities of trial line   STEP III
FINISHED LINE
Keep eye on pencil point

Fig. 9.4. Steps in sketching a straight line.

the point toward which the movement is directed. With each stroke, an attempt should be made to correct the most obvious defects of the stroke preceding, so that the finished trial line will be relatively straight.

4. Darken the finished line, keeping the eye on the pencil point on the trial line. The final line, replacing the trial line, should be distinct, black, uniform, and straight.

It is helpful to turn the paper through a *convenient angle* so that the horizontal and vertical lines assume a slight inclination (Fig. 9.5). A horizontal line, when the paper is in this position, is sketched to the right and upward, thus allowing the arm to be held slightly away from the body and making possible a free arm motion.

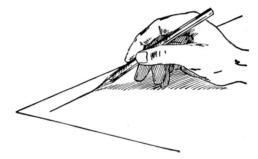

Fig. 9.5. Sketching horizontal lines.

Short vertical lines may be sketched either downward or upward, without changing the position of the paper. When sketching downward, the arm is held slightly away from the body and the movement is toward the sketcher (see Fig. 9.6). To sketch vertical lines upward, the arm is held well away from the body.

Fig. 9.6. Sketching vertical lines.

By turning the paper, a long vertical line may be made to assume the position of a horizontal line and can be sketched with the same general movements used for the latter.

Inclined lines running upward from lower left to upper right may be sketched upward with the same movements used for horizontal lines, but those running downward from upper left to lower right are sketched with the general movements used for either horizontal or vertical ones, depending upon their inclination (Fig. 9.7).   Inclined lines may be more easily sketched by turning the paper to make them conform to the direction of horizontal lines.

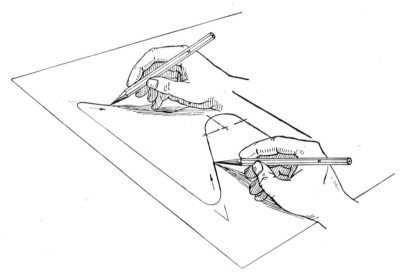

Fig. 9.7.   Sketching inclined lines.

9.7. Circles.   Small circles may be sketched by marking radial distances on perpendicular center lines (Fig. 9.8).   These distances can be marked off either by eye or by measuring with a marked strip of paper (Fig. 9.9).   Larger circles may be constructed more accurately by sketching two or more diagonals, in addition to the center lines, and by sketching short construction lines perpendicular to each, equidistant from the center.   Tangent to these lines, short arcs are drawn perpendicular to the radii.   The circle is completed with a light construction line, and all defects are corrected before darkening (Fig. 9.10).

9.8. Ellipses.   An ellipse of good proportion may be sketched within an enclosing rectangle.   The rectangle, since it is used merely as an aid in forming the ellipse, should be drawn with very light lines, and the required ellipse should be sketched tangent to the sides.

9.9. Making a sketch.   When making orthographic working sketches, a systematic order should be followed and all the rules and conventional practices used in making working drawings should be applied. The following procedure is recommended:

1. Examine the object, giving particular attention to detail.
2. Determine which views are necessary.

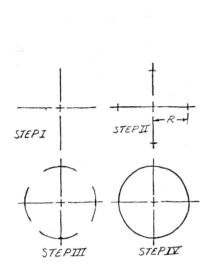

Fig. 9.8.   Sketching small circles.

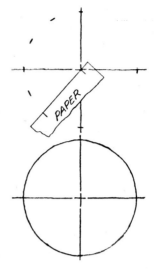

Fig. 9.9.   Marking off radial distances.

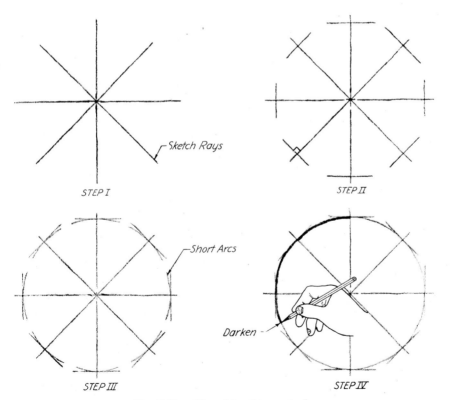

Fig. 9.10.   Sketching large circles.

3. "Block in" the views, using light construction lines.

4. Complete the detail and darken the object lines.

5. Sketch extension lines and dimension lines, including arrowheads.

6. Complete the sketch by adding dimensions, notes, title, date, sketcher's name or initials, and so on.

7. Check the entire sketch carefully to see that no dimensions have been omitted.

The progressive steps in making a working sketch of an object are shown in Fig. 9.11.

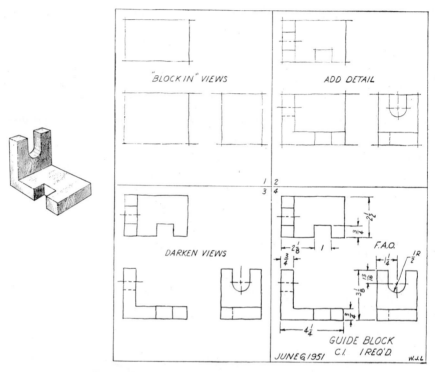

Fig. 9.11. Steps in making a working sketch.

9.10. Making sketches of parts for the purpose of replacement and repair. It quite frequently is necessary to make working sketches of broken or worn parts. Such sketches are used instead of mechanical drawings because they can be made and sent to the shop in a much shorter time. The procedure given in Sec. 9.9 should be followed carefully when making sketches to be used by workmen in the shops.

9.11. Measurements and measuring instruments. If a sketch is to serve as a working drawing, it must contain all the necessary dimensions and instructional notes needed by the workmen. If a sketch is for the manufacture of a part that is to replace a worn or broken part in an existing machine, measurements must be taken from the original part with the same general types of measuring devices to be used in manufacturing the new part. The instrument selected for each particular detail should be of a type that will allow measurements to be made with the correct degree of accuracy. For most machine parts, a steel scale and a set of inside and outside calipers will prove sufficient. When more accurate measurements are necessary, a micrometer must be used. In any case, the selection of the instrument for a measurement should be determined by exercising good judgment. Fig. 9.12 shows how the outside calipers are used to take measurements from an object. Fig. 9.13 shows the use of the inside calipers for measuring the diameter of a hole.

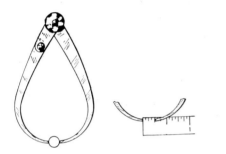

Fig. 9.12. Outside calipers.

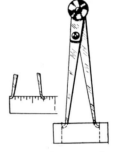

Fig. 9.13. Inside calipers.

When taking measurements, certain practices are recommended. For example, to obtain the distance between holes (shown on the sketch as between centers), measure the distance between corresponding edges. To locate other features and to take off size dimensions, measure from a finished surface whenever possible, for a finished surface is usually a mating surface. The man in the shop must work from such a surface if he is to produce a part accurate enough to function in the existing machine.

9.12. The title. A title is far more important on a working sketch than many persons realize. It serves to identify the sketch and usually contains additional valuable information such as (1) the type of material, (2) the number required, (3) the name or initials of the sketcher, and (4) the date.

9.13. Proportions. The beginner must recognize the importance of being able to estimate comparative relationship between the length, height, and depth of an object being sketched. The complete problem of proportioning a sketch also involves relating the estimated dimensions for any component parts such as slots, holes, and projections to the overall dimensions of the object. It is not the practice to attempt to estimate actual dimensions, for sketches are not usually made to scale. Rather one must decide, for example, that the length of the object is twice its height, that the width of a given slot is equal to one-half the length of the object, and that its depth is approximately one-fourth of the over-all height.

To become proficient at sketching one must learn to recognize proportions and be able to compare dimensions "by eye." Until he is able to do so, he can not really "think with his pencil." Some can develop a keen eye for proportion with only a limited amount of practice and can maintain these estimated proportions when making the views of the sketch. Others have alternatingly discouraging and encouraging experiences. Discouragement comes when one's knowledge of sketching is ahead of his ability and he has not had as much practice as he needs. The many who find it difficult to make the completed views of a sketch agree with the estimated proportions of the object may at the start use the graphical method shown in Fig. 9.14(a), (b), and (c). This method is based on the fact that a rectangle (enclosing a view) may be divided to obtain intermediate distances along any side that are in such proportion of the total length as one-half, one-fourth, one-third and so forth. Those who start with this rectangle method as an aid in proportioning must realize that they should abandon its use when they have developed their eye and sketching skill so that it is no longer needed.

Sketching must be done rapidly and the addition of unnecessary lines consumes much valuable time. Furthermore, the addition of construction lines distract the reader, and it is certain that they do not contribute to the neatness of the sketch.

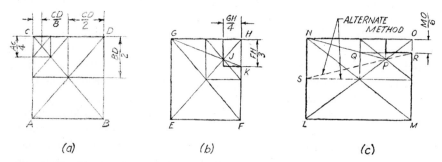

Fig. 9.14. *Methods of proportioning a rectangle representing the outline of a view.*

The mid-point of a rectangle is the point of intersection of the diagonals, as shown in Fig. 9.14(a). A line sketched through this point that is perpendicular to any side will establish the mid-point of that side. Should it be necessary to determine a distance that is equal to one-fourth the length of a side, say AC, the quarter-point may be located by repeating this procedure for the small rectangle representing the upper left-hand quarter of $ABCD$.

With the mid-point J located by the intersecting diagonals of the small rectangle representing one-fourth of the larger rectangle *EFGH* as in (*b*), the one-third point along *FH* may be located by sketching a line from point *G* through *J* and extending it to line *FH*. The point *K* at the intersection of these lines establishes the needed one-third distance.

To determine one-sixth of the length of a side of a rectangle as in (*c*), sketch a line from *N* through point *P* as was done in (*b*) to determine a one-third distance. Point *Q* at which the line *NP* crosses the centerline of the rectangle establishes the one-sixth distance along the centerline.

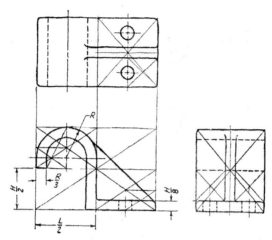

Fig. 9.15. *The rectangle method applied in making an orthographic sketch.*

Fig. 9.15 shows how this method for dividing the sides of a rectangle might be used to proportion an orthographic sketch.

The square may be used to proportion a view after one dimension for the view has been assumed. In using this method, additional squares are added to the initial one having the assumed length as one side (Fig. 9.16). As an example, suppose that it has been estimated that the front view of an object should be three times as long as it is high. In Fig. 9.16 the height of the view has been represented by the line *AB* sketched to an assumed length. The first step in making the construction is to sketch

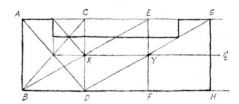

Fig. 9.16. *The build-up method.*

the initial square *ABCD* and extend *AC* and *BD* to indefinite length, being certain that the over-all length from *A* and *D* will be slightly greater than three times the length of *AB*. Then the center line must be sketched through the intersection of *AD* and *BC*. Now *BX* extended to *E* locates

EF to form the second square, and *DY* extended to point *G* locates the line *GH*.   Line *AG* will be three times the length of *AB*.

Fig. 9.17 shows how the build-up method might be used to make an orthographic sketch.   The starting line is *AB*.   The three principal squares were divided as needed using the method for proportioning a rectangle.

The method for determining a length that is equal to some full number and fractional number of times a given height is shown in Fig. 9.18.   In this case the length of the block is two and one-half times the height *AB*.

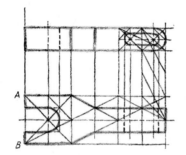

Fig. 9.17.   *An orthographic sketch —build-up method.*

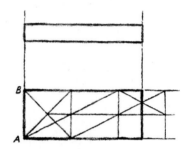

Fig. 9.18.   *Using combined methods.*

9.14. Use of an overlay sheet.   An overlay sheet may be used to an advantage in making any sketch that is complicated with details (Fig. 9.19).   In this case, a quick sketch showing the general outline of the principal parts is made first in a rather rough form.   Then an overlay sheet is placed over this outline sketch and the lines are retraced.   In doing so, slight corrections can be made for any known errors existing in the proportions of the parts or in the position of any of the lines of the original rough sketch.   When this has been done, the representations of the related minor parts are added.   If at any time one becomes discouraged with a sketch that he is making and feels that a new start is needed, an overlay sheet should be used, for there are usually many features on his existing sketch that may be retraced with a great saving of time.

9.15. Use of technical sketching–design by an engineer.   When an engineer is involved in the planning and direction of a project, he finds it necessary to prepare numerous sketches—entirely freehand. Without the ability to prepare quick and accurate sketches as they are needed for both exploratory and explanatory purposes, he would find himself immeasurably handicapped.   In fact, the lack of this ability would reduce his professional efficiency as much as if he were actually tongue-tied or illiterate.   Use of the freehand drafting technique enables one to make frequent changes very rapidly when developing an original

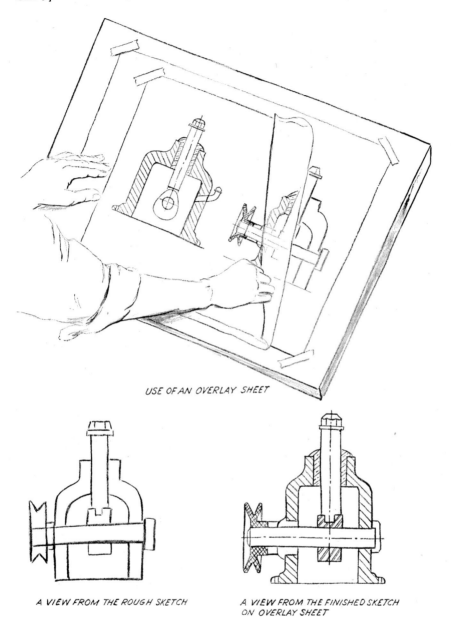

USE OF AN OVERLAY SHEET

A VIEW FROM THE ROUGH SKETCH

A VIEW FROM THE FINISHED SKETCH
ON OVERLAY SHEET

Fig. 9.19.   Use of an overlay sheet for creating a final and complete sketch
of a mechanism.

idea for a design or when modifying a design that has already won partial acceptance.

By making numerous idea sketches an engineer finally is able to crystallize his thoughts and settle some of the perplexing problems that usually arise to plague him.   If he employed instruments to prepare these drawings that are a necessary aid to his thinking, he would find that he was wasting much of his valuable time, for numerous drawings would be required and quite a few might finally be discarded after varied ideas had been explored and found to be unsatisfactory.

In "thinking with a pencil" an engineer's very environment makes the use of instruments undesirable, for much of his work may be done at his office desk, at the conference table, or in the laboratory where instruments are not readily at hand.   It is because of the conditions under which he works that he must learn to sketch rapidly and well and to resist the temptation to use a straight-edge and compass.   To use any aids whatsoever takes away much of the practical advantage to be gained from sketching.

Fig. 9.20 shows an idea sketch that was prepared to satisfy the need for a connector for a mechanical control unit.   Sketches of this type may be turned over to a draftsman for complete development.

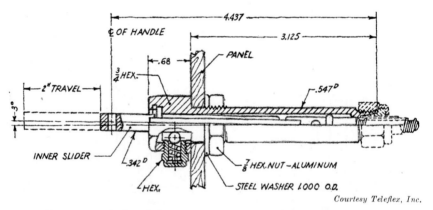

Courtesy *Teleflex, Inc.*

Fig. 9.20.   A sketch for a connector of a remote control unit.

In studying the techniques of sketching, it is advisable to read this chapter and the next at the same time, for multiview and pictorial sketches may be used together when "thinking with the pencil."

An engineer's sketches may show either an idea for a complete unit, or a small sub-assembly of the unit.   Some may be made to show only a few related parts around which a problem exists.

An engineer must usually supply explanatory sketches to the draftsmen who are assisting him in developing a project, for the draftsmen quite frequently come face-to-face with minor problems as the drawings are being prepared.

A wiring diagram in sketch form is shown in Fig. 9.21. This diagram appeared on the original idea sketch shown in Fig. 10.4 in the chapter on pictorial sketching.

9.16. Problems. The problems presented with this chapter have been selected to furnish practice in freehand drafting. The individual pieces that appear in pictorial form have been taken from a wide variety of mechanisms used in different fields of engineering. The student may be required to prepare complete working sketches of these parts if his instructor desires. Such an assignment, however, would presuppose an understanding of the fundamentals of dimensioning as they are presented in the beginning sections of Chapter 16.

A complete set of working sketches may be prepared for a unit mechanism where all of the related parts are shown in pictorial. As part of the assignment an instructor may require a student to prepare a sketch showing all of the parts assembled.

The problems given as assembly drawings provide practice in making

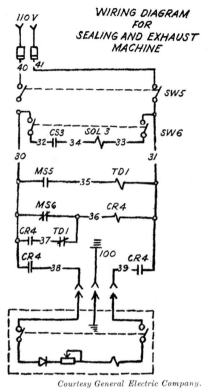

Courtesy General Electric Company.

Fig. 9.21. A wiring diagram.

sketches of individual parts as they are assigned. In sketching a part given on an assembly drawing, the student gains experience in reading drawings and in understanding the functions of different parts. Problems of this type develop the student's power to visualize, for he is forced to form a mental picture of the complete shape of the piece as well as to see the shape of its component forms.

Screw threads may be shown by using either the schematic or simplified form of representation as shown in Figs. 8.18 and 8.19. The student should read Sec. 8.14. If a specification is to be given for the thread, it will be necessary to read the appropriate sections in Chapter 15 that cover the specification of screw threads.

The following practical one-view working sketches were selected to provide practice in lettering and sketching. The pictorial representations of practical machine parts offer the opportunity for practice in sketching and further study of multi-view projection.

1–6. (Figs. 9.22–9.27.) Reproduce an assigned one-view sketch on a sheet of sketching paper.

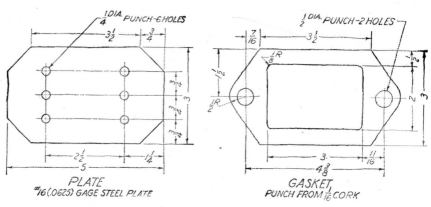

PLATE
#16 (.0625) GAGE STEEL PLATE

Fig. 9.22.

GASKET
PUNCH FROM 1/16 CORK

Fig. 9.23.

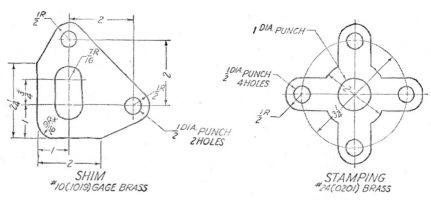

SHIM
#10 (.1019) GAGE BRASS

Fig. 9.24.

STAMPING
#24 (.0201) BRASS

Fig. 9.25.

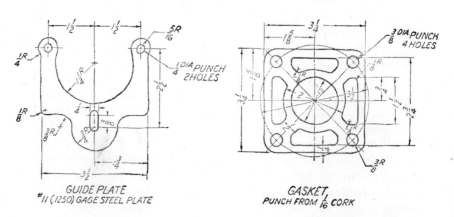

GUIDE PLATE
#11 (.1250) GAGE STEEL PLATE

Fig. 9.26.

GASKET
PUNCH FROM 1/16 CORK

Fig. 9.27.

7–34. (Figs. 9.28–9.55.)   Sketch, freehand, the necessary views of the given objects as assigned.   The selected length for the unit will determine the size of the views.   Assume any needed dimensions that are not given in units.

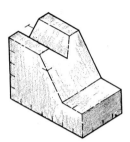

Fig. 9.28.   V-rest.

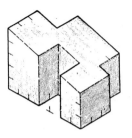

Fig. 9.29.   Support block.

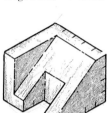

Fig. 9.30.   Wedge block.

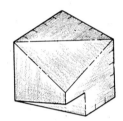

Fig. 9.31.   End block.

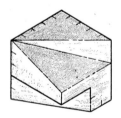

Fig. 9.32.   Adjustment block.

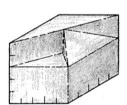

Fig. 9.33.   Slip block.

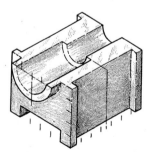

Fig. 9.34.   Bearing block.

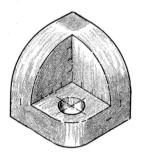

Fig. 9.35.   Corner block.

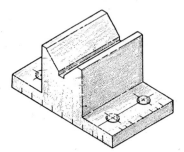

Fig. 9.36.   V-block.

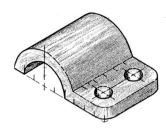

Fig. 9.37.   Control rod bracket.

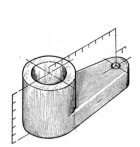

Fig. 9.38.   Link.

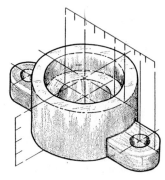

Fig. 9.39.   Collar bracket.

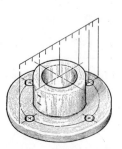

Fig. 9.40.   End plate.

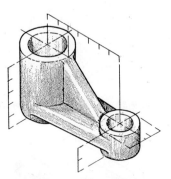

Fig. 9.41.   Trip bracket.

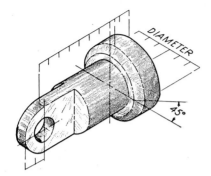

Fig. 9.42.   Guide.

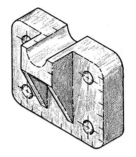

Fig. 9.43.   Support bracket.

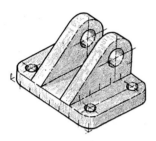

Fig. 9.44.   Strut bracket.

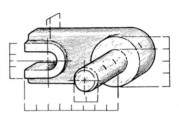

Fig. 9.45.   Stud guide.

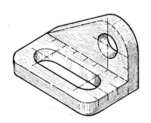

Fig. 9.46.   Feed rod bracket.

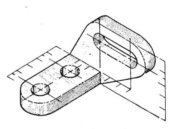

Fig. 9.47.   Automatic feed bracket.

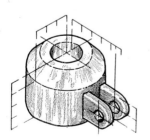

Fig. 9.48.   Feeder cone.

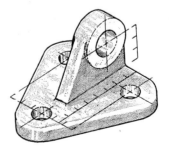

Fig. 9.49.   Bracket.

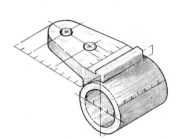

Fig. 9.50.   Shaft bracket.

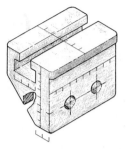

Fig. 9.51.   Offset guide.

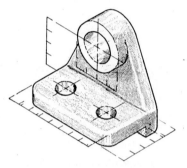

Fig. 9.52.   Support bracket.

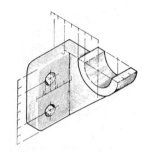

Fig. 9.53.   Offset bracket.

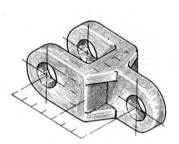

Fig. 9.54.   Link.

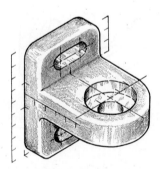

Fig. 9.55.   Bearing bracket.

35–49. (Figs. 9.56–9.70.) These problems are designed to give the student further study in multiview representation and, at the same time, offer him the opportunity to apply good line technique to the preparation of sketches.

Only the necessary views on which all of the hidden lines are to be shown should be drawn.

If dimensions are to be given, ample space must be allowed between the views for their placement. The beginning sections of Chapter 16 present the basic principles of size description.

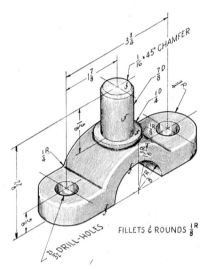

Fig. 9.56.   ***Stud bracket.***

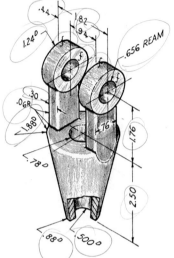

Fig. 9.57.   ***Socket.***

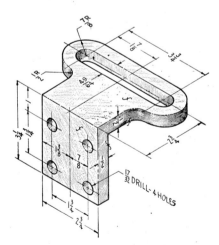

Fig. 9.58.   ***Guide bracket.***

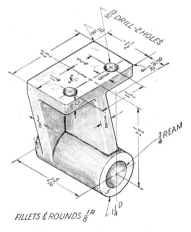

Fig. 9.59.   ***Shifter bracket.***

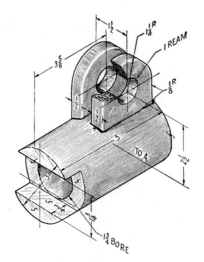

Fig. 9.60.　Control guide.

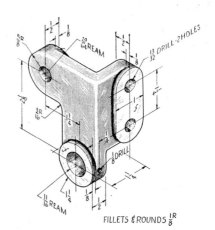

Fig. 9.61.　Link.

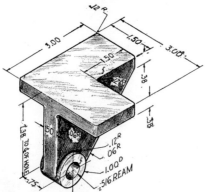

Fig. 9.62.　Tool rest.

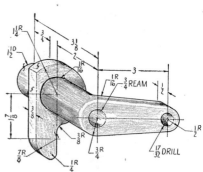

Fig. 9.63.　Offset trip lever.

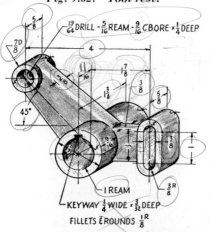

Fig. 9.64.　Control bracket.

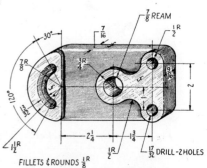

Fig. 9.65.　Control plate.

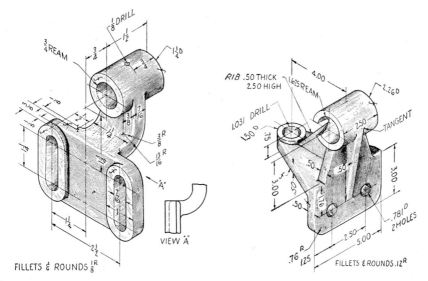

Fig. 9.66. Bearing bracket.   **Fig. 9.67. Control rod guide.**

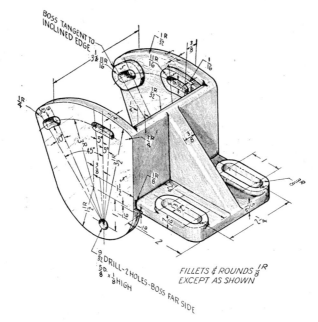

Fig. 9.68. Control bracket (airplane).

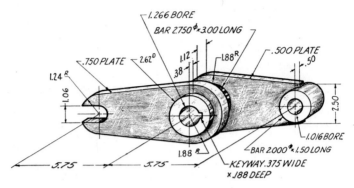

Fig. 9.69.   Idler lever.

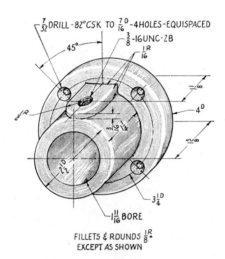

FILLETS & ROUNDS $\frac{1}{8}R$.
EXCEPT AS SHOWN

Fig. 9.70.   Pipe support.

50. (Fig. 9.71.) Make a complete orthographic sketch of the anchor bracket.

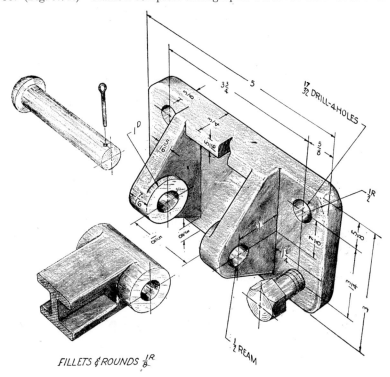

Fig. 9.71. *Anchor bracket.*

51. (Fig. 9.72.) Make a three-view orthographic sketch of the motor bracket.

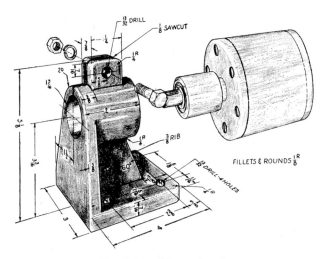

Fig. 9.72. *Motor bracket.*

52–53. (Fig. 9.73.) Make a complete three-view sketch of the tool rest and/or the tool rest bracket. The rectangular top surface of the tool rest is to be $1\frac{1}{8}''$ above the center line of the hole for the $\frac{7}{16}''$ bolt. The over-all dimensions of the top are $1\frac{1}{4}'' \times 2\frac{1}{2}''$. It is to be $\frac{1}{4}''$ thick. The over-all dimensions of the rectangular pad of the bracket are $1\frac{1}{4}'' \times 1\frac{7}{8}''$. The center line of the adjustment slot is $\frac{9}{16}''$ above the center line of the top holes in the rectangular pad and the distance from center line to center line of the slot is $1\frac{3}{8}''$. The bracket is to be fastened to a housing with $\frac{1}{4}''$ round head machine screws.

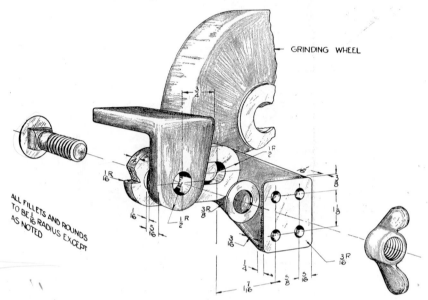

Fig. 9.73. *Tool rest and tool rest bracket.*

54. (Fig. 9.74.) Make a complete three-view sketch of the motor base. The ribs are $\frac{3}{8}''$ thick. At points A, four holes are to be drilled for $\frac{1}{2}''$ bolts that are to be $2\frac{1}{2}''$ center to center in one direction and $3\frac{1}{8}''$ in the other. At points B, four holes are to be drilled for $\frac{1}{2}''$ bolts that fasten the motor base to a steel column. Fillets and rounds are $\frac{1}{8}^{\text{R}}$.

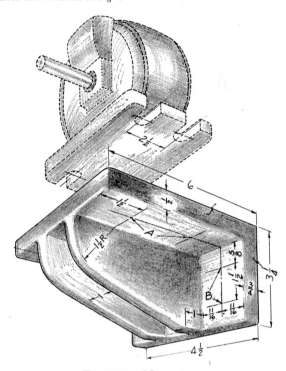

Fig. 9.74. Motor base.

55. (Fig. 9.75.)   Make a complete orthographic sketch of the offset shaft bracket.   *Supplementary information:* (1) The center line of the main shaft is $1\frac{3}{8}''$ above the finished surface of the pad.   The hole in the bracket is to be reamed to accommodate a $1\frac{1}{4}''$ O.D. bushing as shown.   (2) The length of the cylindrical part is $1\frac{1}{4}''$.   Both faces, which are raised $\frac{1}{8}''$ on both sides, are contact faces. The O.D. is $1\frac{3}{4}''$.   (3) The overall dimensions of the pad are to be $2\frac{3}{8}'' \times 2\frac{7}{8}''$. The $2\frac{3}{8}''$ dimension is in the direction parallel to the axis of the main shaft.   (See bottom view.)   (4) The small holes in the base are to be drilled oversize for $\frac{1}{2}''$-UNC cap screws.   (5) The hole for the small shaft should be reamed larger for a $\frac{1}{2}''$ shaft.   (6) The rib is to be $\frac{5}{16}''$ thick.   It should finish tangent to the large cylinder.   (7) Fillets and rounds are $\frac{1}{8}^{R}$ except as noted.   (8) Pay particular attention to tangent runouts.   (9) The near side of the $\frac{3}{8}''$ thick portion of the base is tangent to the $\frac{1}{2}^{R}$ of the $\frac{7}{16}''$ thick base.

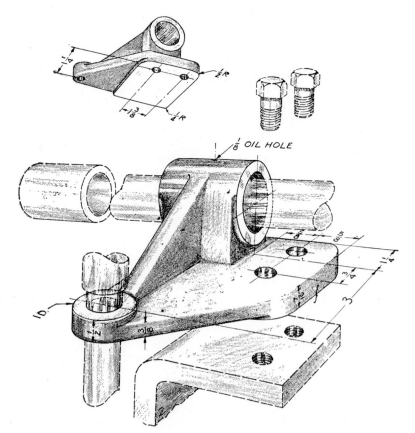

Fig. 9.75.   Offset shaft bracket.

56–57. (Fig. 9.76.)   Make a multiview sketch of the base and/or the pipe roll.

58. (Fig. 9.76.)   Make an orthographic sketch of the pipe stand.   Read Sec. 8.14.

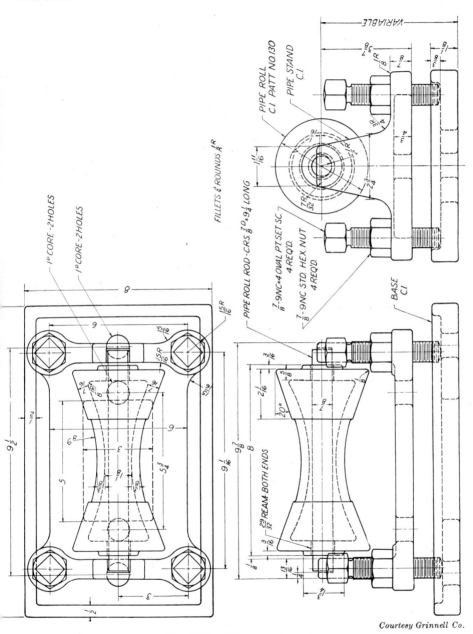

Fig. 9.76.   Pipe stand.

59. (Fig. 9.77.)   Make a multiview sketch of the base of the tool holder.

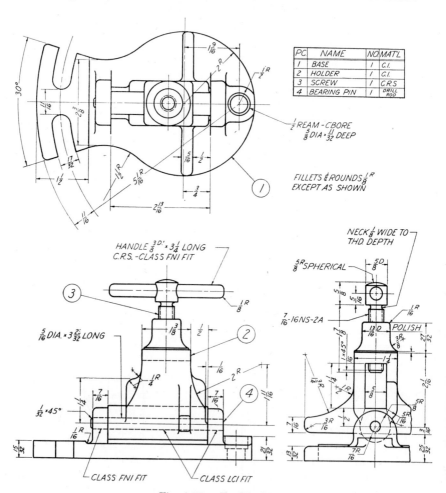

Fig. 9.77.   *Tool holder.*

60–61. (Fig. 9.78.) Make a multiview sketch of the base and/or the swivel fitting.

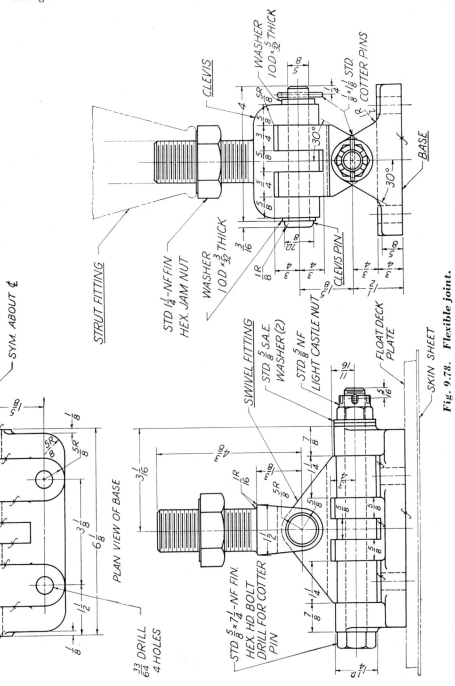

Fig. 9.78. Flexible joint.

62–63. (Fig. 9.79.)   Make an orthographic sketch of the stud arm and/or the clamp arm.   Read Sec. 8.14.

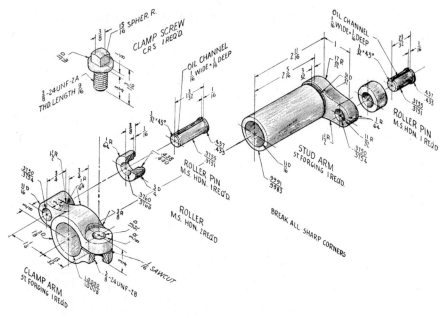

Fig. 9.79.   Roller rest.

64. (Fig. 9.80.)   Make an orthographic sketch of the base of the milling jack.   Read Sec. 8.14.

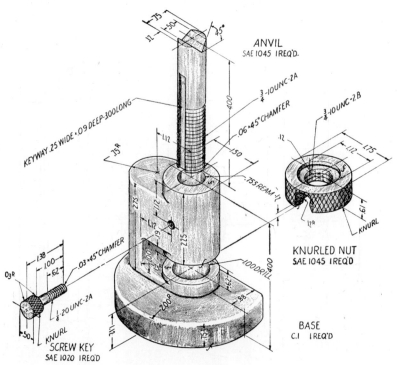

Fig. 9.80.   Milling jack.

10

Pictorial Sketching

10.1. From the earliest times pictorial representations have been the means of conveying the ideas of one person to another person and of one group to another group (Fig. 10.1). There is little doubt that our ancestors traced out in the dust on the cave floor many crude pictures to supplement their gutteral utterances. On their cave walls these same primitive men and women drew pictures which today convey to others the stories of their lives. They used the only permanent means they were aware of at that time.

At present, we have at our command the spoken languages, which no doubt developed from limited semi-intelligent throat sounds, and the written languages, graphical and symbolic in form. The descriptive powers of the various forms of presentation may be compared in Fig. 10.2. The use of sign language representation, (*a*) is rather easy to learn and may be quickly executed but interpretation is restricted to persons who understand the particular language in which it is presented. The multiview representation, shown in (*b*), may be understood world-wide by persons who have been trained in its use. However, the given views will prove to be almost meaningless to the many who have not had the advantage of needed training. What then is the one form of representation that can be understood and may be used by all? It is the pictorial form shown in (*c*).

It is necessary that an engineer be capable of executing well proportioned and understandable freehand pictorial sketches, for it is one of the most important modes of expression that he has available for use. Like other means for conveying ideas it, when depended upon alone, will usually prove to be inadequate. However, when used in combination with the written or spoken language and related graphical representations, it makes a full understanding by others become sure and not just possible. Each method of expression is at hand to supplement another to convey the intended idea.

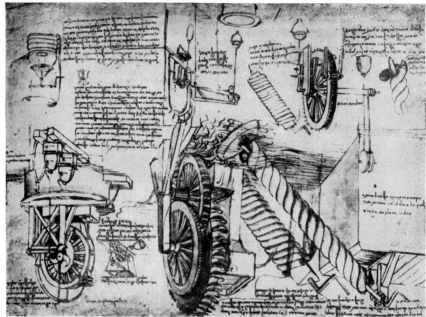

From Collections of Fine Arts Department, International Business Machines Corporation.

Fig. 10.1. *Sketch showing Archimedean screw and wheel by Leonardo da Vinci (1452–1519), engineer, scientist, and painter.*

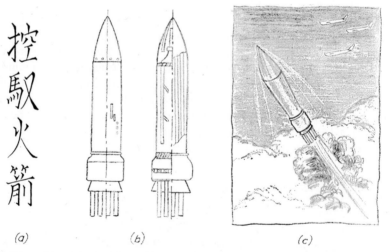

(a)   (b)   (c)

Fig. 10.2. *Graphic methods for presenting ideas (symbolic, multiview, and pictorial).*

The engineer should be capable of speaking his own language and possibly one foreign language fluently; he should be able to write so as to present his ideas clearly and accurately; he should be familiar with the graphical method of presenting shape through the use of multiviews; and

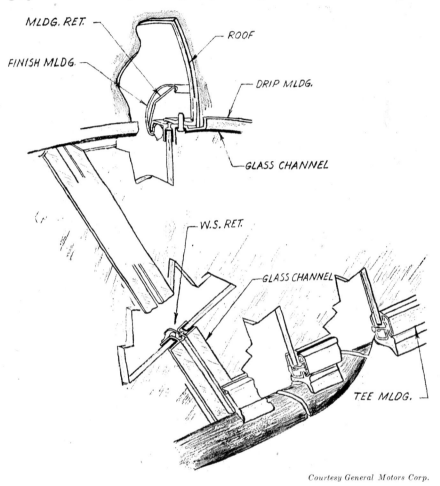

Fig. 10.3.   *A sketch showing a detail of construction.*

finally, he should be competent to execute well proportioned and understandable pictorial sketches, which are needed to clarify and insure complete transfer of his ideas to others.

The engineer is a creative person living in a world where all that he creates must exist in space.   He must visualize space conditions, space distances, and movement in space.   In addition he must be able to retain as well as alter the image of his idea, which will at the very start exist only in his mind.

At this point the engineer nearly always resorts to sketching to organize his thoughts quickly and more clearly visualize the problems that appear. The first ideas may be sketched in pictorial form as they are visualized. Later, in making a preliminary study, a combination of orthographic design sketches and pictorial sketches may quickly pile upon

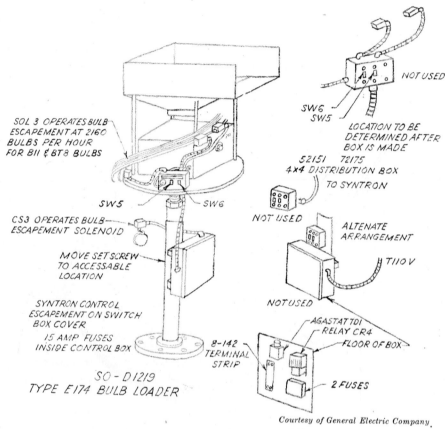

SOL 3 OPERATES BULB ESCAPEMENT AT 2160 BULBS PER HOUR FOR BII & BT8 BULBS

NOT USED

SW6
SW5

LOCATION TO BE DETERMINED AFTER BOX IS MADE

52151   72175
4x4 DISTRIBUTION BOX

TO SYNTRON

SW5   SW6

CS3 OPERATES BULB ESCAPEMENT SOLENOID

NOT USED

ALTENATE ARRANGEMENT

MOVE SET SCREW TO ACCESSABLE LOCATION

T110 V

SYNTRON CONTROL ESCAPEMENT ON SWITCH BOX COVER

NOT USED

15 AMP FUSES INSIDE CONTROL BOX

8-142 TERMINAL STRIP

AGASTAT TDI
RELAY CR4
FLOOR OF BOX

2 FUSES

SO - D1219
TYPE E174 BULB LOADER

Courtesy of General Electric Company

Fig. 10.4.   *A pictorial design sketch.*

his desk as problems are recognized and possible solutions are recorded for reference and for conferences with others.

The engineer's use of sketches, both pictorial and orthographic, continues throughout the preliminary design stages and into the development and detailing stages (Fig. 10.3). This comes about because he is usually called upon to serve as both planner and director. Throughout all stages in the development of a structure, he must solve problems and clarify instructions. Very often a pictorial sketch of some detail of construction will prove to be more intelligible and will convey the idea much better than an orthographic sketch, even when dealing with an experienced draftsman or detailer.

Design sketches may be done in the quiet of the engineer's office or amid the confusion of the conference table. To meet the requirement of speed of preparation, one must resist all temptation to use instruments of any type and rely on the pencil alone, for the true measure of the quality of a finished sketch is neatness and good proportion rather than the straightness of the lines. A pictorial sketch need not be an artistic masterpiece to be useful.

Students may employ pictorial sketches to advantage as an aid in visualizing and organizing problems. Sales engineers may frequently include pictorial sketches with orthographic sketches when preparing field reports on the needs and suggestions of the firm's customers.

With some training anyone can prepare pictorial sketches that will be satisfactory for all practical purposes. Artistic ability is not needed. This fact is important, for many persons lack only the necessary confidence to start making pictorial sketches.

Training for making pictorial sketches must include the presentation of basic fundamentals, as is done with other how-to-do-it subjects. As learning the mechanics of English does not make one a creative writer, so training in sketching will not make one a creative engineer. However, sketching is the means of recording creative thoughts.

Some design sketches, drawn by an electrical engineer, are shown in Fig. 10.4. These sketches were prepared in making a study of the wiring to the electronic control panel for an automatic machine.

10.2. Thinking with a pencil. As an attempt is made to bring actuality to a plan, sketches undergo constant change as different ideas develop. An eraser may be in constant use or new starts may be made repeatedly, even though one should think much and sketch only when it would appear to be worthwhile. Sketching should be done as easily and freely as writing, so that the mind is always centered on the idea and not on the technique of sketching. To reach the point where one can "think with the pencil" is not easy. Continued practice is necessary until one can sketch with as little thought as to how it is done as he gives to how he uses a knife and fork at the dinner table.

Two idea sketches for the dashboard panel of an automobile are shown in Fig. 10.5. Persons who prepare sketches for the styling division of a company must have a feeling for beauty as well as an understanding of engineering design. The engineer of the future must be style conscious if his product is to enjoy a sales advantage over that of a competitor.

Fig. 10.6 shows a form of sketch that might be made by an industrial engineer interested in improving assembly methods. A set of sketches of this type might be prepared to compare the present table arrangement with the planned arrangement, or for presenting a new and well thought-

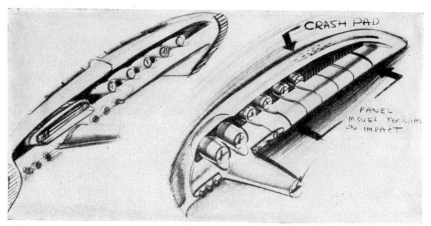

Courtesy General Motors Corp.

Fig. 10.5.   Design sketches for dashboard panel "Wildcat III."

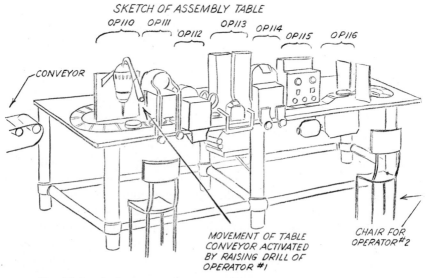

Fig. 10.6.   A planning sketch as made by an industrial engineer.

out plan to experienced employees and interested persons at the management level for their comments.

10.3. Mechanical methods of sketching.   Many engineers have found that they can produce satisfactory pictorial sketches by using one of the so-called mechanical methods. They rely on these methods because of their familiarity with the procedures used in making pictorial drawings with instruments.

It has been assumed that the student has read Chapter 9 covering

"Freehand Drafting," for the techniques discussed there apply to pictorial sketching.

The practices presented in Chapter 11 for the mechanical methods, axonometric, oblique, and perspective, are followed generally in pictorial sketching, except that angles are assumed and lengths are estimated. For this reason, one must develop an eye for good proportion before he will be able to create a satisfactory pictorial sketch that will be in no way misleading.

10.4. Isometric sketching. Isometric sketching starts with three isometric lines, called axes, which represent three mutually perpendicular

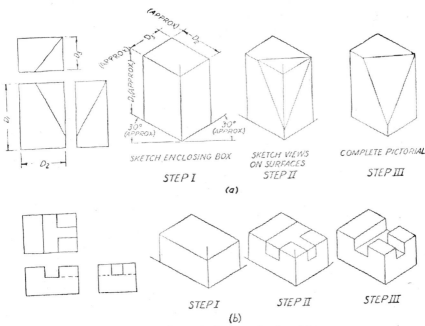

Fig. 10.7. *Steps in isometric sketching.*

lines. One of these axes is sketched vertically, the other two at 30° with the horizontal. In Fig. 10.7 (step I), the near front corner of the enclosing box lies along the vertical axis, while the two visible receding edges of the base lie along the axes receding to the left and to the right.

If the object is of simple rectangular form as in Fig. 10.7, it may be sketched by drawing an enclosing isometric box (step I) upon the surfaces of which the orthographic views may be sketched (step II). Care must be taken in assuming lengths and distances so that the finished view (step III) will have relatively correct proportions. In constructing the enclosing box (step I), the vertical edges are parallel to the vertical axis, and edges receding to the right and to the left are parallel to the right and left axes, respectively.

Objects of more complicated construction may be "blocked in" as shown in Fig. 10.8. Note that the projecting cylindrical features are enclosed in "isometric" prisms, and that the circles are sketched within isometric squares. The procedure in Fig. 10.8 is the same as in Fig. 10.7, except that three enclosing isometric boxes are needed in the formation of the final representation instead of one.

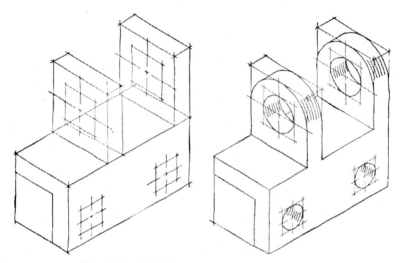

Fig. 10.8. Blocking in an isometric sketch.

In sketching an ellipse to represent a circle pictorially, an enclosing "isometric square" (rhombus) is drawn having sides equal approximately to the diameter of the true circle (step I, Fig. 10.9). The ellipse is formed by first drawing arcs tangent to the mid-points of the sides of the isometric square in light sketchy pencil lines (step II). In finishing the ellipse (step III) with a dark heavy line, care must be taken to obtain a nearly elliptical shape.

SKETCH "ISOMETRIC SQUARE"   SKETCH SHORT ARCS   COMPLETE ELLIPSE
STEP I   STEP II   STEP III

Fig. 10.9. Isometric circles.

Fig. 10.10 shows the three positions for an isometric circle. Note that the major axis is horizontal for an ellipse on a horizontal plane (I).

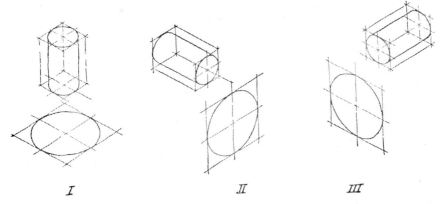

Fig. 10.10. Isometric circles.

10.5. Proportioning. As stated in the previous chapter, one should eventually be able to judge lengths and recognize proportions. Until this ultimate goal has been reached, the graphical method presented in Fig. 9.14 may be used with pictorial sketching (Fig. 10.11). The procedures as used are identical, the only recognizable difference being that the rectangle in the first case now becomes a rhomboid. Fig. 10.12 illustrates

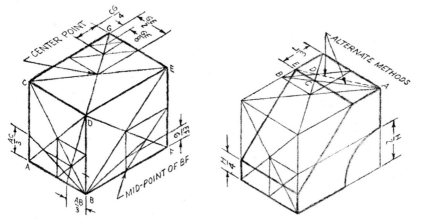

Fig. 10.11. Method for propor-
tioning a rhomboid.

Fig. 10.12. Proportioning method ap-
plied.

how the method might be applied in making a sketch of a simple object. The enclosing box was sketched first with light lines, and then the graphical method was applied as shown to locate the points at one-quarter and one-half of the height. To establish the line of the top surface that is at a distance equal to one-third of the length from the end, a construction line was sketched from A to the mid-point B to locate C at the point of intersection of AB with the diagonal. Point C will fall on the required line.

One might also use the build-up method (Fig. 9.16) to lay-off the estimated proportions of an object. This method is particularly easy to apply when using an approximation of isometric. Suppose that the proportions are to be as shown in Fig. 10.13, and that the axes have been sketched through point D, one being vertical while the other two are at 30 degrees upward to the right and to the left.

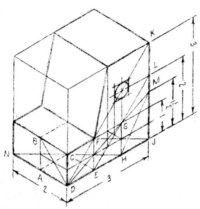

Fig. 10.13.   The build-up method.

A start is made by drawing the two rhombuses $ABCD$ and $CDEF$. The interesting facts that can be observed are:

1. A horizontal line through point C intersects the inclined axes at points H and N, the lower corner points of adjacent rhombuses.

2. A horizontal line through point F intersects the right-hand axis at point J, the far corner of the third rhombus.

3. Line DF extended locates point K. Line KJ is equal in length to the sum of the lengths of the sides of three of the isometric squares (rhombuses).

4. Line EG extended locates point L at two units above DJ.

5. Line DG extended locates the mid-point M of line KJ.

After this means of proportioning has been used a few times, a student will discover the possibilities that are offered by this method of building up an object, and he will become aware that there are varied ways of locating the needed points.

The object shown in Fig. 10.13 can also be thought of as being built-up of cubes. The hidden lines at the lower corner complete the outline of the initial cube. More will be written about the use of cubes when sketching in perspective is presented in the latter portion of this chapter.

10.6. Dimetric sketching. A sketch may be made on dimetric axes to lessen distortion and obtain a more effective representation. In preparing dimetric sketches, one of the axes is usually made vertical and the other two in a choice of several possible arrangements. The two most widely used arrangements of positions are those shown in Figs. 10.14 and 10.15. Either of these arrangements will give a well proportioned view. When the two receding axes are sketched so that they are at approximately 15 degrees with the horizontal, all dimensions taken in the direction of either receding axis are assumed to be approximately three-fourths those in the direction of the vertical axis. In other words, in dimetric sketching an attempt is made to approximate a similar dimetric drawing made with instruments, where a full scale would be used for all dimensions parallel to the vertical axis and a three-fourths size scale for dimensions in the direction of either of the receding axes. If the angles for the

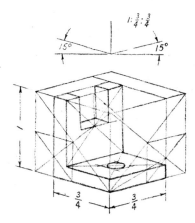

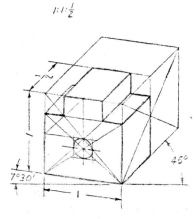

Fig. 10.14. Pictorial sketch (dimetric)—receding axes at approximately 15°.

Fig. 10.15. Pictorial sketch (dimetric)—receding axes at approximately 7° and 45°.

receding axes are approximately 7 degrees and 45 degrees, the dimensions along the vertical axis and the 7 degree axis are considered to be at full size, and those dimensions that are parallel to the axis at 45° are made to appear to be one-half of their assumed lengths.

10.7. Sketches in isometric. In making a sketch in isometric, an experienced person frequently foreshortens the distances in the direction of either of the receding axes until the proportions satisfy the eye. In addition, some who are a little more confident will make the receding lines

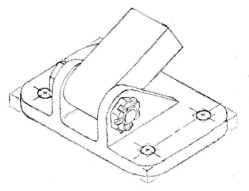

Fig. 10.16. An idea sketch in isometric.

converge slightly. A pictorial sketch treated in this manner is said to be in pseudoperspective.

A sketch giving the parts of a simple mechanism arranged for assembly is shown in Fig. 10.17.

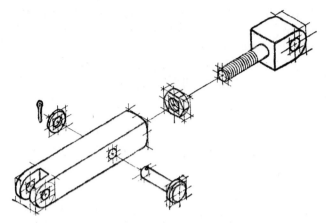

Fig. 10.17.   A sketch of a simple mechanism.

10.8. Oblique projection.   A sketch in oblique shows the front face without distortion, in its true shape.   It has this one advantage over axonometric projection, even though the final result usually will not present so pleasing an appearance.   It is not recommended for objects having circular or irregularly curved features on any but the front plane or in a plane parallel to it.

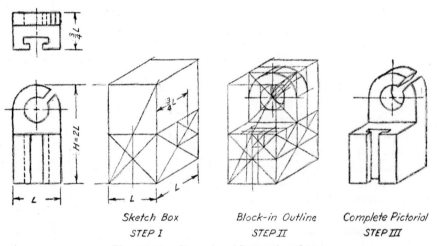

Sketch Box   Block-in Outline   Complete Pictorial
STEP I   STEP II   STEP III

Fig. 10.18.   Steps in oblique sketching.

The beginner who is familiar with axonometric sketching will have very little difficulty in preparing a sketch in oblique, for in general the methods of preparation presented in the previous sections apply to both. The principal difference between these two forms of sketching is in the position of the axes, oblique sketching being unlike the axonometric in that two of the axes are at right angles to each other. The third axis may be at any convenient angle as indicated in Fig. 10.19.

Fig. 10.18 shows the steps in making an oblique sketch using the proportioning methods previously explained for dividing a rectangle and a rhomboid. The receding lines are made parallel when a sketch is made in oblique projection.

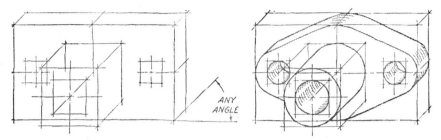

Fig. 10.19. Blocking in an oblique sketch.

The distortion and illusion of extreme elongation in the direction of the receding axis may be minimized by foreshortening to obtain proportions that are more realistic to the eye and by making the receding lines converge slightly. The resulting sketch will then be in a form of pseudoperspective, which resembles parallel perspective to some extent.

10.9. Perspective sketching. A sketch that has been prepared in accordance with the concepts of perspective will present a somewhat more pleasing and realistic effect than one in oblique or axonometric projection.

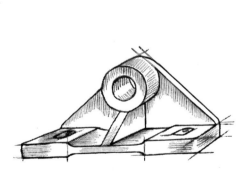

Fig. 10.20. A sketch in parallel perspective.

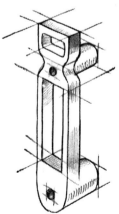

Fig. 10.21. A sketch in angular perspective.

A perspective sketch actually presents an object as it would appear when observed from a particular point. The recognition of this fact, along with an understanding of the concepts that an object will appear smaller at a distance than when it is close, and that horizontal lines converge as they recede until they meet at a vanishing point, should enable one to produce sketches having a perspective appearance.

Fig. 10.20 shows a parallel or one-point perspective which bears some resemblance to an oblique sketch.   All faces in planes parallel to the front show their true shape.   Fig. 10.21 is an angular perspective.

10.10. Principles of perspective sketching. Many engineers hesitate to make perspective sketches, thinking that either too much construction will be needed or that they must have some artistic ability. Both of these ideas are false, for almost anyone who can understand the theory of perspective and can abide by a few simple rules can make a satisfactory representation in perspective. Since sketches that are prepared in perspective surpass those made by any of the other methods, the time consumed in learning to use perspective is well spent.

A two point perspective sketch shows an object as it would appear to the human eye at a fixed point in space and not as it actually exists.   In

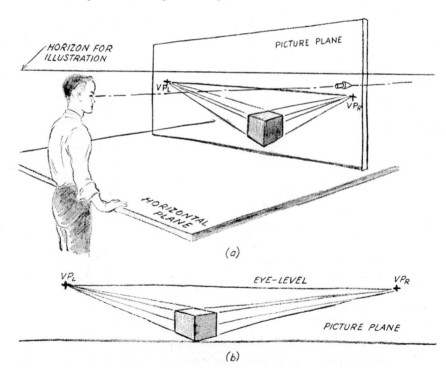

Fig. 10.22.   *Theory of angular perspective.*

perspective, all parallel receding lines converge. Should these receding lines be horizontal, they will converge at a vanishing point on the eye-line. Those lines extending towards the right converge to a vanishing point to the right (VP_R); and those to the left converge to the left (VP_L). These vanishing points are at the level of the observer's eye (Fig. 10.22). A system of lines that is neither perpendicular nor horizontal will converge to a VP for inclined lines (Fig. 10.23).

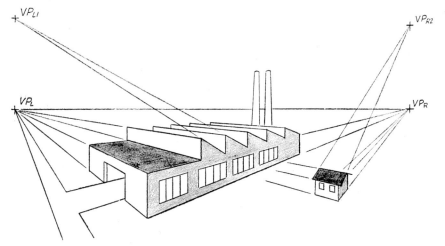

Fig. 19.23.   Inclined lines.

In one point perspective one of the principal faces is parallel to the picture plane. All of the vertical lines will appear as vertical, and the receding horizontal lines converge to a single vanishing point (Fig. 10.24).

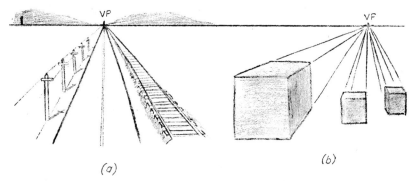

(a)

(b)

Fig. 10.24.   One point perspective.

Those interested in a complete discussion of the geometry of perspective drawing should read Secs. 11.27 through 11.35. The beginner should make two or three mechanically drawn perspectives at the start to fix the fundamentals of the methods of perspective projection in his mind, even though there is some difference between sketching what one sees or imagines and true geometrical perspective.

In making a sketch in artist's perspective, several fundamental concepts must be recognized.

First, a circle sketched in perspective will appear as an ellipse (Fig. 10.25). The long diameter of horizontal circles is always in a horizontal direction.

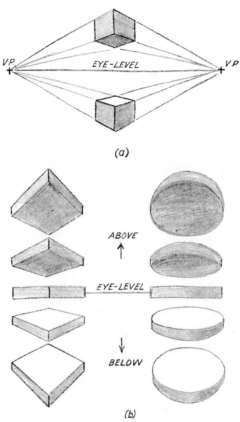

Fig. 10.25.   Objects above and below the eye-line.

Second, if an object or a component part of an object is above the eye-line, it will be seen from below. Should the object be below the eye-line, it will be seen from above (Fig. 10.25). The farther the object is removed above or below the eye-line, the more one can see of the top or the bottom surface. In particular, it can be noted in Fig. 10.25(b) that an ellipse broadens as it is moved away from the eye-line.

Third, the nearest vertical edge of an object will be the longest vertical line of the view as shown in Fig. 10.25(a). When two or more objects of the same actual height appear in a perspective sketch, their represented heights will decrease in the view as they near the vanishing point (Fig. 10.26).

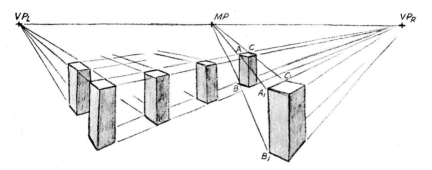

Fig. 10.26. Objects near and far.

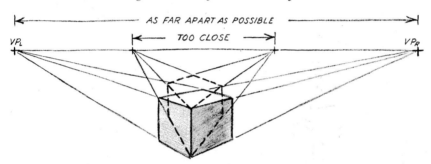

Fig. 10.27. Location of the vanishing points.

Finally, the station point *SP* should be considered as being far enough away from the object so that the vanishing points will not be too close together. Should they be too close, the picture will be distorted (Fig. 10.27).

It is interesting to note that an object may be moved forward in the perspective picture by using the method shown in Fig. 10.26. Lines drawn from *MP* through the corner points *A* and *B* of the block to the rear establish the height of corner points A_1 and B_1. Edge-line A_1B_1 will be in correct length for the perspective.

10.11. Determining proportions. When an object exists only as an image in one's mind, all proportions can be assumed. However, when sketching by eye an object that already exists, it becomes necessary to be able to compare the relationship between the length, width and height dimensions as they are seen. That is, some sort of a measuring stick is needed to compare these lengths in the proportions that they are being seen at the fixed position of the observer, who is at some distance from the object itself. To satisfy this need most sketchers use the most convenient thing that is available—their sketching pencil. Apparent lengths can be determined along the body of the pencil held at arm's length in a plane perpendicular to the line of sight, as shown in Fig. 10.28. One marks with the tip of the thumbnail the length on the object that is covered from the top of the pencil downward. With this basic distance established, the arm is rotated until the pencil coincides with another edge of the object and then an estimate is made as to whether the second line is to be made one-fifth, one-fourth, one-half, or three-fourths as long as the first. To make an estimate of a proportion in terms closer than in fifths is impractical and unnecessary.

Fig. 10.28.　Obtaining proportions by means of the pencil.

The pencil may also be used to determine the direction of a line that will be inclined on a sketch. To do this the sketch board should be held in a position directly in front of the observer and perpendicular to the line of sight. Then the pencil is rotated at arm's length until it coincides with the line of the object. This apparent direction is brought in from space to the paper by moving the pencil parallel to its original position back to the sketch board.

Frequently, it will be possible to transfer an observed length for a starting-line directly from the pencil to the sketch. However, since it is usually undesirable to do this because the resulting sketch will be too large for the paper, the length of one line to start the sketch must be assumed. This first line determines the size of the sketch and all of the other lines must be proportionally related to it.

This method of using the pencil as a measuring stick for determining relative proportions can be used when making sketches that are either in orthographic projection or in some form of pictorial.

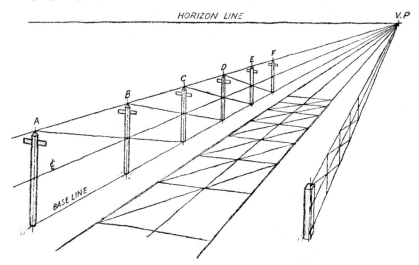

Fig. 10.29.   Spacing by the diagonal line method.

Objects that are of the same height and equally spaced may be located in perspective by using the method illustrated in Fig. 10.29.   To apply this method, three lines must first be drawn to the vanishing point (*VP*). These lines, sketched from the first and near pole, should finally join the top points, the base points, and the mid-points of all poles.   If a line should be sketched from the top of pole *A* straight through the mid-point of pole *B*, the intersection of this line with the base line will locate pole *C*. Likewise, a line sketched from the top of *B* through the mid-point of *C*

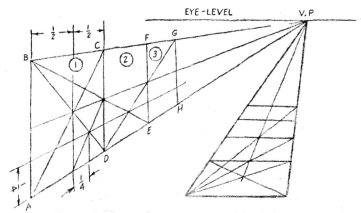

Fig. 10.30.   Proportioning the perspective square,

will locate the base point for pole D.   Pole E and other additional poles may be located similarly.

The method just presented, known as the diagonal line method, is an adaptation of the rectangle method discussed in Sec. 9.13 of the previous chapter.   For those who need some graphical assistance in determining receding distances, at least until they develop an artistic sense for relating proportions in perspective, the method illustrated in Fig. 9.17 may be extended and modified for use as shown in Figs. 10.30 and 10.31.   The

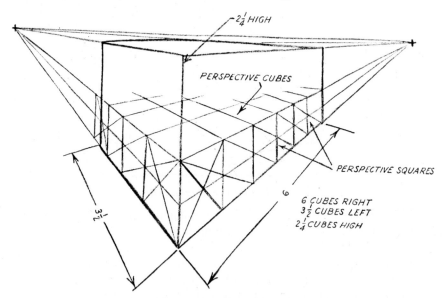

Fig. 10.31.   Proportioning with the perspective cube.

method illustrated in Fig. 10.31, which is known as the "perspective cube" method, combines the use of perspective cubes and the division of their faces as perspective squares.

10.12. To make a perspective sketch. The application of the perspective cube to the construction and division of an enclosing box is shown in Fig. 10.32.   The construction of a required perspective by steps is as follows:

Step I a.   Sketch the eye-line.   This line should be well towards the top of the sheet of sketch paper.

Step II.   Locate VP_L and VP_R on the eye-line.   These vanishing points should be placed as far apart as possible (See Fig. 10.27).

Step III.   Assume the position and length for the near front edge AB. The length of this line, along with the spacing of the vanishing points, establishes the size of the finished sketch.   The position of AB determines how the visible surfaces are to appear.   For instance, if the

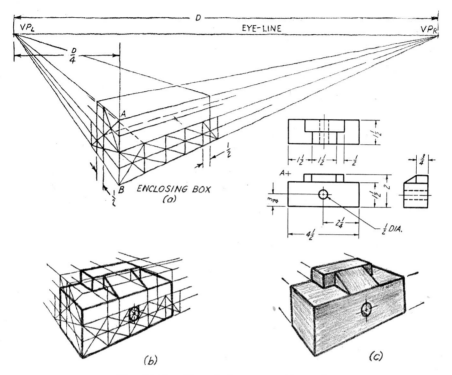

Fig. 10.32.   Use of the perspective cube.

line *AB* had been moved downward from the position shown in (*a*), much more of the top surface would be seen in (*b*) and (*c*). Should *AB* have been moved to the right from its position shown in (*a*), the left side would have become more prominent. If *AB* were placed midway between the two vanishing points, then both the front and left side surfaces would be at 45 degrees with the picture plane for the perspective. As it has been placed in (*a*), the side face is at 60 degrees to the picture plane while the front face is at 30 degrees. Before establishing the position for the near front edge, one must decide which surfaces are the most important surfaces and how they may best be displayed in the sketch.

Step IV. Sketch light construction lines from points *A* and *B* to each vanishing point.

Step V. Determine the proportions for the enclosing box, in this case $4\frac{1}{2}$, 2, and $1\frac{1}{2}$, and mark off one inch units along *AB*.

Step VI. Sketch perspective squares, representing the faces of one inch cubes, starting at *AB* and working towards each vanishing point. In cases where an over-all length must be completed with a partial unit, a full perspective square must be sketched at the end.

Step VII.   Subdivide any of the end squares if necessary and sketch-in the enclosing box (a).

Step VIII.   Locate and block-in the details, subdividing the perspective squares as is required to establish the location of any detail.   When circles are to be sketched in perspective by a beginner, it is advisable to sketch the enclosing box first using light lines (b).

Step IX.   Darken the object lines of the sketch.   Construction lines may be removed and some shading added to the surfaces as shown in (c), if desired.   Read Sec. 10.13.

A sketch in one-point perspective might be made as shown in Fig. 10.33.   For this particular sketch the enclosing box was made to the assumed over-all proportions for the part.   Then the location of the details was established by subdividing the regular rectangle of the front face of the enclosing box and the perspective rectangle of the right side.

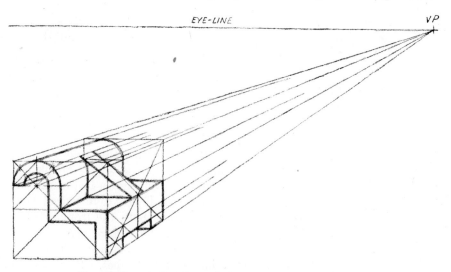

Fig. 10.33.   A sketch made in one-point perspective.

10.13. Pencil shading.   The addition of some shading to the surfaces of a part will force its form to stand out against the white surface of the sketching paper and will increase the effect of depth in a view that might otherwise appear to be somewhat flat.

Seldom are engineers able to do creditable work in artistic shading with cast shadows included as they could many years ago when training in art was part of an engineer's education.   It is unfortunate that they lack this training at the present time, for art and design go hand in hand. This is especially true today, for a pleasing and appealing styling sells more products than good mechanical design (Fig. 10.5).

Within the scope of this chapter, written for beginning students, it will only be possible to present a few simple rules as a guide for those making a first attempt at surface shading.   However, continued practice and some thought should lead one to the point where he can do a creditable job of shading and definitely improve a pictorial sketch.

When shading an imaginary part, an engineer may consider the source of the light to be located in a position to the left, above, and in front of the object.   Of course, if the part actually exists and is being sketched by viewing it, then the sketcher should attempt to duplicate the degrees of shade and shadows as they are observed.

With the light source considered to be to the left, above, and in front of the object, a square part would be shaded as shown in Fig. 10.34(a). The use of gradation of tone on the surfaces gives additional emphasis

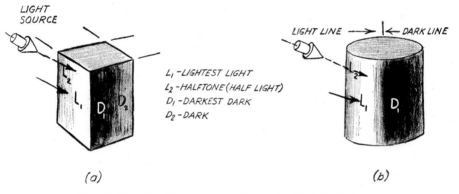

LIGHT
SOURCE

LIGHT LINE ⟶ |← DARK LINE

L_1 –LIGHTEST LIGHT
L_2 –HALFTONE (HALF LIGHT)
D_1 –DARKEST DARK
D_2 –DARK

(a)   (b)

Fig. 10.34.   Shading rectangular and cylindrical parts.

to the depth.   To secure this added effect by shading, the darkest tone on the surface that is away from the light must be closest to the eye.   As the surface recedes the tone must be made lighter in value with a faint trace of reflected light showing along the entire length of the back edge. On the lighted side, the lightest area must be closest to the eye as indicated by the letter L_1 in (a).   To make this lighted face appear to go into the distance, it is made darker as it recedes, but it should never be made as dark as the lightest of the dark tones on the dark surface.

Shading a cylindrical part is not as easy to do as shading a rectangular part but, if it is realized that practically half of the cylinder is in the light and half in the dark and that the lightest light and the darkest dark fall along the elements at the quarter points of each half, then one should not find the task too difficult (b).   The two extremes are separated by lighter values of shade.   The first quarter on the lighted side must be made lighter than the last quarter on the dark side.   In starting at the left and going counterclockwise there is a dark shade of light blending into the full light at the first quarter point.   From this point and passing the center to the dark line, the tone should become gradually darker.   If vertical lines are used for shading, they should be spaced closer and closer together as they approach the dark line.   The extreme right-hand quarter should show the tones of reflected light.

There are two ways that pencil shading may be applied.   If the paper has a medium rough surface, solid tone shading may be used with one shade blending into the other.   For the best results, the light tones are put on first over all areas to be shaded.   The darker tones are then added by building up lighter tones to the desired intensity for a particular area. For this form of shading, a pencil with flattened point is used.

The other form of shading, and the one that is best suited for quick sketches, is produced with lines of varied spacing and weight.   Light lines with wide spacing are used on the light areas and heavy lines that are closely spaced give the tone for the darkest areas.   No lines are needed for the lightest of the light areas.

10.14. Conventional treatment of fillets, rounds, and screw threads.   Sketches that are not given full pencil shading may be given

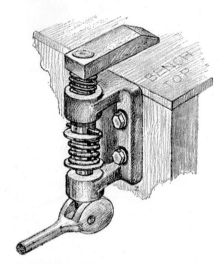

a more or less realistic appearance by representing the fillets and rounds of the unfinished surfaces as shown in Fig. 11.37 in the following chapter. The conventional treatment for screw threads is shown in (*b*) of the same illustration.

10.15. Idea sketches.   A pictorial sketch may be used to advantage in studying an idea for a complete unit, as was done for the quick acting clamp shown in Fig. 10.35. Another example is given in Fig. 10.36, where a suggested arrangement for a remote control system is shown.   Only a minimum number of lines were used to suggest the outline of the boat, for using unnecessary lines on a sketch is

Fig. 10.35.   Idea sketch for a quick acting machine clamp.

undesirable since they make the sketch more difficult to understand.

In Fig. 10.37 the results of some progressive thinking on a particular problem are shown.   The changes that an original design may undergo result from the minor problems that usually develop and from new ideas which seem to improve it.   Frequently these new ideas come as casual thoughts of one's colleagues, or they may arise in a formal way around a conference table when those who represent the design and production departments of a firm meet with the representatives and management and prospective customers. Each new idea that is presented must be thoroughly explored before being discarded as unnecessary or undesirable.

At such conferences, the representation of an idea in some pictorial form assures one that there will be a complete understanding of an idea by all of those who are present, be they engineers or business men.

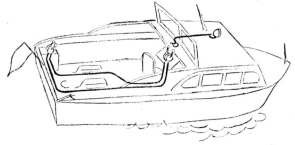

Courtesy Teleflex, Inc.

Fig. 10.36. Idea sketch showing remote control system for a motor boat.

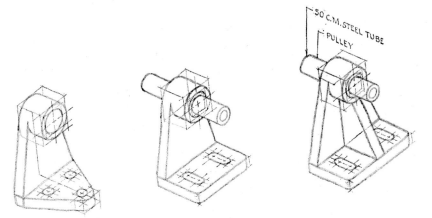

Fig. 10.37. Successive idea sketches made to determine the form for a control rod bracket.

After a rather complete pictorial representation has once been prepared to show a suggested change for an existing mechanism or for showing an entirely new idea for a non-existent structure, subsequent alterations may be represented on transparent overlay sheets (See Sec. 9.14). The sketch on the overlay is made by tracing as much of the original sketch as is needed. Sometimes it will be desirable to make the sketch on the overlay nearly complete; while at other times all that will be needed is a complete sketch of a particular detail along with a few additional lines that will suggest the outline of the main structure or mechanism.

Idea sketches of single parts are made frequently when deciding upon the form that the part must take if it is to fulfill its function. In making such sketches, it is a rare occassion when the first sketch made by the engineer or draftsman proves to be satisfactory (Fig. 10.37). Usually several ideas must be considered and discarded before one is found that will satisfy all concerned with the design or alteration that is being developed

10.16. Creative sketching—beginning student. The spark that sets one off on an engineering project is not the touch of genius, but rather an open-minded recognition of the urgent need and the economic possibilities afforded.   Very little is known as to why some possess the inherent drive that is behind all forms of creativity while others do not, but the opportunity to exercise some creativeness and thoughtful judgement will aid one and strengthen one's confidence.   For this reason a few of the problems offered are presented so as to require the beginning student to create single parts that will satisfy some particular requirements.   In preparing the sketches for these problems, emphasis must necessarily be placed on the form of the part and on the technique of sketching.   Finished sketches can be evaluated only on quality, originality, and how well the part as represented will fulfill the need.   Structural strength and correctness of design, although important, must be overlooked.

One often becomes discouraged with his efforts towards creating even simple parts, when he becomes aware of the amount of time that he is taking in making repeated attempts to satisfy conditions and requirements.   The student, however, should remember that creative work must necessarily be time consuming, for step by step guidance is not at hand. Furthermore, the value of creative work can never be measured in terms of time or money.   For instance, would it be reasonable to evaluate a creation of our great Thomas A. Edison in terms of the number of hours that he worked on that particular project?

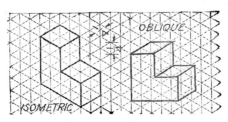

Fig. 10.38. Sketches on isometric paper.

When the mind seems to be stalled on dead-center, it will often be helpful to start a sketch of just anything that might meet the requirements, for as one's mind and pencil work together, new ideas may make an appearance.

10.17. Materials—technique. For pictorial sketching, the materials needed are an HB or F pencil, a soft eraser, and some paper. Although one should become proficient in sketching on plain white bond paper, a specially ruled paper, shown in Fig. 10.38, can be used by those who need the help of guide lines.

10.18. Illustration sketches showing mechanisms exploded. A sketch of a mechanism showing the parts in exploded positions along the

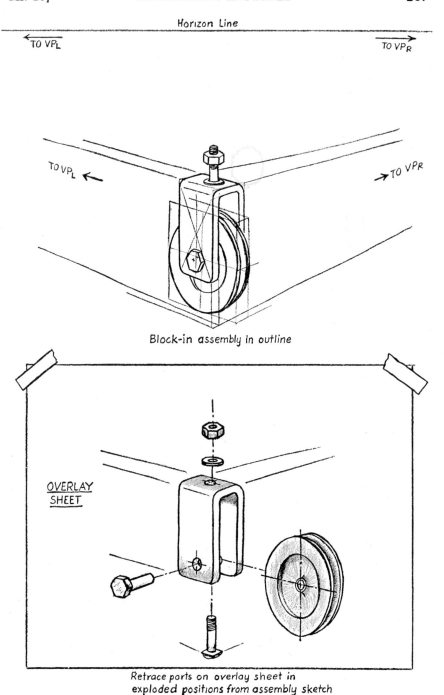

Block-in assembly in outline

OVERLAY
SHEET

Retrace parts on overlay sheet in
exploded positions from assembly sketch

Fig. 10.39.   A sketch showing the parts of a mechanism in exploded positions.

principal axes is shown in Fig. 10.39.   Through the use of such sketches those who have not been trained to read multiview drawings may readily understand how a mechanism should be assembled, for both the shapes of the parts and their order of assembly, as denoted by their space relationship, is shown in pictorial form.

Illustration sketches may be made for discussions dealing with ideas for a design, but more frequently they are prepared for explanatory purposes to clarify instructions for preparing illustration drawings in a more finished form as assembly illustrations, advertising illustrations, catalogue illustrations, and illustrations for service and repair charts.

Many persons find that it is desirable, when preparing sketches of exploded mechanisms, to first block in the complete mechanism with all of the parts in position.   At this initial stage of construction, the parts are sketched in perspective in rough outline and the principal axes and object lines are extended part way towards their vanishing points.

When the rough layout has been completed to the satisfaction of the person preparing the sketch, an overlay sheet is placed over the original sketch and the parts are traced directly from the sketch beneath in exploded positions along the principal axes and along the axes of holes. Frequently some persons make a traced sketch of each individual part and place the sketches in exploded positions before preparing the finished sketch.   Others with more experience accomplish the same results by first tracing the major part along with the principal axes and then moving the overlay sheet as required to trace off the remaining parts in their correct positions along the axes.

It should be recognized that in preparing sketches of exploded mechanisms in this manner the parts are not shown perspectively reduced although they are removed from their original place in the pictorial assembly outward and towards the vanishing points.   To prepare a sketch of this type with all of the parts shown in true geometrical perspective would result in a general picture which would be misleading and one that would be apt to confuse the non-technical person because some parts would appear much too large or too small to be mating parts.

10.19. Problems.   The problems presented in this chapter were selected to give practice in preparing pictorial sketches—axonometric, oblique, or perspective.   In addition to developing proficiency in sketching, these problems offer the student further opportunity to gain experience in reading drawings.   Additional problems that are suitable for pictorial sketching may be found in Chapter 11.

1–6. (Figs. 10.40–10.45.)   Make freehand isometric sketches of the objects as assigned.

7–12. (Figs. 10.40–10.45.)   Make freehand dimetric sketches of the objects as assigned.

13–18. (Figs. 10.40–10.45.) Make freehand perspective sketches of the objects as assigned.

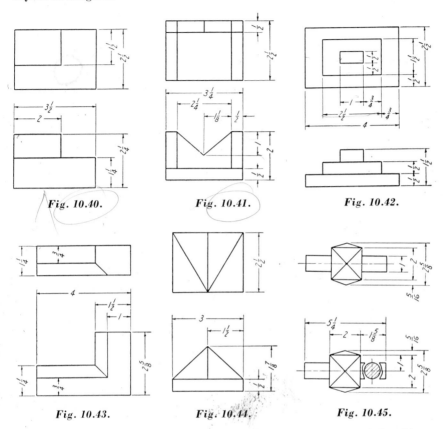

Fig. 10.40.   Fig. 10.41.   Fig. 10.42.

Fig. 10.43.   Fig. 10.44.   Fig. 10.45.

19–21. (Figs. 10.46–10.48.) Make freehand oblique sketches of the objects as assigned.

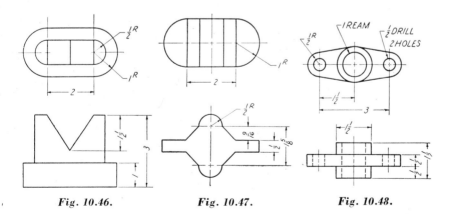

Fig. 10.46.   Fig. 10.47.   Fig. 10.48.

22–26. (Figs. 10.49–10.53.) Make freehand isometric sketches of the objects as assigned.

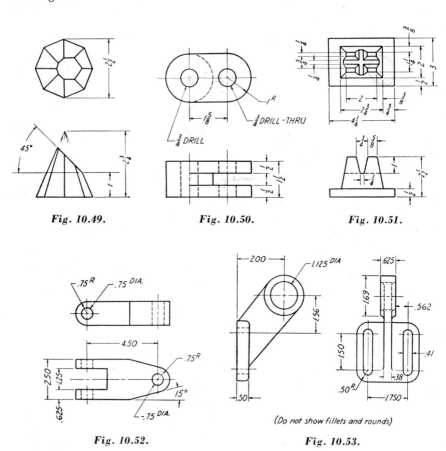

Fig. 10.49.   Fig. 10.50.   Fig. 10.51.

Fig. 10.52.   Fig. 10.53.

(Do not show fillets and rounds)

27–32. (Figs. 10.54–10.65.) Make freehand perspective sketches of the parts as assigned. Use either parallel (one-point) or angular (two-point) perspective as seems desirable in each case.

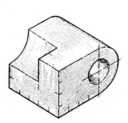

Fig. 10.54. **Stop block.**

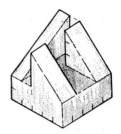

Fig. 10.55. **Angle block.**

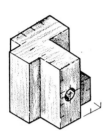

Fig. 10.56.   Alignment block.

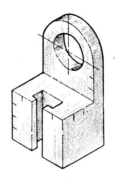

Fig. 10.57.   Slide block.

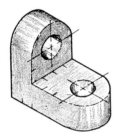

Fig. 10.58.   Angle block.

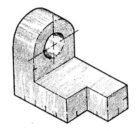

Fig. 10.59.   Alignment guide.

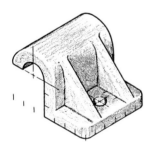

Fig. 10.60.   Index bracket.

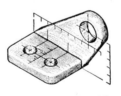

Fig. 10.61.   Control rod bracket.

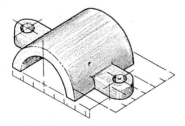

Fig. 10.62.   Saddle clamp.

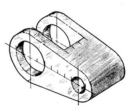

Fig. 10.63.   Control link.

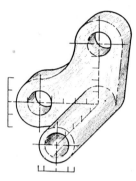

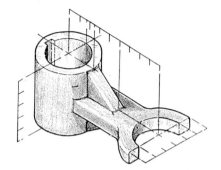

Fig. 10.64.   Bell crank.   Fig. 10.65.   Shifter.

33. (Fig. 9.76.)   Make a pictorial sketch of a part from the pipe stand as assigned.

34. (Fig. 9.77.)   Make a pictorial sketch of the base of the tool holder.

35. (Fig. 9.78.)   Make a pictorial sketch of a part from the flexible joint as assigned.

36. (Fig. 10.66.)   Make a pictorial sketch of the base of the self-aligning shaft support.

37. (Fig. 10.67.)   Make a pictorial sketch of the base of the tumble jig.

38. (Fig. 10.67.)   Make a pictorial sketch of the tumble jig showing the jig assembled.   See Fig. 11.2.

39. (Fig. 10.67.)   Make an exploded perspective sketch of the tumble jig. See Fig. 11.2.

The following problems are offered as suggestions to stimulate creativity and give some additional experience in both pictorial and multiview sketching.   Students who have an inclination to design useful mechanisms should be encouraged to select a problem for themselves, for the creative mind works best when directed to a task in which it already has some interest.   However, the young beginner should confine his activities to ideas for simple mechanisms that do not require extensive training in machine design and the engineering sciences.

40. Prepare design sketches (both pictorial and multiview) for an open-end wrench to fit the head of a bolt (regular series) having a body diameter of 1 inch. Give dimensions on the multiview sketch and specify the material.

41. Prepare design sketches (both pictorial and multiview) for a wrench having a head with four or more fixed openings to fit the heads of bolts having nominal diameters of $\frac{5}{8}''$, $\frac{3}{4}''$, $\frac{7}{8}''$, and $1''$.   Dimension the multiview sketch and specify the material.

42. Prepare a series of design sketches for a bumper hitch (curved bumper) for attaching a light two-wheel trailer to a passenger automobile.   Weight of trailer is 295 pounds.

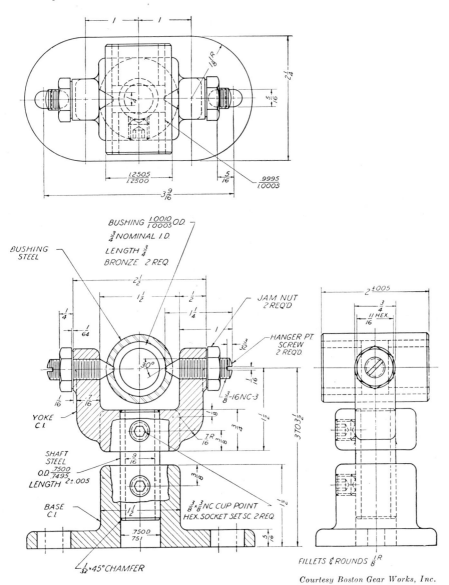

Courtesy Boston Gear Works, Inc.

Fig. 10.66. Self-aligning shaft support.

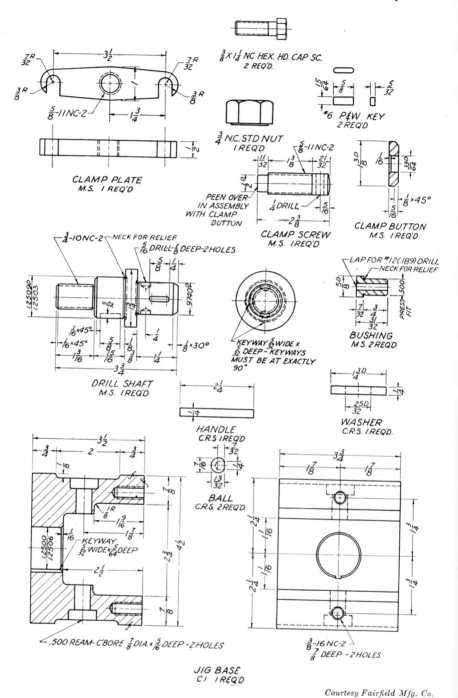

Courtesy Fairfield Mfg. Co.

Fig. 10.67.   Tumble jig.

43. Prepare sketches for a hitch for a glider. The design should allow for release of the cable at the glider after the glider has become air-borne by being pulled by a jeep on the ground.

44. Prepare sketches for a hangar bracket to support a $\frac{1}{2}$ inch control rod. The bracket must be attached to a vertical surface to which the control rod is parallel. The distance between the vertical surface and the center line of the control rod is 4 inches.

45. Prepare sketches for a mechanism to be attached to a two-wheel hand truck to make it easy to move the truck up and down stair steps with a heavy load.

46. Prepare sketches for a quick acting clamp that can be used to hold steel plates in position for making a lap weld.

47. Prepare a pictorial sketch of a bracket that will support an instrument panel at an angle of 45 degrees with a vertical bulkhead to which the bracket will be attached. The bracket should be designed to permit the panel to be raised or lowered a height distance of 4″ as desired.

48. Prepare sketches for an adjustable pipe support for a $1\frac{1}{2}$ inch pipe that is to carry a chemical mixture in a factory manufacturing paint. The pipe is overhead and is to be supported at 10 foot intervals where the adjustable supports can be attached to the lower chords of the roof trusses. The lower chord of a roof truss is formed by two angles $2\frac{1}{2} \times 2\frac{1}{2} \times \frac{5}{16}$ that are separated by $\frac{3}{8}$ inch thick washers.

Pictorial Drawing

11.1. An orthographic drawing of two or more views describes an object accurately in form and size but, since each of the views shows only two dimensions without any suggestion of depth, such a drawing can convey information only to those who are familiar with graphic representation. For this reason, multiview drawings are used mainly by engineers, draftsmen, contractors, and shopmen.

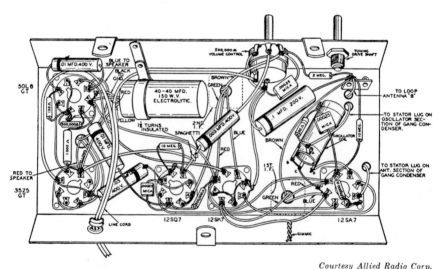

Courtesy Allied Radio Corp.

Fig. 11.1.   Pictorial diagram.

Frequently, however, engineers and draftsmen find they must use conventional picture drawings to convey specific information to persons who do not possess the trained imagination necessary to construct mentally an object from views. To make such drawings, several special schemes of one-plane pictorial drawing have been devised that combine the pictorial effect of perspective with the advantage of having the principal dimensions to scale. But pictorial drawings, in spite of certain advantages, have disadvantages that limit their use. A few of these are as follows:

1. Some drawings frequently have a distorted, unreal appearance that is disagreeable.

2. The time required for execution is, in many cases, greater than for an orthographic drawing.

3. They are difficult to dimension.

4. Some of the lines cannot be measured.

Even with these limitations, pictorial drawings are used extensively for catalogs, Patent Office records, piping diagrams, and furniture designs

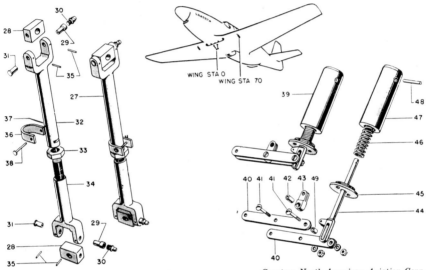

Courtesy North American Aviation Corp.

Fig. 11.2. A pictorial illustration.

(Fig. 11.1). Occasionally they are used, in one form or another, to supplement and clarify machine and structural details which would be difficult to visualize (Fig. 11.2).

11.2. Divisions of pictorial drawing. Single-plane pictorial drawings are classified in three general divisions: (1) axonometric projection, (2) oblique projection, and (3) perspective projection (Fig. 11.3).

Perspective methods produce the most realistic drawings, but the necessary construction is more difficult and tedious than the construction required for the conventional methods classified under the other two divisions. For this reason, engineers customarily use some form of either axonometric or oblique projection. Modified methods, which are not theoretically correct, are often used to produce desired effects.

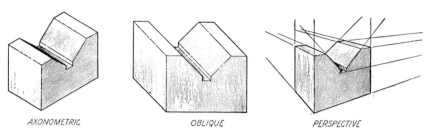

AXONOMETRIC   OBLIQUE   PERSPECTIVE

Fig. 11.3. *Axonometric, oblique, and perspective projection.*

11.3. Divisions of axonometric projection. Theoretically, axono-metric projection is a form of orthographic projection. The distinguish-ing difference is that only one plane is used instead of two or more, and the object is turned from its customary position so that three faces are dis-played (Fig. 5.7). Since an object may be placed in a countless number of positions relative to the picture plane, an infinite number of views may be drawn which will vary in general proportions, lengths of edges, and sizes of angles. For practical reasons, a few of these possible positions have been classified in such a manner as to give the recognized divisions of axonometric projection: (1) isometric, (2) dimetric, and (3) trimetric.

Isometric projection is the simplest of these, because the principal axes make equal angles with the plane of projection and the edges are therefore foreshortened equally.

11.4. Isometric projection (see Sec. 5.4). When the cube in Fig. 5.7 is revolved through an angle of 45 degrees about an imaginary vertical axis, as shown, and is then tilted forward until its body diagonal is per-pendicular to the vertical plane, the edges will be foreshortened equally

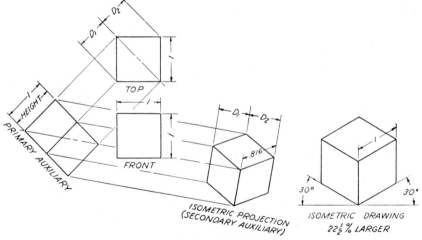

Fig. 11.4. *Comparison of isometric projection and isometric drawing.*

and the cube will be in the correct position to produce an isometric projection.

The three front edges, called isometric axes, make angles of approximately 35° 16′ with the vertical plane of projection or picture plane. In this form of pictorial, the angles between the projections of these axes are 120°, and the projected lengths of the edges of an object, along and parallel to these axes, are approximately 81 per cent of their true lengths. It should be observed that the 90° angles of the cube appear in the isometric projection as either 120° or 60°.

Now, if instead of turning and tilting the object in relation to a principal plane of projection, an auxiliary plane is used that will be perpendicular to the body diagonal, the view projected on the plane will be an axonometric projection. Since the auxiliary plane will be inclined to the principal planes upon which the front, top, and side views would be projected, the auxiliary view, taken in a position perpendicular to the body diagonal, will be a secondary auxiliary view, as shown in Fig. 11.4.

11.5. Isometric scale. An isometric scale (proportional scale) for laying off distances parallel to isometric axes may be made by the simple graphical method shown in Fig. 11.5. Usually, the scale is drawn along the edge of a strip of paper or cardboard. Its use is illustrated in Fig. 11.6.

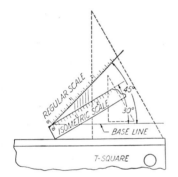

Fig. 11.5. Isometric scale.

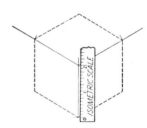

Fig. 11.6. Use of an isometric scale.

11.6. Isometric drawing. Objects seldom are drawn in true isometric projection, the use of an isometric scale being inconvenient and impractical. Instead, a conventional method is used in which all foreshortening is ignored, and actual true lengths are laid off along isometric axes and isometric lines. To avoid confusion and to set this method apart from true isometric projection, it is called isometric drawing.

The isometric drawing of a figure is slightly larger (approximately 22½ per cent) than the isometric projection, but, since the proportions are the same, the increased size does not affect the pictorial value of the representation. (See Fig. 11.4.) The use of a regular scale makes it pos-

sible for a draftsman to produce a satisfactory drawing with a minimum
expenditure of time and effort.

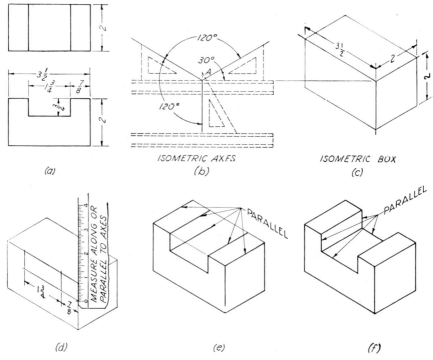

ISOMETRIC AXES   ISOMETRIC BOX
(a)   (b)   (c)

(d)   (e)   (f)

Fig. 11.7.   Procedure for constructing an isometric drawing.

In isometric drawing, lines that are parallel to the isometric axes are
called *isometric lines*.

11.7. To make an isometric drawing of a rectangular object.
The procedure followed in making an isometric drawing of a rectangular
block is illustrated in Fig. 11.7.   The three axes that establish the front
edges, as shown in (*b*), should be drawn through point *A* so that one
extends vertically downward and the other two upward to the right and
left at an angle of 30° from the horizontal.   Then the actual lengths of the
edges may be set off, as shown in (*c*) and (*d*), and the remainder of the
view completed by drawing lines parallel to the axes through the corners
thus located, as in (*e*) and (*f*).

Hidden lines, unless absolutely necessary for clearness, always should
be omitted on a pictorial representation.

The same object may be drawn by starting with the lower right-hand
corner.

11.8. Nonisometric lines.   In a pictorial view, the lines that are
oblique to the isometric axes are called nonisometric lines.   Since a line

of this type does not appear in its true length and cannot be measured directly, its position and projected length must be established by locating its extremities.   In Fig. 11.8, *AB* and *CD*, which represent the edges of the block, are nonisometric lines.   The location of *AB* is established in the pictorial view by locating points *A* and *B*.   Point *A* is on the top edge, *X* distance from the left side surface.   Point *B* is on the upper edge of the base, *Y* distance from the right side surface.   All other lines coincide with or are parallel to the axes, and therefore may be measured off with the scale.

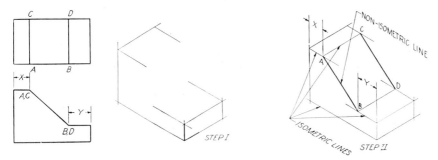

Fig. 11.8.   *Nonisometric lines.*

The pictorial representation of an irregular solid containing a number of nonisometric lines may be conveniently constructed by the box method; that is, the object may be enclosed in a rectangular box so that both isometric and nonisometric lines may be located by points of contact with its surfaces and edges (Fig. 11.9).

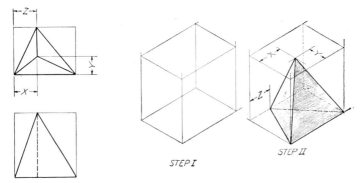

Fig. 11.9.   *Box construction.*

A study of Figs. 11.8 and 11.9 reveals the important fact that lines that are parallel on an object are parallel in the pictorial view, and, conversely, lines that are not parallel on the object are not parallel on the view.   It is often possible to eliminate much tedious construction work by the practical application of this principle of parallel lines.

11.9. Co-ordinate construction method.   When an object contains a number of inclined surfaces, such as the one shown in Fig. 11.10, the use of the co-ordinate construction method is desirable.   In this method, the end points of the edges are located in relation to an assumed isometric base line located upon an isometric reference plane.   For example, the line *RL* is used as a base line from which measurements are made along isometric lines, as shown.   The distances required to locate point *A* are taken directly from the orthographic views.

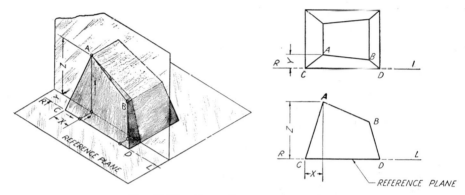

Fig. 11.10.   *Co-ordinate construction.*

Irregular curved edges are most easily drawn in isometric by the offset method, which is a modification of the co-ordinate construction method (Fig. 11.11).   The position of the curve readily can be established by plotted points that may be located by measuring along isometric lines.

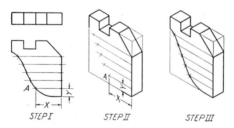

Fig. 11.11.   *Offset construction.*

11.10. Angles in isometric drawing.   When nonisometric lines are located by angular measurements (Fig. 11.12), it is necessary to draw at least a partial orthographic view of the object and take off the dimensions. The scale should be the same as that of the pictorial view (*a*).   A practical application of this principle, to the construction of an isometric drawing of a 60° angle, is shown in (*b*).   By making this construction at the place where the angle is to appear on the isometric drawing, the position of the required line is obtained graphically.

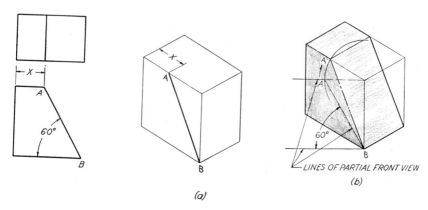

Fig. 11.12. *Angles in isometric.*

11.11. Circle and circle arcs in isometric drawing. In isometric drawing, a circle appears as an ellipse. The tedious construction required for plotting an ellipse accurately (Fig. 11.13) often is avoided by using some approximate method of drawing. The representation thus obtained is accurate enough for most work, although the true ellipse, which is slightly narrower and longer, is more pleasing in shape. For an approximate construction, a four-center method is generally used.

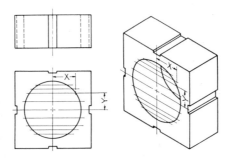

Fig. 11.13. *To plot an isometric circle.*

To draw an ellipse representing a pictorial circle, a square is conceived to be circumscribed about the circle in the orthographic projection. When transferred to the isometric plane in the pictorial view, the square becomes a rhombus (isometric square) and the circle an ellipse tangent to the rhombus at the mid-points of its sides. If the ellipse is to be drawn by the four-center method (Fig. 11.14), the points of intersection of the perpendicular bisectors of the sides of the rhombus will be centers for the four arcs forming the approximate ellipse. The two intersections that lie on the corners of the rhombus are centers for the two large arcs, while the remaining intersections are centers for the two small arcs. Furthermore, the length along the perpendicular from the center of each arc to the point at which the arc is tangent to the rhombus (mid-point) will be the radius. All construction lines required by this method may be made with a T-square and a 30 × 60° triangle.

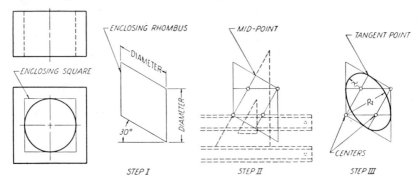

Fig. 11.14. Four-center approximation.

The amount of work may be still further shortened, and the accuracy of the construction improved, by following the procedure shown in Fig. 11.15. The steps in this method are:

Step I. Draw the isometric center lines of the required circle.

Step II. Using a radius equal to the radius of the circle, strike arcs across the isometric center lines.

Steps III–IV. Through each of these points of intersection erect a perpendicular to the other isometric center line.

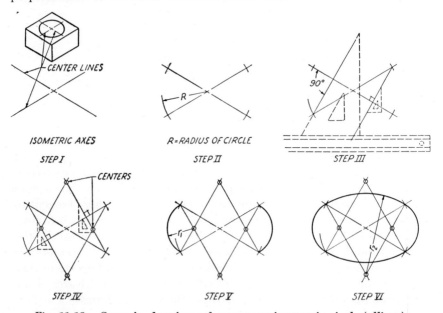

Fig. 11.15. Steps in drawing a four-center isometric circle (ellipse).

Steps V–VI. Using the intersection points of the perpendiculars as centers draw the four arcs that form the ellipse.

A circle arc will appear in pictorial representation as a segment of an ellipse. Therefore, it may be drawn by using as much of the four-center method as is required to locate the needed centers (Fig. 11.17). For

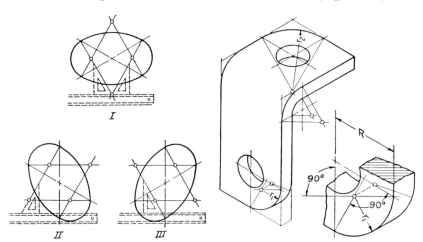

Fig. 11.16.   *Isometric circles.*   Fig. 11.17.   *Isometric circle arcs.*

example, to draw a quarter circle, it is only necessary to lay off the true radius of the arc along isometric lines drawn through the center and to draw intersecting perpendiculars through these points.

To draw isometric concentric circles by the four-center method, a set of centers must be located for each circle.

When several circles of the same diameter occur in parallel planes, the construction may be simplified. Fig. 11.18 shows two views of a cylinder and its corresponding isometric drawing. The centers for the ellipse representing the upper base are found in the usual way, while the four

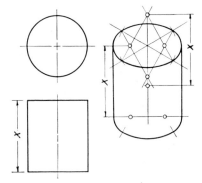

Fig. 11.18.   *Isometric parallel circles.*

centers for the lower base are located by moving the centers for the upper base a distance equal to the height of the cylinder. It should be noted that corresponding centers lie along an isometric line parallel to the axis of the cylinder.

Circles and circle arcs in nonisometric planes are plotted by using the offset or co-ordinate method (Fig. 11.19). Sufficient points for establishing a curve are located by transferring measurements from the ortho-graphic views to isometric lines in the pictorial view, as illustrated for point A.

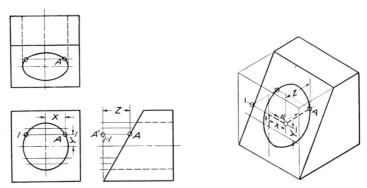

Fig. 11.19.   Circles in nonisometric planes.

The pictorial representation of a sphere is the envelope of all of the great circles which could be drawn on the surface.   In isometric drawing, the great circles appear as ellipses and a circle is their envelope.   In practice it is necessary to draw only one ellipse, using the true radius of the sphere and the four-center method of construction.   The diameter of the circle is the long diameter of the ellipse (Fig. 11.20).

11.12. Positions of isometric axes.   It sometimes is desirable to place the principal isometric axes so that an object will be in position to reveal certain faces to a better advantage (Fig. 11.21).

The difference in direction should cause no confusion, since the angle between the axes and the procedure followed in constructing the view are the same for any position.   The choice of the direction may depend upon the construction of the object, but usually this is determined by the position from which the object ordinarily is viewed.

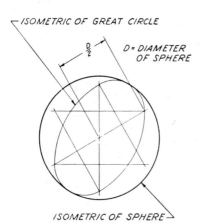

Fig. 11.20.   Isometric drawing of a sphere.

Reversed axes are used in architectural work to show a feature as it would be seen from a natural position below (b).

Sometimes, long objects are drawn with the long axis horizontal, as shown in Fig. 11.22.

(a)

(b)

(c)

(d)

Fig. 11.21. Convenient positions of axes.

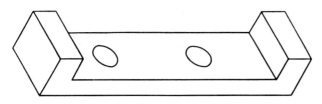

Fig. 11.22. Main axis horizontal—long objects.

11.13. Isometric sectional views (Fig. 11.23). Generally, an isometric sectional view is used for showing the inner construction of an object when there is a complicated interior to be explained or when it is desirable to emphasize features that would not appear in a usual outside view. Sectioning in isometric drawing is based upon the same principles as sectioning in orthographic drawing. Isometric planes are used for cutting an object, and the general procedure followed in constructing the representation is the same as for an exterior view.

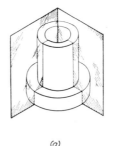
(a)

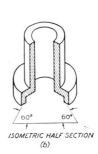
ISOMETRIC HALF SECTION
(b)

Fig. 11.23. Isometric half section.

Fig. 11.24 illustrates a full section in isometric. The accepted procedure for constructing this form of sectional view is to draw the cut face and then add the portion that lies behind.

Fig. 11.23 shows an isometric half section. It is easier, in this case, to outline the outside view of the object in full and then remove a front quarter with isometric planes.

F i g . 1 1 . 2 4 .
Isometric full section.

Section lines should be sloped at an angle that produces the best effect, but they should never be drawn parallel to object lines. Ordinarily, they may be drawn at an angle of 60°.

11.14. Dimetric projection. The view of an object that has been so placed that two of its axes make equal angles with the plane of projection is called a *dimetric projection*. The third axis may make either a smaller or larger angle. All of the edges along or parallel to the first two axes are foreshortened equally, while those parallel to the third axis are foreshortened a different amount. It might be said that dimetric projection, a division of axonometric projection, is like isometric projection in that the object must be placed to satisfy specific conditions. Similarly a dimetric projection may be drawn by using the auxiliary view method. Fig. 11.25 shows the front, top, primary auxiliary, and secondary auxiliary

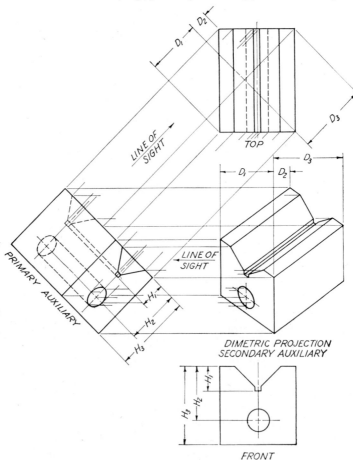

Fig. 11.25. Dimetric projection.

of a part. The secondary auxiliary is the dimetric projection. The procedure is the same as for an isometric projection (see Fig. 11.4), except that the line of sight, instead of being in the direction of a body diagonal, is in a direction to satisfy the conditions of dimetric projection. Obviously, an infinite number of dimetric projections are possible.*

* In *A New Approach to Axonometric Projection and Its Application to Shop Drawings*, by J. G. McGuire, Texas Agricultural and Mechanical College, the auxiliary view method for constructing pictorial representations is associated directly with principal views and working drawings.

In practical application, dimetric projection is sometimes modified so that regular scales can be used to lay off measurements to assumed ratios. This is called dimetric drawing (Fig. 11.26a).

The angles and scales may be worked out* for any ratios such as $1:1:\frac{1}{2}$ (Full size: Full size: Half size), $1:1:\frac{3}{4}$ (Full size: Full size: Three-fourths size). For example, the angles for the ratios $1:1:\frac{1}{2}$ are $7°\ 11'$ and $41°$ $25'$. After the scales have been assumed and the angles computed, an enclosing box may be drawn in conformity to the angles and the view completed by following the general procedure used in isometric drawing, except that two scales must be used. The positions commonly used, along with the scale ratios and corresponding angles, are shown in (b). The first scale given in each ratio is for the vertical axis. Since obviously two of the axes are foreshortened equally, while the third is foreshortened in different ratio, two scales must be used. This is an effective method of representation.

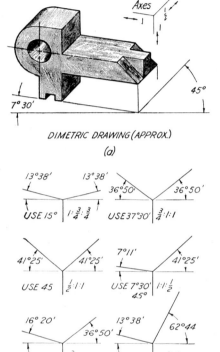

11.15. Trimetric projection. A trimetric projection of an object is the view obtained when each of the three axes makes a different angle with the plane of projection. Fig. 11.27 illustrates the application of the auxiliary view method to the construction of a trimetric projection. This form of pictorial representation has been used to some extent by certain aircraft companies for the preparation of production illustrations.

Fig. 11.26. *Approximate dimetric drawing.*

sentation has been used to some extent by certain aircraft companies for the preparation of production illustrations.

11.16. Oblique projection. In oblique projection, the view is produced by using parallel projectors that make some angle other than 90° with the plane of projection. Generally, one face is placed parallel to the picture plane and the projection lines are taken at 45°. This gives a view that is pictorial in appearance, as it shows the front and one or more

---

* Formula: $\cos \alpha = -\dfrac{\sqrt{2s_1{}^2s_2{}^2 - s_2{}^4}}{2s_1s_2}$. In this formula, α is one of the equal angles; s_1 is one of the equal scales; s_2 is the third scale.

additional faces of an object. In Fig. 5.8, the orthographic and oblique projections of a cube are shown. When the angle is 45°, as in this illustration, the representation is sometimes called cavalier projection. It is generally known, however, as an oblique projection or an oblique drawing.

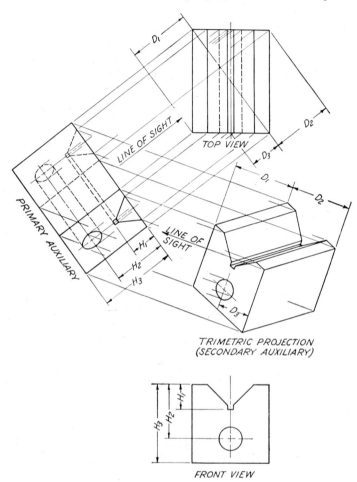

Fig. 11.27.   Trimetric drawing.

11.17. Principle of oblique projection (see Sec. 5.4). The theory of oblique projection can be explained by imagining a vertical plane of projection in front of a cube parallel to one of its faces as shown in Fig. 5.8. When the projectors make an angle of 45° in any direction with the picture plane, the length of any oblique projection $A'B'$ of the edge AB is equal to the true length of AB. Note that the projectors could be parallel to any element of a 45° cone having its base in the plane of projection. With projectors at this particular angle (45°), the face parallel to the plane is projected in its true size and shape and the edges perpendicular to the picture plane are projected in their true length. If the projectors make a greater angle, the oblique projection will be shorter, while if the angle is less, the projection will be longer.

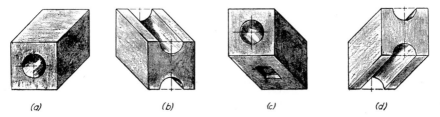

Fig. 11.28. Various positions of the receding axis.

11.18. Oblique drawing. This form of drawing is based upon three mutually perpendicular axes along which, or parallel to which, the necessary measurements are made for constructing the representation. Oblique drawing differs from isometric drawing principally in that two axes are always perpendicular to each other while the third (receding axis) is at some convenient angle, such as 30°, 45°, or 60° with the horizontal (Fig. 11.29). It is somewhat more flexible and has the following advan-

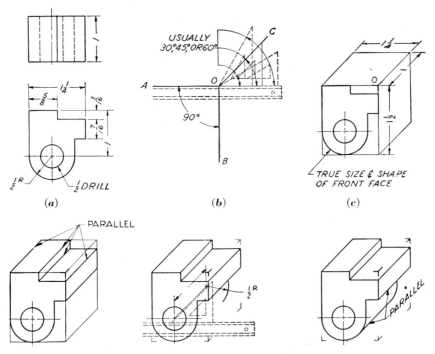

Fig. 11.29. Procedure for constructing an oblique drawing.

tages over isometric drawing: (1) circular or irregular outlines on the front face show in their true shape, (2) distortion can be reduced by foreshortening along the receding axis, and (3) a greater choice is permitted in the selection of the positions of the axes. A few of the various views that can be obtained by varying the inclination of the receding axis are illustrated in Fig. 11.28. Usually, the selection of the position is governed by the character of the object.

11.19. To make an oblique drawing. The procedure followed in constructing an oblique drawing of an adjustable guide is illustrated in Fig. 11.29. The three axes that establish the perpendicular edges in (b)

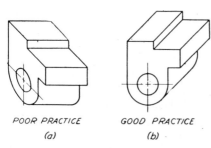

POOR PRACTICE   GOOD PRACTICE

(a)   (b)

**Fig. 11.30.   Irregular contour parallel
to picture plane.**

are drawn through point O representing the front corner. OA and OB are perpendicular to each other and OC is at any desired angle (say 45°) with the horizontal. After the length, height, and depth have been set off, as in (c), the front face may be laid out in its true size and shape and the view can be completed by drawing lines parallel to the receding axes through the established corners. The circle and semicircle are shown parallel to the picture plane in order to avoid distortion and because it is easier to draw a circle than to construct an ellipse.

In general, the procedure for constructing an oblique drawing is the same as for an isometric drawing.

11.20. Rules for placing an object. Generally, the most irregular face, or the one containing the most circular outlines, should be placed parallel to the picture plane, in order to minimize distortion and simplify construction. By following this practice, all or most of the circles and circle arcs can be drawn with a compass, and the tedious construction that would be required to draw their elliptical representations in a receding plane is eliminated. In selecting the position of an object, two rules should be followed. The first is to place the face having the most irregular contour, or the most circular outlines, parallel to the picture plane. Note in Fig. 11.30 the advantage of following this rule.

When the longest face of an object is used as the front face, the pictorial view will be distorted to a lesser degree and, therefore, will have a more realistic and pleasing appearance. Hence, the second rule is to place the longest face parallel to the picture plane. Compare the views shown in Fig. 11.31 and note the greater distortion in (a) over (b).

If these two rules clash, the first should govern. It is more desirable to have the irregular face show its true shape than it is to lessen the distortion in the direction of the receding axis.

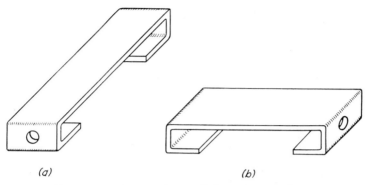

Fig. 11.31.   Long axis parallel to picture plane.

11.21. Angles, circles, and circle arcs in oblique.   As previously stated, angles, circles, and irregular outlines on surfaces parallel to the plane of projection show in true size and shape.   When located on receding faces, the construction methods used in isometric drawing usually may be applied.   Fig. 11.32 shows the method of drawing the elliptical representation of a circle on an oblique face.   Note that the method is identical with that used for constructing isometric circles, except for the slight change in the position of the axes.

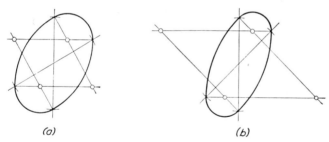

Fig. 11.32.   Oblique circles.

Circle arcs and circles on inclined planes must be plotted by using the offset or co-ordinate method (Fig. 11.33).

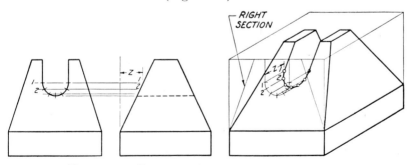

Fig. 11.33.   Curved outlines on an inclined plane.

11.22. Reduction of measurements in the direction of the receding axis. An oblique drawing often presents a distorted appearance that is unnatural and disagreeable to the eye. In some cases the view constructed by this scheme is so misleading in appearance that it is unsatisfactory for any practical purpose. As a matter of interest, the effect of distortion is due to the fact that the receding lines are parallel and do not appear to converge as the eye is accustomed to anticipating (Fig. 11.3).

The appearance of excessive thickness can be overcome somewhat by reducing the length of the receding lines. For practical purposes, measurements usually are reduced one-half, but any scale of reduction may be

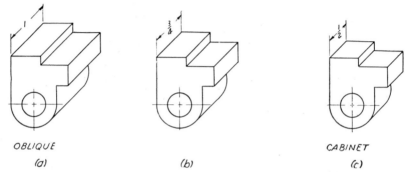

OBLIQUE   CABINET

(a)   (b)   (c)

Fig. 11.34.   *Foreshortening in the direction of the receding axis.*

arbitrarily adopted if the view obtained will be more realistic in appearance. When the receding lines are drawn one-half their actual length, the resulting pictorial view is called a cabinet drawing. Fig. 11.34 shows an oblique drawing (a) and a cabinet drawing (c) of the same object, for the purpose of comparison.

11.23. Oblique sectional views. Oblique sectional views are drawn to show the interior construction of objects. The construction procedure is the same as for an isometric sectional view, except that oblique planes are used for cutting the object. An oblique half section is illustrated in Fig. 11.35.

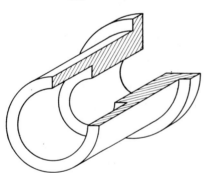

Fig. 11.35.   *Oblique half section.*

11.24. Pictorial dimensioning. The dimensioning of isometric and other forms of pictorial working drawings is done in accordance with the following rules:

1. Draw extension and dimension lines (except those dimension lines applying to cylindrical features) parallel to the pictorial axes in the plane of the surface to which they apply (Fig. 11.36).

2. If possible, apply dimensions to visible surfaces.

3. Place dimensions on the object, if, by so doing, better appearance, added clearness, and easy readings result.

4. Notes may be lettered either in pictorial or as on ordinary drawings. When lettered as on ordinary drawings the difficulties encountered in forming pictorial letters are avoided (Fig. 11.36).

5. Make the figures of a dimension appear to be lying in the plane of the surface whose dimension it indicates, by using vertical figures drawn in pictorial (Fig. 11.36). (Note: Guide lines and slope lines are drawn parallel to the pictorial axes.)

11.25. Conventional treatment of pictorial drawings. When it is desirable for a pictorial drawing or sketch of a casting to present a somewhat more or less realistic appearance, it becomes necessary to represent the fillets and rounds on the unfinished surfaces (Fig. 11.37). One

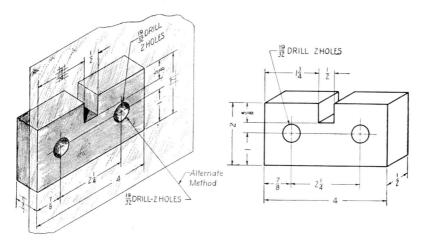

Fig. 11.36.   Extension and dimension lines in isometric (left); numerals, fractions, and notes in oblique (right).

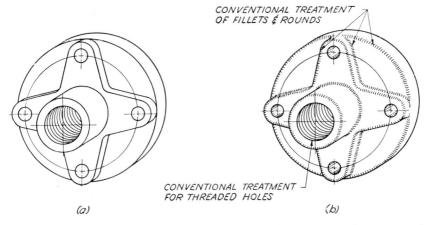

Fig. 11.37.   Conventional treatment of fillets, rounds, and threads in pictorial.

method, commonly used by draftsmen, is shown in (b).   On the drawing
in (a), all of the edges have been treated as if they were sharp.   The
conventional treatment for threads in pictorial is illustrated in (b).

11.26. Perspective.   In perspective projection, an object is shown
much as the human eye or camera would see it at a particular point.
Actually, it is a geometrical method by which a picture can be projected
upon a picture plane in much the same way as in photography.   Perspective drawing differs from the methods previously discussed in that,
although the projectors or visual rays are oblique to the picture plane,
they intersect at a common point known as the station point.   (Fig.
11.41.)

Since perspective shows an object as it appears instead of showing its
true shape and size, it is rarely used by engineers.   It is more extensively
employed by architects to show the appearance of proposed buildings,
by artist-draftsmen for production illustrations, and by illustrators in
preparing advertising drawings.

Fig. 11.2 shows a type of production illustration that has been widely
used in assembly departments as an aid to those persons who find it difficult to read an orthographic assembly.   This form of presentation, which
shows the mechanism both exploded and assembled, has made it possible
for industrial concerns to employ semitrained personnel.   Fig. 11.38
shows a type of industrial drawing made in perspective that has proved
useful in aircraft plants.   Because of the growing importance of this type
of drawing, and also because engineers frequently will find perspective
desirable for other purposes, its elementary principles should be discussed
logically in this text.   Other books on the subject, some of which are listed
in the bibliography, should be studied by architectural students and those
interested in a more thorough discussion of the various methods.

The fundamental concepts of perspective can be explained best if the
reader will imagine himself looking through a picture plane at a formal
garden with a small pool flanked by lamp posts, as shown in Fig. 11.39.
The point of observation, at which the rays from the eye to the objects in
the scene meet, is called the *station point*, and the plane upon which the
view is formed by the piercing points of the visual rays is known as the
picture plane (*PP*).   The piercing points reproduce the scene, the size of
which depends upon the location of the picture plane.

It should be noted that objects of the same height intercept a greater
distance on the picture plane when close to it than when farther away.
For example, rays from the lamp post at 2 intercept a distance 1–2 on the
picture plane, while the rays from the pole at 4, which actually is the same
height, intercept the lesser distance 3–4.   From this fact it should be
observed that the farther away an object is, the smaller it will appear,
until a point is reached at which there will be no distance intercepted at
all.   This happens at the horizon.

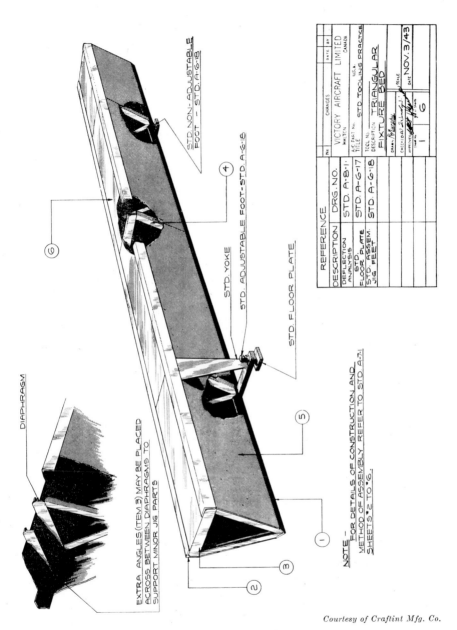

Courtesy of Craftint Mfg. Co.

Fig. 11.38.   A production illustration.

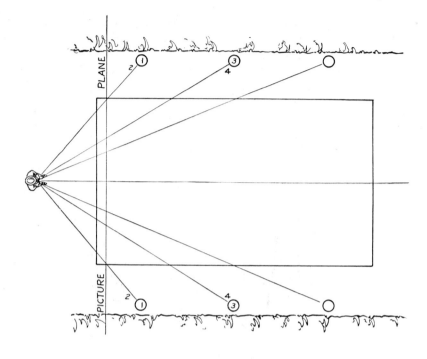

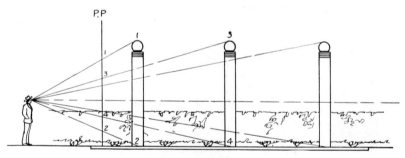

Fig. 11.39.   The picture plane.

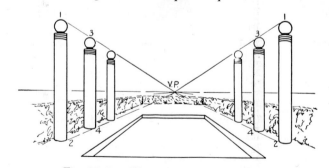

Fig. 11.40.   The picture (perspective).

Fig. 11.40 shows the scene observed by the man in Fig. 11.39 as it would be formed on the picture plane. The posts farther from the picture plane diminish in height, as each one has a height on the picture plane equal to the distance it intercepts, as shown in Fig. 11.39. The lines of the pool and hedge converge to the center of vision or vanishing point, which is located directly in front of the observer, on the horizon.

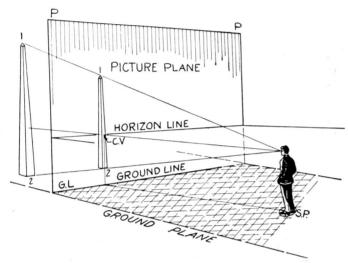

Fig. 11.41. Nomenclature.

11.27. Perspective nomenclature. Fig. 11.41 illustrates pictorially the accepted nomenclature of perspective drawing. The horizon line is the line of intersection of the horizontal plane through the observation point (eye of the observer) and the picture plane. The horizontal plane is known as the *plane of the horizon.* The ground line is the line of intersection of the ground plane and the picture plane. The *CV* point is the center of vision of the observer. It is located directly in front of the eye in the plane of the horizon on the horizon line.

11.28. Location of picture plane. The picture plane is usually placed between the object and the *SP* (station point). In parallel perspective (Sec. 11.33) it may be passed through a face of the object in order to show the true size and shape of the face.

11.29. Location of the station point. The station point should be located in front of the object, where the object can be viewed to the best advantage. It is desirable that it should be at a distance from the picture plane equal to at least twice the height or width of the object, in order to avoid distortion, for at such distance, or greater, the entire object can be viewed without moving the head.

11.30. Position of the object in relation to the horizon. When making a perspective of a tall object, such as a building, the horizon usually is assumed to be at a height above the ground plane equal to the height of a man's eye (5½ feet). A small object may be placed above or below the horizon, depending upon the view desired.

11.31. Lines. The following facts should be recognized concerning the perspective of lines:

1. Parallel horizontal lines vanish at a single *VP* (vanishing point). Usually the *VP* is at the point where a line parallel to the system through the *SP* pierces the *PP* (picture plane).

2. A system of horizontal lines has its *VP* on the horizon.

3. Vertical lines, since they pierce the picture plane at infinity, will appear vertical in perspective.

4. When a line lies in the picture plane, it will show its true length because it will be its own perspective.

5. When a line lies behind the picture plane, its perspective will be shorter than the line.

11.32. Types of perspective. In general, there are two types of perspective: *parallel perspective* and *angular perspective*. In parallel perspective, one of the principal faces is parallel to the picture plane and is its own perspective. All vertical lines are vertical, and the receding horizontal lines converge to a single vanishing point. In angular perspective, the object is placed so that the principal faces are at an angle with the picture plane. The horizontal lines converge at two vanishing points.

11.33. Parallel perspective. Fig. 11.42 shows the parallel perspective of a rectangular block. The *PP* line is the top view of the picture plane, *SP*_H is the top view of the station point, and *CV* is the center of vision. The receding horizontal lines vanish at *CV*. The front face, since it lies in the picture plane, is its own perspective and shows in its true size. The lines representing the edges back of the picture plane are found by projecting downward from the points at which the visual rays pierce the picture plane, as shown by the top views of the rays. Fig. 11.43 shows a parallel perspective of a cylindrical machine part.

11.34. Angular perspective. Fig. 11.44 shows pictorially the graphical method for the preparation of a two-point perspective drawing of a cube. To visualize the true layout on the surface of a sheet of drawing paper, it is necessary to revolve mentally the horizontal plane downward into the vertical or picture plane. Upon completion of this section, it is suggested that the reader turn back and endeavor to associate the development of the perspective in Fig. 11.45 with the pictorial presentation in Fig. 11.44. For a full understanding of the construction in Fig. 11.45, it is necessary to differentiate between the lines that belong to the horizontal plane and those that are on the vertical or picture plane. In addition, it must be fully realized that there is a top view for the perspective that is a line, and that in this line view lie the points that must be projected downward to the perspective representation (front view).

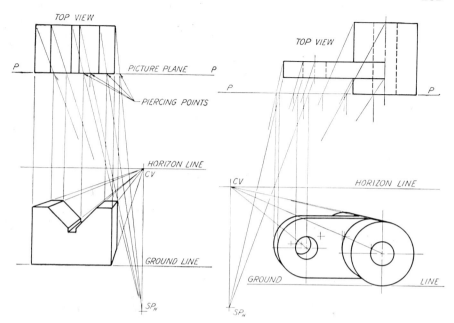

Fig. 11.42. Parallel perspective.

Fig. 11.43. Circles in parallel perspective.

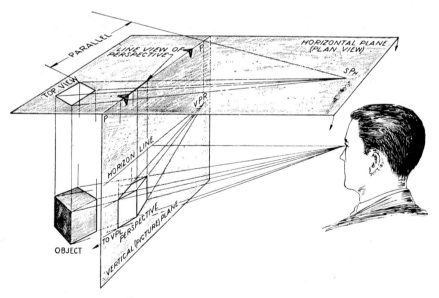

Fig. 11.44. Angular perspective.

Fig. 11.45 shows an angular perspective of a V-block. The block has been placed so that one vertical edge lies in the picture plane. The other vertical edges are parallel to the plane, while all of the horizontal lines are inclined to it so that they vanish at the two vanishing points, *VPL* and *VPR*, respectively.

In constructing the perspective shown in this illustration, an orthographic top view was drawn in such a position that the visible vertical

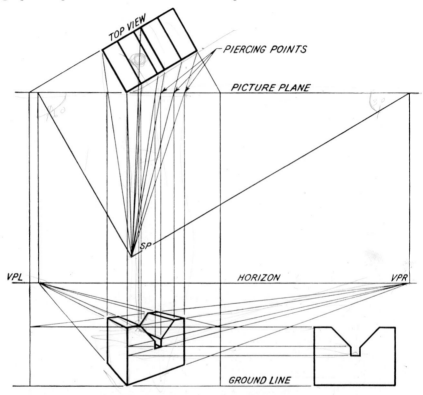

Fig. 11.45.   *Angular perspective.*

faces made angles of 30° and 60° with the picture plane. Next, the location of the observer was assumed and the horizon line was established. The vanishing points *VPL* and *VPR* were found by drawing a 30° line and a 60° line through the *SP*. Since these lines are parallel to the two systems of receding horizontal lines, each will establish a required vanishing point at its intersection with the picture plane. The vertical line located in the picture plane, which is its own perspective, was selected as a measuring line on which to project vertical measurements from the orthographic front view. The lines shown from these division points along this line to the vanishing points (*VPL*–*VPR*) established the direction of the receding horizontal edge lines in the perspective. The position of the back edges was determined by projecting downward from the points at which the projectors from the station point (*SP*) to the corners of the object pierced the picture plane, as shown by the top view of the object and projectors.

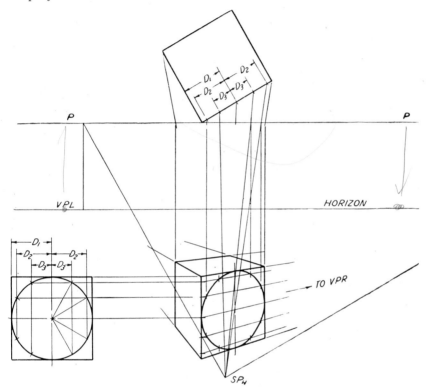

Fig. 11.46. Circles in perspective.

11.35. Circles in perspective. If a circle is on a surface that is inclined to the picture plane (*PP*), its perspective will be an ellipse. It is the usual practice to construct the representation within an enclosing square by finding selected points along the curve in the perspective as shown in Fig. 11.46. Any points might be used, but it is recommended that points be located on 30°, 45°, and 60° lines.

11.36. Problems. The student will find that a preliminary sketch will facilitate the preparation of isometric and oblique drawings of the problems of this chapter. On such a sketch he may plan the procedure of construction.

1–9. (Figs. 11.47–11.55.) Prepare instrumental isometric drawings or free-hand sketches of the objects as assigned.

10–15. (Figs. 11.56–11.61.) Prepare instrumental oblique drawings or free-hand sketches of the objects as assigned.

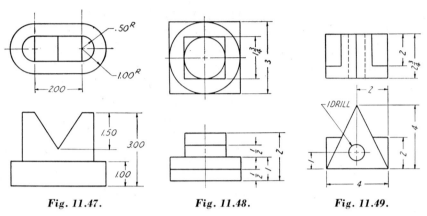

Fig. 11.47.   Fig. 11.48.   Fig. 11.49.

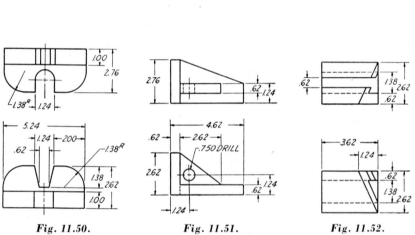

Fig. 11.50.   Fig. 11.51.   Fig. 11.52.

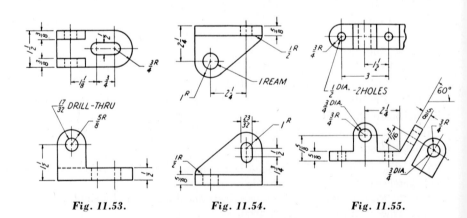

Fig. 11.53.   Fig. 11.54.   Fig. 11.55.

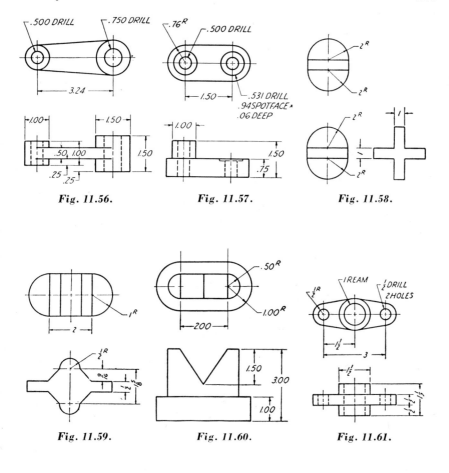

Fig. 11.56.   Fig. 11.57.   Fig. 11.58.

Fig. 11.59.   Fig. 11.60.   Fig. 11.61.

16. (Fig. 11.62.)   Make an oblique drawing of the adjustment cone.
17. (Fig. 11.63.)   Make an oblique drawing of the fork.

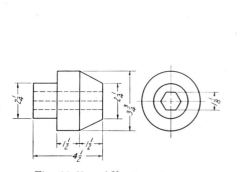

Fig. 11.62.   *Adjustment cone.*

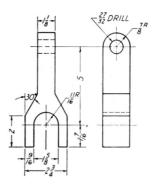

Fig. 11.63.   *Fork.*

18. (Fig. 11.64.) Make an oblique drawing of the feeder guide.

19. (Fig. 11.65.) Make an isometric drawing of the hinge bracket.

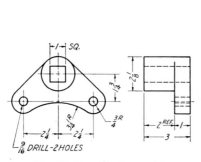

Fig. 11.64. Feeder guide.   **Fig. 11.65. Hinge bracket.**

20. (Fig. 11.66.) Make an isometric drawing of the alignment bracket.

21. (Fig. 11.67.) Make an isometric drawing of the stop block.

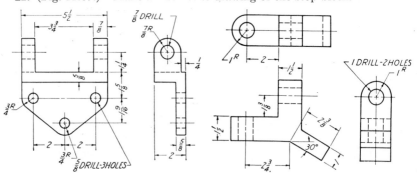

Fig. 11.66. Alignment bracket.   **Fig. 11.67. Stop block.**

22. (Fig. 11.62–11.64.) Make a parallel perspective drawing as assigned.

23. (Fig. 11.65–11.67.) Make an angular perspective drawing as assigned.

24. (Fig. 11.68.) Make a pictorial drawing (oblique, isometric, or perspective) of the slotted bell crank.

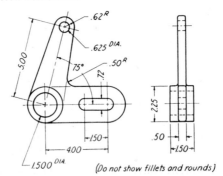

(Do not show fillets and rounds)

Fig. 11.68. Slotted bell crank.

25. (Fig. 11.69.)   Make an isometric drawing of the differential spider.

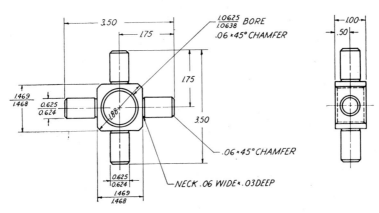

Fig. 11.69.   Differential spider.

26. (Fig. 11.70.)   Make a pictorial drawing (oblique, isometric, or perspective) of the control guide.

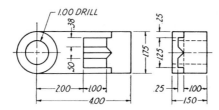

Fig. 11.70.   Control guide.

12

Basic Descriptive Geometry:
Points, Lines, and Planes

12.1. On many occasions, problems arise in engineering design which may be solved quickly by applying the basic principles of orthographic projection.

If one thoroughly understands the solution for each of the problems presented in the illustrations in this chapter, he should find it easy, at a later time, to analyze and solve almost any of the practical problems he may encounter.

It should be pointed out at the very beginning, that to solve most all types of problems one must apply the principles and methods used to solve a few basic problems such as: (1) to find the true length of a line, (2) to find the point projection of a line, and (3) to find the true size and shape of a surface. To find information such as the angle between surfaces, the angle between lines, or the clearance between members of a structure, one must use, in proper combination, the methods of solving these basic problems. Success in solving problems by projection depends largely upon the complete understanding of the principles of projection, the ability to visualize space conditions, and the ability to analyze a given situation. Since the ability to analyze and to visualize are of utmost importance in engineering design, the student is urged to develop these abilities by resisting the temptation to memorize step procedures.

12.2. The projection of a point. Fig. 12.1(a) shows the projection of point S upon the three principle planes of projection and a supplementary plane A. The notation used is as explained in Sec. 6.7. Point s^F is the view of point S on the frontal plane; s^H is the view of S on the horizontal plane; and s^P is its view on the profile plane. For convenience and ease in recognizing the projected view of a point on a supplementary plane, the supplementary planes are designated as A-planes and O-planes. A (auxiliary) planes are always perpendicular to one of the principal planes. Point s^A is the view of S on the A-plane. The view of S on an O (oblique) plane would be designated s^O. Additional O-planes are identified as O_1, O_2, O_3, etc. in the order that they follow the first O-plane.

Since it is necessary to represent on one plane (the working surface of our drawing paper) the views of point S which lie on mutually perpendicular planes of projection, the planes are assumed to be hinged so that they can be revolved as shown in Fig. 12.1(b) until they are in a single plane as in (c). The lines about which the planes of projection are hinged are called reference lines. A reference line is identified by the use of capital letters representing the adjacent planes as F-H, F-P, F-A, H-A, A-O, and so forth. See Fig. 12.1.

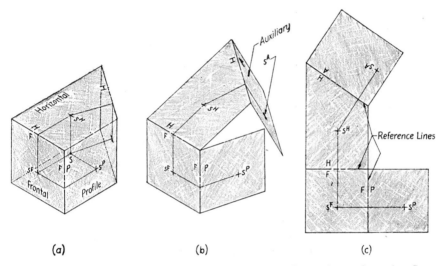

(a)   (b)   (c)

Fig. 12.1. Frontal, horizontal, profile, and auxiliary views of a point S.

It is important to note in (c) that the projections s^F and s^H fall on a vertical line; s^F and s^P lie on a horizontal line, and s^H and s^A lie on a line perpendicular to the reference line H-A. In each case this results from the fact that point S and its projections on adjacent planes lie in a plane perpendicular to the reference line for those planes. See Fig. 12.1(a). This important principal of projection determines the location of views when the relationship of lines and planes form the problem.

12.3. The projection of a straight line. Capital letters are used for designating the end points of the actual line in space. In the projected views, these points are identified as shown in Fig. 12.1. The student should read Sec. 6.7, which presents the principles of multiview drawing. In particular, he should study the related illustration which shows some typical line positions.

12.4. Analysis of views.   It may be desirable at this point to review and restate some of the principles of projection which must be thoroughly understood.

First, each of the principal views of a drawing shows two dimensions. The F (frontal) view gives height and length; the H (horizontal) view reveals length and depth; and, the P (profile) view, height and depth. Each principal view has a dimension common with each of the other views.

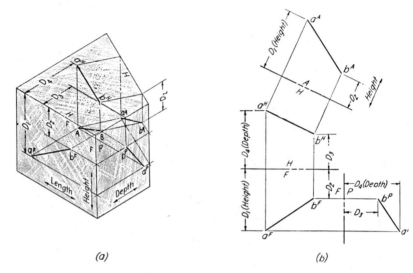

(a)   (b)

Fig. 12.2.   Adjacent views.

What then are the basic relationships of projection that can be observed from a study of the four views in Fig. 12.2?   They might be stated as follows:

1. Since the two views of a point, projected on adjacent planes, will be on a straight line that is perpendicular to the reference line for the planes, a point in one view may be projected to an adjacent view (b).

2. Since the F-, P-, and A-planes shown are all perpendicular to the H-plane; the distance D_1 that A is below the H-plane is the same in all three views.   The height distance D_2 for point B locates point b^A in the A-view and could be transferred from the F-view when constructing a required A-view.

3. Since both the H- and P-planes are perpendicular to the F-plane, the depth distances D_3 and D_4 are the same in both the H- and P-views.

4. Since the two outside planes of three successive planes of projection are perpendicular to the central plane, the distance of the projected views of a point from the respective reference lines will be equal.   Fig. 12.3 shows a series of views and the related dimensions.

From these observations it should be evident that a needed view may be obtained by first drawing projectors from a view that will become a central view, and then laying off along these projection lines (from the reference line) the corresponding distances measured from the reference line of the central plane to the projections of the points on the adjacent view, *i.e.*, to locate b^A construct a projector perpendicular to $H\text{-}A$ and lay off the distance D_2.

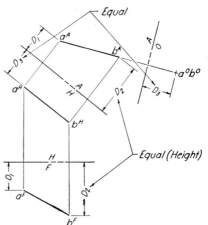

Fig. 12.3. Dimensions on consecutive planes.

12.5. Classification of lines. As has been indicated, a straight line in space can be described graphically on the surface of a sheet of drawing paper by showing the necessary principal and supplementary views and by labeling its extremities. In the written discussion in this chapter a particular line may be identified as being either; (1) vertical, (2) horizontal, (3) inclined, (4) oblique, or (5) normal (Fig. 12.4).

A vertical line has only one direction, perpendicular to the "earth's surface." It can be a frontal-line and a profile-line in that it will be parallel to both of these principal planes of projection. A vertical line will be normal to the horizontal plane of projection and will appear on that plane as a point.

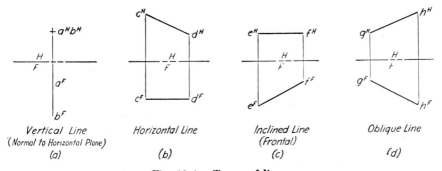

Fig. 12.4. Types of lines.

A horizontal line may have an infinite number of positions but it must have all points of equal elevation. It may also be an inclined line when its position is related to the frontal and profile planes of projection.

An inclined line is one that is parallel to the frontal or profile planes of projection. It is always parallel to one of the principal planes of projection and is inclined to the others.

An oblique line is inclined to all of the principal planes of projection. It can be neither vertical or horizontal, nor can it ever be a frontal, horizontal, or profile line.

A normal line, in accordance with geometry, is any line that is perpendicular to a given line or surface.

12.6. A point on a line. When a point is on a line, the projected views of that point must appear on all of the respective views of the line. Thus, in Fig. 12.5(a) point X is on line AB because x^H lies on a^Hb^H while x^F is on a^Fb^F.

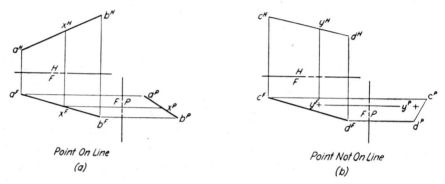

Point On Line	Point Not On Line
(a)	(b)

Fig. 12.5.   Point and line.

In Fig. 12.5(b), the point Y does not lie on line CD because y^F, the frontal view of point Y, does not lie on the frontal view c^Fd^F.

12.7. Intersecting and non-intersecting lines. When two lines intersect they meet or cut each other at a common point (Fig. 12.6a).

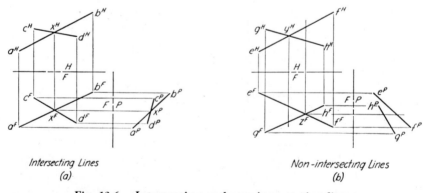

Intersecting Lines	Non-intersecting Lines
(a)	(b)

Fig. 12.6.   Intersecting and non-intersecting lines.

The projections of this point must lie on the same projector. In Fig. 12.6(a), the lines AB and CD meet at point X and the projection of this point of intersection x^H must lie directly above x^F. Likewise, the projected point x^P must lie on a horizontal projector from x^F.

Two intersecting lines can determine a plane.

In Fig. 12.6(*b*) it can be discovered after careful inspection of all views that the lines *EF* and *GH* do not intersect. At a first glance at the top (horizontal) view it would appear that they do intersect at point *Y* but the projection line extended downward from y^H reveals the fact that this is not true because y^F cannot lie on both lines.

12.8. Parallel lines. Any two lines in a space relationship must be either parallel as shown in Fig. 12.7, or they must be intersecting, non-intersecting and non-parallel, in which case they are called skew-lines. If they intersect, they could be normal (perpendicular) to each other. It

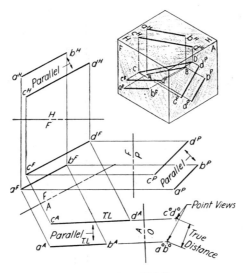

Fig. 12.7. Parallel lines.

might be stated as a rule of projection, with one exception, that when two lines are parallel their projections will be parallel in every view (Fig. 12.7). In other words the lines will appear to be parallel in every view in which both appear. This is true even though in specific views they may appear as points or their projections may coincide. In either case they are still parallel because both conditions indicate that the lines have the same direction. The exception that has been mentioned occurs when the projections in adjacent views are perpendicular to the intervening reference line for those views. For proof of parallelism a supplementary view should be drawn which may or may not be the profile view.

The true or shortest distance between two parallel lines can be determined on the view which will show these lines as points. The true distance can be measured between the points (Fig. 12.7).

12.9. Perpendicular lines. With one or two exceptions, lines that are perpendicular in space will have their projections perpendicular in any view which shows either or both of the lines in true length.   A second rule of perpendicularity might be that, when a line is perpendicular to a

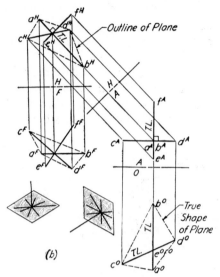

plane, it will be perpendicular to every line in that plane.   A careful study of Fig. 12.8 will verify these rules.   For instance it should be noted that the lines AB and CD lie in a plane which is outlined with broken lines and that $e^{H}f^{H}$ is perpendicular to $a^{H}b^{H}$ because $a^{H}b^{H}$ shows the true length of the line AB.   In the A-view, we see that $e^{A}f^{A}$ is perpendicular to the line view of the plane and is therefore perpendicular to both AB and CD.   The O-view shows the true shape (TSP) of the plane and the line EF as a point.   This again verifies the fact that EF is perpendicular to the plane and to lines AB and CD.

Fig. 12.8.   Perpendicular lines.

Otherwise line EF would not appear as a point.   Note also, that the O-view shows the true length (TL) of AB and CD.

12.10. To determine the true length of a line.   An observer can see the true length of a line when he looks in a direction perpendicular to it.   It is suggested that the student hold a pencil before him and move it into the following typical line positions to observe the conditions under which the pencil, representing a line, appears in true length.

1. *Vertical line.*   The vertical line is perpendicular to the horizontal and will therefore appear as a point in the H (top) view.   It will appear in true length in the F (frontal) view, in true length in the P (profile) view, and in true length in any auxiliary view that is projected upon an auxiliary plane that is perpendicular to the horizontal plane of projection.

2. *Horizontal line.*   The horizontal line will appear in true length when viewed from above because it is parallel to the H-plane of projection and its end points are theoretically equidistant from an observer looking downward.

3. *Inclined line.*   The inclined line will show true length in the F-view or P-view, for by definition (Sec. 12.5) an inclined line is one that is parallel to either the F-plane or the P-plane of projection.   However, it can not be parallel to both planes of projection at the same time.

4. *Oblique line.*   The oblique line will not appear in true length in any of the principal views because it is inclined to all of the principal planes of projection.   It should be apparent that in viewing the pencil

alternately from the directions used·to obtain the principal views, namely from the front, above, and side, that one end of the pencil is always farther away from the observer than the other.   Only when looking directly at

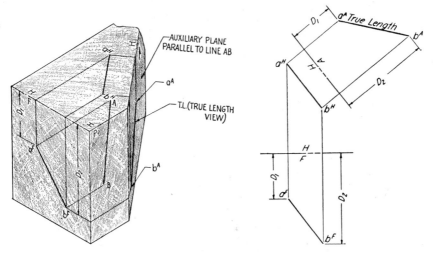

Fig. 12.9.   To find the true length of an oblique line.

the pencil from such a position that the end points are equidistant from the observer can the true length be seen.   On a drawing, the true length projection of an oblique line will appear in a supplementary A (auxiliary) view that is parallel to the line.

12.11. To determine the true length of an oblique line.   In order to find the true length of an oblique line, it is necessary to select an auxiliary plane of projection which will be parallel to the line (Figs. 12.9 and 12.10).

Given: The F (frontal) view $a^F b^F$ and the H (top) view $a^H b^H$ of the oblique line AB (Fig. 12.9).

Solution: (1) Draw the reference line H-A parallel to the projection $a^H b^H$.   The A-plane for this reference line will be parallel to AB and perpendicular to the H-plane. See pictorial drawing.   (2) Draw lines of projection from points a^H and b^H perpendicular to the reference line.   (3) Transfer height measurements from the F-view to the A-view to locate a^A and b^A.   In making this transfer of measurements, the student

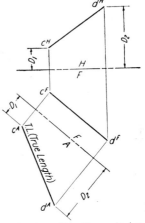

Auxiliary Plane Perpendicular to Frontal Plane

Fig. 12.10.   To find the true length of a line.

should attempt to visualize the space condition for the line and understand that, since the F-view and A-view both show height and because
the planes of projection for these views are perpendicular to the H-plane,
the perpendicular distance D_1 from the reference line H-F to point a^F must
be the same as the distance D_1 from reference line H-A to point a^A.

The projection $a^A b^A$ shows the true length of the line AB.

It was not necessary to use an auxiliary plane perpendicular to the
H-plane to find the true length of line AB in Fig. 12.9. The auxiliary
plane could just as well have been perpendicular to either the F- or
P-planes. Fig. 12.10 shows the use of an auxiliary plane perpendicular
to the frontal plane to find the true length of the line CD. In this case
the auxiliary view has depth distances in common with the top view as
indicated.

12.12. Bearing of a line. The bearing of a line is the horizontal
angle between the line and a north-south line. A bearing is given in
degrees with respect to the meridian and is measured from 0° to 90° from
either north (N) or south (S). The bearing reading indicates the quadrant in which the line is located by use of the letters N and E, S and
E, S and W, or N and W, as N 31° E or S 42° 10′ W. The bearing of a
line is measured in the H-view (Fig. 12.11).

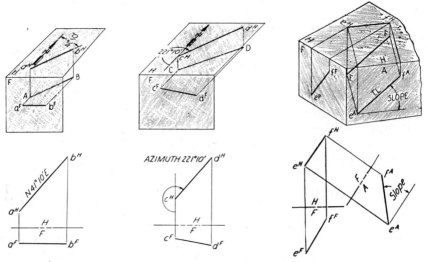

Fig. 12.11. Bearing of   Fig. 12.12. The azi-   Fig. 12.13. The slope
      a line.   muth of a line.   of a line.

12.13. The azimuth of a line. The azimuth of a line may be given
in degrees from either the north or south. In the past, it has been customary to reckon azimuth in degrees from the south in clockwise direction
from 0° to 360° (Fig. 12.12). Thus a line 10° east of north would have
an azimuth of 190°. Recently, some of our government services decided

that azimuth could be measured equally well from the north point of the horizon either to the east or to the west with an azimuth range from 0° to 180°. No difficulty arises if the origin is stated with the azimuth as: 32° W of S (west of south), 172° W of N (west of north), or 69° E of N.

12.14. The slope of a line. In engineering practice the position of a line is given frequently by specifying both the bearing and slope. The slope or grade of a line is the inclination of the line with the horizontal. Slope may be expressed either in percentage, in which case it is the rise in elevation in feet per one-hundred feet of horizontal length, or as an angle in degrees and minutes. The slope of a line can be seen and measured only in a view which shows vertical height and the line in true length (Fig. 12.13).

12.15. Point view of a line. It was pointed out in the first section of this chapter that the solutions of many types of problems depended upon an understanding of a few basic constructions. One of these basic constructions involves the finding of the view showing the point view or point projection of a line. For instance, this construction is followed when it is necessary to determine the dihedral angle between two planes, for the true size of the angle will appear in the view which shows the line common to the two planes as a point.

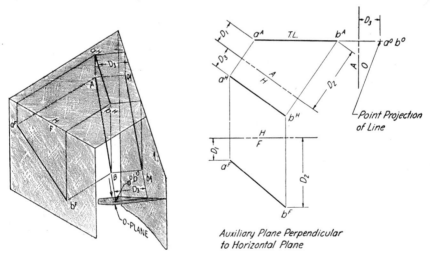

Fig. 12.14. *Point view of a line.*

A line will show as a point on a projection plane that is perpendicular to the line. The observer's direction of sight must be along and parallel to the line. When a line appears in true length on one of the principal planes of projection, only an auxiliary view is needed to show the line as a point. However, in the case of an oblique line both an auxiliary and an oblique view are required, for a point view must always follow a true length view.   In other words, the plane of projection for the view showing the line as a point must be adjacent to the plane for the true view and be perpendicular to it.

Given: The F-view a^Fb^F and the H-view a^Hb^H of the oblique line AB (Fig. 12.14).

Solution: (1) Draw the view showing the TL (true length) of AB. This is an auxiliary view drawn as explained in Sec. 12.11.   (2) Draw reference line A-O perpendicular to the true length projection a^Ab^A.   This reference line is for an O-plane that is perpendicular to the A-plane. (3) Draw a projection line from a^Ab^A and transfer the distance D_3 from the H-view to the O-view.   It should be noted from the pictorial drawing that the distance D_3 is common to both of these views, and that points a^O and b^O coincide to give a point or end view of line AB.

12.16. To find the shortest distance from a point to a line. The shortest distance between a given point and a given straight line must be measured along a perpendicular drawn from the point to the line. Since lines that are perpendicular will have their projections show perpendicular in any view showing either or both lines in true length (Sec. 12.9),

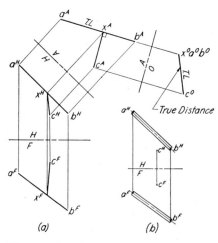

the perpendicular must be drawn in the view showing the given line in true length.

Given: The F- and H-views of the line AB and point C (Fig. 12.15).

Solution: (1) Draw the A (auxiliary) view showing the true length view a^Ab^A of line AB and view c^A of point C.   (2) Draw c^Ax^A perpendicular to a^Ab^A.   Line c^Ax^A is a view of the required perpendicular from point C to its juncture with line AB at point X. (3) Draw reference line A-O parallel to c^Ax^A.   This reference line locates an O-plane which will be parallel to the perpendicular CX and perpendicular to the A-plane.

Fig. 12.15.   To find the shortest distance from a point to a line.

The O-view will show the true length of CX.   Line CX does not show true length in any of the other views.

12.17. To find the shortest distance between two skew lines. As was stated in Sec. 12.8, any two lines that are not parallel and do not intersect are called skew lines.   The shortest distance between any such lines must be measured along one line and only one line that can be drawn perpendicular to both.   This common perpendicular can be drawn in a view which is taken to show one line as a point.   Its projection will be perpendicular to the view of the other line and will show in true length (Fig. 12.16).

Given: The F- and H-views of two skew lines AB and CD.

Solution: (1) Draw an A-view adjacent to the H-view so as to show line AB in true length (a^Ab^A). Line CD should also be shown in this same view (c^Ad^A). (2) Draw reference line A-O perpendicular to a^Ab^A and draw the O-view in which line AB will appear as a point (a^ob^o). It is in this view that the exact location of the required perpendicular can be established. (3) Draw the line e^of^o through point a^ob^o perpendicular to c^od^o. The shortest distance between the skew lines now appears in

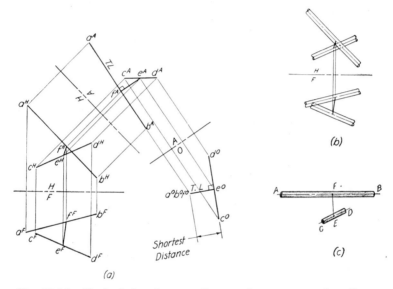

Fig. 12.16.   *To find the shortest distance between two skew lines.*

true distance as the length of e^of^o. Although line CD does not appear in true length in the O-view, e^of^o does, and hence c^od^o and e^of^o will appear perpendicular. (4) Complete the A-view by first locating point e^A on c^Ad^A and then draw e^Af^A parallel to reference line A-O. (5) Locate points E and F in the H- and F-views remembering that point E is located on line CD and point F on line AB.

In engineering design an engineer frequently has to locate and find the length of the shortest line between two skewed members in order to determine clearance or the length of a connecting member. In underground construction work one might use this method to locate a connecting tunnel.

In Fig. 12.16(b) and (c) we see the two rods for which the clearance distance was determined in (a). Lines AB and CD represent the center lines of the rods.

12.18. The direct or natural method. In the solution of space problems, many persons prefer to think of the object or the parts as being definitely fixed in position and that no change will take place. The engineer or draftsman then simply imagines that he changes his position to look at the object or structural members, as he should to determine the information needed. This method is sometimes called the direct method and is identical with the so-called natural method discussed in Sec. 6.4 when the object is considered as being fixed in position.

Up to this point the "glass-box" and supplementary planes of projection have been used freely to present the solution of problems dealing with points and lines because the "glass-box" is useful in explaining the theory of projection and in understanding the position of the views on the surface of a sheet of drawing paper. However, since both the "glass-box" method with planes of projection and the direct method produce the same results, the student should use the method which seems to be best suited to his thinking. In either case, the same notations for the identification of points, lines, and reference lines must be used.

12.19. A plane. A plane may be defined and located by: 1. three points, 2. a straight line and a point, 3. two intersecting straight lines, or 4. two parallel straight lines. Although usually a plane is limited in extent and is bounded by straight or curved lines, it is frequently necessary to consider a plane to extend indefinitely in order to solve some of the problems that are encountered.

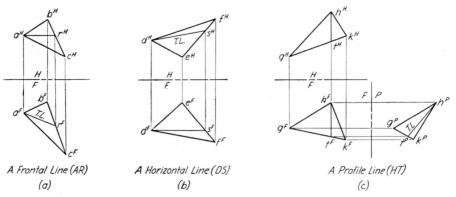

A Frontal Line (AR)   A Horizontal Line (DS)   A Profile Line (HT)

(a)   (b)   (c)

Fig. 12.17. The location of a principal line in a plane.

12.20. The principal lines of a plane (Fig. 12.17). Those lines which are parallel to the principal planes of projection are the principal lines of a plane. A principal line may be either a horizontal line, a frontal line, or a profile line. Principal lines are true length lines and one such line may be drawn in any plane so as to appear true length in any one of the principal views as desired. This is an important principle that is the basis for the solution of many problems involving lines and planes.

12.21. The strike and dip of a plane.   Mining engineers and geologists employ the terms strike and dip to describe the direction and inclination of strata of the earth's formations.   The strike of a plane is the direction of a horizontal line in the plane.   Strike is specified by the bearing of the line.   The dip of a plane is the slope angle of the plane (angle the plane makes with the horizontal).

12.22. To obtain the edge view of a plane.   When a plane is vertical, an edge view of it will be seen from above and it will be represented by a line in the top view.   Should a plane be horizontal, it will appear as an edge in the frontal view.   However, planes are not always vertical or horizontal; frequently they are inclined or oblique to the principal planes of projection.

Finding the edge view of a plane is a basic construction that is used to determine the slope of a plane (dip), to determine clearance, and to establish perpendicularity.   The method presented here is part of the construction used to obtain the true size and shape of a plane, to determine the angle between a line and plane, and to establish the location at which a line pierces a plane.

The edge view of an oblique plane can be obtained by viewing the plane with direction of sight parallel to it.   The edge view will then appear in an auxiliary view. When the auxiliary view shows height, the slope of the plane is shown (Fig. 12.18).

Given: The F- and H-views of plane ABC.

Solution: (1) Draw the horizontal line AX in the plane.   Because AX is parallel to the horizontal, $a^F x^F$ will be horizontal and must be drawn before the position of $a^H x^H$ can be established.   (2) Draw reference line H-A perpendicular to $a^H x^H$.   (3) Construct the A-view which will show the plane ABC as a straight line.   Since the F-view and

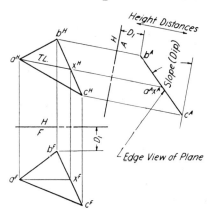

Fig. 12.18.   *To find the edge view of a plane.*

A-view have height as a common dimension, the distances used in constructing the A-view were taken from the F-view.

12.23. To find the true shape (*TSP*) of an oblique plane. Finding the true shape of a plane by projection is another of the basic constructions that the student must understand, for it is used to determine the solution of two of the problems which are to follow.   In a way the construction shown in Fig. 12.19 is a repetition of that shown in Fig. 6.38.   However repetition in the form of another presentation should help even those students who may think that they understand the method for finding the true shape of an oblique surface of an object.

To see the true size and shape of an oblique plane an observer must view it with a line of sight perpendicular to it. To do this he must, as the first step in the construction, obtain an edge view of the plane. An O-view taken from the A-view will then show the true shape of the plane.

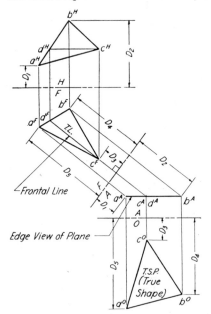

Given: The F- and H-views of plane ABC.

Solution: (1) Draw a frontal line CD in plane ABC. (2) Draw reference line F-A perpendicular to $c^F d^F$ and construct the A-view showing the edge view of the plane. The auxiliary view has depth in common with the H-view. (3) Draw reference line A-O parallel to the edge view in the A-view and construct the O-view which will show the true size and shape of plane ABC. The needed distances from the reference line to points in the O-view are found in the F-view.

Fig. 12.19. To find the true shape (TSP) of an oblique plane.

12.24. To determine the angle between a line and a given plane. The true angle between a given line and a given plane will be seen in the view which shows the plane as an edge (a line) and the line in true length. The solution shown in Fig. 12.20 is based on this premise. The solution as presented might be called the edge view method.

Given: The F- and H-views of plane ABC and line ST.

Solution: (1) Draw the frontal line BX in the plane ABC. (2) Draw reference line F-A perpendicular to $x^F b^F$ and construct the A-view. This view will show plane ABC as line ($a^A b^A c^A$); however, since this view does not show ST in true length, the true angle is not shown. (3) Draw reference line A-O parallel to the edge view of the plane and construct the O-view that will show line ST viewed obliquely and plane ABC in its true size and shape. (4) Draw reference line $O-O_1$ parallel to $s^o t^o$.

Line $s^{o_1} t^{o_1}$ will show the true length of ST in this second oblique view. Plane ABC will be seen again as an edge (line) for it now appears on an adjacent view taken perpendicular to the view showing true shape (TSP). The required angle can now be measured between the true length view line ST and the edge view of plane ABC.

In the illustration in Fig. 12.20 three supplementary views were

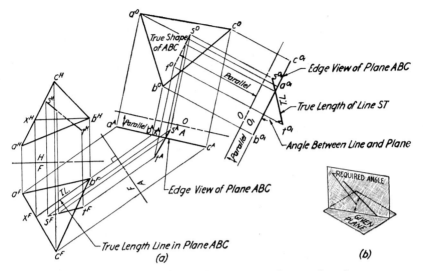

Fig. 12.20.   *To find the angle between a line and a plane.*

required to obtain the true angle.   If the plane had appeared as an edge
in one of the given views, only two supplementary views would have been
needed; if it had appeared in true shape in a given view only one additional view, properly selected to show the plane as an edge and the line
in true length, would be needed.

**12.25. To determine the true angle between two intersecting
oblique lines.**   Since, as previously stated, two intersecting lines estab-

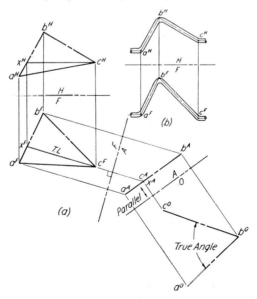

Fig. 12.21.   *To find the true angle between two intersecting lines,*

lish a plane, the true angle between the intersecting lines may be seen in a true shape view of a plane containing the lines (Fig. 12.19). In Fig. 12.21 line AC completes plane ABC containing the given lines AB and BC. It is necessary to find the true angle between AB and BC.

Solution: (1) Draw the frontal line XC. (2) Draw reference line FA perpendicular to $c^F x^F$ and construct the A-view showing an edge view of plane ABC. (3) Draw reference line A-O parallel to the edge view $a^A c^A b^A$ and construct the O-view which will show the TSP of plane ABC. In this view it is desirable to show only the given lines. The true angle between AB and BC is shown by $a^O b^O c^O$. As a practical application this method might be used to determine the angle between two adjacent sections of bent rod as shown in (b).

12.26. To find the piercing point of a line and a plane. Determining the location of the point where a line pierces a plane is another fundamental operation with which one must be familiar. A line, if it is not parallel to a plane, will intersect the plane at a point that is common to both. In a view showing the plane as an edge, the piercing point appears where the line intersects (cuts) the edge view. This method is known as the edge view method to distinguish it from the cutting plane method which may be found in some of the descriptive geometry texts listed in the bibliography.

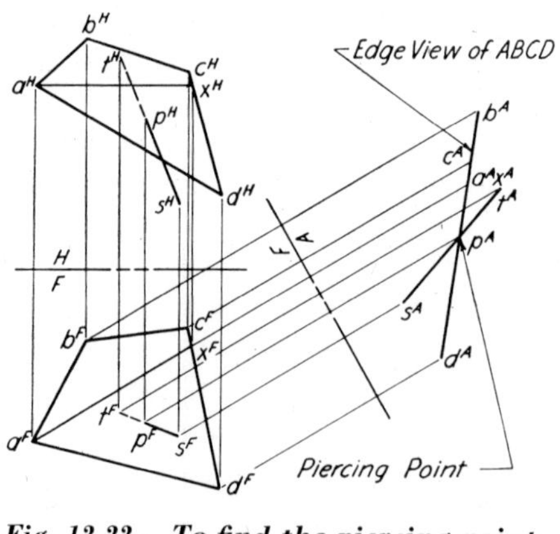

The simple cases occur when the plane appears as an edge in one of the principal views. The general case, for which we use an oblique plane, is given in Fig. 12.22.

Given: Plane $ABCD$ and line ST.

Solution: (1) Draw the frontal line AX in $ABCD$. (2) Draw reference line F-A perpendicular to $a^F x^F$ and construct the A-view showing an edge view of the plane as line $a^A b^A c^A d^A$ and the view of the line $s^A t^A$. Point p^A where the line cuts the edge view of the plane is the A-view of the piercing point. (3) Project point P back from the A-view first to the F-view and then to the H-view.

Fig. 12.22.   *To find the piercing point of a line and a plane.*

12.27. To find the shortest distance from a point to a plane. Frequently it is desirable to determine the shortest distance from a point to a plane in order to check clearance and for other reasons.

The edge view method shown in Fig. 12.23 may be used when it becomes necessary to draw a perpendicular to a plane through a given point, for the problems solutions are related. The student should recognize this fact as he studies this section.

The shortest distance from a point to a plane must be measured along a perpendicular from the point to the plane. This perpendicular can be seen in true length in any view that shows an edge view of the plane.

Given: Plane ABC and point D.

Solution: (1) Draw the horizontal line AX in plane ABC. (2) Draw reference line H-A perpendicular to $a^H x^H$ and construct the A-view showing an edge view of the plane and point D. (3) Draw a perpendicular to the edge view of the plane through d^A. This establishes the location of p^A, the A-view of the point where the perpendicular pierces the plane. (4) Measure $d^A p^A$ to obtain the shortest distance. (5) Draw a line through d^H parallel to reference line H-A and project p^A to the H-view to establish the location of p^H. Line $d^H p^H$ must be parallel to H-A because the adjacent A-view shows the true length of the perpendicular.   (6) Locate p^F in the F-view. Point p^F is the same distance from reference line H-F as p^A is from reference line H-A.

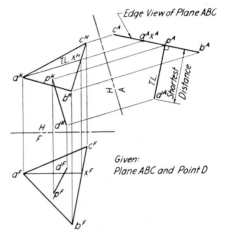

Fig. 12.23.   *To find the shortest distance from a point to a plane.*

12.28. To find the line of intersection of two planes.   The intersection of two planes can be found by using an edge view method.   That is, a view of the line of intersection can be seen in an auxiliary view which shows one plane as an edge.   However the required line of intersection can be found quickly and without resorting to an extra view if the cutting plane method shown in Fig. 12.24 is used.   Those who are interested can find the edge view method in almost any good descriptive geometry text. In the limited coverage of this book it is impossible to present all of the alternate methods that one might find advantageous.   However the simple basic constructions that have been given will serve most of the needs of the professional man.

Since any two planes that are not parallel will intersect in a straight line it is necessary to find only two points that lie in both planes to fix the line in position and direction.   To find these required two points, one could select any two lines in one plane and find the piercing points of these lines.   This would be more work than is necessary.   The cutting plane method is much easier.

The cutting plane method requires the use of only two cutting planes. Although these planes may be taken at random, as far as position is concerned, each must show as an edge view in one of the given views. In order to clarify the theory underlying this method, a pictorial view has been added to Fig. 12.24. It should be noted that when a third plane cuts two given planes the intersection lines for all three planes meet at a point P_1. This point P_1 is one of two points along the line of intersection that must be found.

Given: The planes $ABCD$ and EFG.

Solution: (1) Draw the edge view of cutting plane CP_1 in the F-view. Although drawn through point D it could have been taken elsewhere.

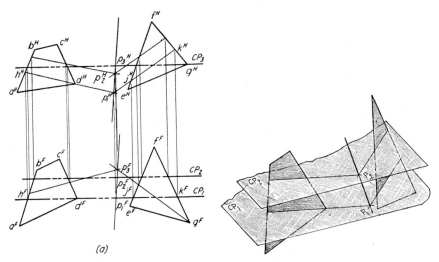

(a)

Fig. 12.24. To find the line of intersection of two planes.

The intersection of CP_1 and plane $ADCD$ is line DH. CP_1 also intersects plane EFG along the line JK. The F-views of these lines appear in the cutting plane line CP_1. (2) Find the H-views of DH and JK and extend them to establish the location of $p_1{}^H$, the H-view of point P_1 on the line of intersection. (3) Project $p_1{}^H$ downward to locate point $p_1{}^F$, the F-view of point P_1. (4) Draw the edge view of CP_2 in the F-view. (5) Locate point $p_2{}^H$ and $p_2{}^F$ by following the general procedure set forth for locating the H- and F-views of point P_1. (6) Locate the H-view of the line of intersection by drawing a line through $p_1{}^H$ and $p_2{}^H$. (7) Locate the F-view of the line of intersection.

Although point P_1 and P_2 definitely establish the line of intersection, it is well to take a third plane (CP_3) as a check.

12.29. To find the dihedral angle between two planes. The angle between two planes is known as a dihedral angle. The true size of this angle between intersecting planes may be seen in a plane that is perpendicular to both. For this condition as set forth, the intersecting planes will appear as edges and the line of intersection of the two planes as a point. The true angle may be measured between the edge views of the planes (Fig. 12.25).

Given: The intersecting planes *ABCD* and *CDEF*. The line of intersection is line *CD* as shown in the pictorial drawing.

Solution: (1) Draw reference line *F-A* parallel to $c^F d^F$ and construct the *A*-view. This view will show *CD* in true length ($c^A d^A$). (2) Draw reference line *A-O* perpendicular to $c^A d^A$ and construct the adjacent *O*-view. Since this view was taken looking along line *CD*, points *C* and *D* are coincident and appear as a single point identified as $c^0 d^0$. The intersecting planes show as edge views and the true angle between the given planes may be measured between these

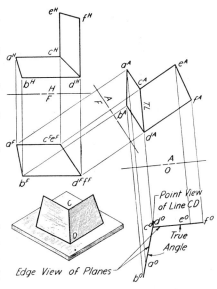

Fig. 12.25. To find the dihedral angle between two planes.

edge view lines. When two planes are given that do not intersect, the dihedral angle may be found after the line of intersection has been determined.

12.30. Visibility. Most often visibility can be determined by inspection of the given views and by remembering; (1) that the extreme outline (outside lines) is always visible, (2) that an edge or corner closest to the viewer is visible, and (3) that an edge or corner falling within the outline and away from the viewer will generally be invisible. A study of the two views of Fig. 12.26(*a*) reveals that in the frontal view, part of the outline of the block must be invisible because the horizontal (top) view shows clearly that the rod is in front of the block, so as to hide a portion of it when viewed from the front. Part of the outline of the block in the horizontal view must be shown as being invisible as well, for the front view shows that the rod is between the observer and the block when looking downward from above.

To assist one in determining visibility in cases where this is difficult to do without resorting to an extra view, a general method has been devised. This method, as it applies to the views of a solid, is illustrated in Fig. 12.26(*b*). In the horizontal (top) view lines $a^H b^H$, $b^H c^H$, $c^H o^H$, and $o^H a^H$ must all be visible because they form the outline of the view. However, since $a^H c^H$ and $o^H b^H$ fall inside the view, their visibility must be determined. Although in this particular case this question could be answered by inspection of the given views, the general method will be applied. In considering $o^H b^H$ and $a^H c^H$ the apparent intersection is in reality two points, one above the other. One point is on OB and the other on AC. To apply our general method, suppose that these points on the edges of the solid be assigned the numbers *1* and *2*, which will be seen in the H-view as 1^H and 2^H. Although in the H-view these points are coincident, the frontal view shows that 1^F is on $o^F b^F$ and is well above 2^F, which lies on $a^F c^F$. Since point *1* on OB is above point *2* on AC, edge OB is visible when the solid is viewed from above.

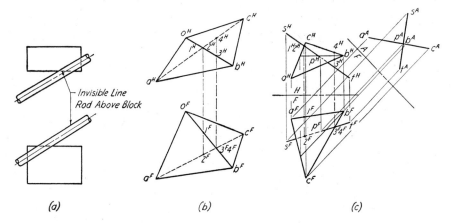

Fig. 12.26.   To determine visibility.

In the frontal view $o^F b^F$ and $a^F c^F$ must be considered for visibility. Numbers *3* and *4* will be assigned to the points on the edges. This time 3^H and 4^H are coincident in the frontal view. When 3^H and 4^H are located in the horizontal view, it becomes evident that point *4* is in back of point *3* and lies on the edge AC. Therefore, since point *4* is farther from the observer than point *3*, edge AC must be invisible.

In Fig. 12.26(*c*) this method for determining visibility is shown applied to an oblique plane and a line which pierces it. The student is urged to analyze the solution carefully.

12.31. To determine the true length of a line by revolution. A method for determining the true length of a line by revolution is discussed in Sec. 6.36. Additional illustrations and further information can be found in Chapter 13.

12.32. Problems. The problems of this chapter have been selected and arranged to offer the student an opportunity to apply the basic principles of descriptive geometry.

The problems in groups I to VI can be reproduced to a suitable size by transferring the needed distances from the drawing to the scale that has been provided for each group of problems. The distances, as they are determined, should be laid off on the drawing paper using a full size scale. The spacing between the views may be increased, if necessary, to prevent the possible overlapping of the views of the finished drawing.

All of the problems of a group may be reproduced on a $11'' \times 17''$ sheet of drawing paper, or one or more problems, as selected and assigned, may be drawn on an $8\frac{1}{2}'' \times 11''$ sheet.

1. (Fig. 12.27.) Group I. This group of problems offers a student the opportunity to visualize space situations and to determine the position of lines by applying the principles of projection.

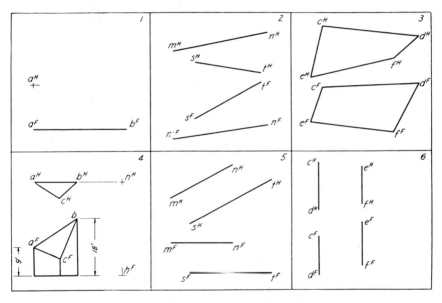

Fig. 12.27. Problems, Group I.

1. Draw the H-view of the 3.4″ line AB.
2. Show proof that the line ST and MN are or are not in a plane.
3. Show proof that $ECDF$ is or is not a plane.
4. *By observation only,* estimate the height of the post H shown in the H-view and partially drawn in the F-view. The top of the post is in the plane of ABC.
5. Without using additional views show proof that lines MN and ST are or are not in a plane.
6. Show proof that the lines CD and EF are not parallel.

2. (Fig. 12.28.) Group II. These problems are intended to give some needed practice in manipulating views to obtain certain relationships of points and lines.

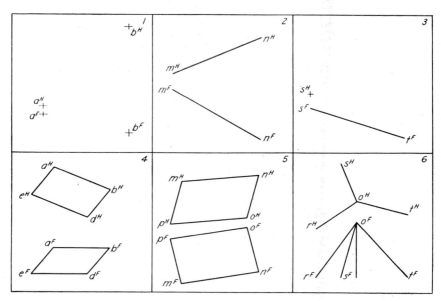

Fig. 12.28.   Problems, Group II.

1. Determine the distance between points A and B.
2. Draw the H- and F-views of a $\frac{1}{2}''$ perpendicular erected from point N of the line MN.
3. Draw the H-view of the $3\frac{3}{4}''$ line ST.
4. Draw the H- and F-views of a plane represented by an equilateral triangle and containing line AB as one of the edges. The added plane ABC is to be at an angle of 30 degrees with plane $ABDE$.
5. If the figure $MNOP$ is a plane surface, an edge view of the surface would appear as a line. Draw such a view to determine whether or not $MNOP$ is a plane.
6. A vertical pole with top O is held in place by three guy wires. Determine the slope in tangent value of the angle for the guy wire which has a bearing of N 23° W.

3. (Fig. 12.29.) Group III. This group of problems offers the opportunity to determine the piercing point of a line and plane. Included also is the requirement to determine the visibility of lines in views.

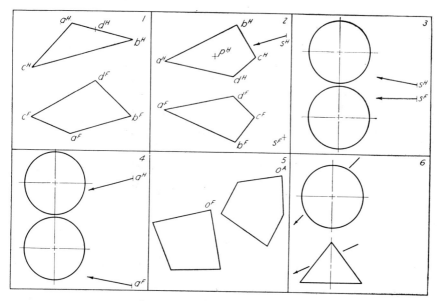

Fig. 12.29. Problems, Group III.

1. Complete the *H*- and *F*-views of the tetrahedron *ABCD*. Show proof for the visibility of the lines.
2. The arrow *S* will pierce the plane *ABCD* at point *P*. Draw the *F* frontal view of the arrow.
3. Two views of a sphere and two views of an arrow are shown. The arrow moves in the direction shown at S^H. Locate the *F*- and *H*-views of the piercing point where the arrow enters the sphere.
4. Two views of a sphere and two views of an arrow are shown. Without using an ellipse in your construction, locate the *F*- and *H*-views of the piercing point where the arrow enters the sphere.
5. *F* (frontal) and *A* (auxiliary) views of a square base pyramid with vertex at *O* are shown incomplete. Complete the two views and show proof of the visibility of the lines.
6. *H*- and *F*-views of a cone and an arrow are shown. Show the *H*- and *F*-views of the piercing points of the arrow as it enters and passes out of the cone.

4. (Fig. 12.30.) Group IV. In this group of problems it is required to determine the shortest distance between skew lines and the angle formed by intersecting lines.

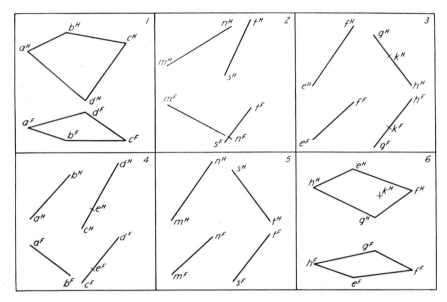

Fig. 12.30.   Problems, Group IV.

1. Show proof that the plane $ABCD$ is an oblique plane.
2. Determine the shortest distance between the lines MN and ST.
3. Through point K on line GH draw the F- and H-views of a line that will be perpendicular to line EF.
4. Determine the angle between line AB and a line intersecting AB and CD at the level of point E.
5. Through a point on line MN that is $1\frac{1}{4}''$ from point N, draw the F- and H-views of a line that will be perpendicular to line ST.
6. Erect a $1''$ perpendicular at point K in the plane $EFGH$. Connect the outer end point L of the perpendicular with F. Determine the angle between LF and KF.

5. (Fig. 12.31.)   Group V.   These problems require that the student determine the angle between a line and a plane and the angle between two given
planes.

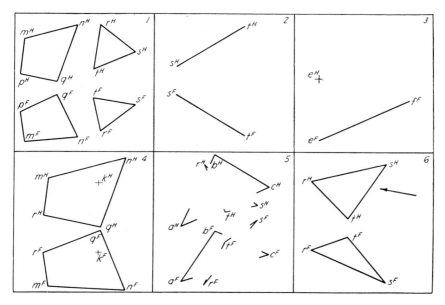

Fig. 12.31.   Problems, Group V.

1. Determine the angle between the planes $MNQP$ and RST.
2. Determine the angle between the line ST and:
   a. The H-plane.
   b. The F-plane.
3. The line EF has a bearing of N. 53° E.   What angle does this line make
   with the P-plane?
4. Draw the F- and H-views of a line through point K that forms an angle of
   35° with plane $MNQR$.
5. The top and front views of planes ABC and RST are partially drawn.
   a. Complete the views including the line of intersection.
   b. Determine the angle between the line of intersection and the H plane
   of projection.
6. Two views of a plane RST and the top view of an arrow are shown.   The
   arrow, pointing downward and toward the left, is in a plane that forms
   an angle of 68 degrees with plane RST.   The arrow point is $\frac{1}{4}''$ from the
   plane RST.
   a. Draw the front view of the arrow.
   b. Draw the top and front views of the line of intersection of the 68
   degree plane and plane RST.

6. (Fig. 12.32.)   Group VI.   These problems are intended to offer a general review of the fundamental methods as presented in this chapter.

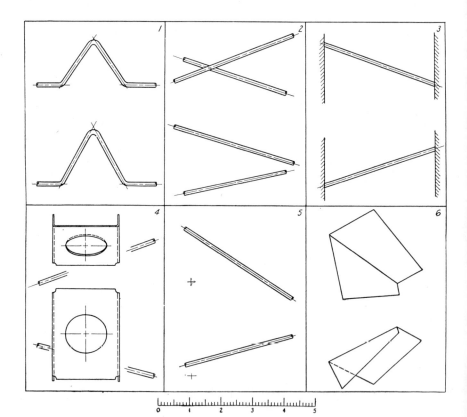

Fig. 12.32.   Problems, Group VI.

1. Determine the angle between the two center lines at each of the bends in the rod.
2. The *F*- and *H*-views of two rods are shown.   Determine the shortest distance between the centerlines.
3. The walls of a cooling room are shown in plan and elevation (*F*- and *H*-views).   Determine the length of the pipe in the given position.
4. Determine the location of the point where the centerline of the rod would pierce the plane of the bulkhead shown.
5. The cross lines indicate the position of a point *P* from which it is desired to know the shortest distance to the center line of the rod.   Determine this distance.
6. The *F*- and *H*-views of intersecting planes are shown.   Determine the true angle between these planes.

7. (Fig. 12.33.)   A trough for the passage of cans of 4″ diameter was made of hard wood $\frac{3}{4}$″ thick.   The V shape of the trough was such that the centerlines of the cans and the top edge of the trough were in the same plane.   The inside surfaces of the trough measured 5″ along a side.   Show the *H*- and *F*-views of an 18″ section of the trough using the *F*- and *H*-views of the centerline *AB* as the centerline of the cans.

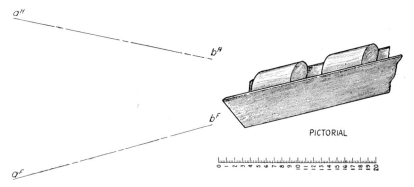

Fig. 12.33.   Trough.

8. (Fig. 12.34.)   The *F*- and *H*-views of a certain control system involving pipe lines and cables operating over pulleys are shown.   Find the shortest distance between the cable and the outside of the pipe (O.D. 1.660″) at a position where the cable runs under the pipe.

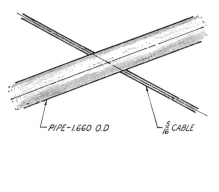

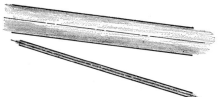

Fig. 12.34.   Clearance for control cable.

9. (Fig. 12.35.) An airplane takes off from a carrier at point C and flies in a direction of N 68° W while gaining altitude at an angle of 15 degrees. At what horizontal distance from the take off point will the plane be at the nearest vertical height from the ground? Use the tangent method for laying out the direction of flight.

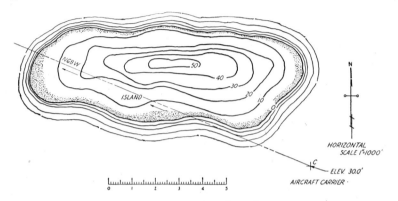

Fig. 12.35. Flight of airplane.

10. (Fig. 12.36.) A vein of ore the top layer of which proved to be a plane surface, was located by the following borings: Hole A, at a depth of 15.0′; B, at a depth of 26.0′; C, at a depth of 68.0′; and D, at a depth of 80.0′.

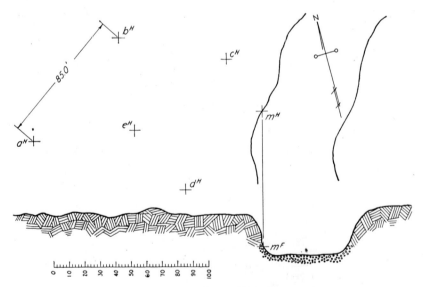

Fig. 12.36. Tunnel problem.

Because an old riverbed provided a roadbed for transportation to a highway near by, it was decided to tunnel directly west and downward at an angle of 15 degrees with the horizontal from point M to gain access to the ore vein.

a. What was the length of the tunnel needed to reach the ore vein?

b. How deep would a check hole need to be drilled at position E to strike the ore?

11. (Fig. 12.37.)   A plot of ground is shown with contours and sections. Along cutting plane AB the positions for a number of drilled holes are shown. Each of the drilled holes struck a vein of ore at depths as follows:

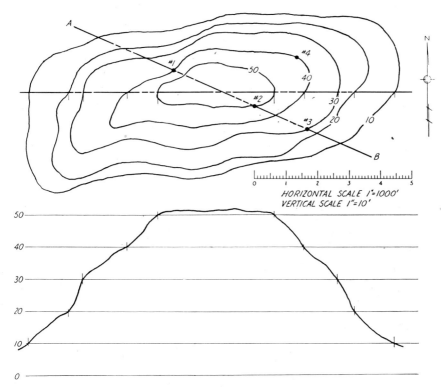

HORIZONTAL SCALE 1"=1000'
VERTICAL SCALE 1"=10'

Fig. 12.37.   Strike and dip problem.

Hole 1 on contour 40' at 15 feet.

Hole 2 on contour 50' at 34 feet.

Hole 3 on contour 30' at 20 feet.

Another hole on contour 40' (4) struck the ore vein at 10 feet.   Determine the "strike" and the "dip" of the ore vein.

13

Developments and Intersections

13.1. A comprehensive study of intersections and developments is logically a part of the subject of descriptive geometry. A few of the many practical applications that can be handled without advanced study in projection, however, are presented in this chapter. Desired lines of intersection between geometrical surfaces may be obtained by applying the principles of orthographic projection with which the student is already familiar. Although developments are laid out and are not drawn by actual projection in the manner of exterior views, their construction nevertheless requires the application of orthographic projection in finding the true lengths of elements and edges.

13.2. Geometric surfaces. A geometric surface is generated by the motion of a geometric line, either straight or curved. Surfaces that are generated by a moving straight line are known as *ruled surfaces*, and those generated by a curved line are known as *double curved surfaces*. Any position of the generating line, known as a generatrix, is called an *element of the surface*.

Ruled surfaces include planes, single curved surfaces, and warped surfaces.

A *plane* is generated by a straight line moving in such a manner that one point touches another straight line as it moves parallel to its original position.

A *single curved surface* is generated by a straight line moving so that in any two of its near positions it is in the same plane.

A *warped surface* is generated by a straight line moving so that it does not lie in the same plane in any two near positions.

Double curved surfaces include surfaces that are generated by a curved line moving in accordance with some mathematical law.

13.3. Geometric objects. Geometric solids are bounded by geometric surfaces. They may be classified as follows:

1. Solids bounded by plane surfaces:
    Tetrahedron, cube, prism, pyramid, and others.

2. Solids bounded by single curved surfaces:
   Cone and cylinder (generated by a moving straight line).
3. Solids bounded by warped surfaces:
   Conoid, cylindroid, hyperboloid of one nappe, and warped cone.
4. Solids bounded by double curved surfaces:
   Sphere, spheroid, torus, paraboloid, hyperboloid, and so on (surfaces of revolution generated by curved lines).

DEVELOPMENTS

13.4. A layout of the complete surface of an object is called a development or pattern. The development of an object bounded by plane surfaces may be thought of as being obtained by turning the object, as illustrated in Figs. 13.1 and 13.2, so as to unroll the imaginary enclosing

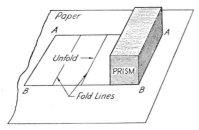

Fig. 13.1. *The development of a prism.*

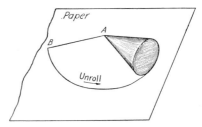

Fig. 13.2. *The development of a pyramid.*

surface upon a plane. Practically, the drawing operation consists of drawing the successive surfaces in their true size with their common edges joined.

The surfaces of cones and cylinders also may be unrolled upon a plane. The development of a right cylinder (Fig. 13.3) is a rectangle having a

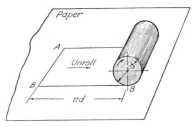

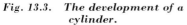

Fig. 13.3. *The development of a cylinder.*

Fig. 13.4. *The development of a cone.*

width equal to the altitude of the cylinder and a length equal to the cylinder's computed circumference (πd). The development of a right circular cone (Fig. 13.4) is a sector of a circle having a radius equal to the slant height of the cone and an arc length equal to the circumference of its base.

Warped and double curved surfaces cannot be developed accurately, but they may be developed by some approximate method. Ordinarily, an approximate pattern will prove to be sufficiently accurate for practical purposes if the material of which the piece is to be made is somewhat flexible.

Plane and single curved surfaces (prisms, pyramids, cylinders, and cones), which can be accurately developed, are said to be developable. Warped and double curved surfaces, which can be only approximately developed, are said to be nondevelopable.

13.5. Practical developments. On many industrial drawings, a development must be shown to furnish the necessary information for making a pattern to facilitate the cutting of a desired shape from sheet metal. Because of the rapid advance of the art of manufacturing an ever-increasing number of pieces by folding, rolling, or pressing cut sheet-metal shapes, one must have a broad knowledge of the methods of constructing varied types of developments. Patterns also are used in stone cutting as guides for shaping irregular faces.

A development of a surface should be drawn with the inside face up, as it theoretically would be if the surface were unrolled or unfolded as illustrated in Figs. 13.1-13.4. This practice is further justified because sheet-metal workers must make the necessary punch marks for folding on the inside surface.

Although in actual sheet-metal work extra metal must be allowed for lap at seams, no allowance will be shown on the developments in this chapter. Many other practical considerations have been purposely ignored, as well, in order to avoid confusing the beginner.

13.6. To develop a right truncated prism. Before the development of the lateral surface of a prism can be drawn, the true lengths of the edges and the true size of a right section must be determined. In the right truncated prism, shown in Fig. 13.5, the true lengths of the prism edges are shown in the front view and the true size of the right section is shown in the top view.

The lateral surface is "unfolded" by first drawing a "stretch-out line" and marking off the widths of the faces (distances 1-2, 2-3, 3-4, and so on, from the top view) along it in succession. Through these points light construction lines are then drawn perpendicular to the line 1_D-1_D, and the length of the respective edge is set off on each by projecting from the front view. When projecting edge lengths to the development, the points should be taken in a clockwise order around the perimeter as indicated by the order of the figures in the top view. The outline of the development is completed by joining these points. Thus far, nothing has been said about the lower base or the inclined upper face. These may be joined to the development of the lateral surface, if so desired.

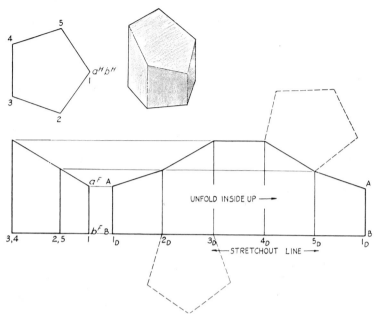

Fig. 13.5.   The standard method of developing the lateral surface of a right prism.

In sheet-metal work, it is usual practice to make the seam on the shortest element in order to save time and conserve solder or rivets.

13.7. To develop an oblique prism.   The lateral surface of an oblique prism, such as the one shown in Fig. 13.6, is developed by the same general method used for a right prism.   Similarly, the true lengths of the edges are shown in the front view, but it is necessary to find the true size of the right section by auxiliary plane construction.   The width of the faces, as taken from the auxiliary right section, are set off along the stretch-out line, and perpendicular construction lines representing the edges are drawn through the division points.   The lengths of the portions of each respective edge, above and below plane X-X, are transferred to the corresponding line in development.   Distances above plane X-X are laid off above the stretch-out line, and distances below X-X are laid off below it.   The development of the lateral surface is then completed by joining the end points of the edges by straight lines.   Since an actual fold will be made at each edge line when the prism is formed, it is the usual practice to heavy these edge (fold) lines on the development.

The stretch-out line might well have been drawn in a position perpendicular to the edges of the front view (see Fig. 13.7), so that the length of each edge might be projected to the development (as in the case of the right prism).

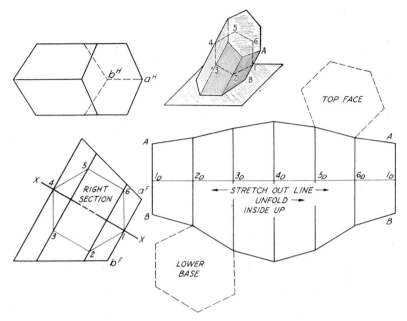

Fig. 13.6.   The development of an oblique prism.

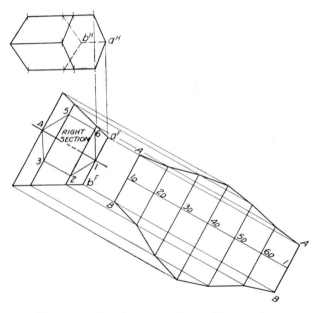

Fig. 13.7.   Development of an oblique prism.

13.8. To develop a right cylinder.   When the lateral surface of a right cylinder is rolled out upon a plane, the base develops into a straight line (Fig. 13.8). The length of this line, which is equal to the circumference of a right section ($\pi \times$ dia.), may be calculated and laid off as the stretch-out line 1_D-1_D.

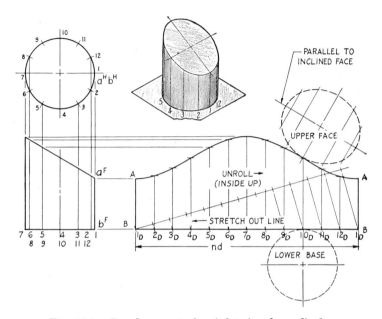

Fig. 13.8.   Development of a right circular cylinder.

Since the cylinder can be thought of as being a many-sided prism, the development may be constructed in a manner similar to the method illustrated in Fig. 13.5. The elements drawn on the surface of the cylinder serve as edges of the many-sided prism. Twelve or twenty-four of these elements ordinarily are used, the number depending upon the size of the cylinder. Usually they are spaced by dividing the circumference of the base, as shown by the circle in the top view, into an equal number of parts. The stretch-out line is divided into the same number of equal parts, and perpendicular elements are drawn through each division point. Then the true length of each element is projected to its respective representation on the development, and the development is completed by joining the points with a smooth curve. In joining the points, it is advisable to sketch the curve in lightly, freehand, before using the French curve. Since the surface of the finished cylindrical piece forms a continuous curve, the elements on the development are not heavied. When the development is symmetrical, as in this case, only one-half need be drawn.

A piece of this type might form a part of a two-piece, three-piece, or four-piece elbow. The pieces are usually developed as illustrated in Fig. 13.9. The stretch-out line of each section is equal in length to the computed perimeter of a right section.

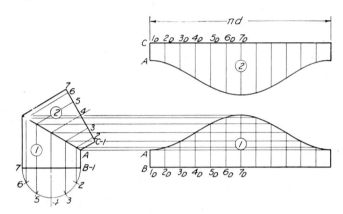

Fig. 13.9. Two-piece elbow.

13.9. To develop an oblique cylinder. Since an oblique cylinder theoretically may be thought of as enclosing a regular oblique prism having an infinite number of sides, the development of the lateral surface of the cylinder shown in Fig. 13.10 may be constructed by using a method similar to the method illustrated in Fig. 13.6. The circumference of the right section becomes stretch-out line 1_D-1_D for the development.

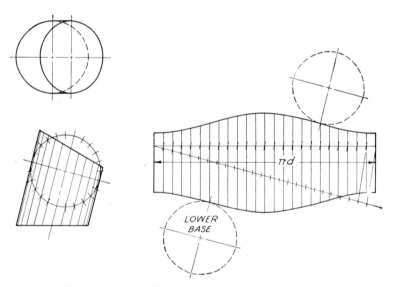

Fig. 13.10. Development of an oblique cylinder.

13.10. To determine the true length of a line. In order to construct the development of the lateral surface of some objects, it frequently is necessary to determine the true lengths of oblique lines that represent the edges. The general method for determining the true lengths of lines inclined to all of the co-ordinate planes of projection has been explained in detail in Sec. 6.36. This article should be reviewed before reading the discussion that follows.

If a line is oblique to each of the three planes of projection, none of its principal projections will show its true length. Note in Fig. 13.11 that the principal projections of the edge AB are inclined. To determine the true length of AB, it may be revolved into a position parallel to either the H, F, or P co-ordinate planes, as shown in Figs. 13.11, 13.12, and 13.13. In Fig. 13.11, AB has been revolved into a position parallel to the F (frontal) plane. The view of AB revolved, a^Fb^Fr, shows the true length. In Fig. 13.12, AB was revolved parallel to the H (top) plane, and a^Hb^Hr shows the true length. In Fig. 13.13, the edge is shown revolved parallel to the P (profile) co-ordinate plane.

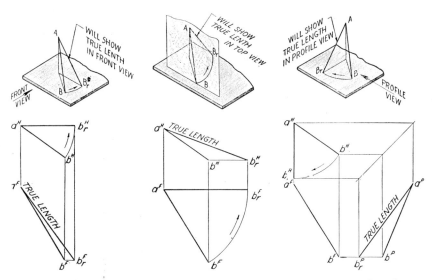

Fig. 13.11. Revolution to position parallel to frontal plane.

Fig. 13.12. Revolution to position parallel to horizontal plane.

Fig. 13.13. Revolution to position parallel to profile plane.

13.11. True-length diagrams. When it is necessary, in developing a surface, to find the true lengths of a number of edges or elements, some confusion may be avoided by constructing a true-length diagram adjacent to the orthographic view as shown in Fig. 13.14. The elements were revolved into a position parallel to the F (frontal) plane so that their true lengths show in the diagram. This practice prevents the front view in the illustration from being cluttered with lines, some of which would represent elements and others their true lengths.

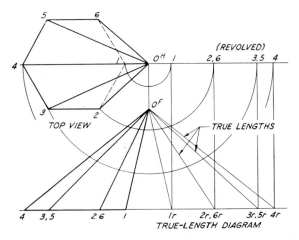

Fig. 13.14. *A true-length diagram (the revolution method).*

Fig. 13.15 shows a diagram that gives the true lengths of the edges of the pyramid. Each line representing the true length of an edge is the hypotenuse of a right triangle whose altitude is the altitude of the edge in the front view and whose base is equal to the length of the projection of the edge in the top view. The lengths of the top projections of the edges of the pyramid are laid off horizontally from the vertical line $o^F X$, which could have been drawn at any distance from the front view. Since all the edges have the same altitude, this line is a common vertical leg for all the right triangles in the diagram. For example, $o^F X 1'$ is a true-length triangle having the line $o^F X$ as a vertical leg and $X 1'$, which is equal in length to $o^H 1$ in the top view, as a base. Other triangles are

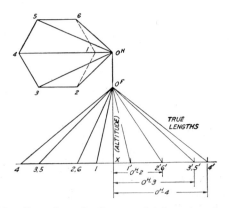

Fig. 13.15. *True-length diagram (right triangle method).*

$o^F X2'$, $o^F X3'$, $o^F X4'$, and so on. The true-length diagram shown in Fig. 13.14 could very well have been constructed by this method.

13.12. To develop a right pyramid. To develop (unfold) the lateral surface of a right pyramid, it is first necessary to determine the true lengths of the edges and the true size of the base. With this information, the development can be constructed by laying out the faces in successive order with their common edges joined. If the surface is imagined to be unfolded by turning the pyramid, as shown in Fig. 13.2, each triangular face is revolved into the plane of the paper about the edge that is common to it and the preceding face.

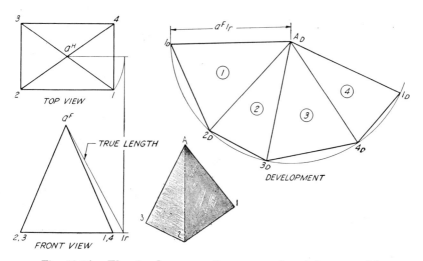

Fig. 13.16. *The development of a rectangular right pyramid.*

Since the edges of the pyramid shown in Fig. 13.16 are all equal in length, it is necessary only to find the length of the one edge $A1$ by revolving it into the position a^F1r. The edges of the base, 1-2, 2-3, and so on, are parallel to the horizontal plane of projection and consequently show in their true length in the top view. With this information, the development is easily completed by constructing the four triangular surfaces.

13.13. To develop the surface of a frustum of a pyramid. To develop the lateral surface of the frustum of a pyramid (Fig. 13.17), it is necessary to determine the true lengths of edges of the complete pyramid as well as the true lengths of edges of the frustum. The desired development is obtained by first constructing the development of the complete pyramid and then laying off the true lengths of the edges of the frustum on the corresponding lines of the development.

It may be noted with interest that the true length of the edge $B3$ is equal to the length $b'3'$ on the true-length line a^F3', and that the location of point b' can be established by the short-cut method of projecting horizontally from point b^F.   Point b' on a^F3' is the true revolved position of point B, because the path of point B is in a horizontal plane that projects as a line in the front view.

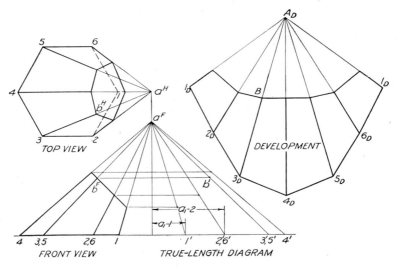

Fig. 13.17.   *Development of the frustum of a pyramid.*

13.14. To develop a right cone.   As previously explained in Sec. 13.4, the development of a regular right circular cone is a sector of a circle. The development will have a radius equal to the slant height of the cone and an included angle at the center equal to $\dfrac{r}{s} \times 360°$ (Fig. 13.18).   In this equation, r is the radius of the base and s is the slant height.

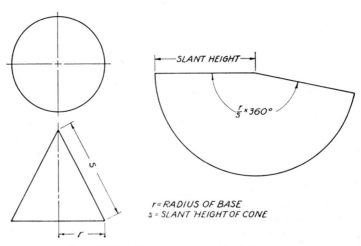

Fig. 13.18.   *Development of a right cone.*

13.15. To develop a right truncated cone.   The development of a right truncated cone must be constructed by a modified method of triangulation, in order to develop the outline of the elliptical inclined surface. This commonly used method is based upon the theoretical assumption that a cone is a pyramid having an infinite number of sides.   The development of the incomplete right cone shown in Fig. 13.19 is constructed upon a layout of the whole cone by a method similar to the standard method illustrated for the frustum of a pyramid in Fig. 13.17.

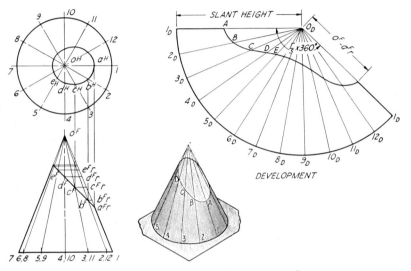

Fig. 13.19.   Development of a truncated cone.

Elements are drawn on the surface of the cone to serve as edges of the many-sided pyramid.   Either twelve or twenty-four are used, depending upon the size of the cone.   Their location is established upon the developed sector by dividing the arc representing the unrolled base into the same number of equal divisions, into which the top view of the base has been divided.   At this point in the procedure, it is necessary to determine the true lengths of the elements of the frustum in the same manner that the true lengths of the edges of the frustum of a pyramid were obtained in Fig. 13.17.   With this information, the desired development can be completed by setting off the true lengths on the corresponding lines of the development and joining the points thus obtained with a smooth curve.

13.16. The triangulation method of developing approximately developable surfaces.   A nondevelopable surface may be developed approximately if the surface is assumed to be composed of a number of small developable surfaces (Fig. 13.21).   The particular method ordinarily used for warped surfaces and the surfaces of oblique cones is known as the triangulation method.   The procedure consists of completely cov-

ering the lateral surface with numerous small triangles that will lie approximately on the surface (Fig. 13.20). These triangles, when laid out in
their true size with their common edges joined, produce an approximate
development that is accurate enough for most practical purposes.

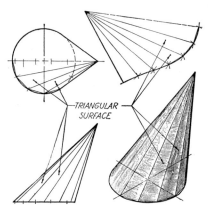 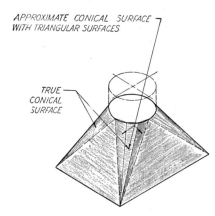

APPROXIMATE CONICAL SURFACE
WITH TRIANGULAR SURFACES

TRUE
CONICAL
SURFACE

TRIANGULAR
SURFACE

Fig. 13.20. Triangulation of an ob-   Fig. 13.21. Triangulation of a sur-
           lique cone.   face.

Although this method of triangulation is sometimes used to develop
the lateral surface of a right circular cone, it is not recommended for such
purpose. The resulting development is not as accurate as it would be if
constructed by one of the standard methods (see Secs. 13.14 and 13.15).

**13.17. To develop an oblique cone using the triangulation
method.** A development of the lateral surface of an oblique cone is
constructed by a method similar to that used for an oblique pyramid.
The surface is divided into a number of unequal triangles having sides
that are elements on the cone and bases that are the chords of short arcs
of the base.

The first step in developing an oblique cone (Fig. 13.22) is to divide
the circle representing the base into a convenient number of equal parts
and draw elements on the surface of the cone through the division points
(1, 2, 3, 4, 5, and so on). To construct the triangles forming the development, it is necessary to know the true lengths of the elements (sides of
the triangles) and chords. In the illustration, all the chords are equal.
Their true lengths are shown in the top view. The true lengths of the
oblique elements may be determined by one of the standard methods
explained in Sec. 13.11.

Since the seam should be made along the shortest element, $A1$ will
lie on the selected starting line for the development and $A7$ will be on
the center line. To obtain the development, the triangles are constructed
in order, starting with the triangle A-1-2 and proceeding around the cone
in a clockwise direction (as shown by the arrow in the top view). The

first step in constructing triangle A-1-2 is to set off the true length a^F1' along the starting line. With point A_D of the development as a center, and with a radius equal to a^F2', strike an arc; then, with point 1_D as a center, and with a radius equal to the chord 1-2, strike an arc across the first arc to locate point 2_D. The triangle $A_D2_D3_D$ and the remaining triangles are formed in exactly the same manner. When all the triangles have been laid out, the development of the whole conical surface is completed by drawing a smooth curve through the end points of the elements.

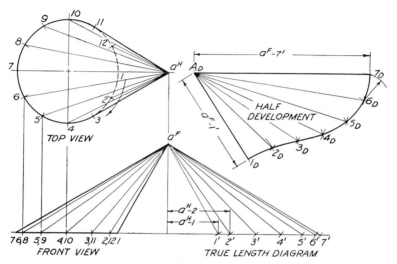

Fig. 13.22. *Development of an oblique cone.*

After the beginner has constructed a few such developments, he will find that much time can be saved by drawing all the long arcs before striking off any of the short ones. To offset any errors in judgment about their approximate correct location, the long arcs may be made fairly long.

13.18. Transition pieces. A few of the many types of transition pieces used for connecting pipes and openings of different shapes and sizes are illustrated pictorially in Fig. 13.23.

13.19. To develop a transition piece connecting rectangular pipes. The transition piece shown in Fig. 13.24 is designed to connect two rectangular pipes of different sizes on different axes. Since the piece is a frustum of a pyramid, it can be accurately developed by the method explained in Sec. 13.13.

13.20. To develop a transition piece connecting two circular pipes. The transition piece shown in Fig. 13.25 connects two circular pipes on different axes. Since the piece is a frustum of an oblique cone, the surface must be triangulated, as explained in Sec. 13.17, and the development must be constructed by laying out the triangles in their true size in regular order. The general procedure is the same as that illus-

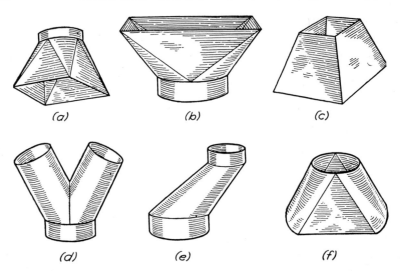

Fig. 13.23.   Transition pieces.

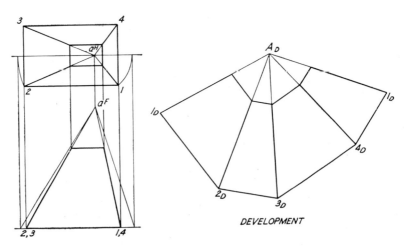

Fig. 13.24.   Transition piece.

trated in Fig. 13.22.   In this case, however, since the true size of the base is not shown in the top view, it is necessary to construct a partial auxiliary view to find the true lengths of chords between the end points of the elements.

13.21.   To develop a transition piece connecting a circular and a square pipe.   A detailed analysis of the transition piece shown in Fig. 13.26 reveals that it is composed of four isosceles triangles whose bases form the square base of the piece and four conical surfaces that are parts of oblique cones.   It is not difficult to develop this type of transition piece because, since the whole surface may be "broken up" into compo-

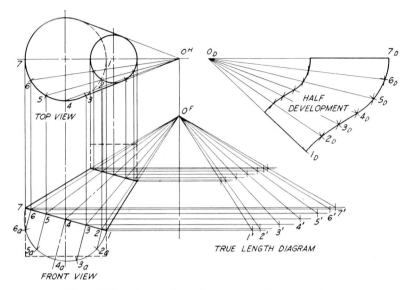

Fig. 13.25. *Transition piece connecting two pipes.*

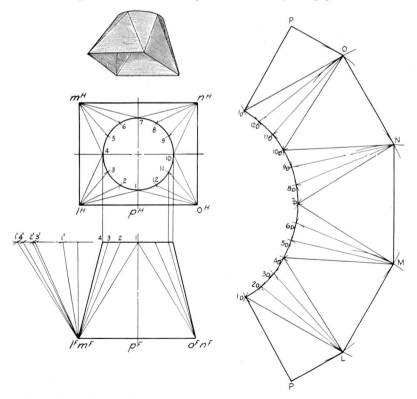

Fig. 13.26. *Transition piece connecting a circular and square pipe.*

nent surfaces, the development may be constructed by developing the first and then each succeeding component surface separately (Fig. 13.21). The surfaces are developed around the piece in a clockwise direction, in such a manner that each successive surface is joined to the preceding surface at their common element. In the illustration, the triangles 1LO, 4LM, 7MN, and 10NO are clearly shown in top view. Two of these, 1LO and 10NO, are visible on the pictorial drawing. The apexes of the conical surfaces are located at the corners of the base.

Before starting the development, it is necessary to determine the true lengths of the elements by constructing a true-length diagram as explained in Sec. 13.11. The true lengths of the edges of the lower base (LM, MN, NO, and OL) and the true lengths of the chords (1-2, 2-3, 3-4, and so on) of the short arcs of the upper base are shown in the top view. The development is constructed in the following manner: First, the triangle 1$_D PL$ is constructed, using the length $p^H l^H$, taken from the top view, and true lengths from the diagram. Next, using the method explained in Sec. 13.17, the conical surface whose apex is at L is developed in an attached position. Triangle 4$_D LM$ is then added, and so on, until all component surfaces have been drawn.

13.22. To develop a transition piece having an approximately developable surface by the triangulation method. Fig. 13.27 shows

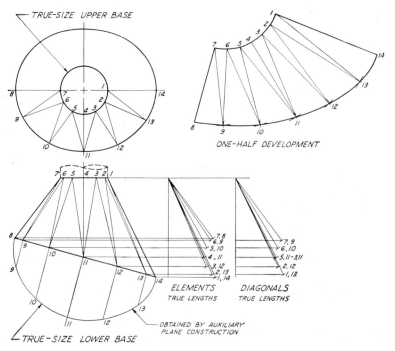

Fig. 13.27. Development of transition piece by triangulation.

a half development of a transition piece that has a warped surface instead of a partially conical one like that discussed in Sec. 13.21.   The method of constructing the development is somewhat similar, however, in that it is formed by laying out, in true size, a number of small triangles that approximate the surface.   The true size of the circular intersection is shown in the top view, and the true size of the elliptical intersection is shown in the auxiliary view, which was constructed for that purpose.

The front half of the circle in the top view should be divided into the same number of equal parts as the half-auxiliary view.   By joining the division points, the lateral surface may be initially divided into narrow quadrilaterals.   These in turn may be subdivided into triangles, by drawing diagonals which, though theoretically they are curved lines, are assumed to be straight.   The true lengths of the elements and the diagonals are found by constructing two separate true-length diagrams by the method illustrated in Fig. 13.15.

13.23. To develop a sphere.   The surface of a sphere is a double curved surface that can be developed only by some approximate method. The standard methods commonly used are illustrated in Fig. 13.28.

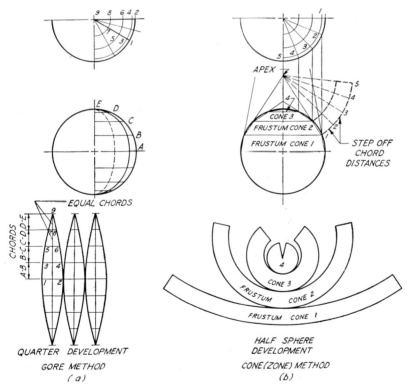

Fig. 13.28.   *The approximate development of a sphere.*

In (a) the surface is divided into a number of equal meridian sections of cylinders. The developed surfaces of these form an approximate development of the sphere. In drawing the development it is necessary to develop the surface of only one section, for this can be used as a pattern for the developed surface of each of the others.

In (b) the sphere is cut by parallel planes, which divide it into a number of horizontal sections, the surfaces of which approximate the surface of the sphere. Each of these sections may be considered the frustum of a right cone whose apex is located at the intersection of the chords extended.

INTERSECTIONS

13.24. Lines of intersection of geometric surfaces. The line of intersection of two surfaces is a line that is common to both. It may be considered the line that would contain the points in which the elements of one surface would pierce the other. Almost every line on a practical orthographic representation is a line of intersection; therefore, the following discussion may be deemed an extended study of the same subject. The methods presented in this chapter are the recognized easy procedures for finding the more complicated lines of intersection created by intersecting geometric surfaces.

In order to complete a view of a working drawing or a view necessary for developing the surfaces of intersecting geometric shapes, one frequently must find the line of intersection between surfaces. On an ordinary working drawing the line of intersection may be "faked in" through a few critical points. On a sheet-metal drawing, however, a sufficient number of points must be located to obtain an accurate line of intersection and an ultimately accurate development.

The line of intersection of two surfaces is found by determining a number of points common to both surfaces and drawing a line or lines through these points in correct order. The resulting line of intersection may be straight, curved, or straight and curved. The problem of finding such a line may be solved by one of two general methods, depending upon the type of surfaces involved.

For the purpose of simplifying this discussion of intersections, it should be assumed that all problems are divided into these two general groups:

Group I. Problems involving two surfaces, both of which are composed of plane surfaces.

Group II. Problems involving two surfaces which are either single curved or double curved.

For instance, the procedure for finding the line of intersection of two prisms is the same as that for finding the line of intersection of a prism and a pyramid; hence, both problems belong in the same group (Group I). Since the problem of finding the line of intersection of two cylinders and the problem of finding the line of intersection of a cylinder and a cone both involve single curved surfaces, these two also belong in the same group (Group II).

Problems of the first group are solved by locating the points through which the edges of each of two geometrical shapes pierce the other. These points are vertices of the line of intersection. Whenever one of two intersecting plane surfaces appears as a line in one view, the points through which the lines of the other surfaces penetrate it usually may be found by inspecting that view.

Problems of the second group may be solved by drawing elements on the lateral surface of one geometrical shape in the region of the line of intersection. The points at which these elements intersect the surface of the other geometrical shape are points that are common to both surfaces and consequently lie on their line of intersection. A curve, traced through these points with the aid of a French curve, will be a representation of the required intersection. To obtain accurate results, some of the elements must be drawn through certain critical points at which the curve changes sharply in direction. These points usually are located on contour elements. Hence, the usual practice is to space the elements equally around the surface, starting with a contour element.

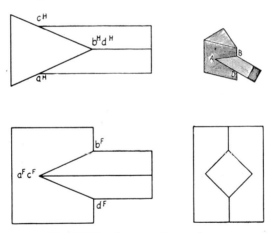

Fig. 13.29. *Intersecting prisms.*

13.25. To find the intersection of two prisms. In Fig. 13.29 (see pictorial), points A, B, C, and D, through which the edges of the horizontal prism pierce the faces of the triangular prism, are the critical points or vertices of the closed intersection. The location of these piercing points may be found in the top view by inspection. Then they may be projected to the front view, to establish their location there. For example, the top view shows that the front edge of the horizontal prism pierces the near face of the vertical triangular prism at point a^H. Point a^H, projected downward to the line representing that edge in the front view, locates

point a^F in the front view.   After the piercing points B, C, and D have
been found and projected to the front view in a similar manner, the intersection is completed by joining, in order, the projected points a^F, b^F, c^F,
and d^F with straight lines.

**13.26. To establish the location of the piercing point of an edge
intersecting an inclined surface.**   In Fig. 13.30, points A, C, and D,
through which the edges of the horizontal prism pierce the vertical prism,
are first found in the top view and are then projected downward to the
corresponding edges in the front view.   Point B, through which the edge
of the vertical prism pierces the near face of the triangular prism, cannot
be found in this manner because the side view from which it could be
projected to the front view is not shown.   Its location, however, can be

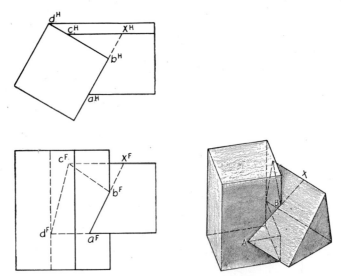

Fig. 13.30.   Intersecting prisms.

established in the front view without even drawing a partial side view,
if some scheme like the one illustrated in the pictorial drawing is used.
In this scheme, the intersection line AB, whose direction is shown in the
top view as line a^Hb^H, is extended on the triangular face to point X on the
top edge.   Point x^H is projected to the corresponding edge in the front
view and a light construction line is drawn between the points a^F and x^F.
Since point B is located on line AX (see pictorial) at the point where the
edge of the prism pierces the line, its location in the front view is at point
b^F where the edge cuts the line a^Fx^F.

13.27. To find the intersection of a pyramid and a prism.   The
intersection of a right pyramid and a prism (see Fig. 13.31) may be found
by the same general method used for finding the intersection of two prisms
(Sec. 13.25).

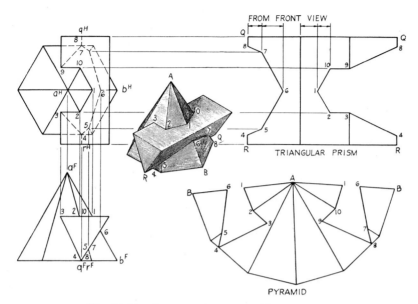

Fig. 13.31.   Intersecting pyramid and prism.

13.28. To find the intersection of two cylinders. If a series of elements are drawn on the surface of the small horizontal cylinder, as in Fig. 13.32, the points A, B, C, and D in which they intersect the vertical cylinder will be points on the line of intersection (see pictorial). These points, which are shown as a^H, b^H, c^H, and d^H in the top view, may be located in the front view by projecting them downward to the corresponding elements in the front view where they are shown as points a^F, b^F,

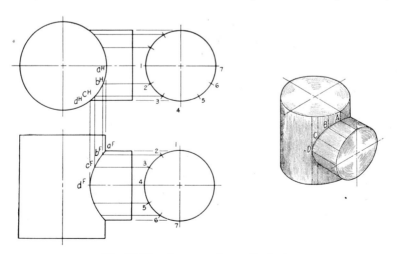

Fig. 13.32.   Intersecting cylinders.

c^F, and d^F. The desired intersection is represented by a smooth curve drawn through these points.

13.29. To find the intersection of two cylinders oblique to each other. The first step in finding the line of intersection of two cylinders that are oblique to each other (see Fig. 13.33) is to draw a revolved right section of the oblique cylinder directly on the front view of that cylinder. If the circumference of the right section then is divided into a number of equal divisions (say six) and elements are drawn through the division points, the points A, B, C, and D in which the elements intersect the

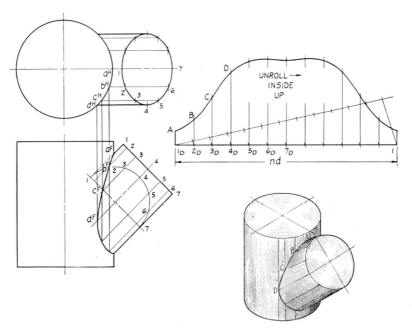

Fig. 13.33.   Intersecting cylinders.

surface of the vertical cylinder will be points on the line of intersection (see pictorial). In the case of the above illustration, these points are found first in the top view and then are projected downward to the corresponding elements in the front view. The line of intersection in the front view is represented by a smooth curve drawn through these points.

13.30. To find the intersection of a cylinder and a cone. The intersection of a cylinder and a cone may be found by assuming a number of elements upon the surface of the cone. The points at which these elements cut the cylinder are on the line of intersection (see pictorial drawings in Figs. 13.34 and 13.35). In selecting the elements, it is the usual practice to divide the circumference of the base into a number of equal parts and draw elements through the division points. To obtain needed

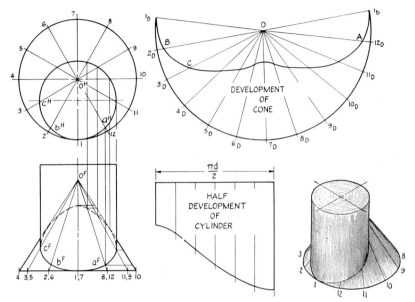

Fig. 13.34.   *Intersecting cylinder and cone.*

points at locations where the intersection line will change suddenly in curvature, however, there should be additional elements.

In Fig. 13.34, the points at which the elements pierce the cylinder are first found in the top view and are then projected to the corresponding elements in the front view.   A smooth curve through these points forms the figure of the intersection.

In Fig. 13.35, the intersection points are first found in the side view.

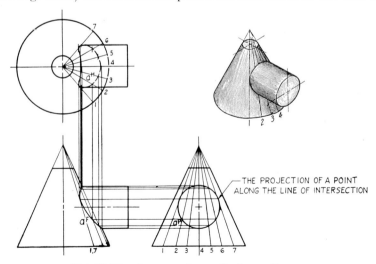

Fig. 13.35.   *Intersecting cylinder and cone.*

An alternate method for finding the line of intersection of a cylinder and a right cone is illustrated in Fig. 13.36.   Here horizontal cutting planes are passed through both geometrical shapes in the region of their line of intersection.   In each cutting plane, the circle cut on the surface of the cone will intersect elements cut on the cylinder at two points common to both surfaces (see pictorial).   A curved line traced through a number of such points in different planes is a line common to both surfaces and is therefore the line of intersection.

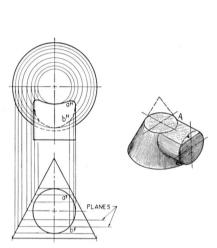

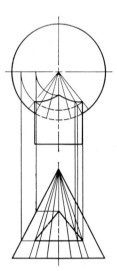

Fig. 13.36.   Intersecting cylinder and   Fig. 13.37.   Intersecting cone and
cone.   prism.

13.31. To find the intersection of a prism and a cone.   The complete line of intersection may be found by drawing elements on the surface of the cone (see Fig. 13.37) to locate points on the intersection as explained in Sec. 13.30.   To obtain an accurate curve, however, some thought must be given to the placing of these elements.   For instance, although most of the elements may be equally spaced on the cone to facilitate the construction of its development, additional ones should be drawn through the critical points and in regions where the line of intersection changes sharply in curvature.   The elements are drawn on the view that will reveal points on the intersection, then the determined points are projected to the corresponding elements in the other view or views.   In this particular illustration a part of the line of intersection in the top view is a portion of the arc of a circle that would be cut by a horizontal plane containing the bottom surface of the prism.

If the surfaces of the prism are parallel to the axis of the cone, as in Fig. 13.38, the line of intersection will be made up of the tips of a series of hyperbolas. The intersection may be found by passing planes that will cut circles on the surface of the cone. The points at which these cutting circles pierce the faces of the prism are points common to the lateral surfaces of both shapes and are therefore points on the required line of intersection. It should be noted that the resulting solution represents a chamfered bolthead.

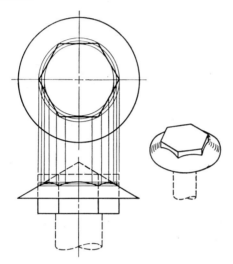

Fig. 13.38.   Cone and hexagonal prism.

13.32. Problems.   The problems of this chapter have been selected to offer opportunities to apply the principles of projection to the determination of lines of intersection and to offer some experience in the construction of developments of the lateral surfaces of geometrical forms.

1. (Fig. 13.39.)   Develop the lateral surface of one or more of the prisms as assigned.

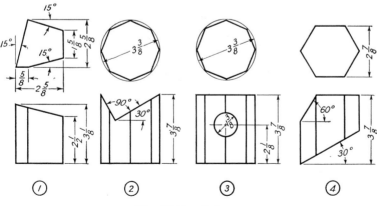

Fig. 13.39.   Prisms.

2. (Fig. 13.40.)   Develop the lateral surface of one or more of the pyramids as assigned.   Make construction lines light.   Show construction for finding the true lengths of the lines.

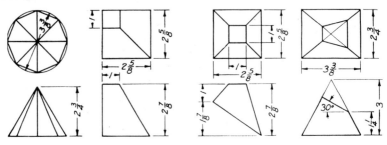

Fig. 13.40.   Pyramids.

3. (Fig. 13.41.)   Develop the lateral surface of one or more of the pyramids as assigned.   With a hard pencil, show the construction for finding the true lengths of the lines.

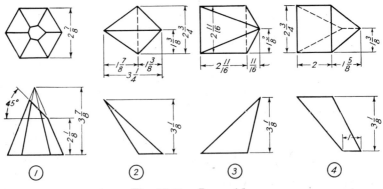

Fig. 13.41.   Pyramids.

4. (Fig. 13.42.)   Develop the lateral surface of one or more of the cylinders as assigned.   Use a hard pencil for construction lines and make them light.

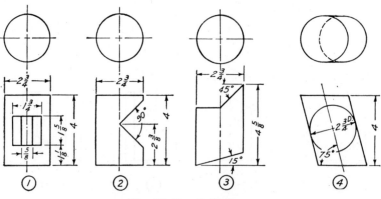

Fig. 13.42.   Cylinders.

5. (Fig. 13.43.) Develop the lateral surface of one or more of the cones as assigned. Show all construction. Use a hard pencil for construction lines and make them light. In each case start with the shortest element and unroll, inside up. It is suggested that 12 elements be used, in order to secure a reasonably accurate development.

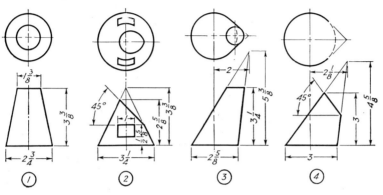

Fig. 13.43. Cones.

6. (Fig. 13.44.) Develop the lateral surface of one or more of the transition pieces as assigned. Show all construction lines in light sharp pencil lines. Use a sufficient number of elements on the curved surfaces to assure an accurate development.

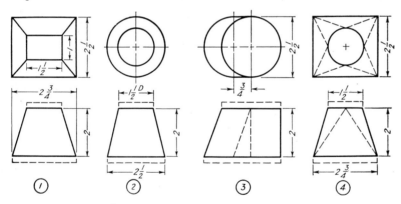

Fig. 13.44. Transition pieces.

7. (Fig. 13.45.)   Develop the sheet-metal connections.   On pieces 3 and 4, use a sufficient number of elements to obtain a smooth curve and an accurate development.

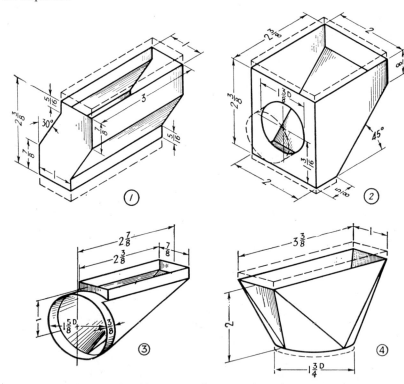

Fig. 13.45.   Sheet-metal connections (transitions).

8–9. (Figs. 13.46–13.47.)   Draw the line of intersection of the intersecting geometrical shapes as assigned.   Show the invisible portions of the lines of intersection as well as the visible.   Consider that the interior is open.

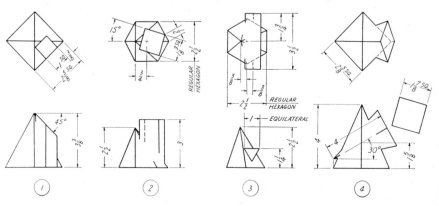

Fig. 13.46.   Intersecting surfaces.

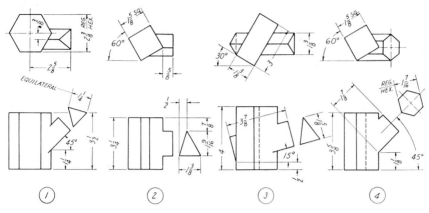

Fig. 13.47.   Intersecting surfaces.

10–11. (Figs. 13.48–13.49.)   Draw the line of intersection of the intersecting geometrical shapes as assigned.   It is suggested that the elements that are used to find points along the intersection be spaced 15 degrees apart.   Do not erase the construction lines.   One shape does not pass through the other.

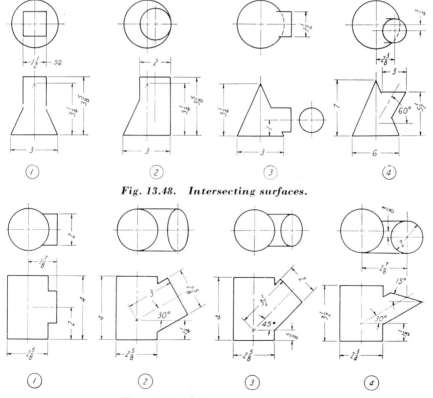

Fig. 13.48.   Intersecting surfaces.

Fig. 13.49.   Intersecting surfaces.

12. (Fig. 13.50.)   Draw the line of intersection of the intersecting geometrical shapes as assigned.   Show the invisible portions of the line of intersection as well as the visible.   Show construction with light sharp lines drawn with a hard pencil.   The interior of the combination is hollow.   One shape does not pass through the other.

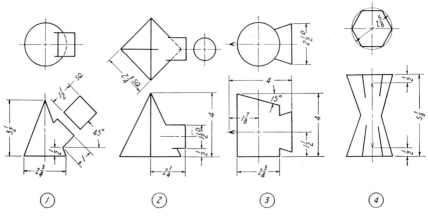

Fig. 13.50.   Intersecting surfaces.

14

Vector Geometry

14.1. In order to be successful in solving some types of problems that arise in design, a well-trained engineer should have a working knowledge of "vector geometry." The methods presented in this chapter should furnish the student with some background knowledge for solving force problems as they appear in the study of mechanics, strength of materials, and design. Through discreet use of the methods of vector geometry, as well as mathematical methods, it is possible to solve engineering problems quickly within a fully acceptable range of accuracy. Since any quantity having both magnitude and direction may be represented by a fixed or rotating vector, vector operations are commonly used for problems in the design of frame structures, problems dealing with velocities in mechanisms, and for problems arising in the study of electrical properties. Because a student in a beginning course in engineering graphics should have basic principles presented to him rather than specialized cases, the methods given in this chapter for solving both two-dimensional and three-dimensional force problems deal mainly with static structures or, in other words, structures with forces acting so as to be in equilibrium. In a study of physics, graphical methods are useful for the composition and resolution of forces.

It is hoped that as a student progresses through his other undergraduate courses, he will desire to learn more about the use of vector methods for solving problems, and that he will become able to recognize the cases where he may have a choice between a graphical and an algebraic method. The graphical method is the better for many cases because it is much quicker and can be more easily checked.

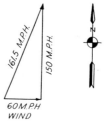

Fig. 14.1. *A vector problem.*

An example of a vector addition is shown in Fig. 14.1. An airplane is flying north with a cross wind from the west. If the speed of the plane

349

is 150 mph (miles per hour) and the wind is blowing towards the east at 60 mph, the plane will be flying NE (northeast) at 161.5 mph.   Vectors can be used for problems of this type because forces acting on a body have both magnitude and direction.

14.2. A force.   In our study of vector methods, a force may be defined as a cause which tends to produce motion in an object.

A force has four characteristics which determine it.   First, a force has "magnitude."   The value of this magnitude may be expressed in terms of some standard unit.   It is usually given in pounds.   Second, a force has a "line of action."   This is the line along which the force acts.   Third, a force has "direction."   This is the direction in which it tends to move the object upon which it acts.   Fourth, and last, a force has a "point of application."   This is the place at which it acts upon the object, often assumed to be a point at the center of gravity.

14.3. A vector.   A force can be represented graphically by a straight

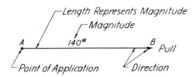

Fig. 14.2.   A vector.

line segment with an arrowhead at one end.   Such an arrow when used for this purpose is known as a "vector" (Fig. 14.2).   The position of the body of the arrow represents the line of action of the force while the arrowhead points out the direction.   The magnitude is represented to some selected scale by the over-all length of the arrow itself.

When a force acts in a two-dimensional plane, only one view of the vector is needed.   However, if the force is in space, two views of the vector must be given.

14.4. Addition of vector forces—two forces.   For a thorough understanding of the principles of vector addition, two simple examples will be considered first.

Fig. 14.3.   A vector addition.

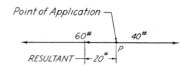

Fig. 14.4.   Forces in opposite directions.

If one of two men who find it necessary to move a supply cabinet pushes on it with 60 pounds force while the other pushes in the same direction with 40 pounds force, the total force exerted to move the cabinet is 100 pounds.   The representation of two or more such forces in the manner shown in Fig. 14.3 amounts to a vector addition.   Should these men be in a prankish mood and decide to push in opposite directions, as illustrated in Fig. 14.4, the cabinet might move provided the 20 pound resultant force were sufficient to overcome friction. The 20 pound resultant comes from a graphical addition.

Now let it be supposed that force A represented by F_A and force B represented by F_B in Fig. 14.5 act from a point P, the point of application. The resultant force on the body will not now be the sum of forces A and B, but instead will be the graphical addition of these forces as represented by the diagonal of a parallelogram having sides equal to the scaled length of the given forces. This single force R of 105.5 pounds would produce an effect upon the body that would be equivalent to the combined forces F_A and F_B. The single force which could replace any given force system, is known as the "resultant" (R) for the force system.

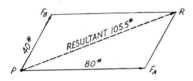

Fig. 14.5.   Parallelogram of forces.   **Fig. 14.6.   A vector triangle.**

Fig. 14.5 shows that the resultant R divides the parallelogram into two equal triangles. Therefore, R could have been found just as well by constructing a single triangle as shown in Fig. 14.6 provided that the vector F_B is drawn so that its tail-end touches the tip-end of F_A, and R is drawn with its arrow-end to the tip-end of F_B. Since either of the triangles shown in Fig. 14.5 could have been drawn to determine R, it should be obvious the resultant is the same regardless of the order in which the vectors are added. However, it is important that they be added tip-end to tail-end and that the vector arrows show the true direction for the action of the concurrent forces in the given system.

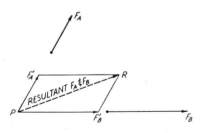
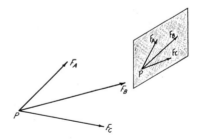

Fig. 14.7.   Resultant of two forces.   **Fig. 14.8.   Coplanar, concurrent forces.**

To find the resultant of two forces, which are applied as shown in Fig. 14.7, it is first necessary to move the vector arrows along their lines of action to the intersection point P before one can apply the parallelogram method.

The forces of a system whose lines of action all lie in one plane are called "coplanar forces." Should the lines of action pass through a common point, the point of application, the forces are said to be "concurrent." Fig. 14.8 shows a system of forces that are both concurrent and coplanar.

14.5. Addition of vectors—three or more forces. The parallelogram method may be used to determine the resultant for a system of three or more forces that are concurrent and coplanar. In applying this method to three or more forces, it is necessary to draw a series of parallelograms, the number depending upon the number of vector quantities that are to be added graphically. For example, in Fig. 14.9 two parallelograms are required to determine the resultant R for system. The resultant R_1 for forces F_A and F_B is determined by the first parallelogram to be drawn, and then R_1 is combined in turn with F_C by forming the second and larger

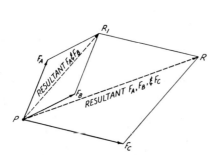

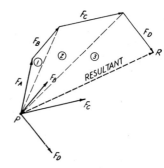

Fig. 14.9. Resultant of three or more forces with a common point of application (parallelogram method).

Fig. 14.10. Resultant of forces (polygon of forces).

parallelogram. By combining the forces in this way R becomes the resultant for the complete system.

Where a considerable number of vectors form a system, a somewhat less complicated diagram results, and less work is required when the triangle method is extended and applied to the formation of a vector diagram such as the one shown in Fig. 14.10. In this case the diagram is formed by three vector triangles, one adjacent to the other, and the resultant of forces F_A and F_B is combined with F_C to form the second triangle. Finally, by combining the resultant of the three forces F_A, F_B, and F_C with F_D, the vector R is obtained, which represents the magnitude and direction of the resultant of the four forces. In the construction F_B, F_C, and F_D in the diagram must be drawn so as to be parallel respectively to their lines of action in the system. However, the order in which they are placed in the diagram is optional as long as one vector joins another tip to tail.

14.6. Forces in equilibrium. A body is said to be in equilibrium when the opposing forces acting upon it are in balance. In such a state the resultant of the force system will be zero.   The concurrent and coplanar force system shown in Fig. 14.11 is in a state of equilibrium, for the vector triangle closes and each vector follows the other tip to tail.

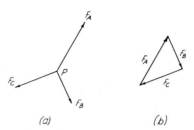

An "equilibrant" is the force which will balance two or more forces and produce equilibrium.   It is a force that would equal the resultant of the system but would necessarily have to act in an opposite direction.

Fig. 14.11.   Forces in equilibrium.

Fig. 14.12 shows a weight supported by a short steel cable.   The force to be determined is that needed to hold the weight in a state of equilibrium when it is swung from the position indicated by the broken lines into the position shown by solid lines.

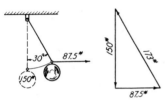

This may be done by drawing a vector triangle with the forces in order from tip to tail.   The 87.5 pound force vector represents the equilibrant, the force that will balance the 150 pound force and the 173 pound tension force now in

Fig. 14.12.   Determination of forces (graphically).

the cable.   The reader may wonder at the increase in the tension force in the cable from a 150 pound force when hanging straight down to a 173 pound force when the cable is at an angle of 30 degrees with the vertical.   It might help to realize that as the weight is swung outward towards a position where the cable will be horizontal, the tension force and the equilibrant will both increase.   Theoretically it would require forces infinitely large to hold the system in equilibrium with the cable in a horizontal position.

In solving a force system graphically it is possible to determine two unknowns in a coplanar system.

Now suppose that is desired to determine the forces acting in the members of a simple truss as shown in Fig. 14.13(a).   To determine these forces graphically, one should isolate the joint supporting the weight and draw a diagram, known as a free-body diagram to show the forces acting at the joint (b).   Although the lines of this diagram may have any length, they must be parallel to the lines in the space diagram in (a).   Since the boom will be in compression, a capital letter C has been placed along the line that represents the boom in the diagram.   A letter T has been placed along the line for the cable because it will be in tension.   Although the diagram may not have been essential in this particular case, such a diagram does play an important part in solving more complex systems.

In constructing the force polygon, it is necessary to start by drawing the vertical vector, for the load is the only force having a known magnitude and direction.   After this vertical vector has been drawn to a length representing 1200 pounds, using a selected scale, the force polygon (triangle) may be completed by drawing the remaining lines representing the unknown forces parallel to their known lines of action as shown in (a). The force polygon will close since the force system is in equilibrium.

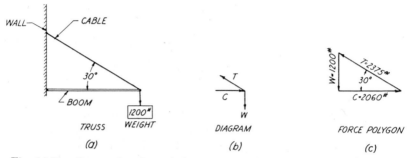

Fig. 14.13.   Determination of the forces at the joint of a simple truss.

The magnitude of the unknown forces in the members of the truss can now be determined by measuring the lines of the diagram using the same scale selected to lay out the length of the vertical vector.   This method might be used to determine the forces acting in the members at any joint in a truss.

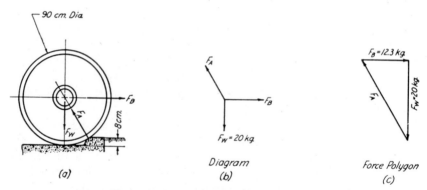

Fig. 14.14.   Determination of forces.

It is possible to solve many of the simple force problems of physics graphically by drawing a force polygon.   For example, suppose that it should be desirable to determine the least horizontal force necessary to move a wheel over an obstacle.   The space diagram shown in Fig. 14.14(a) gives the diameter of the wheel as 90 cm. and its weight as 20 kg.   The height of the obstacle is 8 cm.   The forces acting on the wheel are F_W, its weight, which is known, the reaction force F_A, unknown, and F_B the horizontal force that must be applied at the instant the wheel is just at the point of rising over the obstacle. The magnitude of F_B can be found on the force triangle in (c).

14.7. Coplanar, nonconcurrent force systems. Forces in one plane having lines of action that do not pass through a common point are said to be coplanar, nonconcurrent forces (Fig. 14.15).

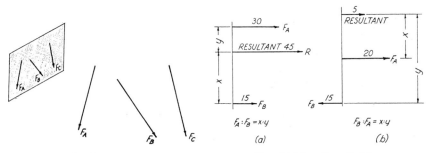

Fig. 14.15. Coplanar, nonconcurrent
forces.

Fig. 14.16.　Parallel forces.

14.8. Two parallel forces. When two forces are parallel and act in the same direction, their resultant will have a line of action that is parallel to the lines of action of the given forces and it will be located between them. The magnitude of the resultant will be equal to the sum of the two forces (Fig. 14.16a), and it will act through a point that divides any perpendicular line joining the lines of action of the given forces inversely as the forces.

Should the two forces act in opposite directions, as shown in (b), the resultant will be located outside of them and will have the same direction as the greater force. Its magnitude will be equal to the difference between the two given forces. The proportion shown with the illustration in (b) may be used to determine the location of the point of application of the resultant.

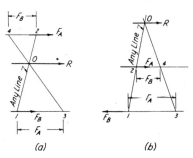

Fig. 14.17.　Determination of the
position of the resultant of parallel
forces (graphical method).

Those who prefer to determine graphically the location of the line of action for the resultant may use the method illustrated in Fig. 14.17. This method is based on well known principles of geometry.

With the two forces F_A and F_B given, any line 1–2 is drawn joining their lines of action. From this line two distances must be laid off along the lines of action of the given forces. If the given forces act in the same direction, then the distances are laid off in opposite directions from the line 1–2 (a). If they act in opposite directions, the distances must be laid off on the same side of line 1–2 (b).   In Fig. 14.17(a), a length equal by scale to F_A was laid off from point 1 on the line of action of F_B.   Then from point 2 a length equal to F_B was marked off in an opposite direction. These measurements located points 3 and 4, the end points of the line intersecting line 1–2 at point O.   Point O is on the line of action of the resultant R.   In Fig. 14.17(b) this method has been applied to establish the location of the resultant for two forces acting in opposite directions.

14.9. Moment of a force.   The "moment of a force" with respect to a point is the product of the force and the perpendicular distance from the given point to the line of action of the force.   In the illustration, Fig. 14.18, the moment of the force F_A about point P is Mom. $= F_A \times d$. The perpendicular distance d is known as the lever arm of the force. Should the distance d be measured in inches and the force be given in pounds, the moment of the force will be in inch-pounds.

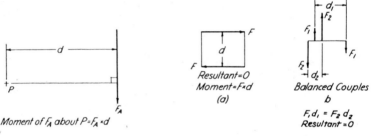

Fig. 14.18.   *Moment of a force.*   Fig. 14.19.   *Force couples.*

14.10. Force couples.   Two equal forces that act in opposite directions are known as a "couple."   A couple does not have a resultant, and no single force can counteract tendency to produce rotation.   The measurement of this tendency is the moment of the couple that is the product of one of the forces and the perpendicular distance between them.

To prevent the rotation of a body that is acted upon by a couple, it is necessary to use two other forces that will form a second couple.   The body acted upon by these couples will be in equilibrium if each couple tends to rotate the body in opposite directions and the moment of one couple is equal to the other.

14.11. String polygon—Bow's notation.   A system for lettering space and force diagrams, known as "Bow's notation," is widely used by technical authors.   Its use in this chapter will tend to simplify the discussions which follow.

In the space diagram, shown in Fig. 14.20(a), each space from the line of action of one force to the line of action of the next one is given a lowercase letter such as a, b, c, and d in alphabetical order.   Thus the line of action for any particular force can be designated by the letters of the areas on each side of it.   For example, in Fig. 14.22 the line of action for the

1080 pound force, acting downward on the beam, would be designated as line of action *bc*. On the force diagram, corresponding capital letters are used at the ends of the vectors. In Fig. 14.20(*b*), *AB* represents the magnitude of *ab* in the space diagram and *BC* represents the magnitude of *bc*.

To find the resultant of three or more parallel forces graphically, the "funicular" or "string polygon" is used. The magnitude and direction of the required resultant for the system shown in Fig. 14.20, are known. The magnitude, representing the algebraic sum of the given forces, appears as the heavy line *AD* of the force polygon. It is required to determine

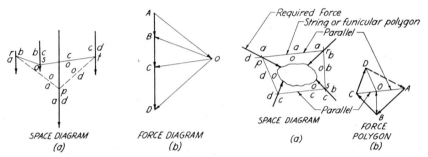

| SPACE DIAGRAM | FORCE DIAGRAM | SPACE DIAGRAM | FORCE POLYGON |
| (a) | (b) | (a) | (b) |

Fig. 14.20.   Resultant of parallel forces —Bow's notation.   **Fig. 14.21.   Funicular or string polygon.**

the location of its line of action. With the forces located in the space diagram and the force polygon drawn, the steps for the solution are as follows:

1. Assume a pole point *O* and draw the rays *OA*, *OB*, *OC*, and *OD*. Each of the triangles formed is regarded as a vector triangle with one side representing the resultant of the forces represented by the other two sides. For example: If we consider *AB* to be a resultant force, then *OA* and *OB* are two component forces that could replace *AB*. For the second vector triangle, *OB* and *BC* have *OC* as their resultant. *OC*, when combined with *CD*, will have *OD* as the resultant. *OA* and *OD* combines with *AD*, the final resultant of the system.

2. Draw directly on the space diagram the corresponding strings of the funicular polygon. The funicular polygon may be started at any selected point *r* along the line of action *ab*. The string *ob* will then be parallel to *OB* of the force polygon. From point *s*, where *ob* intersects *bc*, draw *oc* parallel to *OC*. The line *oc* extended to *cd* establishes the location of point *t*. Line *od* drawn parallel to *OD* and line *oa* drawn parallel to *OA* intersect at point *p*. Point *p* is a point on the line of action of force *ad*, the resultant force *AD* for the given force system.

When one or more of a system of parallel forces are directed oppositely from the others, the magnitude and direction of the resultant will be equal to the algebraic sum of the original forces.

14.12. Coplanar, nonconcurrent, nonparallel forces. In further study of coplanar and nonconcurrent forces it might be supposed that it is necessary to determine the magnitude, direction, and line of action of the one force that will establish a state of equilibrium when combined with the given forces AB, BC, and CD of the force system shown in Fig. 14.21. The direction and line of action of the original forces are given in both the space diagram in (a) and the force polygon in (b). The magnitude and direction of the force that will produce equilibrium is represented by DA, the force needed to close the force polygon. With the force polygon completed, the next step is to assume a pole point O and draw the rays OA, OB, OC, and OD. Now OA and OB are component forces of AB, and AB might be replaced by these forces. To clarify this statement; each of the four triangles may be considered to be a vector triangle, and in the case of vector triangle OAB, AB can be regarded as the resultant for the other two forces OA and OB. It should be noted that component force OB of the vector triangle OBC must be equal and opposite in direction to component force OB of OAB.

All that remains to be done is to determine the line of action of the required force DA by drawing the string diagram as explained in Section 14.11, remembering that point r may be any point along the line of action of ab. The intersection point p for strings oa and od is a point along the line of action da of force DA. Although lines of action ab, bc, cd, and da were drawn to a length representing their exact magnitude in Fig. 14.21(a), they could have been drawn to a convenient length to allow for the construction of the string polygon for these lines merely represent lines of action for the forces AB, BC, CD, and DA. They were presented in scaled length for illustrative purposes.

14.13. Equilibrium of three or more coplanar parallel forces. When a given system, consisting of three or more coplanar forces, is in equilibrium, both the force polygon and the funicular polygon must close. If the force polygon should close and the funicular polygon not close, the resultant of the given system will be found to be a force couple.

Two unknown forces of a parallel coplanar force system may be determined graphically by drawing the force and funicular polygons as shown in Fig. 14.22, since the forces are known to be in equilibrium, and all are vertical. Although one may be aware that the sum of the two reaction forces R_1 and R_2 is equal to the sum of forces AB, BC, CD, and DE, the magnitude of R_1 and R_2 as single forces is unknown. The location of point F in the force polygon, which is needed if one is to determine the magnitudes of R_1 and R_2, may be found by fulfilling the requirement that the funicular polygon be closed.

The funicular polygon is started at any convenient point along the known line of action of R_1, and successive strings are drawn parallel to corresponding rays of the force polygon. In area b the string will be parallel to OB, in area c the string will be parallel to oc and so on until the string that is parallel to OE has been drawn. String of may then be added to close the funicular polygon. This closing line from point x to the starting point y determines the position of OF in the force polygon, for ray OF must be parallel to the string of. The magnitude of the reaction R_1 is represented to scale by the vector FA, and R_2 is represented by the vector FE.

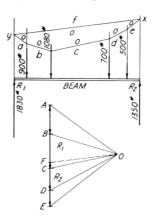

The graphical method for determining the values of wind load reactions for a roof truss having both ends fixed is shown in Fig. 14.23. The solution given is practically identical with the solution applied to the beam in Fig. 14.22.

14.14. Concurrent, noncoplanar force systems. Up to this point in our study of force systems, the student's attention has been directed solely to systems lying in one plane in order that the graphical methods

Fig. 14.22. To determine the reaction forces of a loaded beam.

dealing with the composition and resolution of forces could be presented in a clear and simple manner, free from the thinking needed for understanding force systems involving the third dimension.

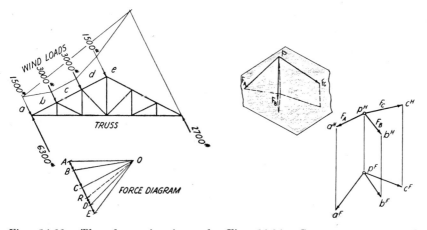

Fig. 14.23. The determination of the reactions for wind loads.

Fig. 14.24. Concurrent, noncoplanar forces.

In dealing with noncoplanar forces it is necessary to use at least two views to represent a structure in space. Although the methods as applied to coplanar force systems for solving problems may be extended to noncoplanar systems, the vector diagram for noncoplanar forces must have two views instead of one view as in the case of coplanar forces. If the student is to understand the discussions that are to follow he must grasp the idea that for the composition and resolution of noncoplanar forces he will work with two distinct and separate space representations, the space diagram for the given structure and the related vector diagram (force polygon). Fig. 14.24 shows two views of a concurrent, noncoplanar force system not in equilibrium.

There are a few basic relationships that exist between a space diagram and its related vector diagram, which must be kept in mind when solving noncoplanar force problems. These relationships are: (1) in corresponding views (*H*-view and *H*-view, or *F*-view and *F*-view), each vector in the vector diagram will be parallel to its corresponding representation in the space diagram, (2) if a system of concurrent, noncoplanar forces is in equilibrium, the force polygon in space closes and the projection on each plane will close, and (3) the true magnitude of a force can be measured only in the vector diagram when it appears in true length or is made to do so.

14.15. Determination of the resultant of a force system of concurrent, noncoplanar forces. The parallelogram method for determining the resultant of concurrent forces as explained in Sec. 14.5 may

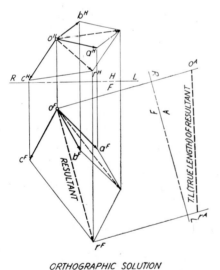

ORTHOGRAPHIC SOLUTION

Fig. 14.25. Determination of the resultant of concurrent, noncoplanar forces.

be employed to find the resultant of the three forces *OA*, *OB*, and *OC* in Fig. 14.25. Any number of given concurrent noncoplanar forces can be combined into their resultant by this method. In the illustration, forces *OA* and *OB* were combined into their resultant, which is the diagonal of the smaller parallelogram, then this resultant in turn was combined with the third force *OC* to obtain the final resultant *R* for the given system. Since the true magnitude of *R* can be scaled only in a view showing its true length, an auxiliary view was projected from the front view. The true length of *R* could also have been determined by revolution.

Since the single force needed to hold a force system in balance, known as the equilibrant, is equal to the resultant in magnitude but is opposite in direction, this method might be used to determine the equilibrant for a system of concurrent noncoplanar forces.

In presenting this problem and the two problems that follow this one, it has been assumed that the student has read the previous sections of this chapter and that his knowledge of the principles of projection is sufficient for him to find the true length of a line, having two views given, and to draw the view of a plane so that it will appear as an edge.

14.16. To find the three unknown forces of a simple load-bearing frame—special case.   In dealing with the simple load-bearing frame in Fig. 14.26, it should be realized that this is a special case rather than a general one, for two of the truss members appear as a single line

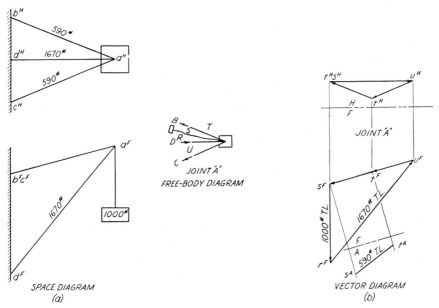

Fig. 14.26.   *Solution of a concurrent, noncoplanar force system—special case.*

in the frontal view of the space diagram. This condition considerably simplifies the task of finding the unknown forces acting in the members, and it is this particular spatial situation that makes this a special case. However, it should be pointed out now that this condition must exist or be set up in a projected view when a vector solution is to be applied to any problem involving a system of concurrent, noncoplanar forces. More will be said about the necessity for having two unknown forces coincide in one of the views in the discussion of the problem that is to follow this one.

After the space diagram has been drawn to scale, the steps toward the final solution are as follows:

1. Draw a free-body diagram showing the joint at A, the joint at which the load is applied. The lines of this diagram may be of any length,

but each line in it must be parallel respectively to a corresponding line in the view of the space diagram to which the free-body diagram is related. In this case, it is the horizontal (top) view. A modified form of Bow's notation was used for convenience in identifying the forces. The vertical load has been shown pulled to one side in order that this force can be made to fall within the range of the notation. This diagram is important to the solution of this problem, for it enables one to see and note the direction of all of the forces that the members exert upon the joint (note arrowheads). Capital letters were used on the free-body diagram to identify the spaces between the forces, rather than lower case letters as is customary, so that lower case letters could be used for the ends of the views of the vectors in the vector diagram.

2. Using a selected scale, start the two views of the vector diagram (b) by laying out vector RS representing the only known force, in this case the 1,000-pound load. Since RS is a force acting in a vertical direction $r^F s^F$ will be in true length in the F-view and will appear as point $r^H s^H$ in the H-view.

3. Complete the H- and F-views of the vector diagram. Since each vector line in the top view must be parallel to a corresponding line in the top view of the space diagram, $s^H t^H$ must be drawn parallel to $a^H b^H$, $t^H u^H$ parallel to $a^H c^H$, and $u^H r^H$ parallel to $a^H d^H$. Since the forces acting at joint A are in equilibrium, the vector triangle will close and the vectors will appear tip to tail.

In the frontal view of the vector diagram, $s^F t^F$ will be parallel to $a^F b^F$, and $t^F u^F$ will be parallel to $a^F c^F$ and $r^F u^F$ will be parallel to $d^F a^F$.

4. Determine the magnitude of the forces acting on joint A. Since vector RU shows its true length in the F-view, the true magnitude of the force represented may be determined by scaling $r^F u^F$ using the same scale used to lay out the length of $r^F s^F$. Although it is known that vectors ST and TU are equal in magnitude, it is necessary to find the true length representation of one or the other of these vectors by some approved method before scaling to determine the true value of the force.

An arrowhead may now be added to the line of action of each force in the free-body diagram to indicate the direction of the action. Since the free-body diagram was related to the top view of the space diagram, the arrowhead for each force will point in the same direction as does the arrowhead on the corresponding vector in the H-view of the vector diagram. These arrowheads show that the forces in members AB and AC are acting away from joint A and are therefore tension forces. The force in AD acts toward A and thus is a compression force.

14.17. To find the three unknown forces of a simple load-bearing truss—general case. For the general case shown in Fig. 14.27, the known force is in a vertical position as in the previous problem, but no two of the three unknown forces appear coincident in either of the two given views.   For this reason, it is necessary at the very start to add a complete auxiliary view to the space diagram that will combine with the existing top view to give a point view of one member and a line view of two of the three unknown forces.   To obtain this desired situation, one should start with the following steps, which will transform the general case into the special case with which one should now be familiar.

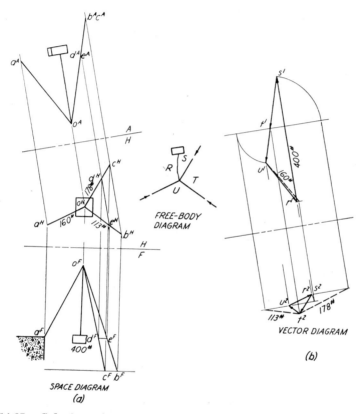

Fig. 14.27.   Solution of a concurrent, noncoplanar force system—general case.

Step 1.   Draw a true length line in the plane of two of the members. In Fig. 14.27(a) this line is *DE*, which appears in true length (*TL*) in the *H*-view.

Step 2.   Draw the needed auxiliary view, taken so that *DE* will appear as a point ($d^A e^A$) and *OB* and *OC* will be coincident (line $o^A b^A c^A$). This construction involves finding the edge view of a plane.   See Sec. 12.22.   In this particular case, the auxiliary view has height in common with the frontal view.

Step 3.   Draw the two views of the vector diagram by assuming the

H-view and the *A*-view to be the given views of the special case.   Proceed
by the steps set forth for the special case in Sec. 14.16.

Step 4.   Determine the magnitude of the forces and add arrowheads
to the free-body diagram to show the direction of action of the forces
acting on point *O*.

14.18. In practice, engineers find wide use for methods that solve
problems through the use of three-dimensional vector diagrams, for any
quantity having both magnitude and direction may be represented by a
vector.   And, although the examples used in the chapter dealt with static
structures, which are in the field of the structural engineer, vector diagram methods are used frequently by the electrical engineer for solving
problems arising in his field and by the mechanical engineer for problems
dealing with bodies in motion.   The student will without doubt encounter
some of these methods in a textbook for a later course or will have them
presented to him by his instructor.

14.19. Problems.   The following problems have been selected to
emphasize the basic principles underlying vector geometry.   By solving
a limited number of the problems presented, the student should find that
he has a working knowledge of some vector methods that are useful for
solving problems in design that involve the determination of the magnitude of forces as well as their composition and resolution.   The student
is to select his own scale remembering that a drawing made to a large scale
usually assures more accurate results.

1. (Fig. 14.28.)   A force of 900 pounds acts downward at an angle of
60 degrees with the horizontal.   Determine the vertical and horizontal components of this force.

2. (Fig. 14.29.)   Determine the resultant force for the given coplanar, concurrent force system.

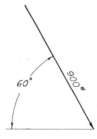

Fig. 14.28.

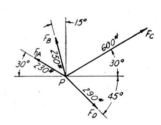

Fig. 14.29.

3. (Fig. 14.30.)   Determine the magnitude of the force F_C and the angle
that the resultant force *R* makes with the horizontal for the given coplanar,
concurrent force system.

4. (Fig. 14.31.)   Determine the magnitude and direction of the equilibrant
for the given coplanar, concurrent force system.

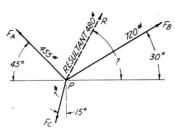

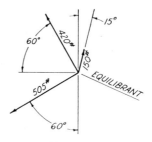

Fig. 14.30.   *Fig. 14.31.*

5. (Fig. 14.32.) A block weighing 45 pounds is to be pulled up an inclined plane sloping at an angle of 30 degrees with the horizontal. If the frictional resistance is 16 pounds, what is the magnitude of the force F_M that is required to move the block uniformly up the plane?

6. (Fig. 14.33.) Determine the magnitude of the force F needed to start the 800 pound wheel over the obstacle.

7. (Fig. 14.33.) Determine the horizontal force needed to start the wheel over the obstacle. See Problem 6.

8. If the wheel shown in Fig. 14.33 were 2 feet in diameter instead of 3 feet, what is the magnitude of the force needed to start the wheel?

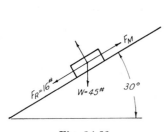

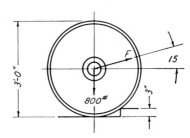

Fig. 14.32.   *Fig. 14.33.*

9. (Fig. 14.34.) A horizontal beam AB is hinged at B as shown. The end of the beam at A is connected by a cable to a hook in the wall at C. The load at A is 250 pounds. Using the dimensions as given, determine the tension

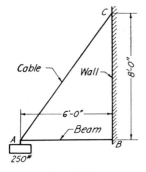

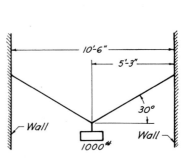

Fig. 14.34.   *Fig. 14.35.*

force in the cable and the reaction on the hinge at B. The weight of the beam is to be neglected.

10. (Fig. 14.35.) A 1,000 pound load is supported as shown. Determine the magnitude of the tension in the cables.

11. (Fig. 14.36.) A 600 pound load is supported by cables as shown. Determine the magnitude of the tension in the cables.

12. (Fig. 14.37.) A 250 pound body hangs vertically as shown by broken lines. If a cable is attached and a side pull is applied in a horizontal direction until the body is drawn to a position with the cable at 30 degrees from the vertical, what will be the magnitude of the applied force F? Determine the magnitude of the tension in the cable with the body in this new position.

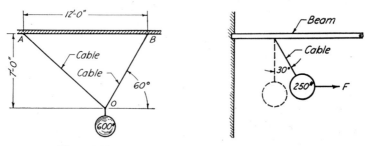

Fig. 14.36.   Fig. 14.37.

13. (Fig. 14.38.) A ship that is being pulled through the entrance of a harbor is headed due east through a cross current moving at 4 knots as shown. If the ship is moving at 12 knots, what is the speed of the tug boat?

14. (Fig. 14.39.) A 170 pound man stands 4 feet to the right of the middle of the wire, which is supported at points 30 feet apart. Determine the magnitude of the tension in the wire if the feet of the man are 5 feet below the platforms.

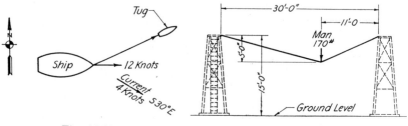

Fig. 14.38.   Fig. 14.39.

15. (Fig. 14.40.) Determine the magnitude of the reactions R_1 and R_2 of the beam with loads as shown.

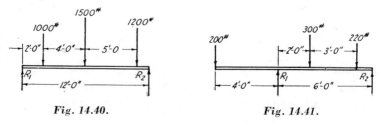

Fig. 14.40.   Fig. 14.41.

16. (Fig. 14.41.) Determine the magnitude of the reactions R_1 and R_2 of the beam.

17. (Fig. 14.42.) Determine the magnitude of the reactions R_1 and R_2 for the roof truss shown. Each of the six panels is of the same length.

18. (Fig. 14.43.) Determine the magnitude of the reactions R_1 and R_2 to the wind loads acting on the roof truss as shown.

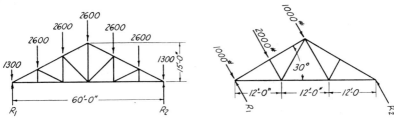

Fig. 14.42.   Fig. 14.43.

19. (Fig. 14.44.) Determine the magnitude of the reactions R_1 and R_2 for the roof truss acting under loads as shown.

20–21. (Figs. 14.45–14.46.) Using the scale given below the drawing, reproduce the given views of the concurrent, noncoplanar force system shown. Assume the magnitudes of the forces and determine the resultant of the system.

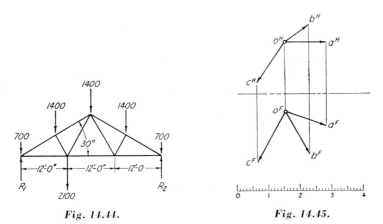

Fig. 14.44.   Fig. 14.45.

22. (Fig. 14.47.) A tripod with an 85 pound load is set up on a level floor as shown. Determine the stresses in the three legs due to the vertical load on the top.

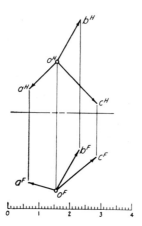

Fig. 14.46.

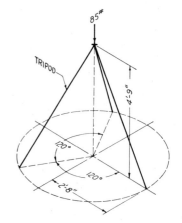

Fig. 14.47.

23–25. (Figs. 14.48–14.50.) Determine the stresses in the members of the space frame shown.

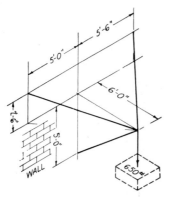

Fig. 14.48.

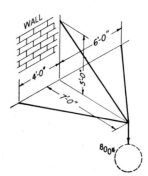

Fig. 14.49.

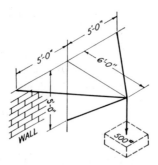

Fig. 14.50.

15

Representation and Specification
of Threads, Fasteners, Welds,
and Piping

SCREW THREADS

15.1 In the commercial field, where the practical application of engineering drawing takes the form of working drawings, knowledge of

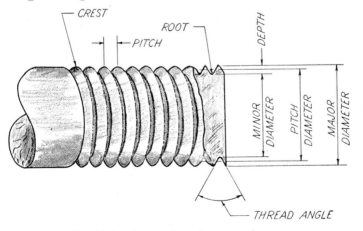

Fig. 15.1. *Screw thread nomenclature.*

screw threads and fasteners is important. There is always the necessity for assembling parts either with permanent fastenings such as rivets, or with bolts, screws, and so forth, which may be removed easily.

Engineers, detailers, and draftsmen must be completely familiar with the common types of threads and fastenings, as well as with their use and the correct methods of representation, because of the frequency of their occurrence in structures and machines.   Information concerning special types of fasteners may be obtained from manufacturers' catalogues.

A young engineer in training should study Fig. 15.1 to acquaint himself with the terms commonly associated with screw threads.

15.2. Threads.   The principal uses of threads are: (1) for fastening, (2) for adjusting, and (3) for transmitting power.   To satisfy most of the requirements of the engineering profession, the different forms of threads shown in Fig. 15.2 are used.

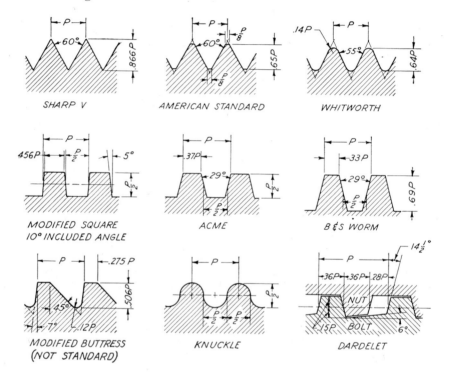

Fig. 15.2.   Screw threads.*

The American Standard form (National Form N) thread which is being replaced by the new unified thread form is still widely used in the United States.   The sharp V is used to some extent where adjustment and holding power are essential.

For the transmission of power and motion, the modified square, Acme, and Brown and Sharpe worm threads have been adopted.   The modified square thread, which is now rarely used, transmits power parallel to its axis.   A still further modification of the square thread is the stronger

---

* ASA B1.3–1941.
  Handbook H-28 (1944) National Bureau of Standards.

Acme, which is easier to cut and more readily disengages split nuts (as lead screws on lathes). The Brown and Sharpe worm thread, with similar proportions but with longer teeth, is used for transmitting power to a worm wheel.

The knuckle thread, commonly found on incandescent lamps, plugs, and so on, can be cast or rolled.

The Whitworth and buttress threads are not often encountered by the average engineer. The former, which fulfills the same purpose as the American Standard thread, is used in England but is also frequently found in this country. The buttress or breech-block thread, which is designed to take pressure in one direction, is used for breech mechanisms

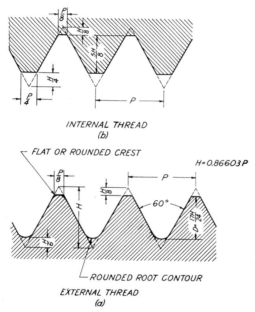

INTERNAL THREAD
(b)

EXTERNAL THREAD
(a)

Fig. 15.3. American-British unified thread.

of large guns and for airplane propeller hubs. The thread form has not been standardized and appears in different modified forms.

The Dardelet thread is self-locking in assembly.

15.3. American-British unified thread. A new Unified Thread Standard (ASA BI.1–1949) came into existence after the representatives of the United States, Great Britain, and Canada signed a unification agreement on Nov. 18, 1948 in Washington, D. C. This accord, which made possible the interchangeability of threads for these countries, created a new thread form (Fig. 15.3) that is a compromise between our own American Standard design and the British Whitworth. The external thread of the new form has a rounded root and may have either a flat or rounded crest.

15.4. Multiple threads. Whenever a quick advance is desired, as on fountain pens, valves, and so on, two or more threads are cut side by side. Two threads form a double thread, three a triple thread, and so on. A thread that is not otherwise designated is understood to be a single thread.

In drawing a single, triple, or an odd-number multiple thread, a crest is always diametrically opposite a root; in a double or even-number multiple thread, a crest is opposite a crest and a root opposite a root.

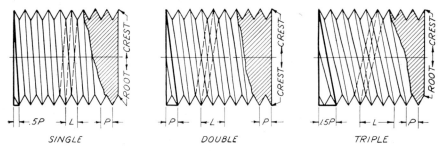

Fig. 15.4.   Single, double, and triple threads.

15.5. Right-hand and left-hand threads. A right-hand thread advances into a threaded hole when turned clockwise; a left-hand thread advances when turned counter-clockwise. They can be easily distinguished by the thread slant. A right-hand thread on a horizontal shank always slants upward to the left\ and a left-hand upward to the right/. A thread is always considered to be right-hand if it is not otherwise specified. A left-hand thread is always marked *L.H.* on a drawing.

15.6. Pitch. The pitch of a thread is the distance from any point on a thread to the corresponding point on the adjacent thread, measured parallel to the axis as shown in Fig. 15.1.

15.7. Lead. The lead of a screw may be defined as the distance advanced parallel to the axis when the screw is turned one revolution (Fig. 15.4). For a single thread, the lead is equal to the pitch; for a double thread, the lead is twice the pitch; for a triple thread, the lead is three times the pitch, and so on.

15.8. Detailed screw-thread representation. The true representation of screw threads by helical curves, requiring unnecessary time and laborious drafting, is rarely used. The detailed representation, closely approximating the actual appearance, is preferred in commercial practice, for it is much easier to represent the helices with slanting lines and the truncated roots and crest with sharp "V's" (Fig. 15.5). Since detailed rendering is also time consuming, its use is justified only in those few cases where appearance and permanency are important factors, and when it is necessary to avoid the possibility that confusion might result from the use of one of the symbolic methods.   The preparation of a detailed representation is a task that belongs primarily to a draftsman, the engineer being concerned only with specifying that this form be used.

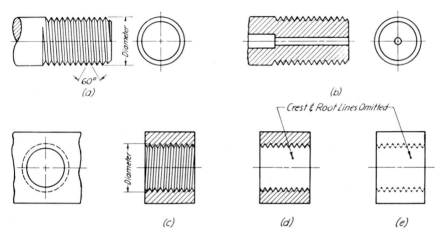

Fig. 15.5.   Detailed representation.

An effective relief and finish is given to the detailed representation of a Unified-American or sharp V thread by drawing all lines fine except the root lines.

Detailed representations for modified square and Acme threads are shown in Fig. 15.6.

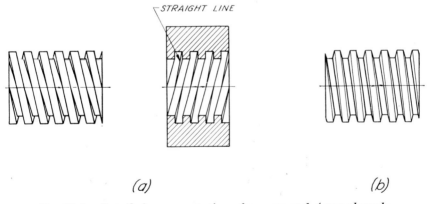

Fig. 15.6.   Detailed representation of square and Acme threads.

15.9. American Standard thread symbols (Fig. 15.7).   To save valuable time and expense in the preparation of drawings, the American Standards Association has adopted the "schematic" and "simplified" series of thread symbols to represent threads having a diameter of one inch or less.   Read Sec. 8.14; study Figs. 8.18 and 8.19.

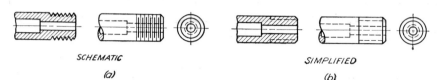

SCHEMATIC

(a)

SIMPLIFIED

(b)

Fig. 15.7.   External thread symbols.*

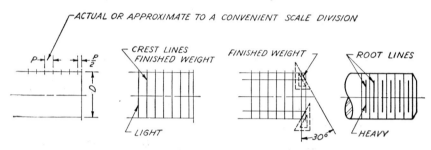

ACTUAL OR APPROXIMATE TO A CONVENIENT SCALE DIVISION

CREST LINES
FINISHED WEIGHT

FINISHED WEIGHT

ROOT LINES

LIGHT

30°

HEAVY

Fig. 15.8.   Drawing conventional threads.

The root of the thread for the simplified representation is shown by invisible lines drawn parallel to the axis.

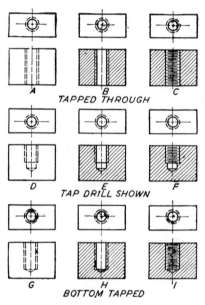

A   B   C

TAPPED THROUGH

D   E   F

TAP DRILL SHOWN

G   H   I

BOTTOM TAPPED

Fig. 15.9.   Internal thread symbols.   American Standard (ASA Z14.1–1946).

The schematic representation consists of alternate long and short lines perpendicular to the axis. Although these lines, representing the crests and roots of the thread, are not spaced to actual pitch, their spacing should indicate noticeable differences in the number of threads per inch of different threads on the same working drawing or group of drawings. The root lines are made heavier than the crest lines (Fig. 15.8).

Before a hole can be tapped (threaded), it must be drilled to permit the tap to enter. See Table II for tap drill sizes for standard threads. Since the last of the thread cut is not well formed or usable, the hole must be shown drilled and tapped deeper than the screw will enter (Fig. 15.9D, E, F). To show the threaded portion extending to the bottom of the drilled hole indicates the use of a bottoming tap to cut full threads at the

* ASA Z14.1–1946.

bottom.   This is an extra and expensive operation not justified except in cases where the depth of the hole and the distance the screw must enter are limited (Fig. 15.9*G*, *H*, *I*).

Fig. 15.10 shows a simplified method of representation for square threads.

15.10. Threads in section. The detailed representation of threads in section, which is used for large diameters only, is shown in

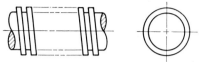

Fig. 15.10.   Simplified representation of a square thread.

Fig. 15.5.   Since the far side of an internal thread in section is visible, the crest and root lines incline in the opposite direction to those of an external thread having the same specifications.

Schematic and simplified symbols for threads of small diameter are shown in Figs. 15.7 and 15.9.

Sectional assembly drawings are treated as shown in Fig. 15.11. When assembled pieces are both sectioned, the detailed representation is used, and the thread form is drawn as sharp "V's."

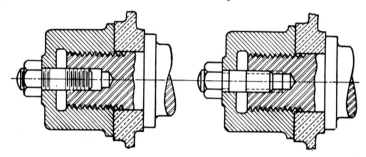

*Fig. 15.11.   Threads in section.**

15.11. Unified and American screw thread series.   The Unified and American screw thread series as given in ASA B1.1–1949 consists of six series and a selection of special threads that cover special combinations of diameter and pitch.   Each series differs from the other by the number of threads per inch for a specific diameter.   See Tables II and III, Appendix.

The coarse thread series (UNC and NC) is designated UNC for sizes above $\frac{1}{4}''$ in diameter.   This series is recommended for general industrial use.

The fine thread series (UNF and NF) designated UNF for sizes above $\frac{1}{4}''$, was prepared for use when a fine thread is required and for general use in the automotive and aircraft fields.

The extra-fine thread series, designated NEF is used for automotive

---

* ASA Z14.1–1946.

and aircraft work when a maximum number of threads is required for a given length.   A few specific sizes of this series are designated UN.

The 8 thread series (8N) is a uniform pitch series for large diameters. It is sometimes used in place of the course thread series for diameters greater than 1″.   This series was originally intended for high pressure joints.

The 12 thread series (12UN or 12N) is a uniform pitch series intended for use with large diameters requiring threads of medium fine pitch.   This series is used as a continuation of the fine thread series for diameters greater than $1\frac{1}{2}$ inches.

The 16 thread series (16UN or 16N) is a uniform pitch series for large diameters requiring a fine pitch thread.   This series is used as a continuation of the extra-fine thread series for diameters greater than 2 inches.

15.12. Unified and American screw thread fits.   Classes of fits are determined by the amounts of tolerance and allowance specified. Under the new unified system classes 1A, 2A, and 3A apply only to external threads; classes 1B, 2B, and 3B apply to internal threads. Classes 2 and 3 from the former American Standard have been retained without change in the new Unified and American Thread Standard for use in the United States only, but they are not among the Unified classes even though the thread forms are identical.   These fits are used with the American thread series (NC, NF, and N series) which covers sizes from size 0 (.060) to 6″.

Class 1A and Class 1B replace class 1 of the old American Standard.

Class 2A and Class 2B were adopted as the recognized standards for screws, bolts, and nuts.

Class 3A and Class 3B invoke new classes of tolerances.   These classes along with class 2A and class 2B should eventually replace class 2 and class 3 now retained from the American Standard.   Class 2 and class 3 are defined in the former standard ASA B1.1–1935 as follows:

Class 2 fit.   Represents a high quality of commercial thread product and is recommended for the great bulk of interchangeable screw-thread work.

Class 3 fit.   Represents an exceptionally high quality of commercially threaded product and is recommended only in cases where the high cost of precision tools and continual checking is warranted.

15.13. Identification symbols for Unified screw threads. Threads are specified under the new unified system by giving the diameter, number of threads per inch, initial letters (UNC, UNF, etc.), and class of fit (1A, 2A, and 3A; or 1B, 2B, and 3B).   See Fig. 15.12.

15.14. Identification symbols for American Standard, Square, and Acme Threads.   American Standard, Square, and Acme threads are specified on drawings, in specifications, and in stock lists by thread information given as shown in Fig. 15.13.

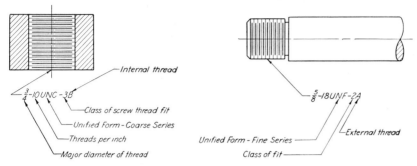

Fig. 15.12.   Unified thread identification symbols.

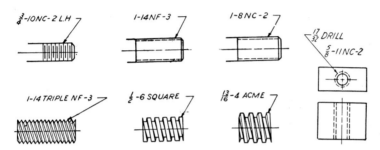

Fig. 15.13.   Thread identification symbols.

15.15. American Standard pipe thread. The American Standard pipe taper thread, illustrated in Fig. 15.14, is similar to the ordinary American Standard thread and has the same thread angle; but it is tapered $\frac{1}{16}''$ per inch, to insure a tight joint at a fitting. The crest is flattened and the root is filled in so that the depth of the thread is $0.80P$. The num-

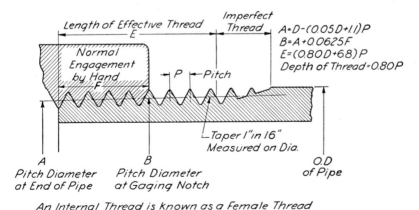

Fig. 15.14.   American Standard pipe thread.

ber of threads per inch for any given nominal diameter can be obtained from Table XVI in the Appendix.

An American National straight pipe thread, having the same number of threads per inch as the taper thread, is in use for pressure-tight joints for couplings, for pressure-tight joints for grease and oil fittings, and for hose couplings and nipples. This thread may also be used for free-fitting mechanical joints. Usually a taper external thread is used with a straight internal thread, as pipe material is sufficiently ductile for an adjustment of the threads.

In specifying pipe threads, the ASA recommends that the note be formulated using symbolic letters as illustrated in Fig. 15.15. For example, the specification for a 1″ standard pipe thread should read, 1″-*NPT*. The letters *NPT*, following the nominal diameter, indicate that the thread is American National (*N*), pipe (*P*), taper (*T*) thread. Continuing with the same scheme of using letters, the specification for a 1″ straight pipe thread would read, 1″-*NPS* [National (*N*)—pipe (*P*)—straight (*S*)]. The form of note given in (*a*), reading *1″ AM. STD. PIPE THD*, is quite commonly used in practice. Identification symbols and dimensions of American National pipe threads are given in the American Standard for Pipe Threads (ASA B2.1–1945).

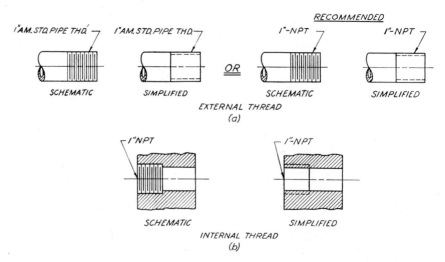

Fig. 15.15.   *American Standard representation of pipe threads.*

15.16. Drawing pipe threads. The taper on a pipe thread is so slight that it will not attract attention on a drawing unless it is exaggerated. If it is shown at all, it is usually magnified to $\frac{1}{8}$″ per inch.

Pipe threads are generally represented by the same conventional symbols used for ordinary American Standard thread (Fig. 15.15).

FASTENERS

15.17. American Standard bolts and nuts (Fig. 15.16). Commercial producers of bolts and fasteners manufacture their products in accordance with the standard specifications given in the American Standard entitled "Square and Hexagon Bolts and Nuts" (Revised 1955).* See table in Appendix.

The ASA has approved the specification for three series of bolts and nuts:

1. *Regular series.* The regular series was adopted for general use.
2. *Heavy series.* Heavy boltheads and nuts are designed to satisfy the special commercial need for greater bearing surface.
3. *Light series nuts.* Light nuts are used under conditions requiring a substantial savings in weight and material. They are usually supplied with a fine thread.

The amount of machining is the basis for further classification of hexagonal bolts and nuts in both the regular and heavy series as unfinished and semifinished.

Square-head bolts and nuts are standardized as unfinished only.

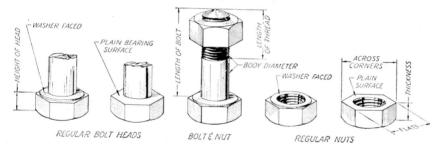

Fig. 15.16.   American Standard bolts and nuts.

Unfinished heads and nuts are not washer-faced, nor are they machined on any surface.

Semifinished bolt heads and nuts are machined or treated on the bearing surface so as to provide a washer face for bolt heads and either a washer face or a circular bearing surface for nuts. Nuts not washer-faced have the circular bearing surface formed by chamfering the edges.

Bolts and nuts are *always* drawn across corners in all views. This recognized commercial practice, which violates the principles of true projection, prevents confusion of square and hexagonal forms on drawings.

The chamfer angle on the tops of heads and nuts is 30 degrees on hexagons and 25 degrees on squares, but both are drawn at 30 degrees on bolts greater than 1″ in diameter.

---

* ASA B18.2–1955.

Bolts are specified in parts lists and elsewhere by giving the diameter, number of threads per inch, series, class of fit, length, finish, and type of head.

EXAMPLE: $\frac{1}{2}$-13 UNC-2A $\times$ $1\frac{3}{4}$ SEMI-FIN. HEX. HD. BOLT.

Frequently it is advantageous and practical to abbreviate the specification thus:

EXAMPLE: $\frac{1}{2}$ $\times$ $1\frac{3}{4}$ UNC SEMI-FIN. HEX. HD. BOLT.

15.18. To draw boltheads and nuts. Using the dimensions given in Table IV in the Appendix, draw the lines representing the top and contact surface of the head or nut and the diameter of the bolt. Lay out a hexagon about an inscribed chamfer circle equal to the width across flats (Fig. 15.17) and project the necessary lines to block in the view. Draw in the arcs after finding the centers as shown.

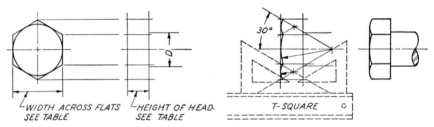

Fig. 15.17.   Steps in drawing a hexagonal bolt head.

A square-head bolt or nut may be drawn by following the steps indicated in Fig. 15.18.

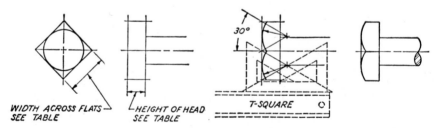

Fig. 15.18.   Steps in drawing a square bolt head.

The engineer and experienced draftsman wisely resort to some form of template for drawing the views of a bolthead or nut. See Fig. 2.43. To draw the views as shown in Figs. 15.17 and 15.18 consumes valuable time needlessly.

15.19. Studs. Studs, or stud bolts, which are threaded on both ends, as shown in Fig. 15.19, are used where bolts would be impractical and for parts that must be removed frequently (cylinder heads, steam chest covers, pumps, and so on). They are first screwed permanently into the

tapped holes in one part before the removable member with its corresponding clearance holes is placed in position. Nuts are used on the
projecting ends to hold the parts together.

Since studs are not standard they must be produced from specifications
given on a detail drawing. In dimensioning a
stud, the length of thread must be given for
both the stud end and nut end along with an
over-all dimension. The thread information is
given by note.

In a bill of material, studs may be specified
as follows:

EXAMPLE: $\frac{1}{2}$-13UNC-2A $\times$ $2\frac{3}{4}$ STUD.

It is good practice to abbreviate the specification thus:

EXAMPLE: $\frac{1}{2}$ $\times$ $2\frac{3}{4}$ STUD.

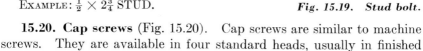

Fig. 15.19.   Stud bolt.

15.20. Cap screws (Fig. 15.20).   Cap screws are similar to machine
screws.   They are available in four standard heads, usually in finished
form.   When parts are assembled,
the cap screws pass through clear
holes in one member and screw into
threaded holes in the other (Fig.
15.20).   Hexagonal cap screws
have a washer face $\frac{1}{64}''$ thick with
a diameter equal to the distance
across flats.   All cap screws $1''$ or
less in length are threaded to the
head.

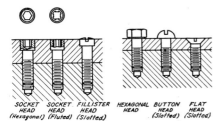

SOCKET   SOCKET   FILLISTER   HEXAGONAL   BUTTON   FLAT
HEAD   HEAD   HEAD   HEAD   HEAD
(Hexagonal) (Fluted) (Slotted)   (Slotted) (Slotted)

Fig. 15.20.   Cap screws.

Cap screws are specified by giving the diameter, number of threads
per inch, series, class of fit, length, and type of head.

EXAMPLE: $\frac{5}{8}$-11UNC-2A $\times$ 2 FIL. HD. CAP
SC.

It is good practice to abbreviate the specification thus:

EXAMPLE: $\frac{5}{8}$ $\times$ 2 UNC FIL. HD. CAP SC.

15.21. Machine screws.   Machine screws,
which fulfill the same purpose as cap screws, are
used chiefly for small work having thin sec-

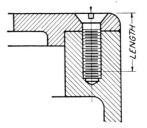

**Fig. 15.21.   Use of a ma-
chine screw.**

tions (Fig. 15.21).   Under the approved American Standard they range
from No. 0 (0.060″ dia.) to $\frac{3}{4}''$ (0.750″ dia.) and are available in either the

American Standard Coarse or Fine-Threaded Series.   The four forms of heads shown in Fig. 15.22 have been standardized.

To specify machine screws, give the diameter, threads per inch, thread series, fit, length, and type of head.

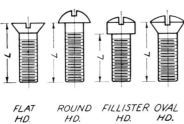

FLAT   ROUND   FILLISTER   OVAL
HD.   HD.   HD.   HD.

Fig. 15.22.   Types of machine screws.

EXAMPLE: No. 12–24NC–3 × $\frac{3}{4}''$ FIL. HD. MACH. SC.

It is good practice to abbreviate by omitting the thread series and class of fit.

EXAMPLE: No. 12–24 × $\frac{3}{4}''$ FIL. HD. MACH. SC.

15.22. Commercial lengths: studs, cap screws, machine screws. Unless a fastening of any of these types carries a constant and appreciable fatigue stress, the usual practice is to have it enter a distance related to its nominal diameter.   If the depth of the hole is not limited, it should be drilled to a depth of 1 diameter beyond the end of the fastener to permit tapping to a distance of $\frac{1}{2}$ diameter below the fastener.

The length of the fastening should be determined to the nearest commercial length that will allow it to fulfill minimum conditions.   In the case of a stud, care should be taken that the length allows for a full engagement of the nut.   Commercial lengths for fasteners increase by the following increments:

Standard length increments:
For fastener lengths $\frac{1}{4}''$ to $1'' = \frac{1}{8}''$
For fastener lengths $1''$ to $4'' = \frac{1}{4}''$

For fastenings and other general purpose applications, the engagement length should be equal to the nominal diameter (D) of the thread when both components are of steel.   For steel external threads in cast iron, brass, or bronze, the engagement length should be $1\frac{1}{2}D$.   When assembled into aluminum, zinc, or plastic the engagement should be $2D$.

15.23. Set screws.   Set screws are used principally to prevent rotary motion between two parts, such as that which tends to occur in the case of a rotating member mounted on a shaft.   A set screw is screwed through one part until the point presses firmly against the other part (Fig. 15.23).

The several forms of safety heads shown in Fig. 15.24 are available in combination with any of the points.   Headless set screws comply with safety codes and should be used on all revolving parts.   The many serious injuries that have been caused by the projecting heads of square-head set screws have led to legislation prohibiting their use in some states (Fig. 15.23).

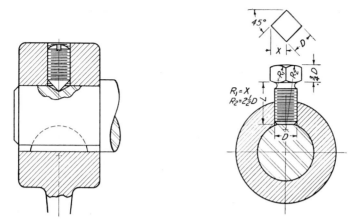

Fig. 15.23. Use of set screws.

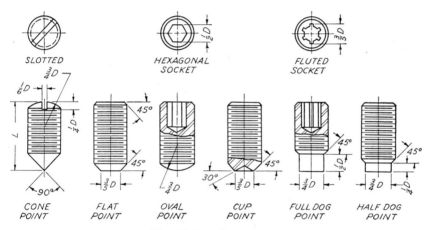

Fig. 15.24. Set screws.

Set screws are specified by giving the diameter, number of threads per inch, series, class of fit, length, type of head, and type of point.

EXAMPLE: $\frac{1}{4}$-20 UNC-2A $\times \frac{1}{2}$ SLOTTED CONE PT. SET SC.

The preferred abbreviated form gives the diameter, number of threads per inch, length, type of head, and type of point.

EXAMPLE: $\frac{1}{4}$-20 $\times \frac{1}{2}$ HEX. SOCKET CONE PT. SET SC.

15.24. Keys. Keys are used in the assembling of machine parts to secure them against relative motion, generally rotary, as is the case between shafts, cranks, wheels, and so on. When the relative forces are not great, a round key, saddle key, or flat key is used (Fig. 15.25). For heavier duty, rectangular keys are more suitable.

The square key (Fig. 15.26) and the Pratt and Whitney key (Fig. 15.27) are the two keys most frequently used in machine design. A plain milling cutter is used to cut the keyway for the square key, and an end mill is used for the Pratt and Whitney keyway. Both keys fit tightly in the shaft and in the part mounted upon it.

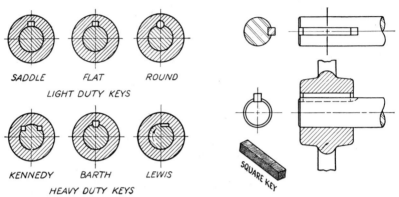

SADDLE   FLAT   ROUND

LIGHT DUTY KEYS

KENNEDY   BARTH   LEWIS

HEAVY DUTY KEYS

Fig. 15.25.   Special light- and heavy-duty keys.

Fig. 15.26.   A square key.

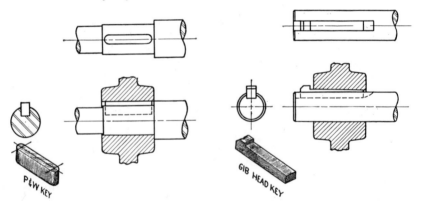

Fig. 15.27.   A Pratt and Whitney key.

Fig. 15.28.   A gib-head key.

The gib-head key (Fig. 15.28) is designed so that the head remains far enough from the hub to allow a drift pin to be driven to remove the key. The hub side of the key is tapered $\frac{1}{8}''$ per foot to insure a fit tight enough to prevent both axial and rotary motion. For this type of key, the keyway must be cut to one end of the shaft.

15.25. Woodruff keys. A Woodruff key is a flat segmental disc with either a flat or a round bottom (Fig. 15.29). It is always specified by a number, the last two digits of which indicate the nominal diameter in eighths of an inch, while the digits preceding the last two give the nominal width in thirty-seconds of an inch.

A practical rule for selecting a Woodruff key for a given shaft is: Choose a standard key that has a width approximately equal to one-fourth of the diameter of the shaft, and a radius nearly equal (plus or minus) to the radius of the shaft.   Table XIII in the Appendix gives the dimensions for American Standard Woodruff keys.

When Woodruff keys are drawn, it should be remembered that the center of the arc is placed above the top of the key at a distance shown in column E in the table.

15.26. Locking devices.   A few of the many types of locking devices that prevent nuts from becoming loose under vibration are shown in Figs. 15.30–15.34.

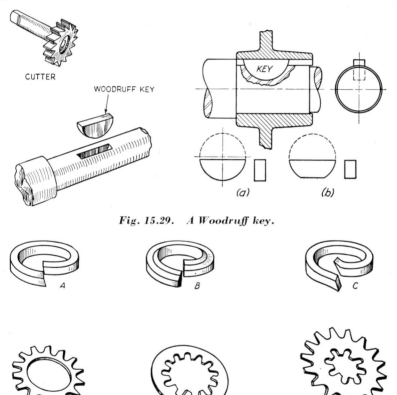

Fig. 15.29.   A Woodruff key.

Fig. 15.30.   Special lock washers.

Fig. 15.30 shows six forms of patented spring washers.   The ones shown in D, E, and F have internal and external teeth.

Fig. 15.31 shows a preassembled nut and washer combination.

Secured in the top of the elastic stop nut shown in Fig. 15.32 is a red fiber locking collar slightly smaller than the diameter of the bolt.

Because this collar is plastic in character, it forms to the bolt thread and grips securely enough to prevent the nut from coming loose under strong vibration.

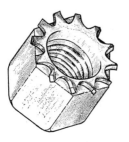

Fig. 15.31. Shake-proof preassembled nut and lock washer.

Fig. 15.32. Elastic stop nut.

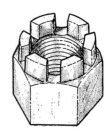

Fig. 15.33. Castellated nut.

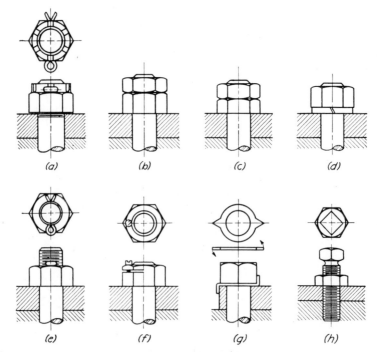

(a)   *(b)*   *(c)*   *(d)*

(e)   *(f)*   *(g)*   *(h)*

Fig. 15.34.   Locking schemes.

In common use is the castellated nut (Figs. 15.33 and 15.34a) with a spring cotter pin that passes through the shaft and the slots in the top. This type is used extensively in automotive and aeronautical work.

Fig. 15.34(b) shows a regular nut that is prevented from loosening by an American Standard jam nut.

In Fig. 15.34(c) the use of two jam nuts is illustrated.

A regular nut with a spring-lock washer is shown in Fig. 15.34(*d*). The reaction provided by the lock washer tends to prevent the nut from turning.

A regular nut with a spring cotter pin through the shaft, to prevent the nut from backing off, is shown in Fig. 15.34(*e*).

Special devices for locking nuts are illustrated in Fig. 15.34(*f*) and (*g*). A set screw may be held in position with a jam nut as in (*h*).

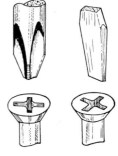

Fig. 15.35. Phillips head screw.

15.27. Phillips head. The Phillips head, shown in Fig. 15.35 for a wood screw, is one of various types of recessed heads. Although special drivers are usually employed for installation, an ordinary screw driver can be used. Machine screws, capscrews, and many special types of fasteners are available with Phillips heads.

15.28. Rivets. Rivets are permanent fasteners used chiefly for connecting members in such structures as buildings and bridges and for assembling steel sheets and plates for tanks, boilers, and ships. They are cylindrical rods of wrought iron or soft steel, with one head formed when manufactured. A head is formed on the other end after the rivet has been put in place through the drilled or punched holes of the mating parts. A hole for a rivet is generally drilled, punched, or punched and reamed $\frac{1}{16}''$ larger than the diameter of the shank of the rivet. Fig. 15.36 illustrates a rivet in position. Small rivets, less than $\frac{1}{2}''$ in diameter, may be driven cold, but the larger sizes are driven hot. For specialized types of engineering

Fig. 15.36. A rivet.

SHOP RIVETS
FIELD RIVETS
BUTTON HEADS
COUNTERSUNK AND CHIPPED
COUNTERSUNK NOT CHIPPED
FLATTENED TO 1/4 HIGH FOR 1/2" AND 5/8" RIVETS
FLATTENED TO 3/8 HIGH FOR 3/4" TO 1" RIVETS
FULL HEADS
COUNTERSUNK AND CHIPPED
BOTH SIDES
BOTH SIDES
NEAR SIDE
FAR SIDE
BOTH SIDES
NEAR SIDE
FAR SIDE
BOTH SIDES
NEAR SIDE
FAR SIDE
BOTH SIDES
NEAR SIDE
FAR SIDE
BOTH SIDES
BOTH SIDES
NEAR SIDE
FAR SIDE
BOTH SIDES

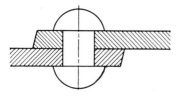

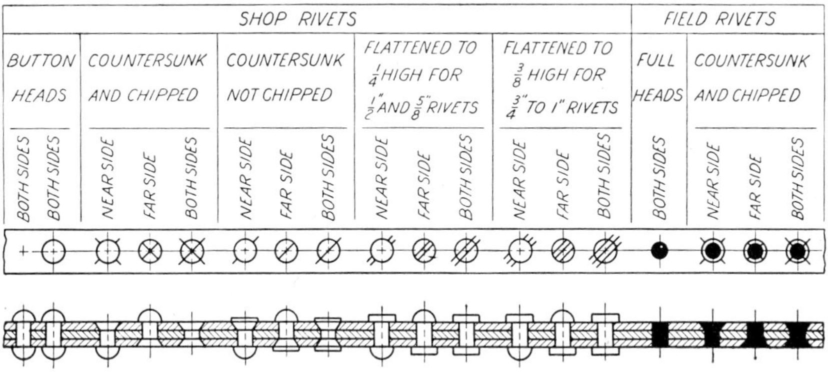

Fig. 15.37. Conventional symbols for rivets.

work, rivets are manufactured of chrome-iron, nickel, brass, copper, and so
on.   Standard dimensions for small rivets are given in Table X in the
Appendix.

The type of rivets and their treatment are indicated on drawings by
the American Standard conventional symbols shown in Fig. 15.37.

Fig. 15.38.   Lap joints.   **Fig. 15.39.   Butt joints.**

The holes for field rivets are indicated in solid black on a drawing, and
shop rivets are shown by open circles with the same diameter as the rivet
head.   Rivets should be drawn with either a drop pen or a bow pencil.
In practice, the circles representing rivets are often drawn freehand on
pencil drawings.

15.29. Riveted joints.   Joints on boilers, tanks, and so on, are classified as either lap joints or butt joints.   Lap joints are generally used
for seams around the circumference (Fig. 15.38).   Butt joints are used
for longitudinal seams, except on small tanks where the pressure is to be
less than 100 pounds per square inch (Fig. 15.39).

15.30. Springs.   In production work, a spring is largely a matter of
mathematical calculation rather than drawing, and it is usually purchased

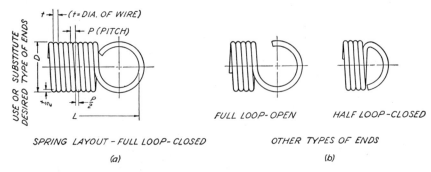

Fig. 15.40.   Tension springs.

from a spring manufacturer, with the understanding that it will fulfill
specified conditions.   For experimental work, and when only one is
needed, it may be formed by winding oil-tempered spring wire or music
wire around a cylindrical bar.   As it is wound, the wire follows the helical
path of the screw thread.   For this reason the steps in the layout of the
representation for a spring are similar to the screw thread.   Pitch distances are marked off, and the coils are given a slope of one-half of the
pitch.   Fig. 15.40(*a*) shows a partial layout of a tension spring.   Other

types of ends are shown in (b).　A compression spring layout, with various types of ends, is illustrated in Fig. 15.41.

When making a detail working drawing of a spring, it should be shown to its free length.　On either an assembly or detail drawing, a fairly accurate representation, neatly drawn, will satisfy all requirements.

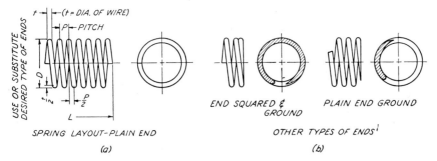

Fig. 15.41.　*Compression springs.*

Single line symbols for the representation of springs are shown in Fig. 8.20.

WELDING

15.31. Welding processes.　For convenience, the various welding processes used in commercial production may be classified into three types: pressure processes, nonpressure processes, and casting processes.

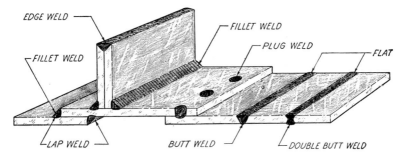

Fig. 15.42.　*Types of welds.*

The nonpressure processes are arc welding and gas welding.　Metallic arc welding is the joining of two pieces of metal through the use of a sustained arc formed between the work and a metal rod held in a holder.　The intense heat melts the metal of the work and at the same time heats the end of the electrode, causing small globules to form and cross the arc to the weld.　In gas welding, the heat is produced by a burning mixture of two gases, which ordinarily are oxygen and acetylene.　The weld is formed by melting a filler rod with the torch flame, along the line of contact, after the metal of the work has been preheated to a molten state. Resistance welding is a pressure process, the fusion being made through heat and mechanical pressure. The work is heated by a strong electrical current which passes through it until fusion temperature is reached; then pressure is applied to create the weld.

The forms of resistance welding are: butt welding, seam welding, spot welding, and flash welding. In spot welding, the parts are overlapped and welds are made at successive single spots. In butt welding, the pieces are so placed that they are butted; then the weld is made by heating electrically and squeezing the parts together. A seam weld is similar to a spot weld, except that a continuous weld is produced. In projection welding, one part is embossed and welds are made at the successive projections.

15.32. Types of welded joints. Fig. 15.42 shows the ordinary types of welded joints.

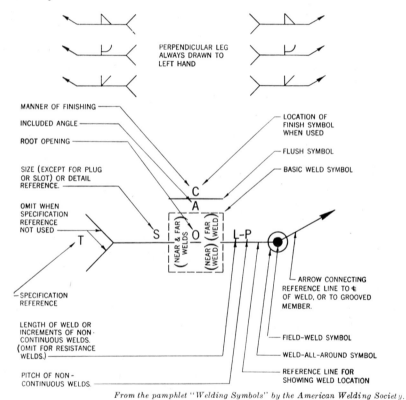

From the pamphlet "Welding Symbols" by the American Welding Society.

Fig. 15.43.   The basic welding symbol.

15.33. Welding symbols. An enlarged drawing of the approved welding symbol is shown in Fig. 15.43, along with explanatory notes which

indicate the proper locations of the marks and size dimensions necessary
for a complete description of a weld.

In order that they may be identified on a drawing and properly specified, welds are classified as *near welds* or *far welds*. A near weld is one
that is parallel to the plane of the paper and toward the observer.

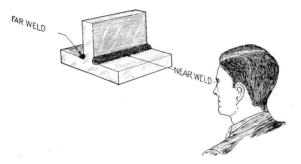

Fig. 15.44. Near welds and far welds.

The arrow is the basic portion of the symbol, as shown in Fig. 15.43.
It points to the joint where the required weld is to be made.

If the weld is on the near side, toward the observer, the symbol indicating the type of weld is placed below or to the right of the base line,
depending upon whether that line is horizontal or vertical. If the weld
is located on the far side, the symbol should be above or to the left.

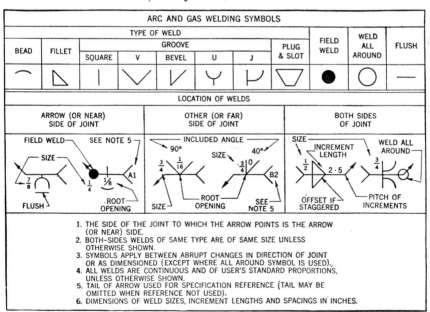

Fig. 15.45. Arc and gas welding symbols.

To indicate that a weld is to be made all around a connection, as is necessary when a piece of tubing must be welded to a plate, a weld-all-around symbol, a circle, is placed as shown in Fig. 15.43.

The size of a weld is given along the base of the arrow, at the side of the symbol, as shown in Fig. 15.45. If the welds on the near side and the far side of a lap joint are the same size, only one dimension should be given. If they are not the same size, each dimension should be placed beside its associated symbol.

15.34. Gas and arc welding symbols. In order to satisfy the need for a standard group of symbols which could be understood in all manufacturing plants, the American Welding Society recommended in 1940 a set of conventional symbols so designed that each symbol resembled in a general way the type of weld it represented. Fig. 15.45 shows a condensed table of symbols. The few examples given here show the proper construction of welding specifications.

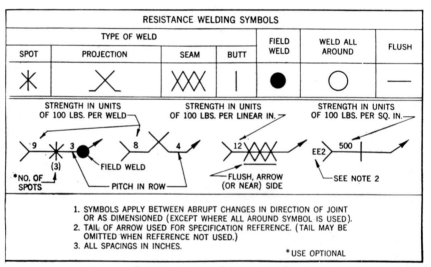

From the pamphlet "Welding Symbols" by the American Welding Society.

Fig. 15.46. Resistance welding symbols.

15.35. Resistance welding. Fig. 15.46 shows the symbols for the four principal types of resistance welding. The method of specifying resistance welds differs from the methods used for arc and gas welds. In the former, the strength of a weld is given in units instead of size, and the symbols do not show the form of the weld. In the table, the strength of spot and projection welds is given in units of 100 pounds per weld. The strength for seam welds is given in units of 100 pounds per linear inch, while for a butt weld the same units are applied to the square inch of weld.

PIPING

15.36. Since piping is used in all types of construction for conveying fluids and gases such as oil, water, steam, and chemicals, some knowledge of it is essential for the engineer, who must select and use pipe in the design of machines, power plants, water systems, and so on. There are so many types of fittings and materials used for various purposes that only the most common can be discussed in this chapter. Additional information may be obtained from publications of research associations and from the catalogs of manufacturers.

15.37. Specification of wrought-iron and steel pipe. The standardized weights commonly used are the standard, extra strong, and double extra strong. All are specified by the nominal inside diameter. All three weights of pipe for any given nominal diameter have the same outside diameter and can be used with the same fittings.

Wrought-iron or steel pipe greater than 12″ in diameter is specified by giving the outside diameter and the thickness of the wall.

15.38. Pipe fittings. Fittings are parts such as elbows, tees, crosses, couplings, nipples, flanges, and so on, which are used to make turns and connections. They fall into three general classes: screwed, welded, and flanged.

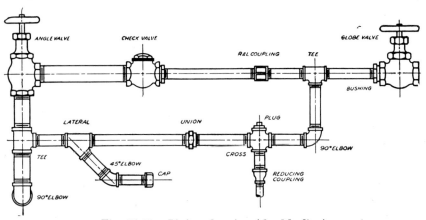

Fig. 15.47. Piping drawing (double-line).

In small piping systems screwed fittings are generally used (Fig. 15.50).

Welded fittings are used where connections are to be permanent (Fig. 15.48). They are manufactured of forged seamless steel, having the same thickness as the pipe. In this type of construction, the weld is depended upon to seal the joint and to carry the pipe-line stresses.

Flanged fittings are used in large piping systems where pressures are high and the connection must be strong enough to carry the weight of large pipes (Fig. 15.49).

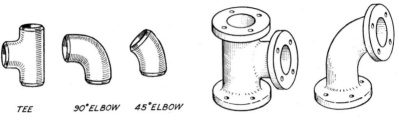

TEE	90°ELBOW	45°ELBOW

Fig. 15.48.   Welded fittings.   **Fig. 15.49.   Flanged fittings.**

15.39. Screwed fittings (Fig. 15.50).   Straight sections of pipe are connected by a short cylindrical fitting (threaded on the inside), which is known as a *coupling*.   A *right and left coupling*, which can be recognized by the ribs on the outside, is often used to close a system.   A *union* is preferable, however, where pipe must be frequently disconnected.

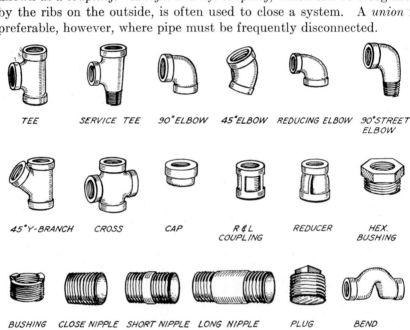

Fig. 15.50.   Screwed fittings.

A *cap* is screwed on the end of a pipe to close it.

A *plug* is used to close an opening in a fitting.

A *nipple* is a short piece of pipe that has been threaded on both ends. If it is threaded the entire length, it is called a *close nipple;* if not, it is called a *short* or *long nipple*.   Extra long nipples may be purchased.

A *bushing* is used to reduce the size of an opening in a fitting when it would be inconvenient to use a reducing fitting.

Tees, crosses, and *laterals* form the connections for lines and branches in a piping system.

Information on screwed fittings may be obtained from manufacturers' catalogs.

15.40. Specification of fittings. A fitting is specified by giving the nominal inside diameter of the pipe for which the openings are threaded, the type of fitting, and the material. If it connects more than one size of pipe, it is called a reducing fitting, and the largest opening of the through run is given first, followed in order by the opposite end and the outlet. Fig. 15.51 illustrates the order of specifying reducing fittings.

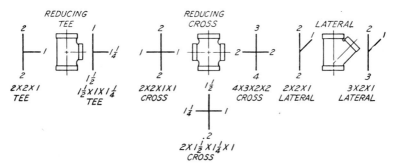

Fig. 15.51. *Specification of fittings.*

If all of the openings are for the same size of pipe, the fitting is known as a straight tee, cross, and so on. A straight fitting is specified by the size of the openings followed by the name of the fitting (2″ tee, 4″ cross, etc.).

15.41. Unions. Screwed or flanged unions connect pipes that must be frequently disconnected for the purpose of making repairs. In many cases, screwed unions are used for making the final closing connection in a line.

15.42. Valves. Valves are used in piping systems to stop or control the movement of fluids and gases. Information on valves may be found in manufacturers' catalogs.

15.43. Piping drawings. A piping drawing usually shows only the arrangement of a system in some conventional form, and gives the size and location of fittings. Read Sec. 8.16.

15.44. Conventional symbols. A few of the conventional symbols for fittings that have been approved by the American Standards Association are given in the Appendix.

15.45. Problems. Excellent practice in drawing (or sketching) the representations of threads, threaded fasteners, keys, and rivets is provided by the problems of this chapter.

1. Draw or sketch the layout shown in Fig. 15.52, and on it show the following fasteners: (1) On center line A-A draw a $\frac{3}{4}''$ unfinished hexagonal-head bolt and nut. (2) On center line B-B draw a $\frac{7}{8}''$ square-head bolt and nut. (3) On center line C-C draw a $\frac{3}{4}''$ fillister-head cap screw. (4) On center line D-D draw a $\frac{5}{8}''$ hexagonal head cap screw. Determine the measurements for the layout by using the given scale. Make each fastener a standard length. Use the schematic symbol for the representation of the threads.

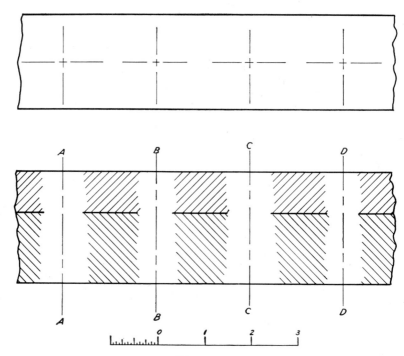

Fig. 15.52.

2. Draw or sketch the three layouts shown in Fig. 15.53 to full size, using the given scale to determine the measurements. On layout (1) complete the drawing to show a suitable fastener on center line A-A. On layout (2) show a $\frac{1}{2}''$ hexagonal-head cap screw on center line B-B. On layout (3) show a $\frac{3}{8}''$ button-head rivet on center line C-C and a No. 608 Woodruff key on center line D-D. Use the schematic symbol for the representation of threads.

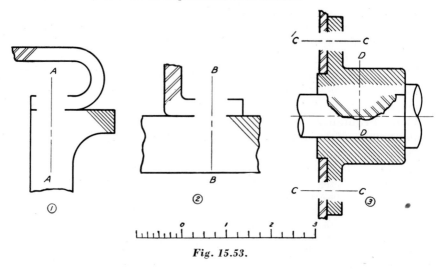

Fig. 15.53.

3. (Fig. 15.54.)   Reproduce the views of the assembly of the alignment bearing.   On C. L.'s. A show $\frac{1}{4}''$ button-head rivets (4 required).   On C. L. B show a $\frac{5}{16}'' \times \frac{1}{2}''$ Am. Std. square-head set screw.   Do not dimension the views.

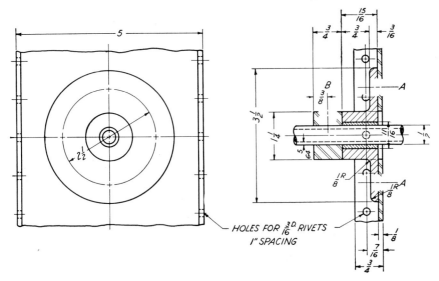

Fig. 15.54.   Alignment bearing.

4. (Fig. 15.55.)   Reproduce the views of the assembly of the impeller drive. On C. L.'s. A show $\frac{1}{4}''$-20 UNC $\times \frac{1}{2}''$ round-head machine screws and regular lock washers.   On C. L. B show a No. 406 Woodruff key.   On C. L. C show a standard No. 2 $\times 1\frac{1}{2}''$ taper pin.

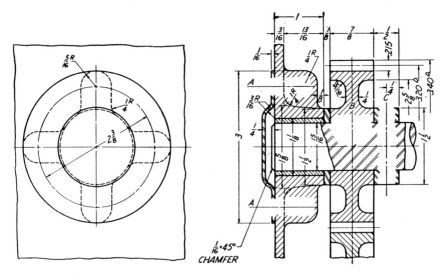

Fig. 15.55.   Impeller drive.

5. (Fig. 15.56.)   Reproduce the views of the assembly of the bearing head. On C. L.'s. A show $\frac{1}{2}''$-UNC studs with regular lock washers and regular semi-finished hexagonal nuts (4 required).   On C. L.'s. B show $\frac{3}{8}''$-UNC $\times$ $1\frac{1}{4}''$ hexagonal-head cap screws (2 required).   On C. L. C drill through and tap $\frac{1}{8}''$ pipe thread.

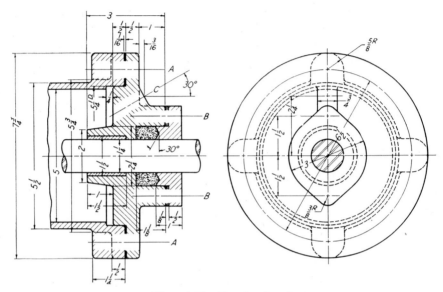

Fig. 15.56.   Bearing head.

6. (Fig. 15.57.)   Reproduce the views of the assembly of the air cylinder. On C. L. A-A at the left end of the shaft show a $1''$-UNF semifinished hexagonal nut.   At the right end show a hole tapped $\frac{3}{4}''$-UNF $\times$ $1\frac{1}{2}''$ deep.   Between the piston and the (right) end plate draw a spring $3''$ O.D., 5 full coils, $\frac{1}{4}''$ wire.   On C. L.'s. B show $\frac{3}{8}''$-UNC $\times$ $1\frac{1}{4}''$ hexagonal-head cap screws.   On C. L.'s. C draw $\frac{1}{4}''$-UNC $\times$ $\frac{3}{4}''$ flat-head cap screws with heads to the left.   On C. L. D show a $\frac{1}{4}''$ standard pipe thread.   On C. L.'s. E show $\frac{1}{2}''$-UNC $\times$ $1\frac{3}{4}''$ semifinished hexagonal-head bolts.   Use semifinished hexagonal nuts.   Show visible fasteners on the end view.

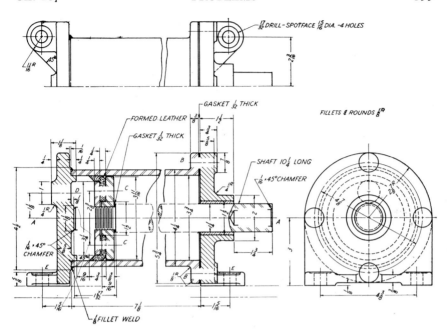

Fig. 15.57. Air cylinder.

7. (Fig. 15.58.) Make a sketch or drawing of an assigned part of the thermostatic radiator trap. Prepare correct specifications for threads.

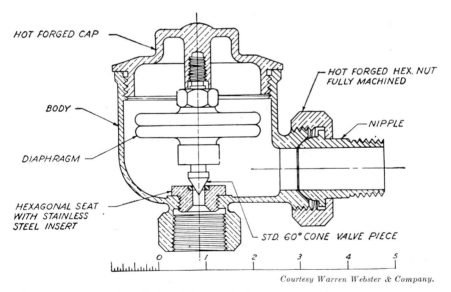

Courtesy Warren Webster & Company.

Fig. 15.58. Thermostatic radiator trap.

8. (Fig. 15.59.)   Make a sketch or drawing of an assigned part of the air cleaner.   For preparing a drawing, the dimensions can be determined by transferring them from the drawing to the accompanying scale with dividers.   Correct specifications should be prepared for all threads.   The views of a sketch or drawing may be completely dimensioned if the beginning sections of Chap. 16 are studied.

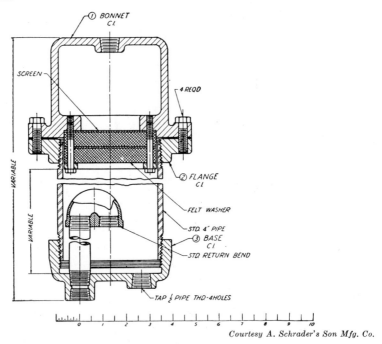

Courtesy A. Schrader's Son Mfg. Co.

Fig. 15.59.   Air cleaner.

9. (Fig. 15.60.)   Make a drawing or sketch of an assigned part of the check valve.   Prepare complete specifications for threads.   If the beginning sections of Chap. 16 are studied, complete detail sketches may be prepared.

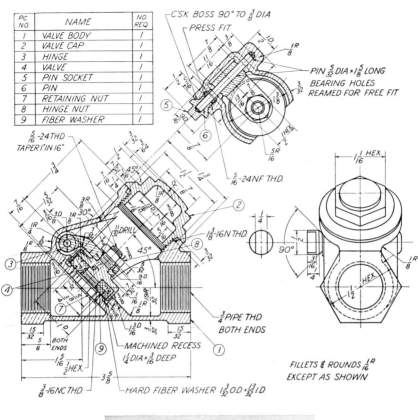

PC NO.	NAME	NO. REQ
1	VALVE BODY	1
2	VALVE CAP	1
3	HINGE	1
4	VALVE	1
5	PIN SOCKET	1
6	PIN	1
7	RETAINING NUT	1
8	HINGE NUT	1
9	FIBER WASHER	1

Fig. 15.60. Check valve.

10. (Fig. 15.61.)   Make a complete set of drawings or sketches of the parts of the vise.   Correct specifications should be given for threads.   Complete working (detail) drawings or sketches may be prepared if the student will first study the beginning sections of Chap. 16.

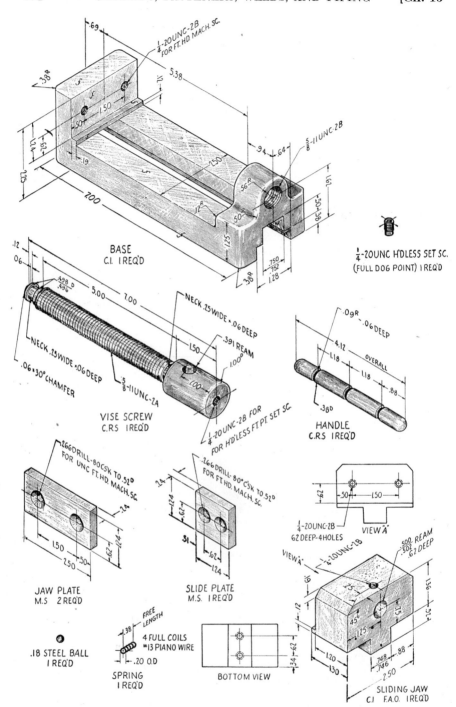

Fig. 15.61. Vise.

11. (Fig. 15.61.) Prepare an assembly drawing or assembly sketch of the vise.

12. (Fig. 15.62.) Make an assembly sketch or drawing of the flexible coupling.

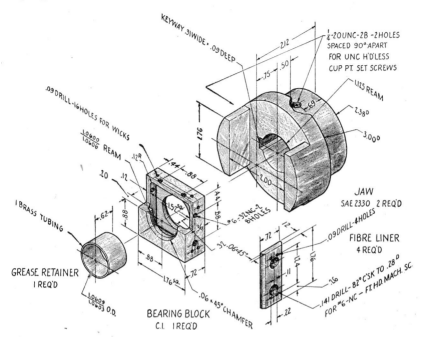

Fig. 15.62. *Flexible coupling.*

13. (Fig. 15.63.)   Prepare an assembly sketch or drawing of the Stock-rest.

14. (Fig. 15.63.)   Prepare a drawing or sketch of the stock-rest body.

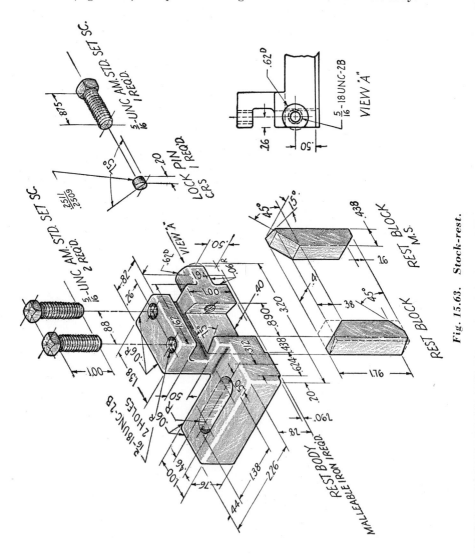

Fig. 15.63.   Stock-rest.

15. Prepare a welding drawing of the bracket shown in Fig. 15.64.

16. Prepare a welding drawing of the caster bracket shown in Fig. 15.65.   The length of the tubing is $2\frac{11}{16}''$.

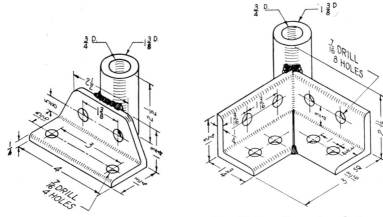

<table>
<tr><td>Fig. 15.64.   Bracket.</td><td>Fig. 15.65.   Caster bracket.</td></tr>
</table>

17. Make a single-line multiview sketch of the portion of a piping system shown in Fig. 8.22.

16

Size Description: Dimensions and Specifications

FUNDAMENTALS AND TECHNIQUES

16.1. A detail drawing, in addition to giving the shape of a part, must furnish information such as the distances between surfaces, locations of holes, kind of finish, type of material, number required, and so forth. The expression of this information on a drawing by the use of lines, symbols, figures, and notes is known as dimensioning.

Intelligent dimensioning requires engineering judgment and a thorough knowledge of the practices of pattern making, forging, and machining.

16.2. Theory of dimensioning. Any part may be dimensioned easily and systematically by dividing it into simple geometrical solids. Even complicated parts, when analyzed, usually are found to be composed principally of cylinders and prisms and, frequently, frustums of pyramids and cones. The dimensioning of an object may be accomplished by dimensioning each elemental form to indicate its size and relative location from a center line, base line, or finished surface. A machine drawing requires two types of dimensions: *size dimensions* and *location dimensions*.

16.3. Size dimensions (Fig. 16.2). Size dimensions give the size of a piece, component part, hole, or slot.

Fig. 16.1 should be carefully analyzed, as the placement of dimensions shown is applicable to the elemental parts of almost every piece.

The rule for placing the three principal dimensions (length, height, and depth) on the drawing of a prism or modification of a prism is: *Give two dimensions on the principal view and one dimension on one of the other views.*

The circular cylinder, which appears as a boss or shaft, requires only *the diameter and length, both of which are shown preferably on the rectangular view.* It is better practice to dimension a hole (negative cylinder) by giving the diameter and operation as a note on the contour view with a leader to the circle (Figs. 16.2 and 16.46).

Cones are dimensioned by giving *the diameter of the base and the altitude on the same view.* A taper is one example of a conical shape found on machine parts (Fig. 16.43).

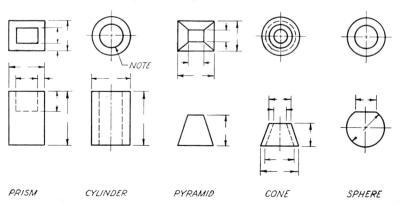

Fig. 16.1. Dimensioning geometrical shapes.

Pyramids, which frequently form a part of a structure, are dimensioned by giving *two dimensions on the view showing the shape of the base.*

A sphere requires only the diameter.

16.4. Location dimensions. Location dimensions fix the relationship of the component parts (projections, holes, slots, and other significant forms) of a piece or structure (Fig. 16.3). Particular care must be exercised in their selection and placing because upon them depend the accuracy of the operations in making a piece and the proper mating of the piece with other parts. To select location dimensions intelligently, one must first determine the contact surfaces, finished surfaces, and center lines of the elementary geometrical forms and, with the accuracy

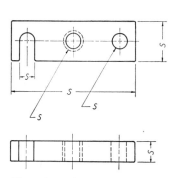

Fig. 16.2. Size dimensions.

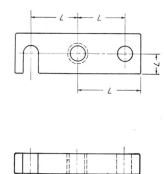

Fig. 16.3. Location dimensions.

demanded and the method of production in mind, decide from what other surface or center line each should be located. Mating location dimensions must be given from the same center line or finished surface on both pieces.

Location dimensions may be from center to center, surface to center, or surface to surface.

16.5. Procedure in dimensioning. The theory of dimensioning may be applied in six steps, as follows:

1. Mentally divide the object into its component geometrical shapes.

2. Place the size dimensions on each form.

3. Select the locating center lines and surfaces after giving careful consideration to mating parts and to the processes of manufacture.

4. Place the location dimensions so that each geometrical form is located from a center line or finished surface.

5. Add the over-all dimensions. (These are usually the summation of the included dimensions in the direction of the length, height, and depth.)

6. Complete the dimensioning by adding the necessary notes.

16.6. Placing dimensions. Dimensions must be placed where they will be most easily understood—in the locations where the reader will

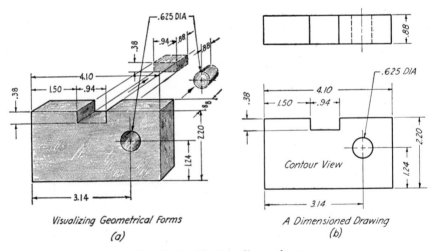

Visualizing Geometrical Forms
(a)

A Dimensioned Drawing
(b)

Fig. 16.4. Placing dimensions.

expect to find them. They generally are attached to the view that shows the contour of the features to which they apply, and a majority of them usually will appear on the principal view (Fig. 16.4). Except in cases where special convenience and ease in reading are desired, or when a dimension would be so far from the form to which it referred that it might be misinterpreted, dimensions should be placed outside a view. They should appear directly on a view only when clarity demands.

All extensions and dimension lines should be drawn before the arrowheads have been filled in or the dimensions, notes, and titles have been lettered. Spacing dimension lines $\frac{1}{2}''$ from the view and $\frac{3}{8}''$ from each other provides an ample distance to satisfy the one rule to which there is no exception: *Never crowd dimensions.* Although it sometimes may be necessary to reduce the distance between dimension lines to a minimum of $\frac{1}{4}''$, the spacing should be uniform throughout. If the location of a dimension forces a poor location on other dimensions, its shifting may allow all to be placed more advantageously without sacrificing clearness. Important location dimensions should be given where they will be conspicuous, even if a size dimension must be moved.

16.7. Dimensioning practices. A generally recognized system of lines, symbols, figures, and notes is used to indicate size and location. Fig. 16.5 illustrates dimensioning terms and notation.

A *dimension line* is lightweight and continuous, broken only near the center to receive the figure giving the distance that it indicates. It is terminated at each end by an arrowhead whose point touches the extension line (Fig. 16.5).

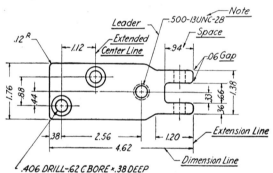

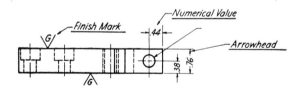

Fig. 16.5.   Terms and dimensioning notation.

Extension lines are light continuous lines extending from a view to indicate the extent of a measurement given by a dimension line that is located outside of a view. They start $\frac{1}{16}''$ from the view and extend $\frac{1}{8}''$ beyond the dimension line (Fig. 16.5).

Arrowheads are drawn for each dimension line, before the figures are lettered. They are made with the same pen or pencil used for the lettering.   The size of an arrowhead, although it may vary with the size of a drawing, should be uniform on any one drawing.   To have the proper proportions, the length of an arrowhead must be approximately three times its spread (American Standard).   This length for average work is usually $\frac{1}{8}''$.   Fig. 16.6 shows an enlarged drawing of an arrowhead of correct proportions.   Although many draftsmen draw an arrowhead with one stroke, the beginner will get better results by using two slightly concaved strokes drawn toward the point (Fig. 16.7a) or, as shown in Fig. 16.7(b), one stroke drawn to the point and one away from it.

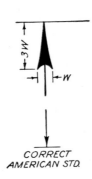

CORRECT
AMERICAN STD.

Fig. 16.6.   Arrowheads.

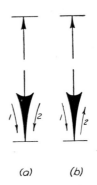

(a)   (b)

Fig. 16.7.   Formation of arrowheads.

A *leader* or *pointer* is a light continuous line (terminated by an arrowhead) that extends from a note to the feature of a piece to which the note applies (Fig. 16.8).   It should be made with a straightedge and should not be curved or made freehand (American Standard's recommendation).

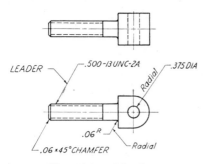

Fig. 16.8.   A leader.

A leader pointing to a curve should be radial, and the first $\frac{1}{8}''$ of it should be in a line with the note (Fig. 16.8).

Finish marks indicate the particular surfaces of a rough casting or forging that are to be machined or "finished."   They are placed in all views, across the visible or invisible lines that are the edge views of surfaces to be machined (Fig. 16.10).

The modified italic *f*, shown in Fig. 16.9(a), is still widely used in spite of the fact that new forms have been recommended by the American Standards Association.   The student will find that careful adherence to the dimensions illustrated here will improve the appearance of those on his drawing.

Fig. 16.9(*b*) shows the ASA recommended 60 degree *V* with its point touching the line view of the surface to be machined. In commercial practice a code letter oftentimes is used to indicate the type of machining required. The code letter or letters are placed in the *V* as shown in (*c*).

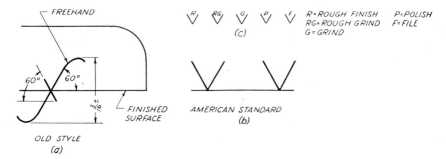

R = ROUGH FINISH   P = POLISH
RG = ROUGH GRIND   F = FILE
G = GRIND

(*c*)

AMERICAN STANDARD
(*b*)

FINISHED SURFACE

OLD STYLE
(*a*)

FREEHAND

Fig. 16.9. Finish marks.

It is not necessary to show finish marks on drilled or reamed holes, when the finish is specified as an operation in a note, such as $\frac{3}{4}''$ Drill or $1''$ Ream. They are also omitted, and a title note, "finish all over," is substituted, if the piece is to be completely machined.

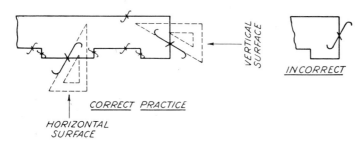

VERTICAL SURFACE

INCORRECT

CORRECT PRACTICE

HORIZONTAL SURFACE

Fig. 16.10. Placing "*f*" marks.

Dimension figures should be lettered either horizontally or vertically with the whole numbers equal in height to the capital letters in the notes. Guide lines and slope lines must be used. Figures must be legible; otherwise, they might be misinterpreted and cause errors which would be embarrassing to the engineer or draftsman.

DIMENSIONING MACHINE DRAWINGS

16.8. Since the use of the decimal system for expressing dimensional values has made rapid gains in American industry and is now accepted in the aircraft and automotive fields, many of the examples in this portion of this chapter will show decimal dimensions (read Sec. 2.15). At present, the fractional system, which dominated the whole of American industry until the Ford Motor Company adopted the decimal-inch some twenty-five years ago, is still used widely in those fields that are not under the direct influence of the automotive and aircraft companies. How long the present co-existence of the two systems will last can not be foretold. It could be only a few years or it could be many years before the decimal system completely replaces the fractional system.

However, this need not be of great concern to the student, for he should be primarily interested in the selection and placement of dimensions. At a later time he will find it easy to use either the fractional or decimal systems as is required in his field of employment. To assist one to use either system, a Standard Conversion Table has been provided in the Appendix (Table I).

16.9. Fractional dimensioning. For ordinary work, where accuracy is relatively unimportant, shopmen work to nominal dimensions given as common fractions of an inch, as $\frac{1}{2}, \frac{1}{4}, \frac{1}{8}, \frac{1}{16}, \frac{1}{32}, \frac{1}{64}$. When dimensions are given in this way, many large corporations specify the required accuracy through a note on the drawing that reads as follows: *Permissible variations on common fraction dimensions to machined surfaces to be plus or minus .010 unless otherwise specified.* It should be understood that the allowable variations will differ among manufacturing concerns because of the varying degrees of accuracy required for different types of work.

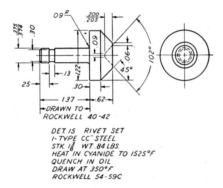

Fig. 16.11. Ford Motor Company decimal system.

16.10. Decimal dimensioning. The ASA recommendation given in the American Standard for Drawings and Drafting Room Practice (ASA Z14.1–1946) reads as follows:

The fundamental basis of the complete decimal system is the use of a two-place decimal, *i.e.*, a decimal consisting of two figures after the decimal point. In all dimensions where a fraction would ordinarily be used, the two-place decimal can be applied. The figures after the decimal point, where applicable, should be in fiftieths (*e.g.*, .02, .04, .08, .84) so that when halved (*e.g.*, diameters to radii) two-place decimals will result. Exceptions, of course, will have to be made, but they should be kept to a minimum.

Fig. 16.11 shows a drawing that was obtained from the Ford Motor Company.

16.11. General dimensioning practices. The reasonable application of the selected dimensioning practices that follow should enable a student to dimension acceptably. The practices in boldfaced type should never be violated. In fact, these have been so definitely established by practice that they might be called rules.

1. Place dimensions so that they can be read from the bottom and right side of the drawing (Fig. 16.12). An exception to this rule should be made in the preparation of drawings in the aircraft and automotive fields. These industries, along with a few manufacturing firms in other fields, use the unidirectional system under which all dimensions are made to read from the bottom of the sheet (Fig. 16.13). This system is also suitable for very large drawings.

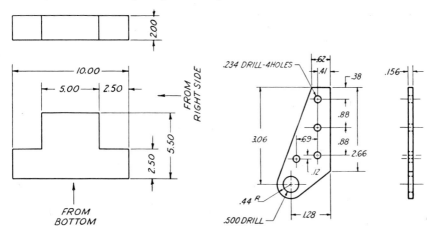

Fig. 16.12.   *Reading dimensions.*   Fig. 16.13.   *Unidirectional system.*

2. Place dimensions outside a view, unless they will be more easily and quickly understood if shown on it (Fig. 16.13).

3. Place dimensions between views unless the rules such as the contour rule, the rule against crowding, and so forth, prevent their being so placed.

4. Do not use an object line or a center line as a dimension line.

5. Locate dimension lines so that they will not cross extension lines.

6. If possible, avoid crossing two dimension lines.

7. A center line may be extended to serve as an extension line (Fig. 16.14).

8. Keep parallel dimensions equally spaced (usually $\frac{3}{8}''$ apart) and the figures staggered (Fig. 16.16).

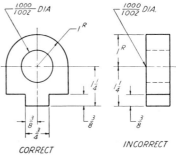

Fig. 16.14.   *Contour principle of dimensioning.*

9. Always give locating dimensions to the centers of circles that represent holes, cylindrical projections, or bosses (Fig. 16.16).

10. If possible, attach the location dimensions for holes to the view upon which they appear as circles (Fig. 16.16).

11. Group related dimensions on the view showing the contour of a feature (Fig. 16.14).

12. Arrange a series of dimensions in a continuous line (Fig. 16.15).

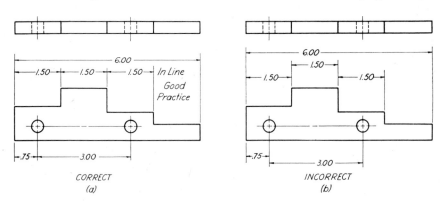

Fig. 16.15.   Consecutive dimensions.

13. Dimension from a finished surface, center line, or base line that can be readily established (Fig. 16.16).

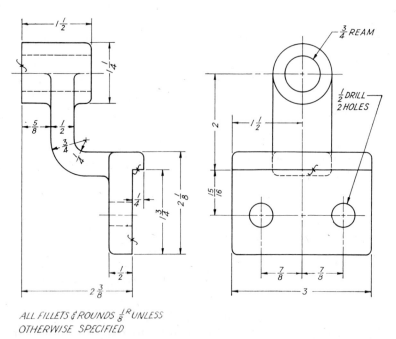

ALL FILLETS & ROUNDS ⅛ᴿ UNLESS OTHERWISE SPECIFIED

Fig. 16.16.   Dimensioning a bracket.

14. Stagger the figures in a series of parallel dimension lines to allow sufficient space for the figures and to prevent confusion (Fig. 16.17).

15. Place longer dimensions outside shorter ones so that extension lines will not cross dimension lines (Fig. 16.16).

16. Give three over-all dimensions located outside any other dimensions (unless the piece has cylindrical ends).

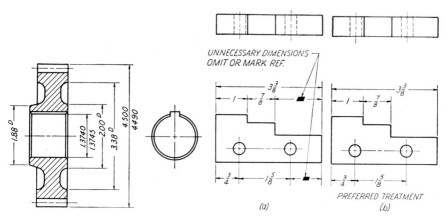

Fig. 16.17.   *Parallel dimensions.*   Fig. 16.18.   *Omit unnecessary dimensions.*

17. When an over-all is given, one intermediate distance should be omitted unless noted (REF) as being given for reference (Fig. 16.18).

18. Do not repeat a dimension.   One of the duplicated dimensions may be missed if a change is made.   Give only those dimensions that are necessary to produce or inspect the part.

19. Make decimal points of a sufficient size so that dimensions cannot be misread.

20. When dimension figures appear on a sectional view, show them in a small uncrosshatched portion so that they may be easily read.   This may be accomplished by doing the section lining after the dimensioning has been completed (Fig. 16.19).

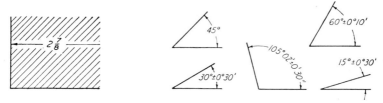

Fig. 16.19.   *Dimension figures on*   Fig. 16.20.   *Angular dimensions.*
        a section view.

21. When an arc is used as a dimension line for an angular measurement, use the vertex of the angle as the center (Fig. 16.20).

22. Place the figures of angular dimensions so they will read from the bottom of a drawing, except in the case of large angles (Fig. 16.20).

23. Show the diameter of a circle, never the radius. If it is not clear that the dimension is a diameter, the figures should be followed by the abbreviation *D* (Figs. 16.21 and 16.22). Often this will allow the elimination of one view.

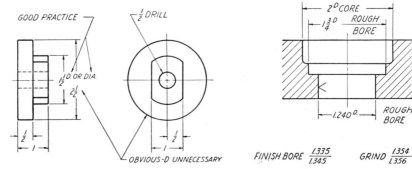

Fig. 16.21.   **Dimensioning a cylindrical piece.**   Fig. 16.22.   **Dimensioning cored and bored holes.**

24. Always dimension an arc by giving its radius followed by the abbreviation *R*, and indicate the center with a small cross. (Note that the arrowhead is omitted at the center in Fig. 16.23.)

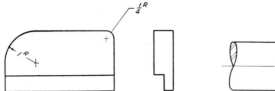

Fig. 16.23.   **Dimensioning radii.**   Fig. 16.24.   **Dimensioning a piece with a spherical end.**

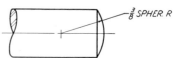

25. When dimensioning a portion of a sphere with a radius the term SPHER. R is added (Fig. 16.24).

26. Letter all notes horizontally.

27. Letter the word *bore* or *core* with the diameter of bored or cored holes (Fig. 16.22).

28. Give the diameter of a circular hole, never the radius, because all hole-forming tools are specified by diameter. If the hole does not go through the piece, the depth may be given as a note (Fig. 16.25).

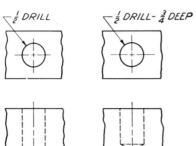

Fig. 16.25.   **Dimensioning holes.**

29. Never crowd dimensions into small spaces. Use the practical methods suggested in Fig. 16.26.

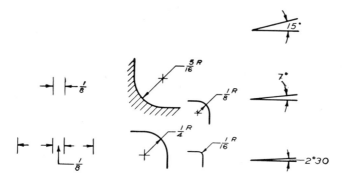

Fig. 16.26.   Dimensioning in limited spaces.

30. Avoid placing inclined dimensions in the shaded areas shown in Fig. 16.27. Place them so that they may be conveniently read from the right side of the drawing. If this is not desirable, make the figures read from the left in the direction of the dimension line (Fig. 16.28a). The unidirectional method is shown in (b).

31. Omit superfluous dimensions. Do not supply dimensional information for the same feature in two different ways.

32. Give dimensions up to 72″ in inches, except on structural and architectural drawings (Fig. 16.29). Omit the inch marks when all dimensions are in inches.

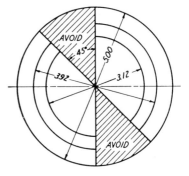

Fig. 16.27.   Areas to avoid.

33. Show dimensions in feet and inches as illustrated in Fig. 16.30. Note that the use of the hyphen in (a) and (b), and the cipher in (b), eliminates any chance of uncertainty and misinterpretation.

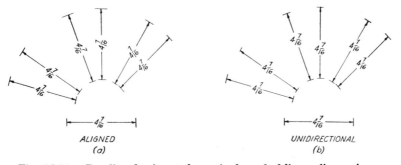

Fig. 16.28.   Reading horizontal, vertical, and oblique dimensions.

Fig. 16.29.   Dimension values.

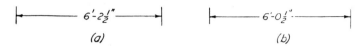

Fig. 16.30.   *Feet and inches.*

34. If feasible, design a piece and its elemental parts to such dimensions as $\frac{3}{8}''$, $\frac{1}{2}''$, $\frac{5}{8}''$, $\frac{3}{4}''$, and $\frac{7}{8}''$. Avoid such fractions as $\frac{17}{32}''$ and $\frac{19}{64}''$.

35. Dimension a 45° chamfer by giving the width and angle as a note (Fig. 16.31a) or as shown in (b).

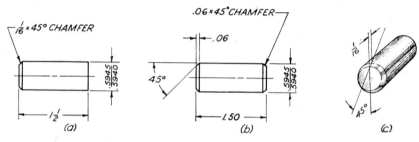

Fig. 16.31.   *Dimensioning a chamfer.*

36. Dimension equally spaced holes in a circular flange by giving the diameter of the bolt circle, across the circular center line, and the size and number of holes in a note.

37. When holes are unequally spaced in a circular flange, give the angles as illustrated in Fig. 16.32.

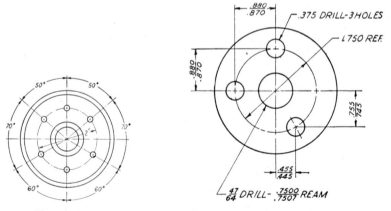

Fig. 16.32.   *Unequally spaced holes.**   Fig. 16.33.   *Accurate location dimensioning of holes.*

38. Holes that must be very accurately located should be dimensioned using a co-ordinate method (Fig. 16.33) rather than through the use of angular measurements as illustrated in Fig. 16.32.

---

* ASA Z14.1–1946.

39. Dimension a curved line by giving offsets (Fig. 16.34) or radii (Fig. 16.35).

40. Show an offset dimension line for an arc having an inaccessible center. Locate with true dimensions the point placed in a convenient location that represents the true center (Fig. 16.35).

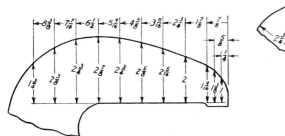

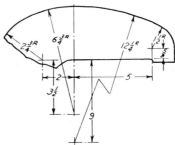

Fig. 16.34. Dimensioning curves by offsets.*

Fig. 16.35. Dimensioning curves by radii.*

41. Dimension, as required by the method of production, a piece with rounded ends. (See Figs. 16.36–16.39.)

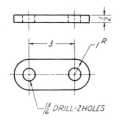

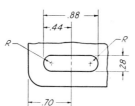

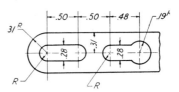

Fig. 16.36. Dimensioning a piece with rounded ends.

Fig. 16.37. Slot to provide for adjustment.

Fig. 16.38. Slots performing a mechanical function.

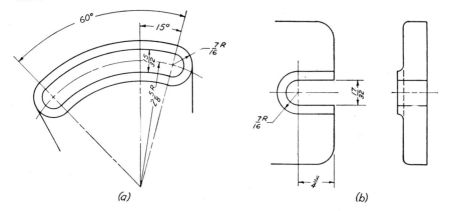

Fig. 16.39. Dimensioning semicircular features.

* ASA Z14.1–1946.

a. Give radii and center-to-center distance on parts that would be laid out by using centers and radii. Do not show an over-all dimension. It is not required. (See Fig. 16.36.)

b. Slots that are to provide for adjustment are dimensioned by over-all length and width dimensions and are located by dimensions given to their center lines (Fig. 16.37).

c. Slots that are to perform a mechanical function are dimensioned from center-to-center as two partial holes. The R is given to indicate a true radius. Slots of this type are subject to gage inspection (Fig. 16.38).

d. Give the width and over-all length for Pratt and Whitney keyways because this is the manner in which the keys are specified.

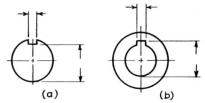

(a)   (b)

*Fig. 16.40. Dimensioning keyways.**

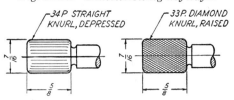

*Fig. 16.41. Dimensioning knurls to provide grip.**

42. A keyway on a shaft should be dimensioned as shown in Fig. 16.40(a). If the keyway is in a hub it is dimensioned as shown in (b).

43. When knurls are to provide a rough surface for better grip, it is necessary to specify the pitch and kind of knurl as shown in Fig. 16.41.

44. In sheet metal work mold lines are used in dimensioning instead of the centers of the arcs (Fig. 16.42). A mold (construction) line is the line at the intersection of the plane surfaces adjoining a bend.

45. Dimension standard and special tapers as illustrated in Fig. 16.43.

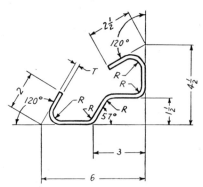

*Fig. 16.42. Profile dimensioning.**

a. Special tapers may be dimensioned by giving one diameter, the length, and a note.

* ASA Z14.1–1946.

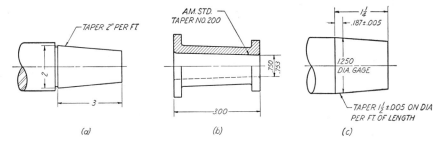

Fig. 16.43.   Dimensioning tapers.

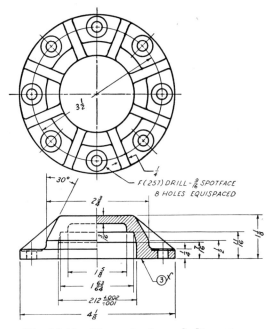

Fig. 16.44.   Dimensioning a half section.

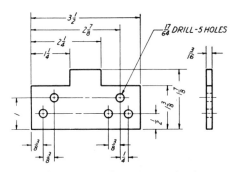

Fig. 16.45.   Base line dimensioning.

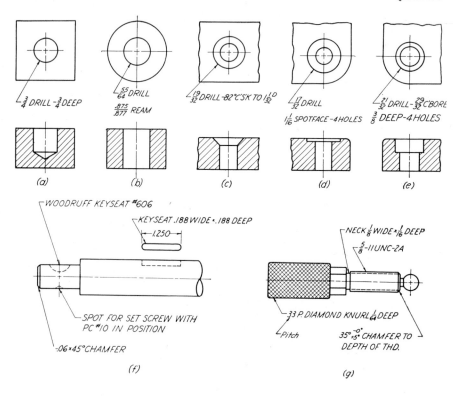

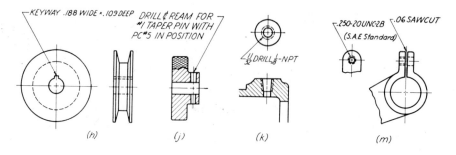

Fig. 16.46. Shop notes.

b. Standard tapers require one diameter, the length, and a note specifying the taper by number.

c. Tapers may be dimensioned with tolerances by giving a diameter with its location as shown in (c).

46. A half section may be dimensioned through the use of hidden lines on the external portion of the view (Fig. 16.44).

47. Make dimensioning complete, so that it will not be necessary for a workman to add or subtract to obtain a desired dimension or to scale the drawing.

16.12. Base-line dimensioning. In certain types of precision work, principally diemaking, all dimensions are given from base lines. These may be finished surfaces at right angles or important center lines. The use of this method prevents cumulative errors, as each dimension is independent of the others (Fig. 16.45).

16.13. Notes (Fig. 16.46). The use of properly composed notes often adds clarity to the presentation of dimensional information involving specific operations. Notes also are used to convey supplementary instructions about the kind of material, kind of fit, degree of finish, and so forth. It is good practice to specify a dimension representing a tool operation or a series of tool operations by a note rather than by figured dimensions. Brevity in form is desirable for notes of general information or specific instruction.

RULES FOR THE FORMULATION AND PLACEMENT OF SHOP NOTES

1. Give the size first, then the machining operation.

Example: $\frac{17}{32}$ *Drill.*

2. In the case of threaded parts, use the terminology recommended by the ASA for the American-British unified thread.

Example: $\frac{1}{2}$ 13UNC–2A. Read Sec. 15.13.

3. Where there are several holes alike in a group, use one note and indicate the number of holes.

Example: $\frac{1}{2}$ *Drill– 4 Holes.*

4. Where there are two or more similar groups, repeat the entire note for each group.

5. For drilled holes and reamed holes, give the diameter, the operation required, and the depth. If the hole goes all the way through the piece, the depth should be omitted.

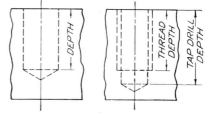

Fig. 16.47. Depth of drilled and tapped holes.

6. For a tapped (threaded) hole, give the tap-drill size, the diameter

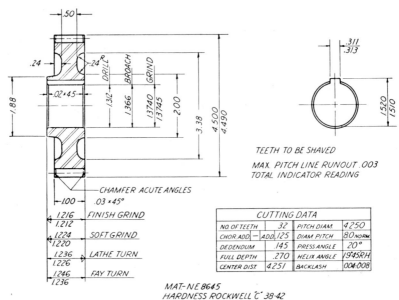

TEETH TO BE SHAVED

MAX. PITCH LINE RUNOUT .003
TOTAL INDICATOR READING

CUTTING DATA			
NO.OF TEETH	32	PITCH DIAM.	4.250
CHOR.ADD.	—ADD..125	DIAM PITCH	8.0 NORM.
DEDENDUM	.145	PRESS ANGLE	20°
FULL DEPTH	.270	HELIX ANGLE	19°45'RH
CENTER DIST.	4.251	BACKLASH	.004-.008

MAT-N.E.8645
HARDNESS ROCKWELL "C" 38-42

Courtesy Fairfield Mfg. Co.

Fig. 16.48. Dimensions and specifications for a helical gear.

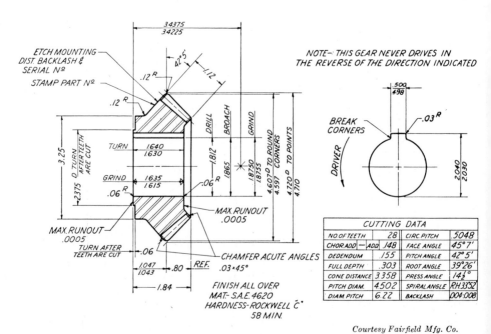

NOTE-: THIS GEAR NEVER DRIVES IN
THE REVERSE OF THE DIRECTION INDICATED

CUTTING DATA			
NO.OF TEETH	28	CIRC PITCH	.5048
CHOR.ADD.	—ADD..148	FACE ANGLE	45°7'
DEDENDUM	.155	PITCH ANGLE	42°5'
FULL DEPTH	.303	ROOT ANGLE	39°26'
CONE DISTANCE	3.358	PRESS ANGLE	14½°
PITCH DIAM.	4.502	SPIRAL ANGLE	RH.33°52'
DIAM PITCH	6.22	BACKLASH	.004-.008

Courtesy Fairfield Mfg. Co.

Fig. 16.49. Dimensions and specifications for a spiral bevel gear.

of the screw, the number of threads per inch, the kind of thread, and the class of fit (Fig. 15.12). The depth is omitted if the hole goes all the way through the piece. Depth measurements for drilled and tapped holes are shown in Fig. 16.47.

7. Locate the notes for a piece in such a way that they will not overlap the adjacent views of another piece on the same drawing.

8. When putting a shop note for a hole on a drawing, if possible make the leader point to the circular view.

16.14. Dimensioning gears. When dimensioning gears, it is recommended that the dimensions be given with the view or views as shown in Figs. 16.48 and 16.49 and that the cutting data be incorporated in an accompanying table.

LIMIT DIMENSIONING AND GEOMETRIC TOLERANCING

16.15. Limit dimensions. Present-day competitive manufacturing requires quantity production and interchangeability for many closely

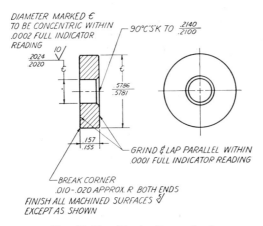

Fig. 16.50. Limit dimensioning.

mating parts. The production of each of these mating parts to an exact decimal dimension, although theoretically possible, is economically unfeasible, since the cost of a part rapidly increases as an absolute correct size is approached. For this reason, the commercial draftsman specifies an allowable error (tolerance) between decimal limits (Fig. 16.50). The determination of these limits depends upon the accuracy and clearance required for the moving parts to function satisfactorily in the machine. Although manufacturing experience is often used to determine the proper limits for the parts of a mechanism, it is better and safer practice to adhere to the fits recommended by the American Standards Association in ASA B4.1–1955. This standard applies to fits between plain cylindrical parts. Recommendations are made for preferred sizes, allowances, tolerances, and fits for use where applicable. Up to a diameter of 20 inches the standard is in accordance with ABC (American-British-Canadian) conference agreements.

There are many factors that a designer must take into consideration when selecting fits for a particular application. These factors might be the bearing load, speed, lubrication, materials, and length of engagement. Frequently temperature and humidity must be taken into account. Considerable practical experience is necessary to make a selection of fits or to make the subsequent adjustments that might be needed to satisfy critical functional requirements. In addition, manufacturing economy must never be overlooked.

Those interested in the selection of fits should consult texts on machine design and technical publications, for coverage of this phase of the dimensioning of cylindrical parts is not within the scope of this book. However, since it is desirable to be able to determine limits of size following the selection of a fit, attention in this section will be directed to the use of Table XVII. Whenever the fit to be used for a particular application has not been specified in the instructions for a problem or has not been given on the drawing, the student should consult his instructor after a tentative choice has been made based on the brief descriptions of fits as given in this section.

To compute limit dimensions it is necessary to understand the following associated terms.*

Nominal Size. The nominal size is the designation which is used for the purpose of general identification.

Basic Size. The basic size is that size from which the limits of size are derived by the application of allowances and tolerances.

Allowance. An allowance is an intentional difference between the maximum material limits of mating parts. It is a minimum clearance (positive allowance) or maximum interference (negative allowance) between mating parts.

Tolerance. A tolerance is the total permissible variation of a size. The tolerance is the difference between the limits of size.

Limits of Size. The limits of size are the applicable maximum and minimum sizes.

Fit. Fit is the general term used to signify the range of tightness which may result from the application of a specific combination of allowances and tolerances in the design of mating parts.

Clearance Fit. A clearance fit is one having limits of size so prescribed that a clearance always results when mating parts are assembled.

Interference Fit. An interference fit is one having limits of size so prescribed that an interference always results when mating parts are assembled.

Transition Fit. A transition fit is one having limits of size so prescribed that either a clearance or an interference may result when mating parts are assembled.

---

* Extracted from American Standard Preferred Limits and Fits for Cylindrical Parts (ASA B4.1–1955) with permission of the publisher, The American Society of Mechanical Engineers, 29 W. 39th St., New York, 18, N.Y.

Basic Hole System. A basic hole system is a system of fits in which the design size of the hole is the basic size and the allowance is applied to the shaft.

Basic Shaft System. A basic shaft system is a system of fits in which the design size of the shaft is the basic size and the allowance is applied to the hole.

Tables XVII-A, B, C, D, and E cover three general types of fits: running fits, locational fits, and force fits. For educational purposes standard fits may be designated by means of letter symbols as follows:

RC—Running or Sliding Fit
LC—Locational Clearance Fit
LT—Transition Fit
LN—Locational Interference Fit
FN—Force or Shrink Fit

It should be understood that these letters are not to appear on working drawings. Only the limits for sizes are shown.

When a number is added to these letter symbols, a complete fit is represented. For example FN4 specifies, symbolically a class 4, force fit for which the limits of size for mating parts may be determined from use of Table XVII-E. The minimum and maximum limits of clearance or interference for a particular application may be read directly from this table.

Classes of fits as given in these tables are as follows:

Running and sliding fits—Classes RC1 through RC9
Clearance locational fits—Classes LC1 through LC11
Transition locational fits—Classes LT1 through LT7
Interference locational fits—Classes LN2 and LN3
Force and shrink fits—Classes FN1 through FN5

*Running and Sliding Fits.** Running and sliding fits are intended to provide a similar running performance, with suitable lubrication allowance, throughout the range of sizes. The clearances for the first two classes, used chiefly as slide fits, increase more slowly with diameter than the other classes, so that accurate location is maintained even at the expense of free relative motion.

A brief description of the fits is given here. For a more complete understanding one should read and study the standard.

RC1—Close sliding fits are intended for accurate location of parts which must assemble without perceptible play.

RC2—Sliding fits are intended for accurate location but with greater maximum clearance than Class RC1.

RC3—Precision running fits are about the closest fits which can be expected to run freely and are intended for precision work at slow speeds and light journal pressures, ...

RC4—Close running fits are intended chiefly for running fits on accurate machinery with moderate surface speeds and journal pressures. . . . .

---

* Extracted from American Standard Preferred Limits and Fits for Cylindrical Parts (ASA B4.1–1955).

RC5⎫ Medium running fits are intended for higher running speeds, or heavy
RC6⎭ journal pressures, or both.

RC7—Free running fits are intended for use where accuracy is not essential
or where large temperature variations are likely to be encountered,

. . . .

RC8⎫ Loose running fits are intended for use where materials such as cold-
RC9⎭ rolled shafting and tubing, made to commercial tolerances, are
involved.

*Locational Fits.** Locational fits are divided into three groups: clearance fits
(LC), transition fits (LT), and interference fits (LN).

LC. Locational clearance fits are intended for parts which are normally
stationary, but which can be freely assembled or disassembled. They run from
snug fits for parts requiring accuracy of location, through the medium clearance
fits for parts such as spigots, to the closer fastener fits where freedom of assembly
is of prime importance.

LN. Locational interference fits are used where accuracy of location is of
prime importance, and for parts requiring rigidity and alignment with no special
requirements for bore pressure.

*Force Fits.** Force or shrink fits constitute a special type of interference fit,
normally characterized by maintenance of constant bore pressures throughout
the range of sizes.

FN1—Light drive fits are those requiring light assembly pressures, and
produce more or less permanent assemblies.

FN2—Medium drive fits are suitable for ordinary steel parts, or for shrink
fits on light sections.

FN3—Heavy drive fits are suitable for heavier steel parts, or for shrink fits
in medium sections.

FN4⎫ Force fits are suitable for parts which can be highly stressed, or for
FN5⎭ shrink fits where the heavy pressing forces required are impractical.

16.16. Computation of limits of size for cylindrical parts. To
obtain the correct fit between two engaging parts, compute limit dimensions that modify the nominal size of both. Numerical values of the
modifications necessary to obtain the proper allowance and tolerances
for various diameters for all fits mentioned previously are given in Tables
XVII-A, B, C, D, and E in the Appendix.

The two systems in common use for computing limit dimensions are
(1) the basic hole system, and (2) the basic shaft system. The same
American Standard tables may be used conveniently for both systems.

16.17. Basic hole system. Because most limit dimensions are computed on the basic hole system, the illustrated example shown in Fig. 16.51
involves the use of this system. If, as is the usual case, the nominal size
is known, all that is necessary to determine the limits is to convert the
nominal size to the basic hole size and apply the figures given under
"standard limits," adding or substracting (according to their signs) to or
from the basic size to obtain the limits for both the hole and the shaft.

* Extracted from American Standard Preferred Limits and Fits for Cylindrical
Parts (ASA B4.1–1955).

EXAMPLE:

Suppose that a $\frac{1}{2}''$ shaft is to have a class RC6 fit in a $\frac{1}{2}''$ hole (Fig. 16.51a). The nominal size of the hole is $\frac{1}{2}''$. The basic hole size is the exact theoretical size 0.5000.

From Table XVII-A it is found that the hole may vary between plus 0.0000 and plus 0.0010, and the shaft between -0.0012 and -0.0022. The tolerance on both mating parts is 0.0010, and the allowance (minimum clearance) is 0.0012 as given in the table.

$$\text{The limits on the hole are:} \frac{(0.5000 \text{ plus } 0.0000)}{(0.5000 \text{ plus } 0.0010)} = \frac{0.5000}{0.5010}$$

$$\text{The limits on the shaft are:} \frac{(0.5000 - 0.0012)}{(0.5000 - 0.0022)} = \frac{0.4988}{0.4978}$$

The limits are placed in the order in which they will be approached when the part is machined (Fig. 16.51c). The minimum limit should appear above the line for an internal dimension, and the maximum limit above for an external dimension.

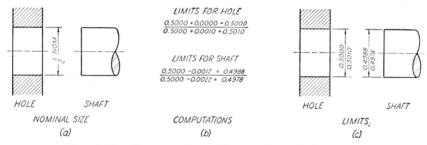

Fig. 16.51. *Computation of limits—basic hole system.*

16.18. Basic shaft system. When a number of parts requiring different fits but having the same nominal size must be mounted upon a shaft, the basic shaft system is used because it is much easier to adjust the limits for the holes than to machine a shaft of one nominal diameter to a number of different sets of limits required by different fits.

For basic shaft fits the maximum size of the shaft is basic. The limits of clearance or interference are the same as those shown in Tables XVII-A, B, C, D and E for the corresponding fits. The symbols for basic shaft fits are identical with those used for the standard fits with a letter S added. For example LC4S, specifies a clearance locational fit, class 4, as determined on a basic shaft basis.

To determine the limits for size under this system, the limits for hole and shaft as given in Tables XVII-A–E are increased for clearance fits, or decreased for transition or interference fits by the value shown for the upper shaft limit which is the amount required to change the maximum shaft to basic size.

16.19. Unilateral tolerances. Unilateral tolerances may be expressed in any one of several ways as shown in Fig. 16.52.

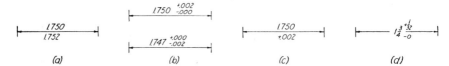

Fig. 16.52.   Unilateral tolerances.

Two limits may be given as in (*a*) or the basic size can be shown to the required number of decimal places, followed by a plus tolerance above a minus tolerance as in (*b*). Another method illustrated in (*c*) gives the preferred dimension with a tolerance that may be plus or minus but not both. When the dimension is given as a fraction the zero tolerance is expressed by a 0 (cipher).

16.20. Bilateral tolerances. Bilateral tolerances are expressed with a divided tolerance (Fig. 16.53). Whenever the plus and minus values are unequal as in (*c*) the plus value is placed above the dimension line.

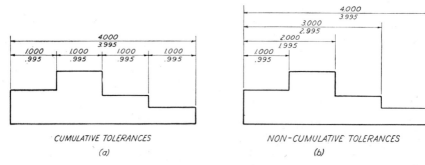

Fig. 16.53.   Bilateral tolerances.

16.21. Cumulative tolerances. An undesirable condition may result when either the location of a surface or an over-all dimension is affected by more than one tolerance dimension. When this condition exists as illustrated in Fig. 16.54(*a*) the tolerances are said to be cumulative. It can be noted in (*a*) where the dimensions are continuous from surface-to-surface that there is a permissible variation of only 0.005 in the over-all length of the piece while at the same time it is not unreasonable to expect all dimensions to vary between either the extreme high or low limits. If minimum tolerances are obtained between all surfaces, the

CUMULATIVE TOLERANCES
(a)

NON-CUMULATIVE TOLERANCES
(b)

Fig. 16.54.   Cumulative tolerances.

length of the part could be 3.980 as against a minimum specified length of 3.995. If it is necessary to maintain the over-all dimension within the specified limits, the allowable variation of 0.005 must be distributed among the four dimensions. This would increase manufacturing costs because the machinist would find it necessary to work to limits closer than those that are specified. In order to avoid this situation, it is the preferred practice to locate the surfaces from a datum plane as shown in (b), so that each surface is affected by only one dimension. The use of a datum plane makes it possible to take full advantage of permissible variations in size and still satisfy all requirements for the proper functioning of the part.

16.22. Production tolerances. Whenever extreme accuracy is required for the production of parts, it becomes necessary to specify tolerances for concentricity, squareness, parallelism, and flatness. The tolerances for these features are usually expressed in notes. See Figs. 16.50 and 16.55.

16.23. Concentricity tolerances. A note expressing the permissible variation in concentricity for mating coaxial cylindrical surfaces on closely fitted precision parts is necessary if the parts are to be produced with an exactness that will permit assembly. A note specifying the tolerance for concentricity might read as follows: *Diameters marked must be concentric within* ■ *total indicator reading.* If this is a general note, given without leaders to the cylindrical surfaces to which the note applies, a letter or the symbol ℭ may be used to identify the diameters as shown in Fig. 16.55.

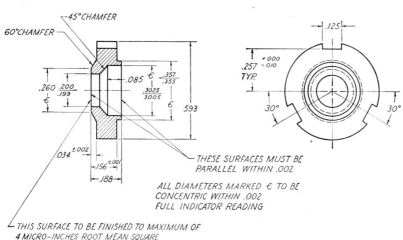

Fig. 16.55. *Tolerance of concentricity and parallelism.*

16.24. Squareness tolerances. A note is used to specify the tolerance governing the squareness of one surface to another. Such a note might read as follows: *This surface must be square with axis of hole within* ■ *total indicator reading at X radius.*

16.25. Parallelism tolerances (Fig. 16.55). A tolerance for parallelism is expressed in a note in terms of the linear deviation from parallel per inch. A note for parallelism tolerance might read as follows: *These surfaces must be parallel within .002 per inch.*

16.26. Flatness tolerances. A note is used to express the tolerance relating to flatness. The note should specify the direction (concave or convex) and give the permitted amount of deviation from flat. Such a note might read: *This surface must be flat to* ■ *concave.*

16.27. True position dimensioning. In the past, it has been the usual practice to locate points by means of rectangular dimensions given with tolerances. A point located in this manner lies within a square or rectangular area. However, this method frequently does not convey the engineering intent nor does it take full account of the relations that must be maintained for the interchangeable assembly of mating parts. True position dimensioning locates the point within a circular area.

Positional tolerancing can be used for specific features of a machine part. When the part contains a number of features arranged in groups, positional tolerances can be used to relate each of the groups to one another as necessary and to tolerance the position of the features within a group independently of the features of the other groups.

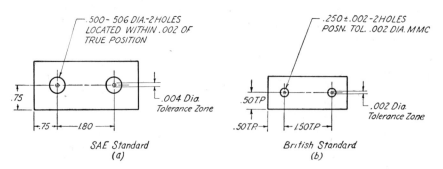

Fig. 16.56.   *True position dimensioning.*

The term "true position" denotes the theoretically exact position for a feature. In practice in the United States, the basic (exact) location of the center point of each hole is given with untoleranced dimensions and the expression "LOCATED WITHIN .XXX of TRUE POSITION" is added to the normal note specifying the size of the holes and their number. See Fig. 16.56(*a*). Another form of "true position" expression based on the present British Standard is shown in Fig. 16.56(*b*). This form has recently appeared in a proposed ASA standard.

The principal difference between the two forms of notes is that the

SAE (American) form gives a tolerance radius whereas the form recommended by the British Standard (*b*) gives a tolerance zone diameter. A joint committee representing both the SAE and ASA has been assigned the task of compromising the differences existing between these two expressions, and it has been agreed to use the designation R (for radius) with the note in (*a*). If this idea is accepted, the note in (*a*) will then read: .500–.506 DIA.–2 HOLES–LOCATED WITHIN .002R OF TRUE POSITION. It is probable that the new ASA–Y14 Standard will show this new form of note with the R added along with the note shown in (*b*), for both methods specify the same thing. American industrial organizations may make their own choice.

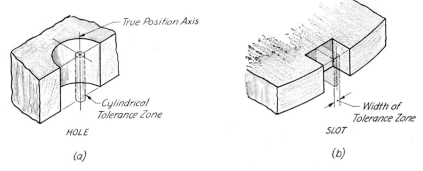

Fig. 16.57. *Meaning of true position dimensioning.*

The requirement of true position dimensioning for a cylindrical feature is illustrated in Fig. 16.57(*a*). As must be understood, the axis of the hole at all points must lie within the specified cylindrical tolerance zone having its center located at true position. This cylindrical tolerance zone also defines the limits within which variations in the squareness of the axis of the hole in relation to the flat surface must be confined.

In applying true position dimensioning to noncylindrical features, such as slots, dovetails, serrations, and so forth, it will be found that the principal difference is in the geometrical form of the tolerance zone. The note specifying slots might read: 6 SLOTS EQUALLY SPACED AND LOCATED WITHIN .005 EACH SIDE OF TRUE POSITION. The expression .005 EACH SIDE OF TRUE POSITION specifies that the axis of the slot must fall within a rectangular tolerance zone as shown in Fig. 16.57(*b*). The tolerance zone must be symmetrically disposed on each side of true position by the amount of the true position tolerance.

In Fig. 16.56(*b*) the letters *T.P.* stand for true position and the letters MMC specify maximum metal condition. Since the most unfavorable assembly relationship exists under a maximum material condition, it is understood that the true position tolerance will apply only to the maximum material condition in (*a*).

The illustrations used with this discussion have been presented with the sole idea of showing briefly what is meant by true position dimensioning. They are not to be thought of as being practical examples. Dotted circles have been added to each illustration to call attention to the imaginary tolerance zones. Those who may have the need for the use of this method of tolerancing should consult the Drafting Standards so as to acquire a full understanding of true position dimensioning.

16.28. Surface quality. The improvement in machining methods within recent years coupled with a strong demand for increased life for machined parts has caused engineers to give more attention to the quality of the surface finish. Not only the service life but also the proper functioning of the part as well may depend upon obtaining the needed smoothness quality for contact surfaces.

On an engineering drawing a surface may be represented by line if shown in profile or it may appear as a bounded area in a related view. Machined and ground surfaces, however, do not have the perfect smoothness represented on a drawing. Actually a surface has three dimensions, namely, length, breadth, and curvature (waviness) as illustrated in Fig. 16.58(*a*). In addition there will be innumerable peaks and valleys of differing lengths, widths, and heights. An exaggerated profile of surface roughness is shown in (*b*). Combined waviness and roughness is illustrated in (*c*).

The following terms must be understood before the surface symbol shown in Fig. 16.59(*a*) can be properly applied.

Roughness. Roughness is the relatively finely spaced surface irregularities that are produced by the cutting action of tool edges and abrasive grains on surfaces that are machined.

Waviness. Waviness is the surface undulations that are of much greater magnitude than the roughness irregularities. Waviness may result from machine or work deflections, vibrations, warping, strains, or similar causes.

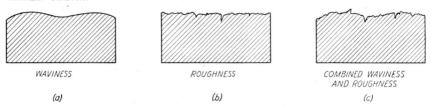

WAVINESS   ROUGHNESS   COMBINED WAVINESS AND ROUGHNESS

(*a*)   (*b*)   (*c*)

Fig. 16.58. Surface definitions illustrated.

Lay. Lay is the predominate direction of the tool marks of the surface pattern. See Fig. 16.59(*b*).

Microinch. A microinch is one millionth (0.000001) of an inch.

The following was abstracted from the American Standard Publication "Drawings and Drafting Room Practice" (ASA Z14.1–1946):

A surface whose finish is to be specified should be marked with the finish mark having the general form of a check mark ($\checkmark$) so that the point of the symbol is

(a) On the line indicating the surface,

(b) On a leader pointing to the surface (Fig. 16.60).

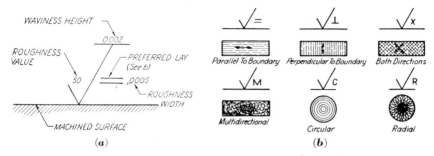

Fig. 16.59. Surface quality symbols.

Where it is desired to specify only the surface roughness height, and the width of roughness or direction of tool marks is not important, the simplest form of the symbol should be used. See Fig. 16.50. This height may be either maximum peak to valley height, average peak to valley height, or average deviation from the mean (RMS or arithmetical). The numerical value is placed in the $\checkmark$ as shown.

Where it is desired to specify waviness height in addition to roughness height a straight horizontal line should be added to the top of the simple symbol. See Fig. 16.59(a). The numerical value of height of waviness would be shown above this line.

Then, if the nature of the preferred lay is to be shown in addition to these two characteristics, it will be indicated by the addition of a combination of lines as shown in Fig. 16.59(a) and (b). The parallel and perpendicular part of the symbol indicates that the dominant lines on the surface are parallel or perpendicular to the boundary line of the surface in contact with the symbol.

The complete symbol, including the roughness width placed to the right of the lay symbol, is shown in Fig. 16.59(a).

The use of only one number to specify the height or width of roughness or waviness shall indicate the maximum value. Any lesser degree of roughness will be satisfactory. When two numbers are used separated by a dash, they indicate the maximum and minimum permissible values.

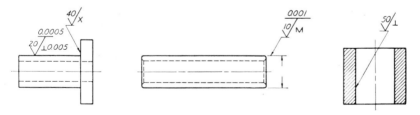

Fig. 16.60. Application of surface finish symbols.

Surface finish should be specified only by experienced personnel because the function of many parts does not depend upon the smoothness quality of a surface or surfaces. In addition, surface quality need not be necessarily indicated for many parts that are produced to close dimensional tolerances because a satisfactory surface finish may result from the required machining processes.   It should be remembered that the cost of producing a part will generally become progressively greater as the specification of surface finish becomes more exacting.

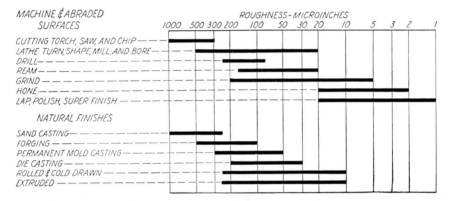

Fig. 16.61.   Surface finishes expected from common production methods.

The chart in Fig. 16.61 shows the expected surface roughness in microinches for surfaces produced by common production methods.

The surface-quality symbol, which is used only when it is desirable to specify surface smoothness, should not be confused with a finish mark that indicates the removal of material.   A surface-quality symbol might be used for a surface on a die-casting, forging, or extruded shape where the surface is to have a natural finish and no material is to be removed.

STRUCTURAL DIMENSIONING

16.29. Location of dimension lines.   All dimensions must be placed in such a manner that they will be easily understood.   Principal dimensions are generally obtained from the design sheets; other dimensions necessary for detailing are found in tables or are determined by the detailer.

Dimensions for rivet spacing, short location and size dimensions, and so on, are placed close to the view, whereas the longer dimensions such as over-all lengths are placed farther away so that extension lines will not cross dimension lines (Fig. 16.62).

Dimension figures are placed above or at the side of continuous (unbroken) dimension lines.   These lines generally should be placed off the view, but usually added clearness may be obtained by putting some dimensions in an open area on the view itself.   Dimension lines ordinarily should not be placed less than $\frac{3}{8}$ inch apart or closer to the view than $\frac{1}{2}$ inch.

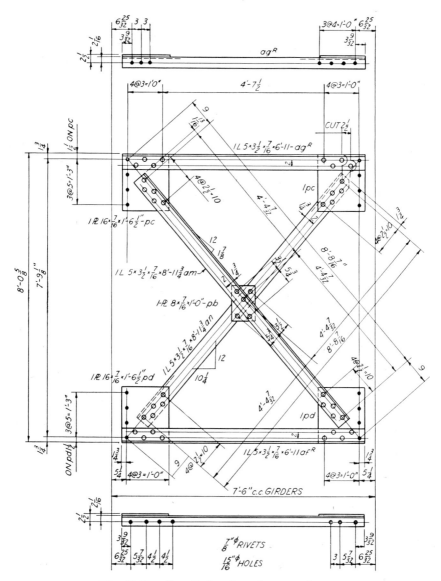

Fig. 16.62. *Detail drawing of a cross frame.*

16.30. Dimensions and notes in structural detailing (Fig. 16.62).

1. Figures can be placed to one side, with a leader to the dimension line, if the available space is very small.

2. Figures and notes must read from the bottom and the right side of the sheet because shopmen are familiar with reading from these positions.

3. For dimensions less than one foot, the inch marks (″) may be omitted.

4. With the exception of widths of plates and depths of sections, all dimensions of one foot or more are expressed in feet and inches.

Correct	Incorrect
$\frac{1}{4}$	$0\frac{1}{4}$
9	$0'-9''$
10	$10''$
$1'-0''$	$12''$
$2'-3\frac{1}{4}''$	$2'-03\frac{1}{2}''$
$4'-0\frac{1}{4}''$	$4'\frac{1}{4}''$

5. Usually, dimensions are given in multiples of $\frac{1}{8}$ inch or, preferably, $\frac{1}{4}$ inch. It is not desirable to use multiples of $\frac{1}{16}''$ or $\frac{1}{32}''$, except in rare cases.

6. Decimals found in tables should be converted into fractions to the nearest $\frac{1}{16}$ inch.

7. Rivets and holes are located by dimensions from center to center.

8. Dimensions *always* should be given to the center lines of I-beams and to the backs of angles and channels.

9. When three or more rivet spaces for a line of rivets are equal, they should be dimensioned as a group (4 @ $3''$ = $1'-0''$). Staggered rivets are dimensioned as if they were on one gage line.

10. Since a workman must use a rule or tape to lay off angles, a slope triangle should be shown to give the inclination of a working line.

11. A general note is usually placed on a detail drawing giving the edge distances, painting instructions, size of rivets, size of open holes, and so on.

12. The size of a member is indicated by a specification (in the form of a note) parallel to it.

13. The width of a plate is always given in inches.

16.31. Problems. The following problems offer the student the opportunity to apply the rules of dimensioning given in this chapter. If it is desired, decimals of an inch may be used in place of fractions. Use Table I in the Appendix.

1–2. (Figs. 16.63–16.64.) Reproduce the given views of an assigned part. Determine the dimensions by transferring them from the drawing to the open-divided scale by means of the dividers. Decimal-inch dimensioning is to be used for the parts given in Fig. 16.64.

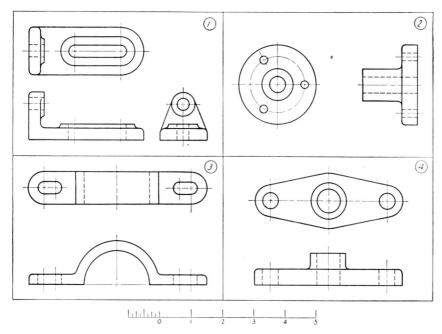

Fig. 16.63.   Dimensioning problems.

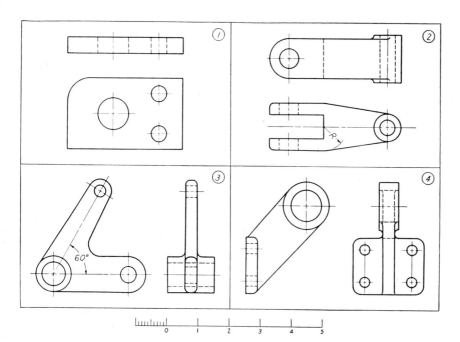

Fig. 16.64.   Dimensioning problems.

3–13. (Figs. 16.65–16.75.)   Make a fully dimensioned multiview sketch or drawing of an assigned part.   Draw all necessary views.   Give a detail title with suitable notes concerning material, number required, etc.   These parts have been selected from different fields of industry—automotive, aeronautical, chemical, electrical, etc.

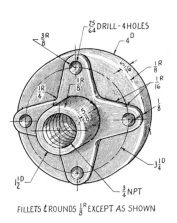

FILLETS & ROUNDS $\frac{1}{8}$R EXCEPT AS SHOWN

Fig. 16.65.   Flange.

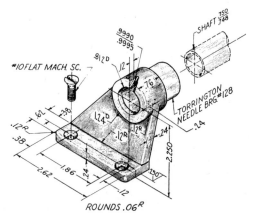

ROUNDS .06^R

Fig. 16.66.   Bearing bracket—airplane control system.

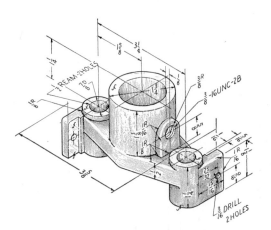

Fig. 16.67.   Guide bracket.

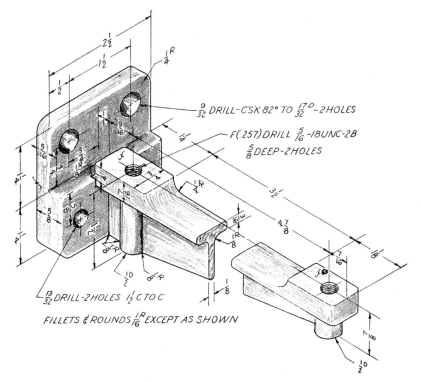

Fig. 16.68.   **Support bracket.**

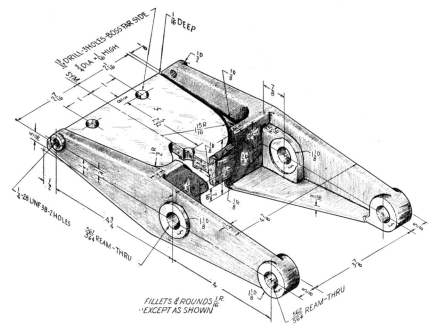

Fig. 16.69.   **Control pedal—airplane control system.**

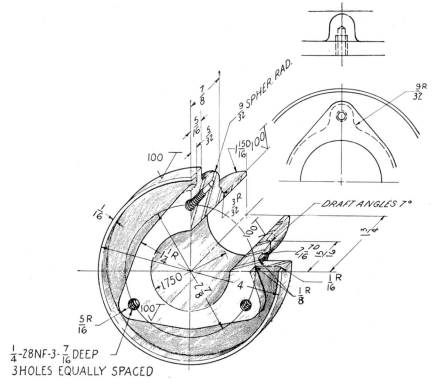

Fig. 16.70. *Inlet flange—airplane cooling system.*

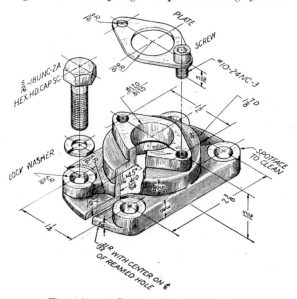

Fig. 16.71. *Cover—mixing machine.*

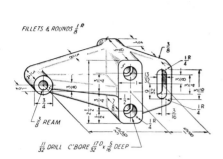

FILLETS & ROUNDS $\frac{1}{8}$ R

Fig. 16.72.   Elevator bracket.

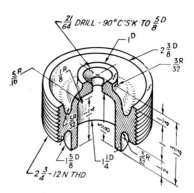

$\frac{21}{64}$ DRILL - 90° C'S'K TO $\frac{5}{8}$ D

Fig. 16.73.   Valve seat.

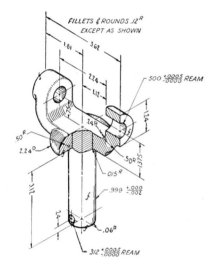

FILLETS & ROUNDS .12 R
EXCEPT AS SHOWN

Fig. 16.74.   Yoke.

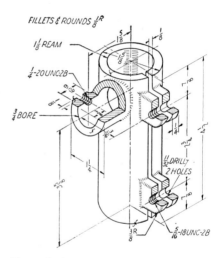

FILLETS & ROUNDS $\frac{1}{8}$ R

Fig. 16.75.   Torch holder—welding.

14. (Fig. 16.76.)   Make a detail working sketch or drawing of the rocker arm. Show a detail section taken through the ribs.   *Supplementary information*: (1) The distance from the center of the shaft to the center of the hole for the pin is 4.00″.   The distance from the shaft to the threaded hole is 4.50″.   (2) The nominal diameter of the hole for the shaft is 1.875″.   The hole in the rocker arm is to be reamed for a definite fit.   Consult your instructor, but *do not* use a limit dimension for either the shaft or the pin.   The diameter of the pin is .969″.   (3) The diameter of the threaded boss is 2.00″.   (4) The diameter of the roller is 2.25″, and its length 1.46″.   Total clearance between the roller and finished faces is to be .03″.   (5) The inside faces of the arms are to be milled in towards the hub far enough to accommodate the roller.   (6) The rib is .62″ thick.   (7) The lock nut has $1\frac{1}{4}$–12 UNF thread.   (8) Fillets and rounds .12″ R except where otherwise noted.

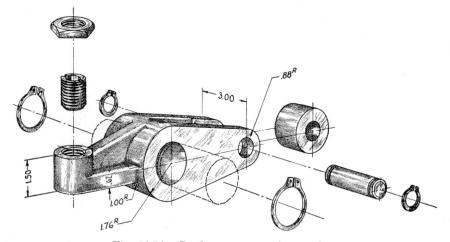

Fig. 16.76.   Rocker arm—marine engine.

15. (See Fig. 9.77.) Make a detail drawing of an assigned part of the tool holder.

16. (Fig. 16.77.) Make a detail drawing of an assigned part of the bearing bracket. Compose a suitable detail title, giving the name of the part, the material, etc.

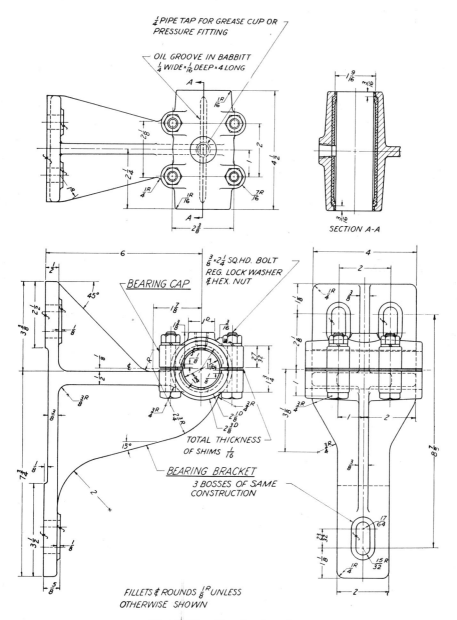

Fig. 16.77. Bearing bracket.

17. (Fig. 16.78.)   Make a detail drawing of an assigned part of the Simplex ball bearing screw jack.

PC.NO.	NAME	QUAN.	MATERIAL	PC. NO.	NAME	QUAN.	MATERIAL
1	STANDARD	1	MALL. IRON	5	GROOVE PIN	3	$\frac{7}{32}D\times\frac{5}{8}$ STEEL ROD
2	SCREW	1	S.A.E.1120 FORGING	6	LEVER BAR	1	REROLLED RAIL STK.
3	CAP	1	S.A.E.1045 FORGING	7	$\frac{7}{8}$ DIA. BALL BEARING	1	STD.
4	THRUST WASHER	1	S.A.E. 2315				

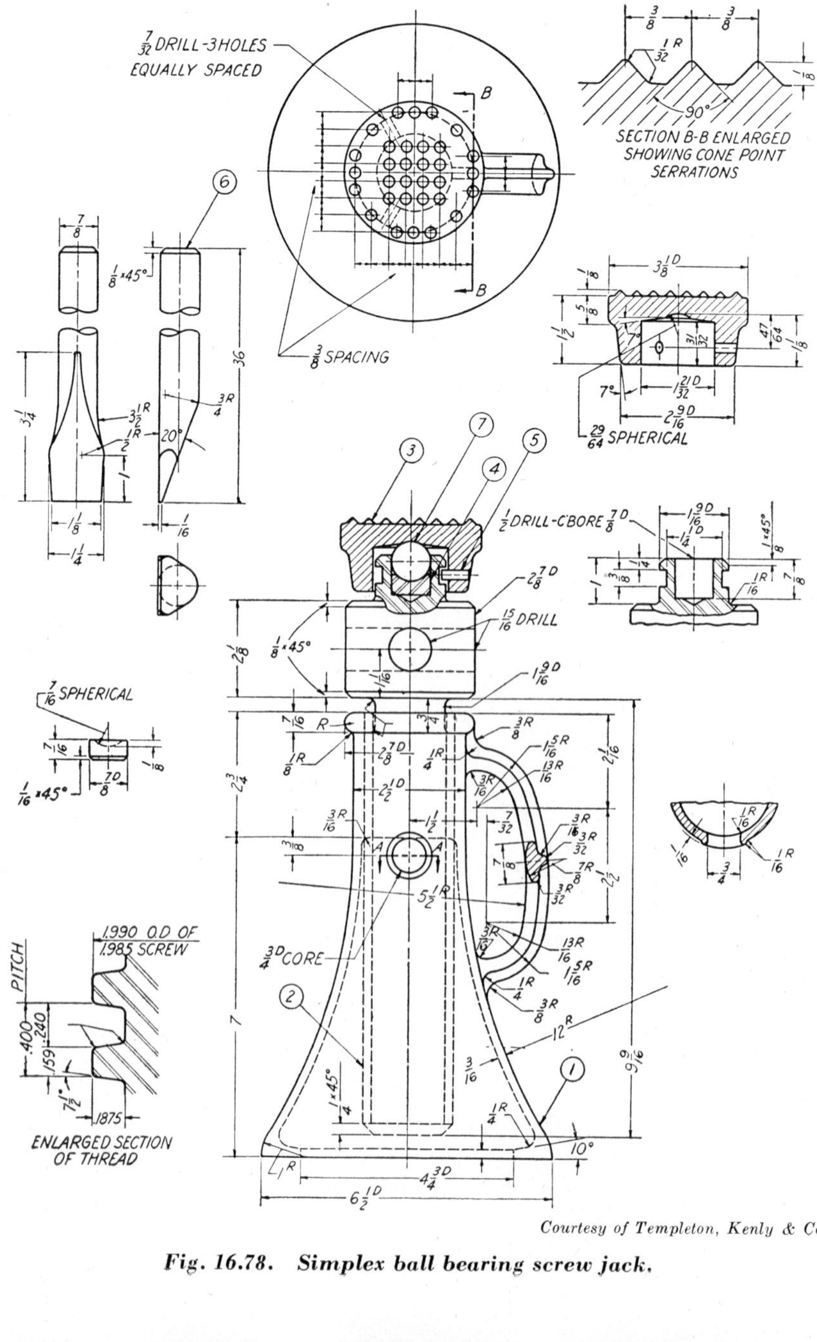

Courtesy of Templeton, Kenly & Co.

Fig. 16.78.   Simplex ball bearing screw jack.

18. (Fig. 16.79.) Make a detail drawing of an assigned part of the shaft support.

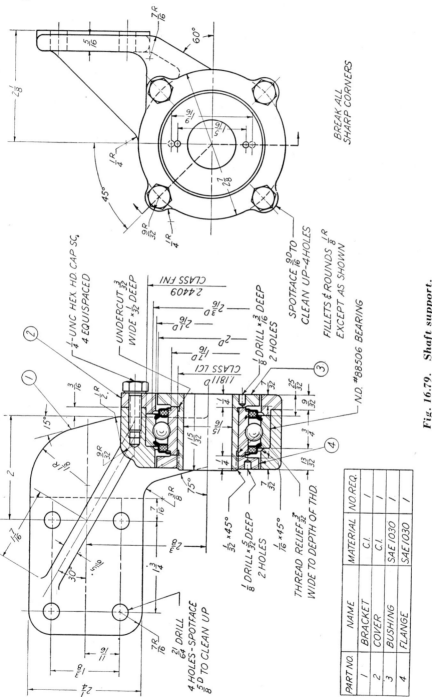

Fig. 16.79. Shaft support.

19. (Fig. 16.80.)   Make a detail drawing of an assigned part of the roller-bearing stud unit.

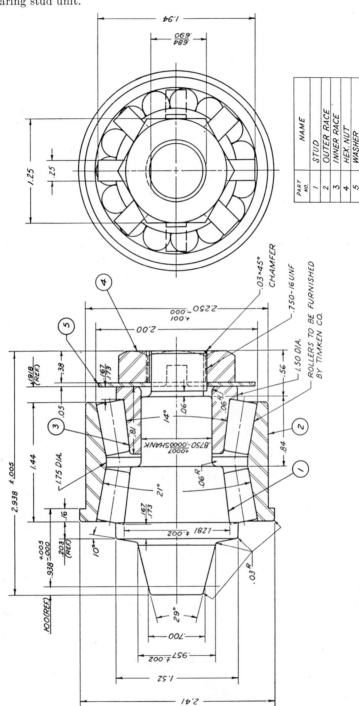

Fig. 16.80.   Roller-bearing stud unit.

Courtesy Ross Gear and Tool Co.

PART NO.	NAME
1	STUD
2	OUTER RACE
3	INNER RACE
4	HEX. NUT
5	WASHER

20. (Fig. 16.81.) Make a detail drawing of an assigned part of the handle.

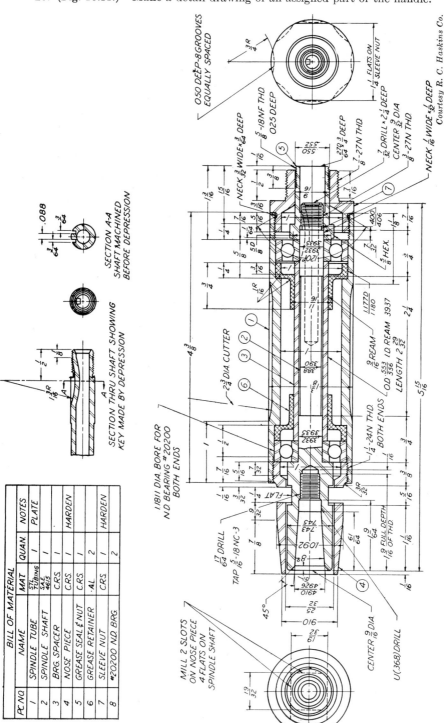

Fig. 16.81. Handle.

Courtesy R. C. Haskins Co.

BILL OF MATERIAL				
PC.NO.	NAME	MAT.	QUAN.	NOTES
1	SPINDLE TUBE	STL. TUBING	1	PLATE
2	SPINDLE SHAFT	SAE 4615	1	
3	BRG. SPACER	C.R.S.	1	
4	NOSE PIECE	C.R.S.	1	HARDEN
5	GREASE SEAL & NUT	C.R.S.	1	
6	GREASE RETAINER	AL.	2	
7	SLEEVE NUT	C.R.S.	1	HARDEN
8	#20200 N.D. BRG.		2	

17

Design and Communication Drawings

17.1. Communication drawings. An engineer must frequently prepare or direct the preparation of one or more types of drawings to convey his ideas to others in an industrial organization. These drawings may be original idea sketches and layout drawings or they may be shop drawings, commonly called working drawings. In addition, catalog representations are often needed, and these too must be made under the direction of someone in the engineering department.

All of these types of drawings, ranging from design drawings to exploded pictorial drawings, have one thing in common and that is that they are prepared to convey needed ideas and facts to others. Since all serve the same purpose, they may be classed together as "communication drawings," this term being almost all inclusive.

In this chapter we will be concerned mainly with the types of drawings that are prepared by draftsmen under an engineer's supervision, and which are to serve as communications to others beyond the engineering department. The preparation of idea sketches, both multiview and pictorial, has been discussed in detail in Chapters 9 and 10. Charts and graphs, which may also be thought of as communication drawings, are presented in Chapter 18. Charts and graphs are used by engineers to supplement written reports and technical papers.

17.2. Sketches and design drawings. The first stage in the development of an idea for a structure or machine is to prepare freehand sketches and to make the calculations required to determine the feasibility of the design. From these sketches the designer prepares a layout, on which an accurate analysis of the design is worked out. It is usually drawn full size and is executed with instruments in pencil. The layout should be complete enough to allow a survey of the location of parts (to

450

avoid interference), the accessibility for maintenance, the requirements for lubrication, and the method of assembly.

Usually, only center distances and certain fixed dimensions are given. The general dimensioning, as well as the determination of material and degree of finish of individual parts, is left for the draftsman who makes the detail drawings while using layout drawing as a guide.

Design layouts require both empirical and scientific design. Empirical design involves the use of charts, formulas, tables, and so forth, which have been derived from experimental studies and scientific computations. Scientific design, which requires a broad knowledge of the allied fields such as mechanics, metallurgy, and mathematics, is used when a new machine is designed to operate under special specified conditions for which data are not available in any handbook.

MACHINE DRAWINGS*

17.3. Classes of machine drawings. There are two recognized classes of machine drawings: detail drawings and assembly drawings.

17.4. Set of working drawings. A complete set of working drawings for a machine consists of detail sheets, giving all necessary shop information for the production of individual pieces, and an assembly drawing showing the location of each piece in the finished machine. In addition, the set may include drawings showing a foundation plan, piping diagram, oiling diagram, and so on.

17.5. Detail drawings. A detail drawing should give complete information for the manufacture of a part, describing with adequate dimensions the part's size. Finished surfaces should be indicated and all necessary shop operations shown. The title should give the material of which the part is to be made and should state the number of the parts that are required for the production of an assembled unit of which the part is a member. A detail drawing is shown in Fig. 17.1.

Since a machinist will ordinarily make one part at a time, it is advisable to detail each piece, regardless of its size, on a separate individual sheet. In some shops, however, custom dictates that related parts be grouped on the same sheet, particularly when the parts form a unit in themselves. Other concerns sometimes group small parts of the same material together thus: castings on one sheet, forgings on another, special fasteners on still another, and so on.

17.6. One-view drawings. Many parts, such as shafts, bolts, studs, and washers, may require only one properly dimensioned view. In the case of each of these parts, a note can imply the complete shape of the piece without sacrificing clearness. Most engineering departments, however, deem it better practice to show two views.

---

* Additional information covering the preparation of machine drawings may be obtained from the author's text *Fundamentals of Engineering Drawing*.

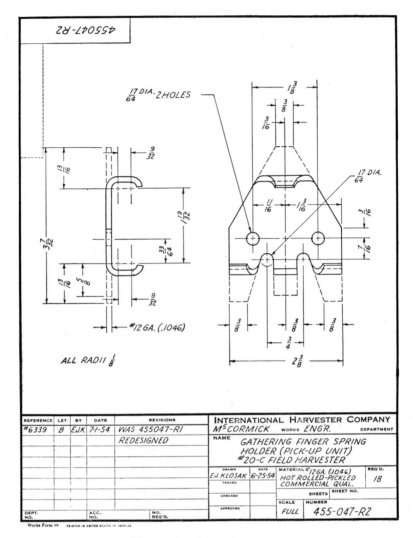

Fig. 17.1.   A detail drawing.

17.7. Pattern-shop drawings. Sometimes special pattern-shop drawings, giving information needed for making a pattern, are required for large and complicated castings.   If the pattern maker receives a drawing that shows finished dimensions, he provides for the draft necessary to draw the pattern and for the extra metal for machining.   He allows for shrinkage by making the pattern oversize.   When, however, the draft and allowances for finish are determined by the engineering department, no finish marks appear on the drawing.   The allowances are included in the dimensions.

17.8. Forge-shop drawings.   If a forging is to be machined, sepa-

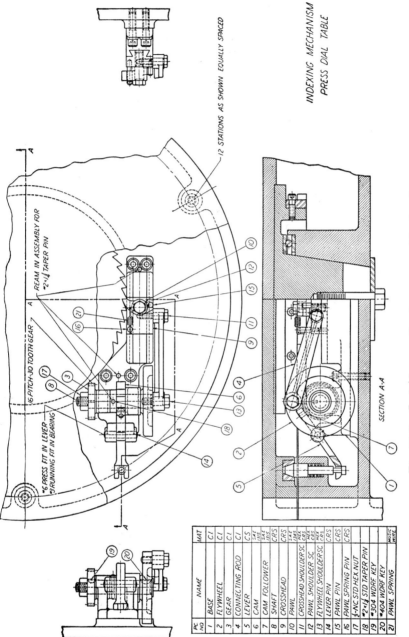

Fig. 17.2. *Indexing mechanism—assembly drawing.*

INDEXING MECHANISM
PRESS DIAL TABLE

12 STATIONS AS SHOWN EQUALLY SPACED

REAM IN ASSEMBLY FOR
2"·4 TAPER PIN

16 PITCH-30 TOOTH GEAR

"6 PRESS FIT IN LEVER
"5 RUNNING FIT IN BEARING

SECTION A-A

PC NO	NAME	MAT
1	BASE	CI
2	FLYWHEEL	CI
3	GEAR	CI
4	CONNECTING ROD	CI
5	LEVER	CS
6	CAM	SAE 1045
7	CAM FOLLOWER	SAE 1315
8	SHAFT	CRS
9	CROSSHEAD	SAE 1045
10	PAWL	CRS
11	CROSSHEAD SHOULDER SC	HEX CRS
12	PAWL SHOULDER SC	HEX CRS
13	FLYWHEEL SHOULDER SC	HEX CRS
14	LEVER PIN	CRS
15	PAWL PIN	CRS
16	PAWL SPRING PIN	CRS
17	½-NC STD HEX NUT	
18	2"·4 STD TAPER PIN	
19	*304 WDRF KEY	
20	*404 WDRF KEY	
21	PAWL SPRING	MUSIC WIRE

rate detail drawings usually are made for the forge and machine shops. A forging drawing gives all the nominal dimensions required by the forge shop for a completed rough forging.

17.9. Machine-shop drawings. Rough castings and forgings are sent to the machine shop to be finished. Since the machinist is not interested in the dimensions and information for the previous stages, a machine-shop drawing frequently gives only the information necessary for machining.

17.10. Assembly drawings (Fig. 17.2). A drawing that shows the parts of a machine or machine unit assembled in their relative working positions is an assembly drawing. There are several types of such drawings: design assembly drawings, working assembly drawings, unit assembly drawings, installation diagrams, and so on, each of which will be described separately.

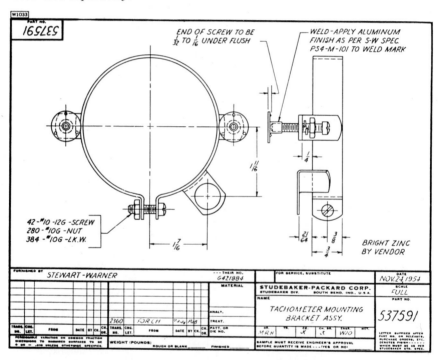

Fig. 17.3. A unit assembly drawing.

17.11. Working assembly drawings. A working assembly drawing, showing each piece completely dimensioned, is sometimes made for a simple mechanism or unit of related parts. No additional detail drawings of parts are required (Fig. 17.3).

17.12. Sub-assembly (unit) drawings. A unit assembly is an assembly drawing of a group of related parts that form a unit in a more complicated machine.   Such a drawing would be made for the tail stock of a lathe, the clutch of an automobile, or the carburetor of an airplane. A set of assembly drawings thus takes the place of a complete assembly of a complex machine (Fig. 17.3).

17.12. Title blocks and record strips.   The purpose of a title or record strip is to present in an orderly manner the name of the machine, name of the manufacturer, date, scale, drawing number, and other drafting room information.

Every commercial drafting room has developed its own standard title forms, whose features depend upon the processes of manufacture, the

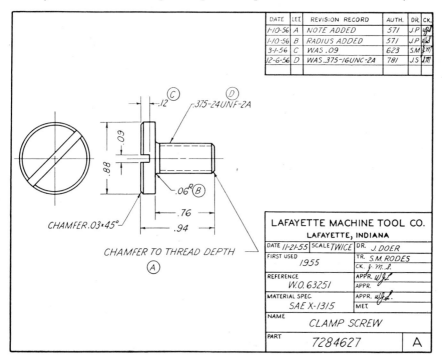

Fig. 17.4.   Title block and alteration record.

Fig. 17.5.   A printed record strip.

Courtesy International Harvester Co.

peculiarities of the plant organization, and the established customs of particular types of manufacturing. In large organizations, the blank form, along with the border line, is printed on standard sizes of drawing or tracing paper. See Figs. 17.4 and 17.5.

A record strip is a form of title extending almost the entire distance across the bottom of the sheet. In addition to the usual title information, it may contain a section for recording revisions, changes, and so on, with the dates on which they were adopted.

17.14. Contents of the title. The title on a machine drawing generally contains the following information:

1. Name of the part.

2. Name of the machine or structure. (This is given in the main title and is usually followed by one of two words: *details* or *assembly*.)

3. Name and location of the manufacturing firm.

4. Name and address of the purchasing firm, if the structure has been designed for a particular company.

5. Scale.

6. Date. (Often spaces are provided for the date of completion of each operation in the preparation of the drawing. If only one date is given, it is usually the date of completion of the tracing.)

7. Initials of the draftsman who made the pencil drawing.

8. Initials of the tracer.

9. Initials of the checker.

10. Initials or signature of the chief draftsman, chief engineer, or another in authority who approved the drawing.

11. Drawing number. This generally serves as a filing number and may furnish information in code form. Letters and numbers may be so combined to indicate departments, plants, model, type, order number, filing number, and so on. The drawing number is sometimes repeated in the upper left-hand corner (in an upside-down position), so that the drawing may be quickly identified if it should become reversed in the file.

Some titles furnish information such as material, part number, pattern number, finish, treatment, estimated weight, superseded drawing number, and so on.

17.15. Corrections and alterations. Alterations on working drawings are made either by cancellation or by erasure. Cancellations are indicated by parallel inclined lines drawn through the views, lines, notes, or dimensions to be changed.

Superseding dimensions should be placed above or near the original ones. If alterations are made by erasure, the changed dimensions are often underlined.

All changes on a completed or approved drawing should be recorded in a revision record that may be located either adjacent to the title block (Fig. 17.1) or at one corner of the drawing (Fig. 17.4). The notation should contain the identification symbol, date, authorization number, character of the revision, and the initials of the draftsman and checker who made the change. The identification symbol is a letter or numeral placed in small circle near the alteration on the body of the drawing (Fig. 17.4).

If changes are made by complete erasure, record prints should be made for the file before the original is altered. Many companies make record prints whenever changes are extensive.

Since revisions on completed drawings are usually necessitated by unsatisfactory methods of production or by a customer's request, they should never be made by a draftsman unless an order has been issued with the approval of the chief engineer's office.

17.16. Title for an assembly drawing. The title strip on an assembly drawing usually is the same as that used on a detail drawing. It will be noted, when lettering in the block, that the title of the drawing is generally composed of the name of the machine followed by the word *assembly* (Figs. 17.3 and 17.6).

17.17. Bill of material. A bill of material is a list of parts placed on an assembly drawing just above the title block, or, in the case of quantity production, on a separate sheet. The bill contains the part number, descriptive name, material, quantity (number) required, and so on, of each piece. Additional information, such as stock size, pattern number castings), and so forth, is sometimes listed.

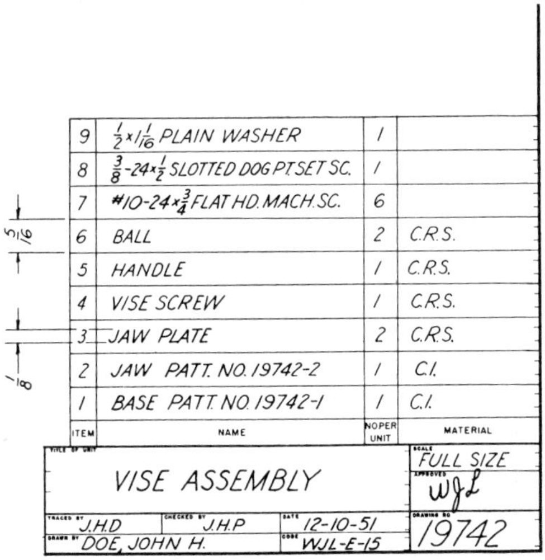

ITEM	NAME	NO PER UNIT	MATERIAL
9	$\frac{1}{2} \times 1\frac{1}{16}$ PLAIN WASHER	1	
8	$\frac{3}{8}$-24×$\frac{1}{2}$ SLOTTED DOG PT. SET SC.	1	
7	#10-24×$\frac{3}{4}$ FLAT HD. MACH. SC.	6	
6	BALL	2	C.R.S.
5	HANDLE	1	C.R.S.
4	VISE SCREW	1	C.R.S.
3	JAW PLATE	2	C.R.S.
2	JAW PATT. NO. 19742-2	1	C.I.
1	BASE PATT. NO. 19742-1	1	C.I.

VISE ASSEMBLY — FULL SIZE — WJL

TRACED BY J.H.D — CHECKED BY J.H.P — DATE 12-10-51 — DRAWING NO. 19742
DRAWN BY DOE, JOHN H. — CODE WJL-E-15

Fig. 17.6.   A bill of material above a title block.

Suggested dimensions for ruling are shown in Fig. 17.6.

When listing standard parts in a bill of material, the general practice is to omit the name of the materials and to use abbreviated descriptive titles.   A pattern number may be composed of the commercial job number followed by the assigned number one, two, three, and so on.   It is suggested that parts be listed in the following order: (*a*) castings, (*b*) forgings, (*c*) parts made from bar stock, (*d*) standard parts.

Sometimes parts lists are first typed on thin paper and then blueprinted.   The form may be ruled or printed.   A parts list serves as a bill of material.

17.18.   Making the assembly drawing.   The final assembly may be traced from the design assembly drawing, but more often it is redrawn to a smaller scale on a separate sheet.   Since the redrawing, being done from both the design and detail drawings, furnishes a check that frequently reveals errors, the assembly always should be drawn before the details are accepted as finished and the blueprints are made.   The assembly of a simple machine or unit is sometimes shown on the same sheet with the details.

17.19.   Checking machine drawings.   Checking, the final assurance that the machine is correctly designed, should be done by a person (checker or squad foreman) who has not prepared the drawings but who is thoroughly familiar with the principles of the design.   He must have a broad knowledge of shop practices and assembly methods.   In commercial drafting rooms, the most experienced men are assigned to this type of work, for the engineers must rely upon their ability and background knowledge.   The assembly drawing is checked against the detail drawings and corrections are indicated with either a soft or a colored pencil.   The checker should:

1. Survey the machine as a whole from the standpoint of operation, ease of assembly, and accessibility for repair work.   He should consider the type, strength, and suitability of the materials.

2. Check each part with the parts adjacent to it, to make certain that proper clearances are maintained.   (To determine whether or not all positions are free of interference, it may be necessary to lay out the extreme travel of moving parts to an enlarged scale.)

3. Study the drawing to see that each piece has been illustrated correctly and that all necessary views, types of views, treatments of views, and scales have been shown.

4. Check dimensions by scaling; calculate and check size and location dimensions which affect mating parts; determine the suitability of dimensions from the standpoint of the various departments' needs, such as pattern, forge, machine, assembly shop, and so on; examine views for proper dimensioning, and mark unnecessary, repeated, or omitted dimensions.

5. Check tolerances, making sure the computations are correct and that proper fits have been used, so that there will be no unnecessary production costs.

6. See that finishes and such operations as drilling, reaming, boring, tapping and grinding are properly specified.

7. Check specifications for material.

8. Examine notes for correctness and location.

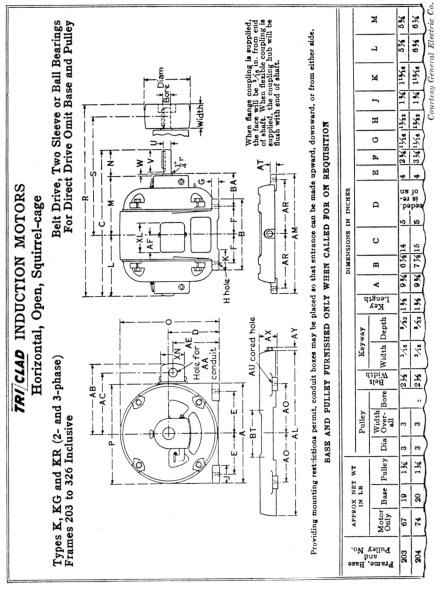

Fig. 17.7.   An outline assembly drawing.

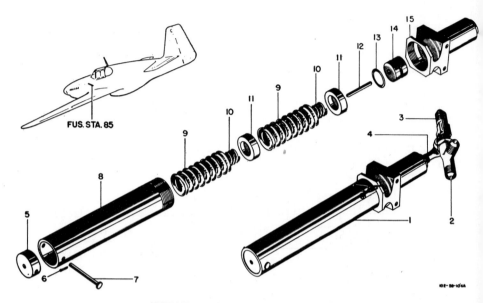

HYDRAULIC PARKING BRAKE COMPENSATOR

FIGURE No. 116

REF NO.	PART NUMBER	TITLE		NO. REQ.	REF NO.	PART NUMBER	TITLE		NO. REQ.
	1 2 3 4 5 6					1 2 3 4 5 6			
Note: See Fig. No. 135 For Attaching Parts.					9	73-33447	Spring - Brake master cylinder compensator	(ALL)	2
1	102-334040	Compensator Assem. - Parking brake complete	(ALL)	1	10	99-33446	Spring - Brake master compensator inner	(ALL)	2
	99-33404	Compensator Assem. - Parking brake	(ALL)	1	11	99-33435	Seat - Parking brake compensator spring & pin	(ALL)	2
2	811MT5	Fitting - Solderless tee	(ALL)	1					
3	5-2-2RST	Tee - (Parker Appliance Co., Cleveland, Ohio.)	(ALL)	1	12	99-33433	Pin - Parking brake compensator piston	(ALL)	1
4	AN914-1	Elbow - Internal & external pipe thread 90°	(ALL)	1	13	AN6227-14	Packing - "O" ring hyd.	(ALL)	1
5	73-33428	Seat - Parking brake compensator spring	(ALL)	1	14	99-33427	Piston - Parking brake compensator	(ALL)	1
6	AN380-2-2	Pin - Cotter	(ALL)	1	15	99-33431	Head - Parking brake compensator cylinder	(ALL)	1
7	AN393-49	Pin - Flat head, 3/16	(ALL)	1					
8	99-33430	Cylinder - Parking brake compensator	(ALL)	1					

Courtesy North American Aviation Corp.

Fig. 17.8. Parts list drawing.

9. See that stock sizes have been used for standard parts such as bolts, screws, keys, and so on. (Stock sizes may be determined from catalogs.)

10. Add any additional explanatory notes that should supply necessary information.

11. Check the bill of material to see that each part is completely and correctly specified.

12. Check items in the title block.

13. Make a final survey of the drawing in its entirety, making certain there is either a check or correction for each dimension, note, and specification.

DRAWINGS FOR CATALOGS, INSTRUCTION MANUALS AND TECHNICAL PUBLICATIONS

17.20. Installation assembly drawings. An installation drawing gives useful information for putting a machine or structure together. The names of parts, order of assembling parts, location dimensions, and special instructions for operating may also be shown.

17.21. Outline assembly drawings. Outline assembly drawings are most frequently made for illustrative purposes in catalogs. Usually they show merely over-all and principal dimensions (Fig. 17.7). Their appearance may be improved by the use of line shading.

17.22. Exploded pictorial assembly drawings for parts lists and instruction manuals. Exploded pictorial assembly drawings are used frequently in the parts lists sections of company catalogs and in instruction manuals. Drawings of this type are easily understood by those with

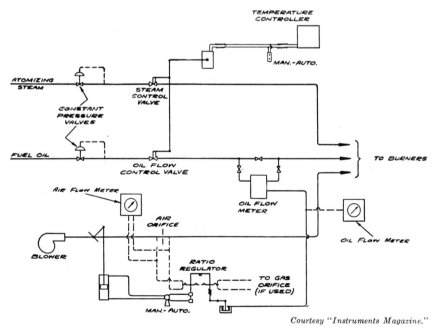

Courtesy "Instruments Magazine."

Fig. 17.9. A diagram assembly drawing.

very little experience in reading multiview drawings.   Fig. 17.8 shows a
commercial example of an exploded pictorial assembly drawing.

17.23. Diagram assembly drawings.   Diagram drawings may be
grouped into two general classes: (1) those composed of single lines and
conventional symbols, such as piping diagrams, wiring diagrams, and so
on (Fig. 17.9), and (2) those drawn in regular projection, such as an
erection drawing, which may be shown in either orthographic or pictorial
projection.

Piping diagrams give the size of pipe, location of fittings, and so on.
To draw an assembly of a piping system in true orthographic projection
would add no information and merely entail needless work.

A large portion of electrical drawing is composed of diagrammatic
sketches using conventional electrical symbols.   Electrical engineers
therefore need to know the American Standard wiring symbols given in
the Appendix.

CHEMICAL ENGINEERING DRAWINGS

17.24. Chemical engineering drawings.   In general, the chemical
engineer is concerned with plant layouts and equipment design.   He must
be well informed on the types of machinery used in grinding, drying,
mixing, evaporation, sedimentation, and distillation, and must be able to
design or select conveying machinery.

It is obvious that the determining of the sequence of operations,
selecting of machinery, arranging of piping, and so on, must be done by
a trained chemical engineer who can speak the basic language of the
mechanical, electrical, or civil engineer with whom he must co-operate.
To be able to do this, he must have a thorough knowledge of the principles
of engineering drawing.

Plant layout drawings, the satisfactory development of which requires
numerous preliminary sketches (layouts, scale diagram, flow sheets, and
so on), show the location of machines, equipment, and the like.   Often,
if the machinery and apparatus are used in the manufacturing of chemicals
and are of a specialized nature, a chemical engineer is called upon to do
the designing.   It even may be necessary for him to build experimental
apparatus.

ELECTRICAL ENGINEERING DRAWINGS

17.25. Electrical engineering drawings.   Electrical engineering
drawings are of two types, machine drawings and diagrammatic assemblies.   Working drawings, which are made for electrical machinery,
involve all of the principles and conventions of the working drawings of
the mechanical engineer.   Diagrammatic drawings have been discussed
in Sec. 17.23.

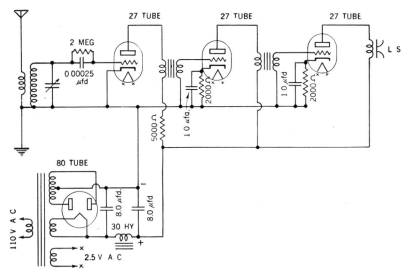

From Marcus and Horton, Elements of Radio, *Prentice-Hall, Inc.*

Fig. 17.10. *A schematic diagram.*

PLANT LAYOUT DRAWINGS

17.26. Floor-plan drawings. An engineer usually is not an architect nor is an architect usually an engineer; therefore, when a new factory is to be built or an addition is to be added to an existing one, both architect and engineer are needed and both must co-operate in the design. In this partnership it becomes the job of the engineer to prepare the floor plans so that the highest possible production efficiency can be obtained. He must study carefully the necessary steps of production and then decide upon the locations for the offices, supply rooms, storage rooms, shops, and finally the production machines. The design becomes a recorded study of the flow of materials and parts through the plant. Frequently it may be necessary to show a conveyor system or a piping system on the plan. In the case of small plants, circumstances may be such that the engineer must assume full responsibility for the design of the entire building.

CIVIL ENGINEERING DRAWINGS

17.27. Civil engineering drawings. The civil engineer is concerned with a broad field of construction and with civic planning. The drawings prepared by civil engineers may be in the nature of maps for city, state, and nationwide planning for streets, water systems, sewerage systems, airports, highways, railroads, harbor and waterways or they may be design, fabrication, and erection drawings for concrete and steel structures as in the case of buildings and bridges.

17.28. Engineering maps.* A map is a drawing that represents a portion of the earth's surface area. Since it usually represents a relatively small part, and the third dimension (the height) is not shown except in some cases by contour lines, a map may be thought of as a one-view orthographic projection. Various forms of maps have been devised to satisfy different requirements. Land maps, plats, and so on, which fulfill their purpose by revealing only the natural and man-made features

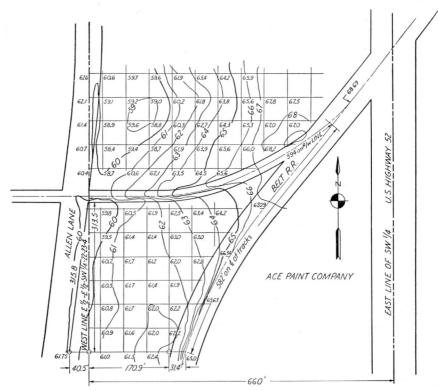

Fig. 17.11. *A contour map of a small area.*

along with imaginary division lines and geometrical measurements, show only two dimensions. Others, such as topographical maps, show three dimensions, by representing height by means of contours (Fig. 17.11).

Working maps prepared for engineering projects are known as engineering maps. They may be drawn for either reconnaissance or construction purposes (Fig. 17.12). They usually are made to a large scale and accurately show the location of all property lines and important features. On maps of a topographic nature, practically all natural and

---

* Additional information covering engineering maps may be obtained from the author's text, *Fundamentals of Engineering Drawing.*

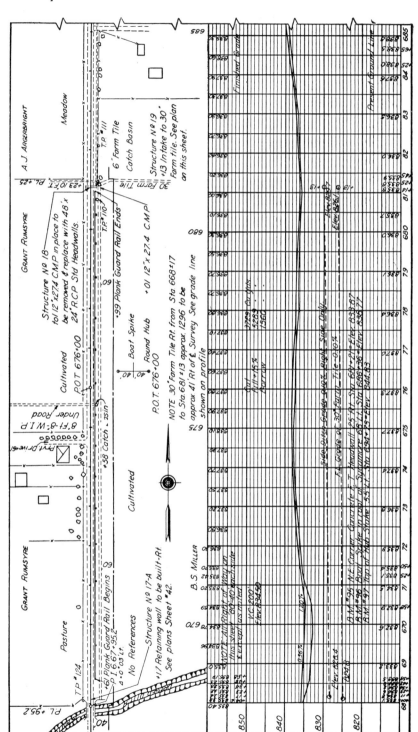

Fig. 17.12.   A plan and profile sheet of a proposed highway project.

man-made features along a right-of-way or on a site are shown, and the
form of the surface of the ground is indicated by means of contours.

17.29. Classes of structural drawings.* Most of the large steel
fabricators maintain a design office and a detailing office. The former
prepares design drawings and estimates costs in the preparation of bids
and frequently serves in a consulting capacity on designs furnished by a
customer. The detailing office, which is usually located at the fabri-

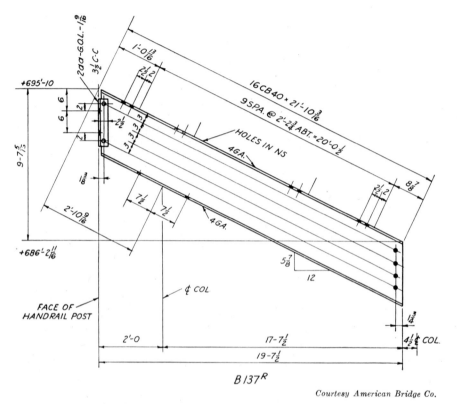

Courtesy American Bridge Co.

Fig. 17.13.   Structural detail drawing.

cating plant, orders material and prepares shop and erection plans from
the design sheets.

Design drawings usually are line diagrams showing the shape of a
structure, the principal dimensions, structural sections, and in some cases
the stresses to be used in detailing the connections.

For the use of the layout man a set of design drawings may contain

---

* Additional information covering structural drawing may be obtained from the
author's text, *Fundamentals of Engineering Drawing.*

elaborate design details, showing the type of connections, thickness of gusset plates, and the number of rivets.

A set of specifications covering special conditions, unit stresses, materials to be used, and so forth, is considered as part of the design information.

Shop detail drawings show all of the information necessary for shop fabrication (Fig. 17.13).

Erection plans, which are prepared primarily for use in the field, consist of line diagrams giving dimensions, shipping marks, and notes in sufficient detail to guide the erector in assembling the parts to complete the finished structure.

17.30. Machine shop drawings. The structural detailer will occasionally be called upon to prepare detail drawings for castings for bridge shoes and roadway expansion joints and at times drawings for complicated gearing and shafting for movable bridges. Regular machine drawing practices apply, the principal difference being that bridge machinery in general is ponderous with single castings often weighing ten or fifteen tons.

17.31. Problems. The four general types of problems presented in this chapter have been designed to furnish practice in the preparation of working drawings or sketches. The first type is composed of dimensioned pictorial drawings of individual pieces taken from a wide variety of mechanisms. The student should prepare complete working detail drawings of these pieces as they may be assigned by his instructor. It should be recognized that dimensions are not necessarily placed the same on orthographic views as they are on pictorial drawings. In order to make it possible for the student to apply the principles presented in Chapter 16, no special effort has been made to place dimensions in accordance with the rules of good practice.

The second type of problem is that which shows in pictorial all the parts of a unit mechanism. This gives the student an opportunity to prepare a complete set of working drawings of a simple unit. It is suggested that the detail drawings be prepared before the assembly is drawn.

The third and fourth types provide practice in both reading and preparing drawings, the third requiring the preparation of detail drawings from given assembly drawings, the fourth requiring the making of assembly drawings from the details.

1–7. Make a detail drawing or sketch of an assigned machine part. Draw all necessary views. Give a detail title with suitable notes concerning material, number required, etc.

Fig. 6.86. Shifter.   Fig. 6.92. Corner bracket.
Fig. 6.87. Tube holder.   Fig. 9.66. Bearing bracket.
Fig. 6.90. Guide bracket.   Fig. 9.67. Control guide.
     Fig. 9.72. Motor bracket.

8. (Fig. 6.95.) Make a detail working drawing of the bell crank. Read the instructions carefully before starting to draw.

9. (Fig. 15.61.) Make a complete set of working drawings of the vise. The complete set of drawings should be composed of detail drawings of the parts (except standard parts) and an assembly drawing.

10. (Fig. 15.62.) Make a complete set of working drawings of the flexible coupling. The complete set should include detail drawings of the individual parts and an assembly drawing complete with bill of material.

11. (Fig. 15.63.) Make a complete set of working drawings of the stock-rest. The complete set should include the necessary detail drawings of the parts and an assembly drawing complete with a bill of material.

12. (Fig. 9.80.) Make a complete set of working drawings of the milling jack. The complete set of drawings should be composed of detail drawings of the parts and an assembly drawing showing the parts in their relative positions.

13. (Fig. 9.76.) Make a detail drawing of an assigned part of the pipe stand. Draw all necessary views and give all dimensions that will be required by the shop. Compose a suitable title, giving the name of the part, the material, and the number required.

14. (Fig. 9.77.) Make a complete set of detail drawings for the tool holder.

15. (Fig. 9.78.) Make a detail working drawing of an assigned part of the flexible joint. Compose a suitable title giving the name of the part, the material, etc.

16. (Fig. 10.66.) Make a detail working drawing of an assigned part of the self-aligning shaft support. Compose a suitable title, giving the name of the part, the material, etc.

17. (Fig. 10.67.) Make an assembly drawing of the tumble jig, using the given details. Use the schematic symbol for screw threads. The pictorial drawing should prove helpful in deciding upon the relative locations of the assembled parts.

18. (Fig. 17.14.) Make a detail drawing (or sketch) of an assigned part of the air cylinder.

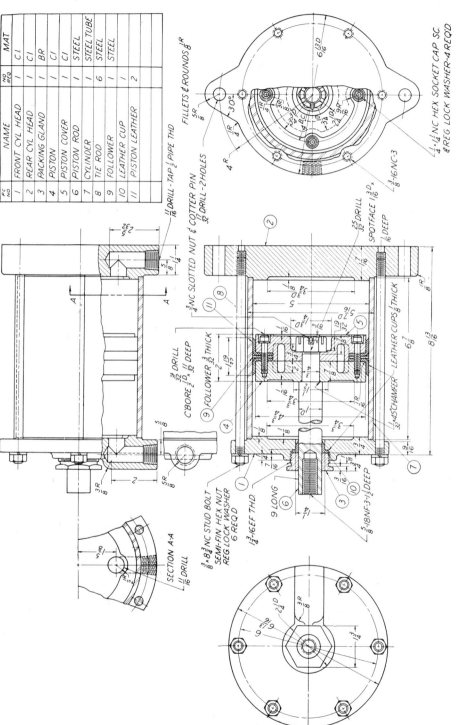

Fig. 17.14. *Air cylinder.*

19. (Fig. 17.15.)   Make a detail drawing (or sketch) of an assigned part of the compensating collet chuck.

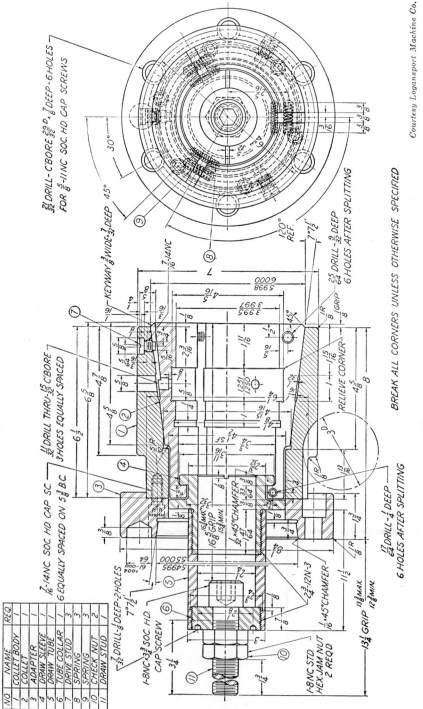

Courtesy Logansport Machine Co.

Fig. 17.15.   *Compensating collet chuck.*

20. (Fig. 17.16.)   Make a detail drawing (or sketch) of an assigned part of the boring fixture.

PART NO.	NAME	MATERIAL	NO. REQ'D
1	HOLDER	C.R.S.	1
2	CLAMP STRAP	C.R.S.	1
3	CLAMP	C.R.S.	1
4	CLAMP SCREW	C.R.S.	1
5	PLUG	BRASS	1
6	THUMB SCREW	C.R.S.	1
7	REST BUTTON	TOOL STEEL	2
8	BUSHING	TOOL STEEL	1
9	PIN	DRILL ROD	1

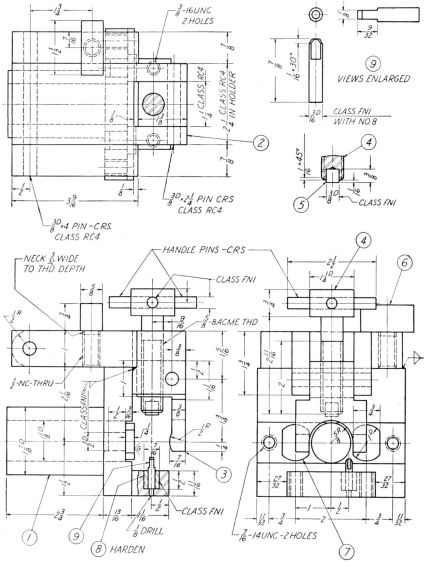

Fig. 17.16.   Boring fixture.

21. (Fig. 17.17.)   Make a detail drawing (or sketch) of an assigned part.

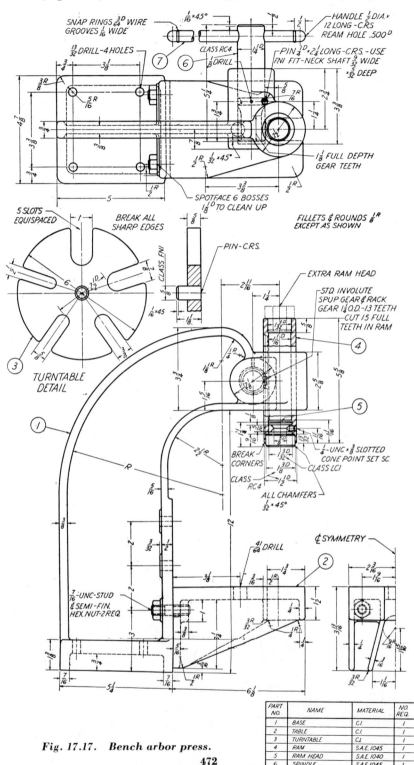

Fig. 17.17.   **Bench arbor press.**

472

PART NO.	NAME	MATERIAL	NO. REQ.
1	BASE	C.I.	1
2	TABLE	C.I.	1
3	TURNTABLE	C.I.	1
4	RAM	S.A.E. 1045	1
5	RAM HEAD	S.A.E. 1040	1
6	SPINDLE	S.A.E. 1045	1
7	HANDLE	C.R.S.	1

22. (Fig. 17.18.) Make a detail drawing (or sketch) of an assigned part of the conveyor take-up unit.

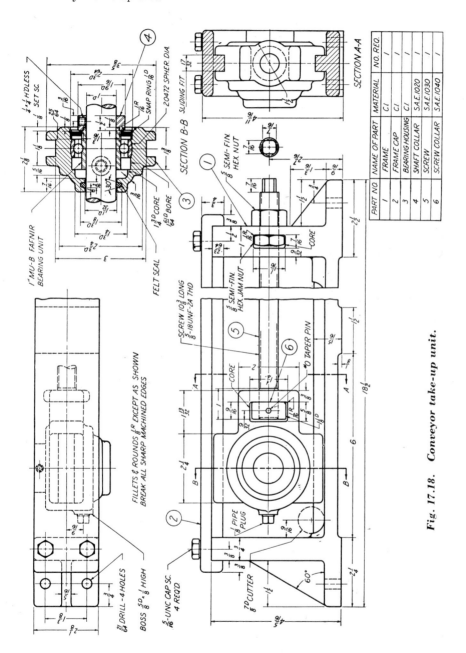

Fig. 17.18. Conveyor take-up unit.

23. (Fig. 17.19.)   Make a detail drawing (or sketch) of an assigned part of the gear pump.

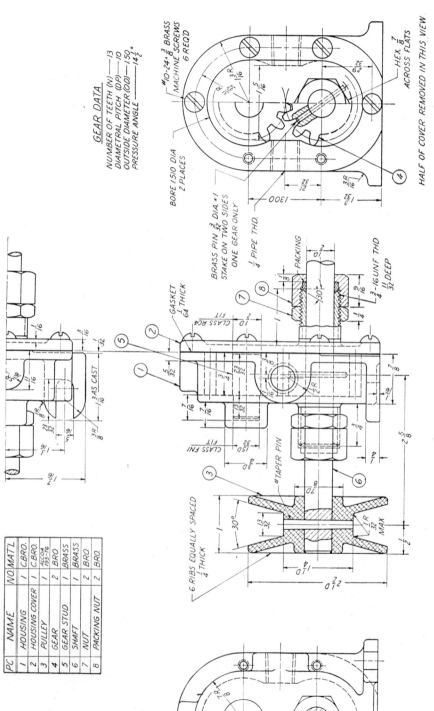

Fig. 17.19.   Gear pump.

24. (Fig. 17.20.)   Make a detail working drawing (or sketch) of an assigned part of the bench grinder.

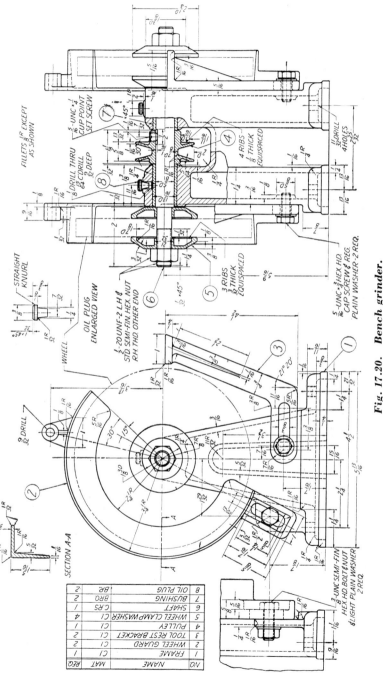

Fig. 17.20. Bench grinder.

NO	NAME	MAT	REQ
1	FRAME	CI	1
2	WHEEL GUARD	CI	2
3	TOOL REST BRACKET	CI	2
4	PULLEY	CI	1
5	WHEEL CLAMP WASHER	CI	4
6	SHAFT	CRS	1
7	BUSHING	BRO	2
8	OIL PLUG	BR.	2

25. (Figs. 17.21–17.23.)   Make detail drawings and an assembly drawing of the speed reducer.

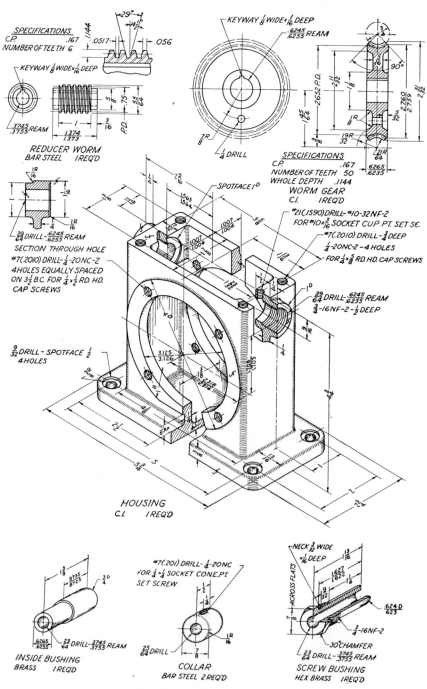

Fig. 17.21.   Speed reducer.

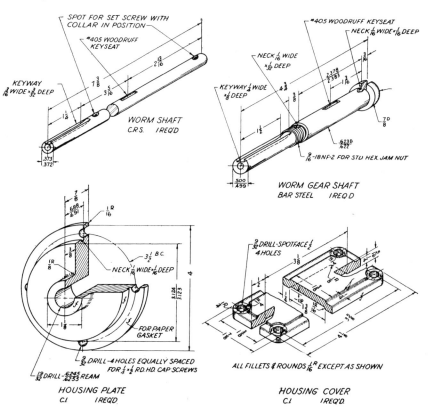

Fig. 17.22.   Speed reducer.

Fig. 17.23.   Speed reducer.

26. (Fig. 17.24.)   Make an assembly drawing of the radial engine unit, using the given details.   It is suggested that one piston be shown in full section so that the relative positions of the parts will be revealed.

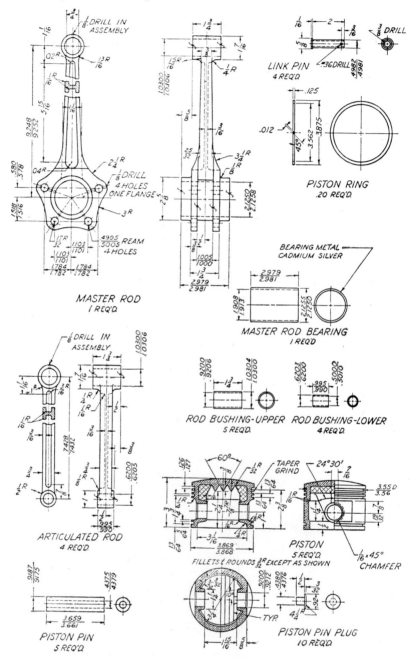

Fig. 17.24.   Radial engine details.

27. (Figs. 17.25–17.26.)   Make an assembly drawing of the idler pulley, using the given details.   Use the schematic symbol for screw threads.

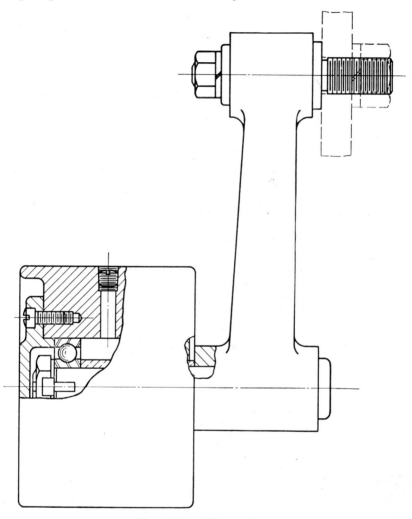

Fig. 17.25.   Idler pulley.

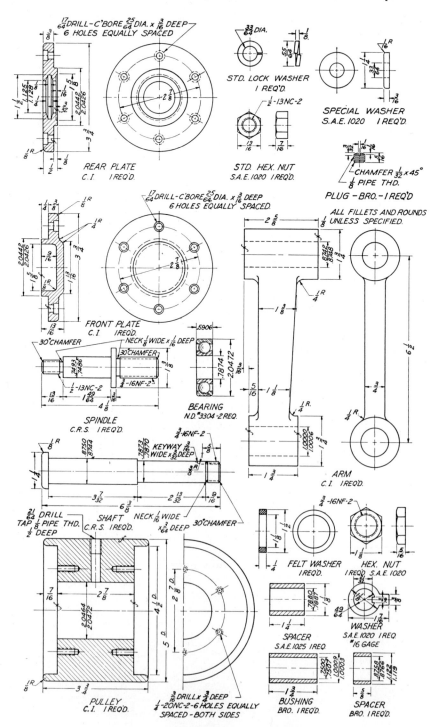

Fig. 17.26.   Idler pully details.

28. (Figs. 17.27–17.29.)   Make an assembly drawing of the hand clamp vise, using the given details.   Use the schematic symbol for screw threads.

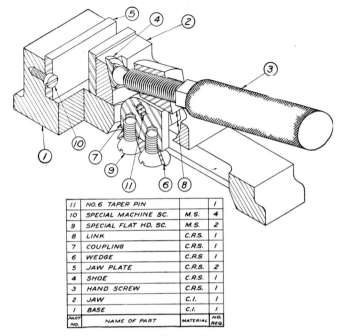

11	NO. 6 TAPER PIN		1
10	SPECIAL MACHINE SC.	M.S.	4
9	SPECIAL FLAT HD. SC.	M.S.	2
8	LINK	C.R.S.	1
7	COUPLING	C.R.S.	1
6	WEDGE	C.R.S.	1
5	JAW PLATE	C.R.S.	2
4	SHOE	C.R.S.	1
3	HAND SCREW	C.R.S.	1
2	JAW	C.I.	1
1	BASE	C.I.	1
PART NO.	NAME OF PART	MATERIAL	NO. REQ.

Fig. 17.27.   *Hand clamp vise.*

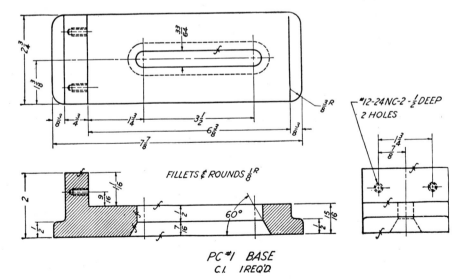

FILLETS & ROUNDS $\frac{1}{8}$ R

*12-24NC-2 -$\frac{1}{2}$ DEEP
2 HOLES

PC #1   BASE
C.I.   1 REQ'D

Fig. 17.28.   *Hand clamp vise details.*

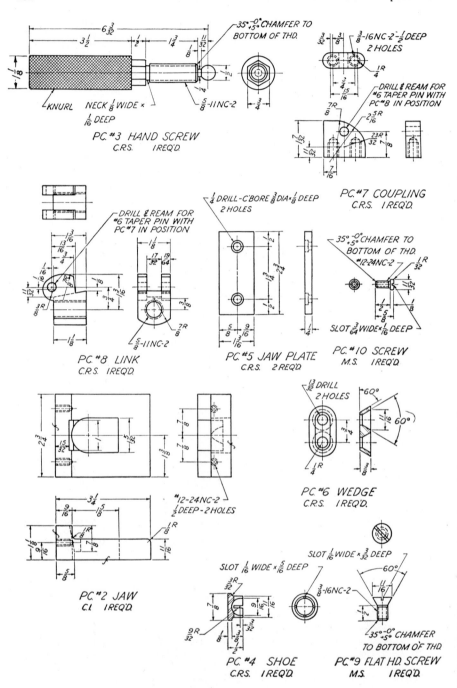

Fig. 17.29. Hand clamp vise details.

29. (Figs. 17.30–17.32.)   Make an assembly drawing of the hand grinder.

Fig. 17.30.   Hand grinder.

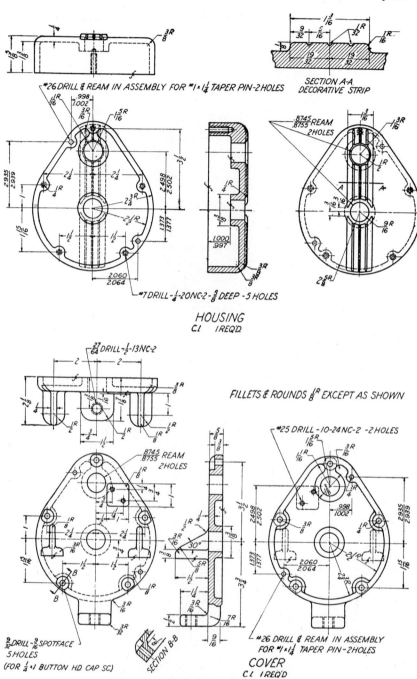

Fig. 17.31.   Hand grinder details.

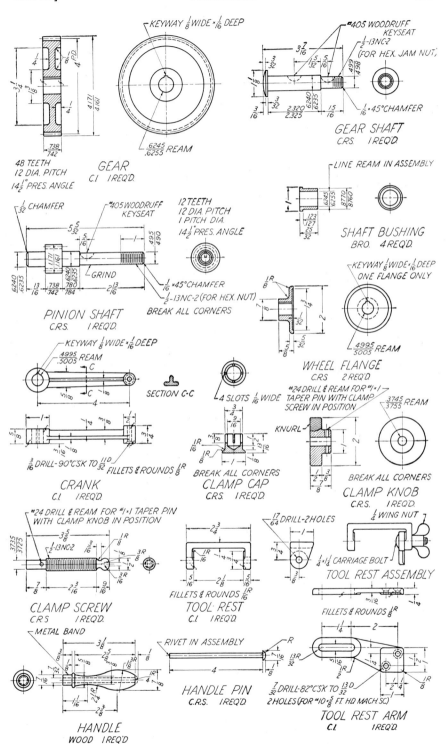

Fig. 17.32.   **Hand grinder details.**

30. (Figs. 17.33–17.35.) Make an assembly drawing of the right-angle head using the given details.

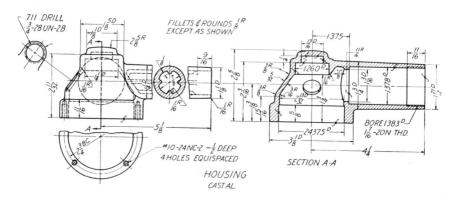

HOUSING
CAST AL.

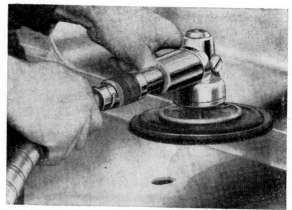

Courtesy R. C. Haskins Company.

Fig. 17.33. Right-angle head details.

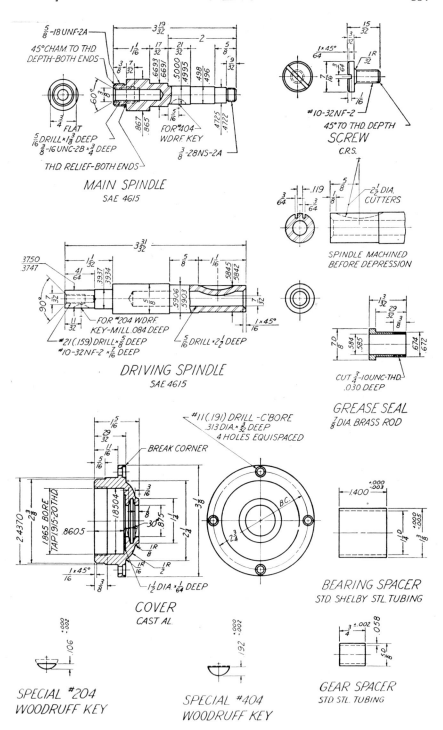

Fig. 17.34.   **Right-angle head details.**

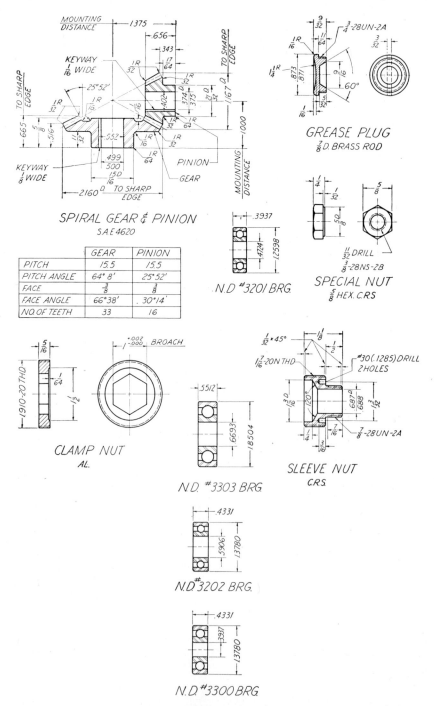

SPIRAL GEAR & PINION
S.A.E.4620

	GEAR	PINION
PITCH	15.5	15.5
PITCH ANGLE	64° 8′	25° 52′
FACE	$\frac{3}{8}$	$\frac{3}{8}$
FACE ANGLE	66° 38′	30° 14′
NO. OF TEETH	33	16

GREASE PLUG
$\frac{7}{8}$ D. BRASS ROD

SPECIAL NUT
$\frac{5}{8}$ HEX. C.R.S.

N.D #3201 BRG.

CLAMP NUT
AL.

N.D. #3303 BRG

SLEEVE NUT
C.R.S.

N.D. #3202 BRG.

N.D. #3300 BRG.

Fig. 17.35. Right-angle head details.

Engineering Graphs, Charts, Alignment Charts

GRAPHS AND CHARTS

18.1. A properly designed graphical representation will convey correlated data and facts to an average individual more rapidly and effectively

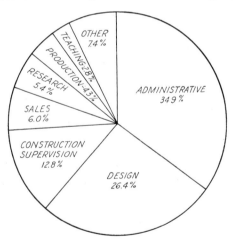

PROFESSIONAL ENGINEERS
THE KIND OF WORK THEY DO

Fig. 18.1. A pie chart.

than a verbal, written, or tabulated description, because a visual impression is easily comprehended and requires less mental effort than would be necessary to ascertain the facts from complex tables and reports (Fig. 18.1). It is because of this that diverse kinds of graphs and charts have been developed to present scientific, statistical, and technical information.

Note how quickly the relationship presented by the line graph in Fig. 18.2 can be interpreted.

Engineers, even though they are concerned mainly with technical graphs, should be familiar also with the popular forms, for every industrial concern frequently must prepare popular types of graphs in order to strengthen its relationship with the public.

It is impossible to treat exhaustively the subject of graphical representation in a single chapter.   Only a few of the most common forms used to analyze economic, scientific, and technical data can be discussed in detail. Many of the principles followed in the construction of engineering graphs, however, apply to the other types.

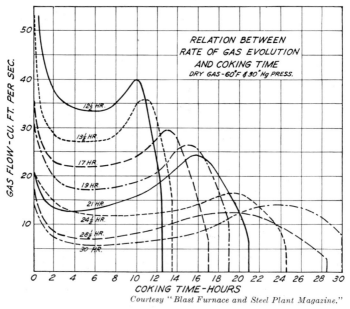

Fig. 18.2.   *An engineering graph prepared for publication.*

As much drafting skill is required in the execution of a graph as in making any other type of technical drawing.   Good appearance is important and can be achieved only with the help of good lettering and smooth, uniform, and properly contrasted lines.

18.2. Classification of charts, graphs, and diagrams. Graphs, charts, and diagrams may be divided into two classes in accordance with their use, and then further subdivided according to type.   When classified according to use, the two divisions are, first, those used for strictly scientific and technical purposes and, second, those used for the purpose of popular appeal.   The classification according to type is as follows:

1. Rectilinear charts
2. Semilogarithmic charts
3. Logarithmic charts
4. Barographs, area, and volume charts
5. Percentage charts
6. Polar charts
7. Trilinear charts
8. Pictorial charts
9. Alignment charts (nomographs)

18.3. Quantitative and qualitative charts and graphs.   In general, charts and diagrams are used for one of two purposes, either to read values or to present a comparative picture relationship between variables. If a chart or graph is prepared for reading values, it is called a *quantitative* graph; if prepared for presenting a comparative relationship, it is called *qualitative*.   Obviously, some charts serve both purposes and cannot be classified strictly as either type.   One of these purposes, however, must be predominant.   Since a number of features in the preparation depend upon the predominant purpose, such purpose must be determined before attempting to construct a graph.

18.4. Ordinary rectangular co-ordinate graphs.   Most engineering graphs, prepared for laboratory and office use, are drawn on ruled rectangular graph paper and are plotted in the first quadrant (upper right-hand), with the intersection of the X (horizontal) axis and Y (vertical) axis at the lower left used as the zero point or origin of co-ordinates.   The paper is ruled with equispaced horizontal and vertical lines, forming small rectangles.   The type most commonly used for chart work in experimental engineering is $8\frac{1}{2}'' \times 11''$ and is ruled to form one-twentieth-inch squares (Fig. 18.3a), every fifth line being heavy.   Another type of paper frequently used, which is suitable for most laboratory reports in technical schools, has rulings that form one-millimeter and one-centimeter squares (Fig. 18.3b).   Other rulings run $\frac{1}{10}''$, $\frac{1}{8}''$, or $\frac{1}{4}''$ apart.   Ordinarily, the ruled lines are spaced well apart on charts prepared for reproduction in popular and technical literature (Fig. 18.2).   The principal advantage of having greater spacing be-

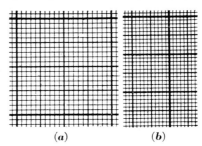

(a)   (b)

Fig. 18.3.   Types of graph paper.

tween the lines is that large squares or rectangles tend to make the graph easier to read.   Ready printed graph papers are available with various rulings in several colors.

Ordinary co-ordinate line graphs are used extensively because they

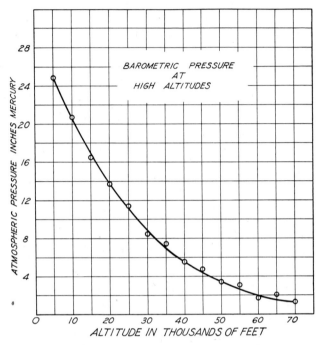

Fig. 18.4.   Rectangular graph.

are easily constructed and easily read.   The known relationship between the variables is expressed by one or more continuous lines, which may be straight, broken, or curved.

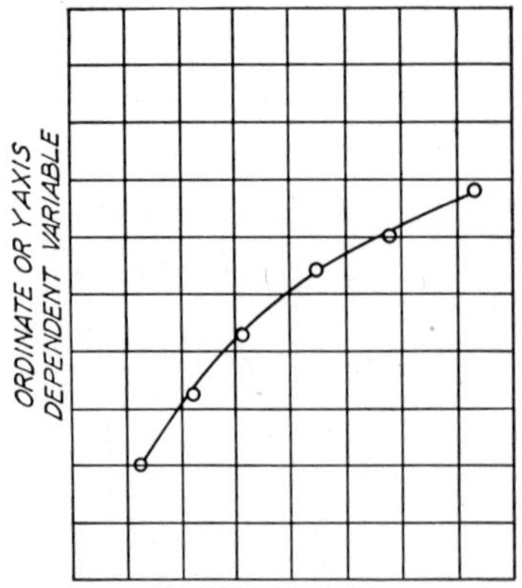

The graph in Fig. 18.4 shows the approximate barometric pressure at different heights above sea level.

A graphical representation may be drawn easily and correctly if, after the required data have been assembled, careful consideration is given to the principles of curve drawing discussed in the following articles.

18.5. The determination of the variables for ordinate and abscissa. The independent variable, the quantity arbitrarily varied during the experiment, usually is chosen for the abscissa (Fig. 18.5).   Certain kinds of experimental data, however, such as a stress-strain diagram (Fig. 18.6), are plotted with the independent variable along the ordinate.

Fig. 18.5. Independent and dependent variables.

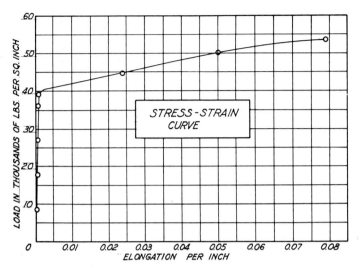

Fig. 18.6.   Stress-strain diagram.

18.6. The selection of suitable scales.* The American Society of Mechanical Engineers in a standard for engineering and scientific graphs recommends:

a. Very careful consideration should be given to the choice of scales since this has a controlling influence on the slope of the curve.   The slope of the curve, as a whole and also at intermediate points, provides a visual impression of the degree of change in the dependent variable for a given increment in the independent variable.   Creating the right impression of the relationship to be shown by a line graph is, therefore, probably controlled more critically by the relative stretching of the vertical and horizontal scales than by any other feature involved in the design of the graph.

b. The range of scales should be chosen to insure effective and efficient use of the co-ordinate area in attaining the objective of the chart.

c. The zero line should be included, if visual comparison of plotted magnitudes is desired.

(If the chart is quantitative, the intersection of the axes need not be at the origin of co-ordinates.   If it is qualitative, however, both the ordinate and abscissa generally should have zero value at the intersection of the axes, as in Fig. 18.2.)

d. For arithmetic scales, the scale numbers shown on the graph and space between co-ordinate rulings should preferably correspond to 1, 2, or 5 units of measurement, multiplied or divided by 1, 10, 100, etc.

(Other units could be used except for the fact that they create situations where it becomes difficult to interpolate values.   For example, one square should equal one of the following.)

---

* These statements were abstracted from the American Standard for Engineering and Scientific Graphs for Publication (ASA Z15.3–1943).

0.01	0.1	1	10	100	etc.
0.02	0.2	2	20	200	etc.
0.04	0.4	4	40	400	etc.
0.05	0.5	5	50	500	etc.
etc.	etc.	etc.	etc.	etc.	etc.

e. The horizontal (independent variable) scale values should usually increase from left to right and the vertical (dependent variable) from bottom to top.

18.7. Locating the axes and marking the values of the variables. On graphs prepared for laboratory reports and not for publication, the axes should be located 1″ or more inside the border of the co-ordinate

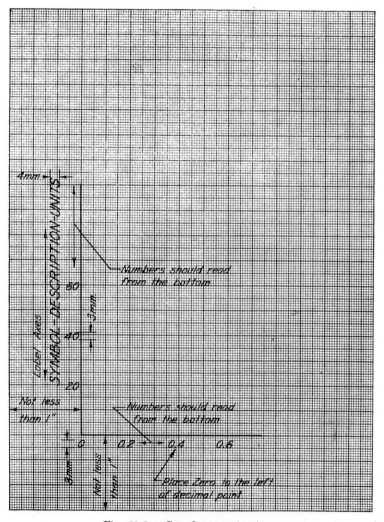

Fig. 18.7.   Graph construction.

ruling. (See Fig. 18.7.) When selecting the scale units and locating the axes, it should be remembered that the abscissa may be taken either the long way or short way of the co-ordinate paper, depending upon the range of the scales.

Concerning the numbers, the ASME standard recommends:

The use of many digits in scale numbers should be avoided. This can usually be accomplished by a suitable designation in the scale caption.

EXAMPLE: PRESSURE, MM. OF HG. $\times$ 10⁻⁵; RESISTANCE, THOU-SANDS OF OHMS.

The numbers should read from the bottom when possible (Fig. 18.7). For the sake of good appearance, they never should be crowded. Always place a cipher to the left of the decimal point when the quantity is less than one.

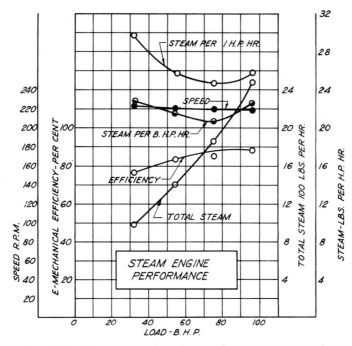

Fig. 18.8.   Representation of several curves on a graph.

Usually, only the heavy co-ordinate lines are marked to indicate their values or distance from the origin, and, even then, the values may be shown only at a regular selected interval. (See Fig. 18.7.) These numbers should be placed to the left of the Y-axis and just below the X-axis.

When several curves representing different variables are to appear on the same graph, a separate axis generally is required for each variable. (See Fig. 18.8.) In this case, a corresponding description should be given along each axis. The axes should be grouped at the left or at the bottom of the graph, unless it is desirable to place some at the right or along the top.

18.8. Indicating plotted points representing the data. If the data represent a set of experimental observations, the plotted points of a

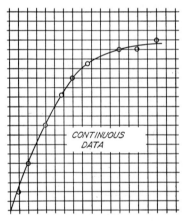

single-curve graph should be marked by small circles approximately 0.1″ in diameter (see Fig. 18.9). The following practice is recommended: open circles, filled-in circles, and partially filled-in circles (○ ● ◔) rather than crosses, squares, and triangles should be used to differentiate observed points of several curves on a graph. Filled-in symbols may be made smaller than those not filled in.

PREFERRED

(a)

PERMISSIBLE

(b)

Fig. 18.9. Identification symbols.

Mathematical curves are frequently drawn without distinguishing marks at computed positions.

18.9. Drawing a curve. Since most physical phenomena are continuous, curves on engineering graphs usually represent an average of plotted points (Fig. 18.10). Discontinuous data should be plotted with a broken line, as shown in Fig. 18.11.

CONTINUOUS DATA

DISCONTINUOUS DATA

Fig. 18.10. Continuous curve.   **Fig. 18.11. Discontinuous data.**

It is preferable to represent curves by solid lines. If more than one curve appears on a graph, differentiation may be secured by varied types of lines; but the most important curve should be represented by a solid one. A very fine line should be used for a quantitative curve, if values are to be read accurately. A heavy line ($\frac{1}{40}$″ width) is recommended for a qualitative curve. It should be observed in Figs. 18.10 and 18.11 that the curve line does not pass through open circles.

For ordinary qualitative graphs, the ASME standard suggests:

a. When more than one curve is presented on a graph, relative emphasis or differentiation of the curves may be secured by using different types of line, *i.e.*, solid, dashed, dotted, etc.   A solid line is recommended for the most important curve.

b. When more than one curve is presented on a graph, each should bear a suitable designation.

c. Curves should, if practicable, be designated by brief labels placed close to the curves (horizontally or along the curves) rather than by letters, numbers or other devices requiring a key (Fig. 18.8).

18.10. The labeling of the scales.   Each scale caption should give a description of the variable represented and the unit of measurement. The captions on engineering graphs frequently contain an added identifying symbol such as "N–EFFICIENCY–PER CENT" or "P–OUTPUT–H.P."

All lettering should be readable from the bottom and right side of the graph (not the left side).   When space is limited, standard abbreviations should be used, particularly for designating the unit of measurement.   To avoid confusing the reader, only recognized word contractions should be used.

18.11. Titles, legends, notes, and so on.   The title of a graph should be clear, concise, complete, and symmetrical.   It should give the name of the curve, the source of the data, the date, and other important information (Fig. 18.12).   It should be so placed that it gives a balanced effect to the completed drawing (Fig. 18.2).   In addition to the title, a wiring diagram, pictorial diagram, formula, or explanatory note is often necessary to give a clear picture of the nature of the experiment. For example, if there is any great irregularity in the plotted points or a condition that may have affected the values as shown by the data, a note of explanation should be given.

STRESS - STRAIN DIAGRAM
FOR
COMPRESSION
IN
CAST IRON

Fig. 18.12.   A title.

A legend or key is sometimes included to explain a set of curves in greater detail.

In commercial practice, alcohol is often used to clear a rectangular area of co-ordinate lines in order that the title may be printed in an open space.

18.12. Procedure for making a graphical representation in ink.

1. Select the type of co-ordinate paper.
2. Determine the variables for ordinate and abscissa.
3. Determine the scale units.
4. Locate the axes and mark the scale values in pencil.
5. Plot the points representing the data.   (Many persons ink the symbols (○ ◑) indicating the points at this stage.)

6. Draw the curve.   If the curve is to strike an average among the plotted points, a trial curve should be drawn in pencil.   If the curve consists of a broken line, as is the case with discontinuous data, the curve need not be drawn until the graph is traced in ink.

7. Label the axes directly in ink.

8. Letter the title, notes, and so on.   The title should be lettered on a trial sheet that can be used as a guide for lettering directly in ink on the graph.

9. Check the work and complete the diagram by tracing the curve in ink.

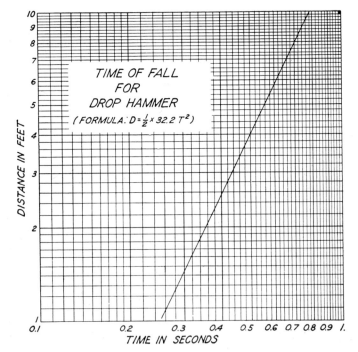

Fig. 18.13.   Logarithmic graph.

18.13. Logarithmic graphs.   Logarithmic co-ordinate graphs are constructed on prepared paper on which the parallel horizontal and parallel vertical rulings are spaced proportional to the logarithms of numbers (Fig. 18.13).   This type of graph has two principal advantages over the ordinary co-ordinate type.   First, the error in plotting or reading values is a constant percentage, and, second, an algebraic equation of the form $y = ax^b$ appears as a straight line if x has a value other than 0.   The exponent b may be either plus or minus.

The equation for a falling body, $D = \frac{1}{2}gt^2$, is represented in Figs. 18.13 and 18.14.   A practical application of interest to engineers is in the design of drop hammers.   In this equation, based on uniform accelerated motion, t represents time in seconds and d the distance traveled in t seconds by a freely falling body with no initial velocity.   Observe that the plotted points form a parabolic curve on ordinary co-ordinate graph paper, and a straight line on logarithmic paper.   To draw the line on the graph in Fig. 18.13, it is necessary to calculate and locate only two points, while in Fig. 18.14 several points must be plotted to establish the location of the corresponding curved-line representation.   The line on Fig. 18.13 has a slope of 2 to 1, because the exponent of t is 2.   Therefore, the line could be drawn by utilizing one point and the slope, instead of plotting two points and joining them with a straight line.

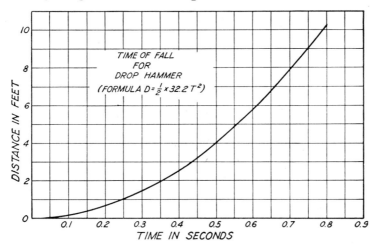

Fig. 18.14.   Co-ordinate graph.

Log paper is available with rulings in one or more cycles for any range of values to be plotted.   Part-cycle and split-cycle papers may also be purchased.

18.14. Semilogarithmic graphs.   Semilogarithmic paper has ruled lines that are spaced to a uniform scale in one direction and to a logarithmic scale in the other direction (Fig. 18.15).   Charts drawn on this form of paper are used extensively in scientific studies because functions having values in the form of geometric progressions are represented by straight lines.   In any case, the main reason for the use of semilogarithmic paper is that the slope of the resulting curve indicates rate of change rather than amount of change, the opposite being true in the case of curves on ordinary co-ordinate graph paper.   If those who are interested desire, they may determine the rate of increase or decrease at any point by measuring the slope.   A straight line indicates a constant rate of change.   In commercial work this form of paper is generally called "ratio paper," and the charts are known as "rate-of-change charts."

As previously stated, the choice of a type of graph paper depends upon the information to be revealed. Curves drawn on uniform co-ordinate graph paper to illustrate the percentage of expansion or contraction of sales, and so on, present a misleading picture. The same data plotted on semilogarithmic paper would reveal the true rate of change to the business management. For this reason, semilogarithmic paper should be used whenever percentage of change rather than quantity change is to be shown. In scientific work, when the value of one variable increases in a geometric progression and the other in an arithmetic progression, this form is valuable.

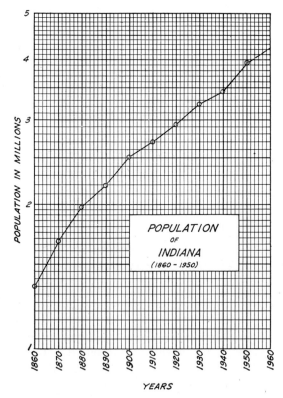

Fig. 18.15.   Semilogarithmic chart.

18.15. Bar charts. Bar charts or barographs are used principally in popular literature covering economic and industrial surveys. They are a simple diagrammatic form giving a pictorial summary of statistical data and can be easily understood by the average person. Logarithmic and uniform co-ordinate graphs are less suited for this purpose because few people know the procedure for reading curves or understand their picture qualities.

Whenever values or quantities are illustrated, as in Fig. 18.16, by consecutive heavy bars whose lengths are proportional to the amounts they represent, the resulting representation is called a *bar chart*.

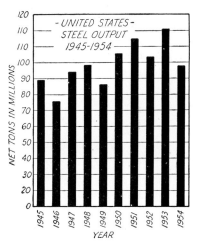

The bars on this type of diagram may be drawn either horizontally or vertically, but all should start at the same zero line. Their lengths should be to some fixed scale, the division values of which may be given in the margin along the bottom or left side of the graph. When it is necessary to give the exact values represented, the figures should be placed along each bar in a direction parallel to it. To place the values at the end gives the illusion of increasing the length of the bars. Usually, the names of the items are lettered to the left of the

Fig. 18.16.   A bar chart.

vertical starting line on a horizontal chart and below the starting line on a vertical chart.

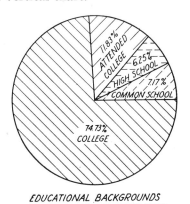

EDUCATIONAL BACKGROUNDS
OF PERSONS LISTED IN WHO'S WHO
Data, Courtesy Equitable Life Ins. Co.

Fig. 18.17.   Pie chart.

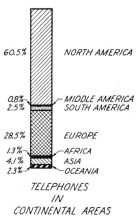

TELEPHONES
IN
CONTINENTAL AREAS

Fig. 18.18.   Percentage bar chart.

18.16. Area (percentage) charts. An area diagram can be used profitably when it is desirable to present pictorially a comparison of related quantities in percentage. This form of representation illustrates the relative magnitudes of the component divisions of a total of the distribution of income, the composition of the population, and so on. Two common types of the various forms of area diagrams used in advertising literature are illustrated in Figs. 18.17 and 18.18. Percentages, when represented by sectors of a circle or subdivisions of a bar, are easy to interpolate.

The pie chart (Fig. 18.17) is the most popular form of area diagram, as well as the easiest to construct. The area of the circle represents 100 per cent and the sectors represent percentages of the total. In order to make the chart effective, a description of each quantity and its corresponding percentage should be lettered in its individual sector. All lettering should

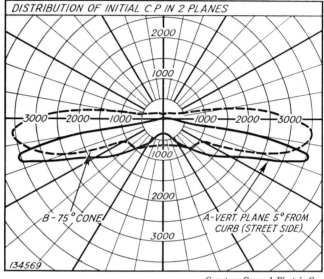

Courtesy General Electric Co.

Fig. 18.19.   Polar chart.

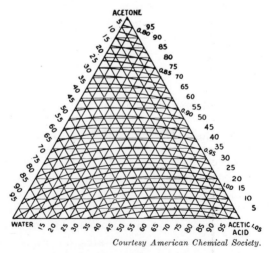

Courtesy American Chemical Society.

Fig. 18.20.   Trilinear chart.

be completed before the areas are crosshatched or colored. The percentage bar chart shown in Fig. 18.18 fulfills the same purpose as the pie chart. The all-over area of the bar represents 100 per cent. Note that each percentage division is crosshatched differently. The descriptions may be placed on either side of the bar; the percentages should be on the bar or at the side.

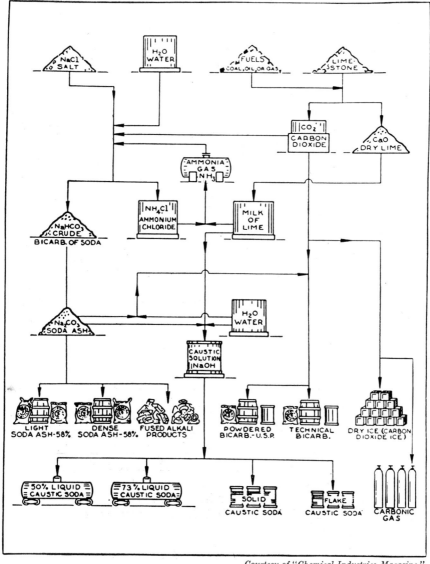

Fig. 18.21. Flow chart of ammonia-soda operations.

18.17. Polar charts. Certain types of technical data can be more easily plotted and better represented on polar co-ordinate paper. Polar charts drawn by self-recording instruments, polar diagrams, and plotted polar curves representing various kinds of scientific data are very common. Polar curves are used to represent the intensity of diffused light, intensity of heat, and so on. The polar chart in Fig. 18.19 gives, in terms of candle power, the intensity of light in two planes.

18.18. Trilinear charts. Trilinear charts are used principally in the study of the properties of chemical compounds, mixtures, solutions, and alloys (Fig. 18.20). Basically, this is a 100 per cent chart the use of which, owing to its geometrical form, is limited to the investigation of that which is composed of three constituents or variables. Its use depends upon the geometrical principle that the sum of the three perpendiculars from any point is equal to the altitude. If the altitude represents 100 per cent, the perpendiculars will represent the percentages of the three variables composing the whole.

The ruling can be accomplished conveniently by dividing any two sides of the triangle into the number of equal percentage divisions desired and drawing through these points lines parallel to the sides of the triangle.

18.19. Chemical engineering charts. Fig. 18.21 shows a type of flow chart that must be prepared frequently by chemical engineers in industrial practice.

18.20. Pictorial charts. Pictorial charts are quite generally used to present data in reports prepared for nontechnical readers.

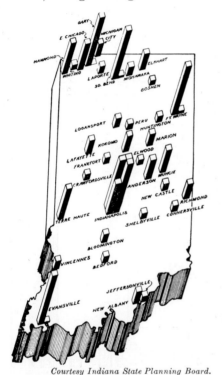

Courtesy Indiana State Planning Board.

Fig. 18.22. *Population chart (pictorial).*

Usually, such charts present comparisons of populations (Fig. 18.22), expenditures, costs, etc. Stacks of silver dollars may represent expenditures, size of animals can represent livestock production, and human figures can present employment data.

ALIGNMENT CHARTS

18.21. Alignment charts (nomographs). The purpose of alignment charts is to eliminate many of the laborious calculations necessary

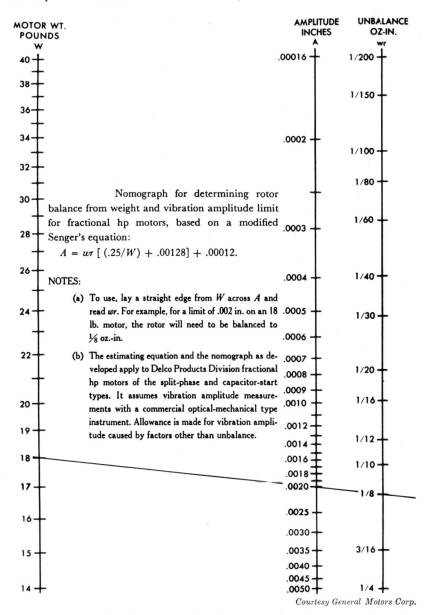

MOTOR WT.
POUNDS
W

AMPLITUDE
INCHES
A

UNBALANCE
OZ-IN.
wr

Nomograph for determining rotor balance from weight and vibration amplitude limit for fractional hp motors, based on a modified Senger's equation:

$$A = wr\left[\,(.25/W) + .00128\right] + .00012.$$

NOTES:

(a) To use, lay a straight edge from W across A and read wr. For example, for a limit of .002 in. on an 18 lb. motor, the rotor will need to be balanced to $\frac{1}{8}$ oz.-in.

(b) The estimating equation and the nomograph as developed apply to Delco Products Division fractional hp motors of the split-phase and capacitor-start types. It assumes vibration amplitude measurements with a commercial optical-mechanical type instrument. Allowance is made for vibration amplitude caused by factors other than unbalance.

Courtesy General Motors Corp.

Fig. 18.23.   An alignment chart.

to solve formulae containing three or more variables.   Such a chart is often complicated and difficult to construct, but if it can be used repeatedly, the labor involved in making it will be justified.   In the commercial field, these charts appear in varied forms, which may be very simple or very complicated.   Figure 18.23 illustrates an alignment chart consisting of three graduated parallel lines.

Briefly stated, the simplest form of alignment chart consists of a set of three or more inclined or vertical scales so spaced and graduated as to represent graphically the variables in a formula. The scales may be divided into logarithmic units or some other types of functions, depending upon the form of equation. As illustrated in Fig. 18.23, the unknown value may be found by aligning a straightedge to the points representing known values on two of the scales. With a scale or triangle so placed, the numerical value representing the solution of the equation can be read on the third scale at the point of intersection.

Since alignment charts in varied forms are being used more and more by engineers and scientists, it is desirable that students studying in the fields dealing with the sciences have some knowledge of the fundamental principles underlying their construction. However, in any brief treatment, directed toward a beginner, it is impossible to explain fully the mathematics involved in the construction of the many and varied types. Therefore, our attention here must be directed toward an understanding of a few of the less complicated straight-line forms with the hope that the student will gather sufficient knowledge to construct simple charts for familiar equations of no more than three variables.

To satisfy the growing demand for training in the construction of graphical aids for engineering computation, several technical schools have added special courses dealing with alignment charts, special slide rules, and so on. Rather thorough coverage of nomographic drawing may be found in any of the several reliable books that are listed in the bibliography of this text.

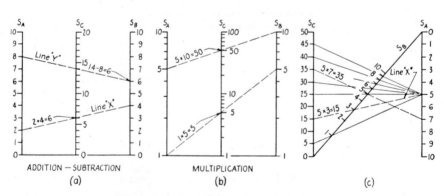

Fig. 18.24.   Parallel-scale and Z-charts.

18.22. Construction of simple alignment charts. In this limited study, the explanation for the constructions will be based on the principles of plane geometry. The two forms to be considered for formulae having no more than three variables are the parallel-scale chart and the Z-chart, also called an N-chart (Fig. 18.24).

Without giving much more than a passing thought at this time to the geometry underlying the construction of alignment charts and to the selection of scales, the methods that might be used to construct simple charts for graphical addition and subtraction and graphical multiplication and division might well be considered. See Fig. 18.24(a) and (b).

A parallel-scale alignment chart of the type shown in (a), prepared for the purpose of making additions and subtractions, could be constructed as follows:

Step 1. Draw three vertical straight lines spaced an equal distance apart.

Step 2. Draw a horizontal base line. This line will align and establish the origins (0) of the three scales.

Step 3. Using an engineer's decimal scale, mark off a series of equal lengths on scales S_A and S_B. Start at the base line in each case. Mark the values of the graduations upward on both scales starting with 0 at the base line.

Step 4. Mark off on the S_C scale a series of lengths that are half as long as those on scales S_A and S_B. Number the graduation marks starting at the base line.

In using this chart to add two numbers, say 2 and 4, one may align the ruling edge of a triangle through 2 on the S_A scale and 4 on the S_B scale, then, read their sum at the point where the edge of the triangle crosses the S_C scale. See line X. To subtract one number from another, say 8 from 14, the edge of the triangle should be placed so as to pass through 8 on scale S_A and 14 on S_C. The difference, read on the S_B scale, will be 6 as shown by line Y.

For proof of this construction, it is necessary to turn to this principle of geometry: that the median of a trapezoid (a line parallel to the bases and located equidistant between them) will have a length equal to one-half the sum of the lengths of the two bases. Let it be supposed then that lines X and Y form the sides of such a trapezoid, and the bases are the lines intercepted between X and Y on the scales S_A and S_B. Then, since S_C is equidistant between S_A and S_B, the segment between points 6 and 14 must represent the line located midway between the bases of the trapezoid. With the lengths of the units on S_C equal to one-half the length of those along scales S_A and S_B, the number of units intercepted along S_C must be equal to the sum of the number of units intercepted on the other two scales. The base line and the line X could also be considered to be the sides of the trapezoid. In this case 6 units on S_C equals the sum of the 2 units on S_A and the 4 units on S_B.

If logarithmic scales are used for this form of chart as in (b) instead of natural scales as in (a), a chart for multiplication and division results, for the log of the product of two numbers is equal to the sum of the logs of the factors. Thus, by a method of addition a product can be obtained.

EXAMPLE: $c = a \times b$ and,

$$\log c = \log a + \log b$$

To find the product of two numbers, say 5 and 10, one should place the ruling edge of a triangle so that it will pass through 5 on the S_A scale and 10 on the S_B scale. The product may be read on the S_C scale. (See (b).)

Necessary information for the construction of logarithmic scales is given in Section 18.24.

A Z-chart (also called an N-chart), which will give the product of two numbers, is shown in (c). For example, if line X is assumed to represent the edge of a triangle so placed as to pass through 5 on the S_A scale and 3 on the S_B scale, it can be seen that $3 \times 5 = 15$.

A simple Z-chart that has been prepared solely for straight multiplication will have outside vertical scales of uniform spacing. The length of the scales and the spacing of the graduation marks can be arbitrarily determined as long as the chart will fit on the paper that is available and provided that the graduations cover the desired range in each case. The two vertical scales begin with 0 (zero) value at opposite ends of the diagonal scale so that the values of the graduations read in increasing magnitude upward on one scale and downward on the other.

The steps in constructing a chart of this type are as follows:

Step 1. Lay out the vertical scales using uniform spacing for the graduation marks.

Step 2. Draw the line for the diagonal scale by joining the two zero points.

Step 3. Graduate the diagonal scale. In order to simplify the construction, it is suggested that one convenient value for the factor (say 5) be selected from which to draw construction lines to the graduation marks on the scale giving the product. The points of intersection of these lines with the diagonal line establish the location of the graduation marks for the diagonal scale. For instance, a line drawn from 5 on S_A to 5 on S_C will give the location of the graduation mark for the 1 on scale S_B. Similarily, a line drawn from 5 on S_A to 45 on S_C will locate the graduation mark for the 9 on S_B.

18.23. Definitions. Before starting a discussion on the construction of scales, it is necessary that the student have an understanding of the meaning of the following terms and expressions that are commonly used when constructing alignment charts for solving equations.

Constant—A quantity whose value remains unchanged in an equation.

Variable—A quantity capable of taking different values in an equation. A variable is designated by some letter, usually one of the latter letters of the alphabet.

Function of a variable—A mathematical expression for a combination of terms containing a variable, usually expressed in abbreviated form as $f(x)$ which is understood to mean "function of x." An equation usually contains several functions of different variables, such as $f(r) + f(s) = f(t)$; or $f(u)$. $f(v) = f(w)$.

Functional modulus—A proportionality multiplier that is used to bring a range of values of a particular function within a selected length for a scale. For instance, with the upper and lower limits of a function known and a definite length L chosen for the scale, the value of the functional modulus (m) can be found by dividing L by the amount of the difference between the upper and lower limits of the function. The scale equation for determining m

may be written: $m = \dfrac{L}{f(u_2) - f(u_1)}$ where $f(u_2)$ and $f(u_1)$ are the upper and lower limits.

Scale—A graduated line that may be either straight or curved. When the graduation marks are equally spaced, that is, when the distance between marks is the same for equal increments of the variable as the variable increases in magnitude, the scale is known as a uniform scale. When the lengths to the graduation marks are laid off to correspond to scale values of the function of a variable, the scale is called a functional scale.

18.24. Construction of a functional scale. Let it be supposed that it is necessary to construct a functional scale, 5 inches in length, for

$f(u) = \dfrac{u^2}{2}$ with u to range from 0 to 10. It will be found desirable to

make the necessary computations by steps and to record the scale data in tabular form (Fig. 18.25).

Step 1.   Record the values of u in the table.

Step 2.   Compute the values of the function.

Step 3.   Determine the functional modulus m.

Step 4.   Multiply the recorded values of the function by the functional modulus.

In this case and in many other cases, the functional modulus may be chosen by inspection. For this problem, the over-all length (L) of the scale will be 5 inches when $m = 0.10$. If the scale equation is used to determine the functional modulus then:

$$m = \frac{L}{f(u_2) - f(u_1)} = \frac{5}{\dfrac{(10)^2}{2} - 0} = \frac{5}{50} = 0.10$$

u	0	1	2	3	4	5	6	7	8	9	10
u^2	0	1	4	9	16	25	36	49	64	81	100
$\dfrac{u^2}{2}$	0	0.5	2.0	4.5	8.0	12.5	18.0	24.5	32.0	40.5	50.0
$m\left(\dfrac{u^2}{2}\right)$	0	0.05″	0.2″	0.45″	0.80″	1.25″	1.80″	2.45″	3.20″	4.05″	5.00″

Fig. 18.25.   Table.

All that now remains to be done to construct the scale is to lay off the computed distances along the line for the scale and mark the values at the corresponding interval points (Fig. 18.26).

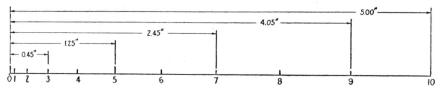

Fig. 18.26. Functional scale for $\dfrac{u^2}{2}$.

Although a logarithmic scale might be constructed in this same manner, much time can be saved by using the graphic method shown in Fig.

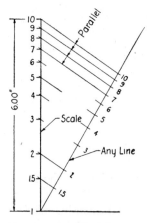

Fig. 18.27. Graduating a log scale.

18.27 for subdividing the scale between its end points. To apply this method to a scale that has already been laid off to a predetermined length with the end points of the range (say 1 to 10) marked, the steps of the construction are as follows:

Step 1. Draw a light construction line through point 1 making any convenient angle with the scale line.

Step 2. Using a printed log scale, mark off points on the auxiliary line.

Step 3. Draw a line through the 10 point on the construction line and the 10 point on the scale, then, through the remaining points draw lines parallel to this line through the 10's. These will divide the scale in proportion to the logarithms of numbers from 1 to 10.

18.25. Parallel-scale charts for equations of the form $f(t) + f(u) = f(v)$. An alignment chart that is designed for solving an equation that can be set up to take this form will have three parallel functional scales that may be either uniform or logarithmic depending upon the equation. More information will be presented later concerning parallel-scale charts with logarithmic scales. In this section, attention will be directed to charts having scales with uniform spacing.

Before one can start constructing the chart, he must determine by calculation certain necessary information. First, he must determine how the scales are to be graduated, and second, he must calculate the ratio for the scale spacing.

To be competent to design parallel-scale charts, one must have a full understanding of the geometrical basis for their construction. The explanation to follow is associated with the line layout in Fig. 18.28. Three parallel scales S_A, S_B, and S_C are shown and the origins t_0, u_0, and v_0 fall on line (isopleth) AB. Line (1) and line (2) are drawn parallel to AB through points v and u respectively. By similar triangles (shown shaded);

$$\frac{L_t - L_v}{a} = \frac{L_v - L_u}{b}$$

Now if, $m_t = \dfrac{L_t}{f(t) - f(t_0)}$ then, $L_t = m_t[f(t) - f(t_0)]$

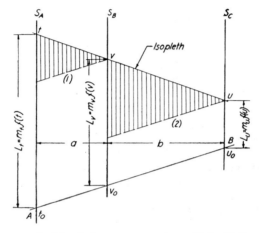

Fig. 18.28.   Geometrical basis for construction of parallel-scale alignment charts.

When the function of t_0 is zero, the equation becomes,

$$L_t = m_t f(t)$$

Similarly, when v_0 is zero, $L_v = m_v f(v)$

and, when u_0 is zero, $L_u = m_u f(u)$

Substituting these values;

$$\frac{m_t f(t) - m_v f(v)}{a} = \frac{m_v f(v) - m_u f(u)}{b}$$

Collecting terms,

$$m_t f(t) + \left(\frac{a}{b}\right) m_u f(u) = \left(\frac{a}{b}\right) m_v f(v) + m_v f(v)$$

$$= m_v \left(1 + \frac{a}{b}\right) f(v)$$

But $f(t) + f(u) = f(v)$ only if the coefficient of the three terms are equal, therefore,

$$m_t = \left(\frac{a}{b}\right) m_u = \left(1 + \frac{a}{b}\right) m_v$$

and, $$\frac{m_t}{m_u} = \frac{a}{b} \qquad \text{Equation (1)}$$

Now since $$m_t = \left(1 + \frac{a}{b}\right) m_v \qquad \text{and} \qquad \frac{a}{b} = \frac{m_t}{m_u}$$

Then, $$m_t = \left(1 + \frac{m_t}{m_u}\right) m_v$$

$$m_v = \frac{m_t}{\left(1 + \dfrac{m_t}{m_u}\right)}$$

and finally, $$m_v = \frac{m_t m_u}{m_t + m_u} \qquad \text{Equation (2)}$$

Now suppose that it is desired to construct a chart having the form of $t + u = v$ and that t is to have a range from 0 to 10 and u from 0 to 20 (Fig. 18.29). It has been determined that the scale lengths should be 6 inches.

Then: $$m_t = \frac{6}{10.0} = \frac{6}{10} = 0.6; \qquad m_u = \frac{6}{20.0} = \frac{6}{20} = 0.3$$

and, $$m_v = \frac{m_t m_u}{m_t + m_u} = \frac{0.6 \times 0.3}{0.6 + 0.3} = \frac{0.18}{0.90} = 0.20 \quad \text{Equation (2)}$$

To determine the ratio of the scale spacing;

$$\frac{m_t}{m_u} = \frac{a}{b} = \frac{0.6}{0.3} = \frac{2}{1} \qquad \text{Equation (1)}$$

For convenience, distance "a" between scales can be made 3 inches. Distance "b" must then be $1\frac{1}{2}$ inches to satisfy the proportion of 2 to 1. The total width of the chart will be $4\frac{1}{2}$ inches.

Since in this particular case the modulus for each of the scales is in full tenths and the scales are to be uniformly divided, an engineer's scale may be used to mark off the scales of the chart. With other conditions, it would be necessary to prepare either a table such as the one shown in Fig. 18.25 or to divide the line between its end points using a geometrical method.

18.26. Parallel-scale charts for equations of the form $f(t) \cdot f(u) = f(v)$. Equations of this form may be rewritten so as to take the form $f(t) + f(u) = f(v)$ by using logarithms for both sides of the equation. For example, suppose that it is desirable to prepare a chart for $M = Wl$, a formula commonly used by designers and engineers. In this equation,

M is the maximum bending moment at the point of support of a cantilever beam; W is the concentrated load; and l is the distance from the
point of support to the load.

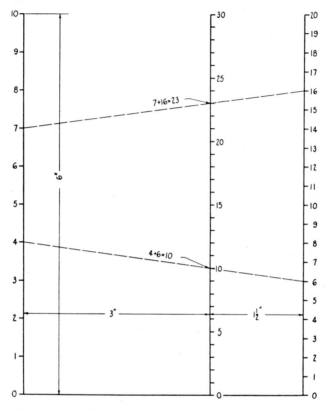

Fig. 18.29.   *Alignment chart for equation of the form*
$$f(t) + f(u) = f(v).$$

Given; $M = Wl$

Rewritten; $\log M = \log W + \log l$

Another example would be the formula for determining the discharge of
trapezoidal weirs.

Given; $Q = 3.367Lh^{3/2}$

Rewritten; $\log Q = \log 3.367 + \log L + 1.5 \log h.$

In this last equation, Q is discharge in cubic feet per second; L is the
length of the crest in feet (width of weir); and h is the observed head
(depth of water).

For the purpose of our discussion, the formula $P = I^2R$ will be used
where P is power in watts; I is current in amperes; and R is resistance in

ohms (Fig. 18.30). It has been determined that I must vary from 1 to 10 amperes and R from 1 to 10 ohms. A chart of this type might be used to determine the power loss in inductive windings. The length of the scales is to be 5 inches.

The steps for the construction are as follows:

Step 1. Write the equation in standard form.

$$\log P = 2 \log I + \log R$$

Step 2. Determine the moduli m_I and m_R for the outside scales.

$$m_I = \frac{5}{2 \log 10 - 2 \log 1} = \frac{5}{2} = 2.5; \quad L_I = 2.5 \, (2 \log I) = 5 \log I$$

$$m_R = \frac{5}{\log 10 - \log 1} = \frac{5}{1} = 5; \quad L_R = 5 \log R$$

Step 3. Determine m_P and L_P for the P-scale.

$$m_P = \frac{2.5 \times 5}{2.5 + 5} = \frac{12.5}{7.5} = \frac{5}{3}; \quad L_P = \frac{5}{3} \log P$$

Step 4. Determine the ratio for the spacing of the scales.

$$\frac{m_I}{m_R} = \frac{2.5}{5} = \frac{1}{2} \, (\text{ratio})$$

Step 5. Draw three vertical lines 1″ and 2″ apart and add a horizontal base line. By using these selected values, the ratio for spacing will be maintained and the chart will have good proportion.

Step 6. Graduate the scales for I and R using the method shown in Fig. 18.27. In this particular case, both logarithmic scales will be alike and will range from 1 on the base line upward to 10.

Step 7. Graduate the P-scale. By substituting values in the equation, it will be found that P will range from 1 watt to 1000 watts; therefore, the scale will be a three-cycle logarithmic scale, and the graphic method may be used for locating the graduation marks.

Figure 18.31 shows another parallel-scale alignment chart. This particular one could be used to determine the volume of a cylindrical tank when the diameter and height are known.

The formula for the volume of a cylinder, as given in the illustration, may be rewritten as: $\log V = \log (\pi/4) + 2 \log D + \log H$. Suppose that it has been decided, as in this case, that both the diameter (D) and the height (H) are to vary from 1 foot to 10 feet, and that the length of the two outside scales is to be 6 inches. For the moment, the constant term $\log (\pi/4)$ can be ignored, for it can be accounted for at a later time by shifting the V-scale for the volume upward until it is in the position for furnishing a correct reading for a particular value as computed using the formula.

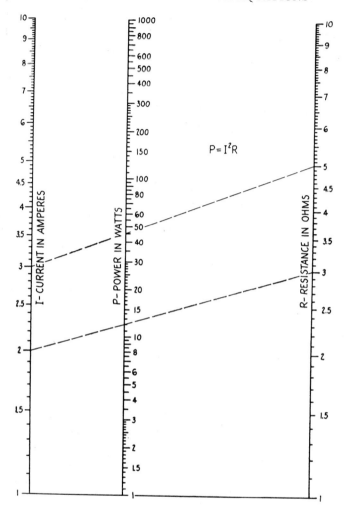

Fig. 18.30.   Alignment chart for the equation P = I²R.

The moduli can be determined as previously explained.

$$m_D = \frac{6}{2 \log 10 - 2 \log 1} = 3 \qquad \text{and,} \quad L_D = 3(2 \log D) = 6 \log D$$

$$m_H = \frac{6}{\log 10 - \log 1} = 6 \qquad \text{and,} \quad L_H = 6 \log H$$

$$m_V = \frac{m_D \times m_H}{m_D + m_H} = \frac{3 \times 6}{3 + 6} = \frac{18}{9} = 2 \qquad \text{and,} \quad L_V = 2(\log V)$$

Scale spacing ratio; $\qquad\qquad \dfrac{m_D}{m_H} = \dfrac{3}{6}$

For convenience, the scales can be spaced at 2″ and 4″, giving a chart that is a square in form.

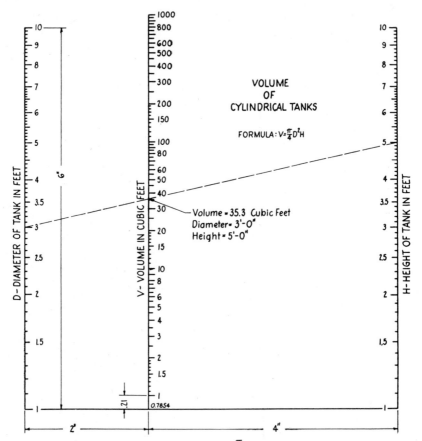

Fig. 18.31. *Alignment chart for* $V = \dfrac{\pi}{4} D^2 H$ *(volume of a cylinder).*

The scales for D and H may be graduated by using the graphical method illustrated in Fig. 18.27. The scale for V will be a three-cycle scale with a 6-inch range of length between the 1 and 1000 values. Since the value of V at the base line must result from the substitution in the equation of the values of 1 and 1 for the other two scales, the resulting value of 0.7854 cubic feet is the volume at the base line. The most convenient procedure to follow in graduating the V-scale is to start with the 0.7854 value at the base line. By so doing, the constant term, log $\pi/4$, is taken into account. Should one desire to determine the distance to be laid off along the V-scale from the base line to the 1, it will be found to be equal to two times the difference between the logs of the numbers in this particular case, for the value of m_v is 2.

18.27. Problems. The following problems have been designed to emphasize the fundamental principles underlying the preparation and use of technical graphs and charts.

1. Determine the values for the following equations, as assigned, and plot the curve in each case for quantitative purposes.

Parabola	$Y = 4x^2$, x from 0 to 5
Ellipse	$Y^2 = 100 - 2x^2$
Sines	$Y = \sin x$, x from 0° to 360°
Cosines	$Y = \cos x$, x from 0° to 360°
Logarithms	$Y = \log x$, x from 1 to 10
Reciprocals	$Y = \dfrac{1}{x}$, x from 1 to 10

2. The freezing temperature for two common antifreeze solutions for various compositions are given below.

PRESTONE			DENATURED ALCOHOL	
% by Vol.	*Temp. °F.*		*% by Vol.*	*Temp. °F.*
10	25		10	25
20	16.5		20	17.5
25	11		25	14
30	5		30	5
35	−3		35	−1
40	−12		40	−11
45	−25		45	−18
50	−38		50	−25
55	−47		55	−32
			65	−45

Prepare a chart for these data, mainly quantitative in character, from which the required per cent volume can be read for any desired freezing temperature. Use India ink and the type of paper shown in Fig. 18.3(*b*).

3. Approximate barometric pressures at different heights above sea level are given below. Prepare a qualitative chart for the given data, using India ink on rectangular co-ordinate paper.

Note that the curve would be straight on semilogarithmic paper.

H—Altitude in miles										
0	1	2	3	4	5	6	7	8	9	10
29.92	24.5	20.0	16.2	13.45	11.0	8.9	7.28	5.95	4.87	4.0
B—Barometric pressure, in. of Hg.										

4. Data on rate of growth are frequently plotted on semilogarithmic paper, because the slope of the curve then represents the rate of growth. On semilogarithmic paper, plot the data for the enrollment in a university.

Year	Enrollment	Year	Enrollment	Year	Enrollment	Year	Enrollment
1920	3199	1930	5745	1940	8,231	1950	12,122
1921	3331	1931	5273	1941	8,457	1951	9,018
1922	3360	1932	4564	1942	6,013	1952	8,976
1923	3414	1933	4278	1943	4,376	1953	9,451
1924	3660	1934	4534	1944	4,122	1954	10,313
1925	4010	1935	5364	1945	4,451	1955	11,287
1926	4239	1936	6332	1946	10,698	1956	12,111
1927	4573	1937	7125	1947	14,291		
1928	4960	1938	7613	1948	14,012		
1929	5364	1939	7923	1949	13,287		

Place the vertical axis 1 unit in from the left edge and the horizontal axis at the extreme bottom of the page ruling. Letter in an appropriate title.

Draw also the curve of the general trend and enter on the chart, just below the title, what the enrollment would be in 1959 if the same rate of growth is maintained.

5. In a hydraulics laboratory, the construction of a quantitative curve that would give the weight of water contained in tubes of various diameters and lengths was desired. This was accomplished by filling tubes of known diameters with water to a depth of one foot and observing the weight of water thus added. The water was kept at a temperature for maximum density and the following data were obtained:

D = Diam. of Tube in Inches	W = Weight of 1 Ft. Col. of Water	D = Diam. of Tube in Inches	W = Weight of 1 Ft. Col. of Water
2	1.362	5	8.512
2½	2.128	5½	10.299
3	3.064	6	12.257
3½	4.171	6½	14.385
4	5.448	7	16.683
4½	6.895	7½	19.152
		8	21.790

On a sheet of graph paper Fig. 18.3(b), plot the above data. Place the axes 3 centimeters in from the edges. Letter the title in any convenient open space.

6. Owing to uncontrollable factors, such as lack of absolute uniformity of material or test procedure, repeated tests of samples of material do not give identical results. Also, it has been observed in many practical situations that:

1. Large departures from the average seldom occur.
2. Small variations from average occur quite often.
3. The variations are equally likely to be above average and below average.

The foregoing statements are borne out by the accompanying data showing the results of 4,000 measurements of tensile strength of malleable iron.

On a sheet of co-ordinate graph paper (Fig. 18.3a or b) prepare a graph showing frequency of occurrence of various strength values as ordinates, and tensile strength as abscissa. Draw a smooth symmetrical curve approximating the given data.

Range of Tensile Strength Values in Lb. per Sq. In.	No. of Observations
Under 45,000	0
45,000–45,999	1
46,000–46,999	2
47,000–47,999	3
48,000–48,999	6
49,000–49,999	20
50,000–50,999	232
51,000–51,999	376
52,000–52,999	590
53,000–53,999	740
54,000–54,999	771
55,000–55,999	604
56,000–56,999	383
57,000–57,999	184
58,000–58,999	60
59,000–59,999	20
Over 60,000	8
	4,000

7. On a sheet of paper, of the type shown in Fig. 18.3(b), using India ink, plot a curve to represent the data given below. *Note:* For *stress-strain diagrams*, although the load is the independent variable, it is plotted as ordinate, contrary to the general rule as given in Sec. 18.5. Fig. 18.6 shows a similar chart. In performing tests of this nature, some load is imposed before any readings of elongation are taken.

It is suggested that the label along the abscissa be marked "Strain, 0.00001 in. per in.," then fewer figures will be required along the axis.

Stress, lb. per sq. in.	Strain, in. per in.	Stress, lb. per sq. in.	Strain, in. per in.
3,000	0.0001	25,000	0.00090
5,000	0.0002	30,000	0.00106
10,000	0.00035	32,000	0.00112
15,000	0.00054	33,000	0.00130
20,000	0.00070	34,000	0.00140

8. Make a vertical multiple bar chart showing the enrollment at _____ University from 1920 to 1956. Obtain data from problem 4.

9. Make a semilogarithmic graph showing the enrollment of your school for the last twenty years.

10-19. Prepare an alignment chart for the given equation. Chart scales should have a sufficient number of division marks to enable the user to obtain some reasonably accurate results (readings). In each problem the range for two of the variables has been given. The range of the third variable must make possible the use of the full range of each of the other two variables.

10. Construct an alignment chart for the multiplication of numbers from 1 to 100. Read Sec. 18.22 and study Fig. 18.24.

11. Construct an alignment chart of the form $t + u = v$. Let t vary from 0 to 10 and u from 0 to 15. Read Sec. 18.25 and study Fig. 18.29.

12. Construct an alignment chart for determining the area of a triangle. The student is to determine for himself the range for each of the scales.

13. Construct an alignment chart for determining the volume of a cylinder. The diameter is to range from 1 to 5 inches and the height from 1 to 10 inches. The volume is to be in cubic inches. Read Sec. 18.26.

14. Make an alignment chart for determining the volume of a paraboloid, $V = 1/8\pi ab^2$, where a is the length (measured along the axis) and b is the diameter of the base. Let a vary from 1 to 20 inches and b from 1 to 10 inches.

15. Construct an alignment chart for the maximum bending moment at the point of support of a cantilever beam, formula $M = Wl$. W is the concentrated load at the end of the beam and l is the distance from the point of support to the load. Read Sec. 18.26. Let W vary from 100 to 1,000 pounds and l from 10 to 20 feet. M will be in foot-pounds.

16. Make an alignment chart for the discharge of trapezoidal weirs, formula $Q = 3.367Lh^{3/2}$. Q is discharged in cubic feet per second; L is length of crest in feet (width of weir); and, h is the head (depth of water). Let L vary from 1 to 10 feet and h from 0.5 to 2 feet. Read Sec. 18.26.

17. Make an alignment chart for the formula $P = I^2R$ as explained in Sec. 18.26. Let I vary from 1 to 20 amps and R from 1 to 10 ohms.

18. Make an alignment chart for the formula $R = \dfrac{E}{I}$ where E is the electromotive force in volts; I is current in amperes; and, R is resistance in ohms. Let R vary from 1 to 20 ohms and I from 1 to 100 amperes. Read Sec. 18.26.

19. Make an alignment chart for the formula $I = \dfrac{bd^3}{36}$ where I is the moment of inertia of a triangular section; b is the length of the base in inches; and d is the depth of the section (altitude of triangle). Let b vary from 1 to 10 inches and d from 1 to 10 inches. Read Sec. 18.26.

Graphical Calculus

19.1. Graphical calculus. In solving engineering problems, it is frequently desirable and often necessary to present a graphical analysis of empirical data. Even though it is often possible to make an evaluation through the use of analytical calculus, a graphical representation is more meaningful because it is pictorial in character. Graphical integration and differentiation are particularly desirable for problems for which only a set of values are known, or for curves that have been produced mechanically, as in the case of steam engine indicator diagrams, or if the results cannot be determined by the analytical methods of calculus.

The following sections are devoted to the graphical rules and methods for determining derived curves. Discussion of the interpretation of results has been intentionally omitted since interpretation is not usually graphical and, therefore, not within the scope of this text.

19.2. Graphical integration. In deriving curves of a higher order, the principle is applied that the area bounded by two successive ordinates, the curve, and the axis is equal to the difference in magnitude of the corresponding ordinates of the integral curve. Figure 19.1 illustrates this principle of graphical integration. In (a) an increment of a curve is shown enlarged. The area under the curve will be approximately equal to the area of the shaded rectangle $ABCD$ when the line AB is drawn so that the area AM1 above the curve is approximately equal to the area MB2 below the curve. With a little practice one will find it easy to establish a line such as AB quite accurately by eye if a strip of celluloid or a triangle is used through which the curve can be seen.

By applying the principle of graphical integration to a series of increments, an integral curve may be drawn as shown in Fig. 19.2. At this point, it should be recognized that since the difference between successive ordinates represents increase in area, the difference between the final ordinate and the initial ordinate represents the total area between these ordinates that is bounded by the curve and the X-axis.

The scale selected for the Y-axis of the integral curve need not be the same as the scale for the given curve.

Portions of a lower-order curve that are above the X-axis are considered to be positive whereas areas below with negative ordinates are

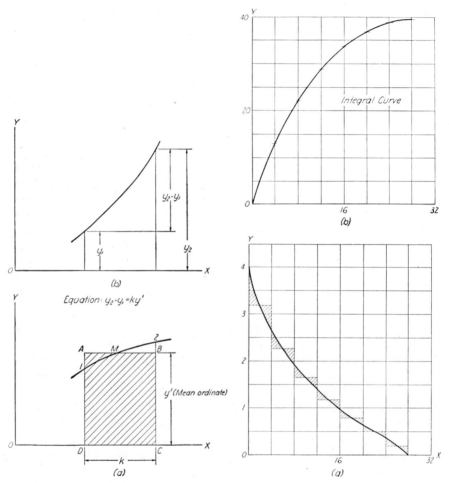

Fig. 19.1. **Illustration of the princi-**   Fig.   19.2.   **The   integration   of   a**
pal of integration.   **curve.**

recognized as negative. See Fig. 19.3(a). Since the negative area between any two ordinates on the lower-order curve represents only the difference in the length of the corresponding ordinates on the integral curve, the length of y_7 is less than the length of y_6 by an amount equal to the negative area.   Also, because areas represent only differences in length of successive ordinates of the integral curve, the initial point on the integral curve might have any value and still fulfill its purpose.   For example, either integral curve shown in Fig. 19.3(b) is a satisfactory solution for the curve in (a).

Fig. 19.4 shows the derived curves for a falling drop hammer.   It is common practice, when drawing related curves, to place them in descending order as shown, that is, the lower-order curve is placed below.

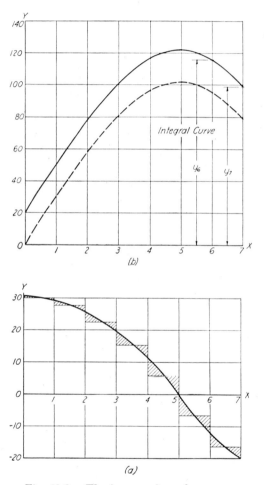

Fig. 19.3.   The integration of a curve.

In (a) the straight line represents a uniform acceleration of 32.2 feet per second per second, which is the acceleration for a freely falling body. The initial velocity is 0.   The units along the X-axis represent time in seconds and the units along the Y-axis represent acceleration in feet per second per second.

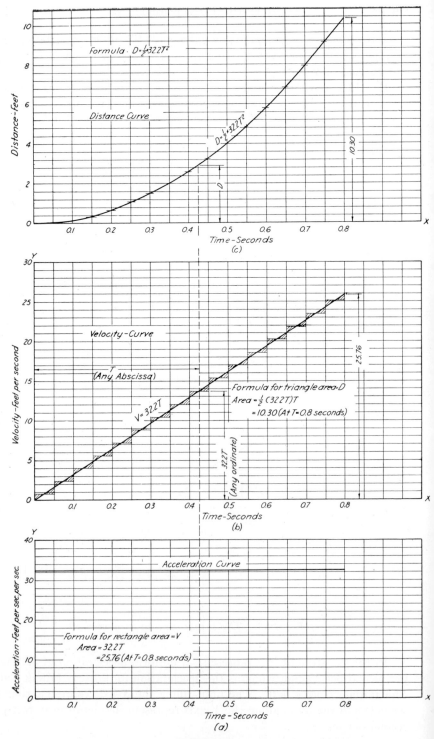

Fig. 19.4. Derived curves for a falling drop hammer.

524

Since the acceleration is uniform, the velocity curve will be a straight line of constant slope, (b).   The length of the last ordinate is equal to the total area under the acceleration curve, namely 25.76 feet per second (fps).

The distance curve, which is obtained by integrating the velocity time curve, is shown in (c).   The length of the ordinate at any interval point is equal to the total area below the velocity curve between the origin and the point [D = A = $\frac{1}{2}$(32,2T)T].   See Figs. 19.1, 19.2, and 19.3.

19.3. To integrate a curve by the ray polygon method.   An integral curve may be drawn by a purely graphical process known as the ray polygon method.

This method of integrating the area under a curve is illustrated in Fig. 19.5.

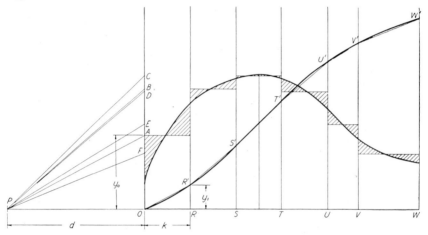

Fig. 19.5.   Use of ray polygon.

Divide the X-axis into intervals and draw ordinates at the division points.   Then, select the pole point P at some convenient location that will make the distance d equal to any number of the full units assigned to the X-axis.   The selection of the number of units for the distance d determines the length of the scale along a Y-axis for the integral curve. To establish relationship between y_1 and y_0 the following equation based on similar right triangles can be written.

$$y_1 : k = y_0 : d$$
$$y_1 \cdot d = k \cdot y_0$$
$$y_1 = \frac{k \cdot y_0}{d} = \frac{k}{d} \cdot y_0$$

Determine the mean ordinate for each strip and transfer its height to the Y-axis as length OA, OB, OC, and so forth.   Draw rays from P to points A, B, C, D, E, and F.

To construct the integral curve, start at O and draw a line parallel to PA cutting the first vertical through R at R'. Through R' draw a line parallel to PB until it cuts the second vertical through S at S'. Repeat this procedure to obtain points T', U', and so on. Points R', S', T', U', V', and W' are points on the required integral curve. In Fig. 19.5 the integral curve is constructed on the same coordinate axes as the lower-order curve.

19.4. Graphical differentiation. Curves of a lower order are derived through the application of the principle that the ordinate at any point on the derived curve is equal to the slope of a tangent line at the

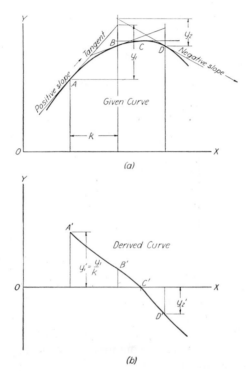

Fig. 19.6.   Illustration of the principle of differentiation.

corresponding point on the given curve. The slope of a curve at a point is the tangent of the angle with the X-axis formed by the tangent to the curve at the point. For all practical purposes, when constructing a derivative curve, the slope may be taken as the rise of the tangent line parallel to the Y-axis in one unit of distance along the X-axis, or the slope of the tangent equals $\dfrac{y_1}{k}$ as shown in Fig. 19.6.

Fig. 19.6 illustrates the application of this principle of graphical differentiation. The length of the ordinate y_1' at point A' on the derived curve

is equal to the slope $\frac{y_1}{k}$ at point A on the given curve as shown in (a).
When the slope is zero as at point C, the length of the ordinate is zero
and point C' lies on the X-axis for the derived curve. When the slope
is negative, as shown at D, the ordinate is negative and lies below the
X-axis.

The graph shown in Fig. 19.7 is composed of segments of straight
lines. Since the slope is constant for the interval 0–1, the derivative
curve in the interval is a horizontal line. In the interval 1–2, the slope
is also constant but of a lesser magnitude. Thus, the derivative curve is
composed of straight line segments as shown in (b).

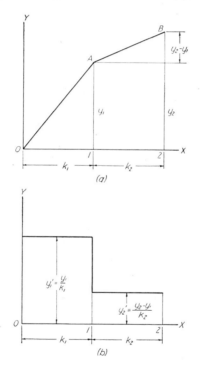

Fig. 19.7. Graphical differentiation.

At this point in the discussion of graphical calculus it becomes possible
to determine the relationship between the principles of integration and
differentiation and to show that one is derived from the other.

From inspection of the graphs shown in Fig. 19.7, equations may be
formulated as follows:

By the principle of differentiation

$$y_2' = \frac{y_2 - y_1}{k_2}$$

in the interval *1–2* where

$$\frac{y_2 - y_1}{k_2}$$

represents the slope of AB. The area under the curve in (*b*) in the interval *1–2* is equal to

$$y_2' \cdot k_2 = \frac{y_2 - y_1}{k_2} \cdot k_2 = y_2 - y_1 \quad \text{(integral curve)}$$

and

$$y_2' = \frac{y_2 - y_1}{k_2} \quad \text{(differential curve)}$$

In constructing a derivative curve, the determination of the tangent lines is often difficult because the direction of a tangent at a particular point is usually not well defined by the curvature of the graph. Two related schemes that may be used for constructing tangents are shown in Fig. 19.8(*a*) and (*b*). In (*a*) the tangent is drawn parallel to a chord of the curve, the arc of which is assumed to approximate the arc of a parabola. A sufficiently accurate location for the point of tangency T_1 may be determined by drawing a line from the mid-point of the chord to the arc, parallel to an assumed direction for the diameter of the parabola. When working with small segments of the curve, one may assume the diameter to be either horizontal or vertical.

(*a*)   (*b*)

Fig. 19.8.   Construction of a tangent line.

A more accurate construction is shown in (*b*) where the tangent is drawn parallel to two parallel chords. The point of tangency T_2 is determined by connecting the mid-points of the chords and extending this line to the curve. This line determines the direction of the diameter.

The construction in (*b*) using two chords to establish a tangent is applicable to any curve that may be approximated by a portion of a circle, ellipse, parabola, or hyperbola.

Since a tangent is assumed to be parallel to a chord, it is common practice to use chords instead of tangents for constructing a derivative curve,

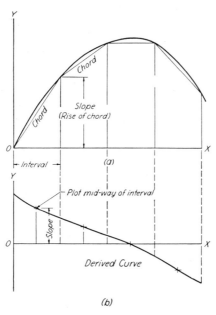

Fig. 19.9.   Use of chords in place of tangents.

as shown in Fig. 19.9(a). The slope is plotted on an ordinate located midway in the corresponding interval of the derived curve.

A derivative curve can also be drawn using the ray polygon method as explained in Sec. 19.3 in reverse. See Fig. 19.10. The lines PA, PB, and PC of the ray polygon are drawn parallel to the tangents at points T_1, T_2, and T_3. Point Q is found by drawing a line horizontally from point

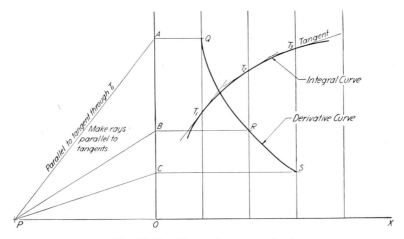

Fig. 19.10.   Ray polygon method.

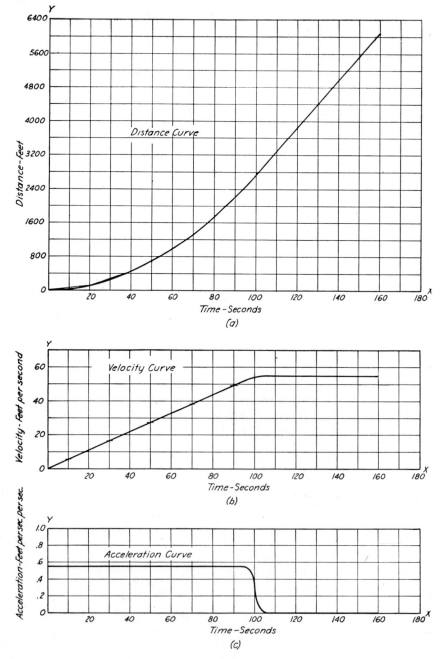

Fig. 19.11.   *Graphical differentiation.*

A to the ordinate through the point of contact of the tangent parallel to PA. Points R and S are found similarly.

Fig. 19.11 shows the differentiation of a curve using chords instead of tangents. The given distance-time curve was plotted from data obtained for a passenger train leaving a small station near a large city. The velocity and acceleration curves reveal that the train moves with a constant acceleration for approximately 100 seconds until it reaches a velocity of fifty-five miles per hour. From this point it travels with a constant velocity toward its destination.

19.5. Problems. The following problems have been designed to emphasize the fundamental principles underlying graphical integration and differentiation and to offer the student an opportunity to acquire a working knowledge of the methods that are commonly used by professional engineers.

1. A beam 10 ft. long is uniformly loaded at 20# per ft. as shown in the accompanying diagram. Plot distance in feet along the X-axis. Draw (1) the integral curve to show the shearing force, and (2) the second integral curve to show the bending moment.

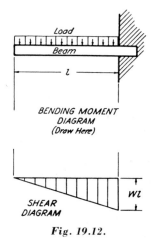

Fig. 19.12.

2. A beam 15 ft. long and supported at both ends is loaded uniformly at 18# per foot as shown in the accompanying diagram.   Plot distance in feet along the X-axis and load along the Y-axis.   Draw (1) the integral curve to show the shearing force, and (2) the second integral curve to show the bending moment.

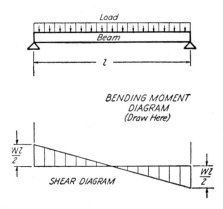

Fig. 19.13.

3. Plot the points given in the table and draw a smooth curve.   Construct the derivative curve.   Write the equation of the derivative curve

x	0	1	2	3	4	5	6	7	8	9	10
y	10	10.5	12	14.5	18	22.5	28	34.5	42	50.5	60

Equation of given curve $y = \frac{1}{2}x^2 + 10$.

4. Construct the distance-time, velocity-time, and acceleration-time curves for an automobile moving as follows: time = 10 seconds, acceleration = 5 feet per second per second throughout the interval, initial velocity = 0.

5. The passenger train for which derived curves are shown in Fig. 19.11 is brought to a stop with a constant negative acceleration of 1.0 feet per second per second.   Before applying the brakes the train was traveling with a constant velocity of 55 feet per second.   Construct the curves showing acceleration-time, velocity-time, and distance-time relationships.

20

Geometry of Machine Elements:
Gears and Cams

20.1. Gears. The engineer frequently is called upon to prepare representations of gears and gear teeth. It is therefore important for him to know the general proportions and nomenclature pertaining to

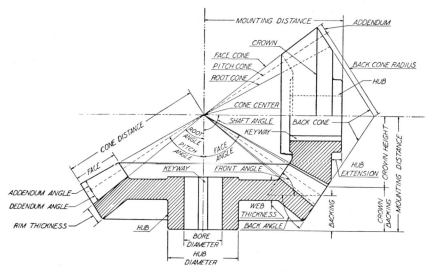

Fig. 20.1. Bevel-gear nomenclature.

gearing. In Fig. 20.1 the nomenclature for bevel gears is shown. Note that the definitions pertaining to gear-tooth parts can generally be represented in a right section of the gear.

The theory of gears is a part of the study of mechanism. In working drawings of gears and toothed wheels it is necessary to draw at least one tooth of each gear. Some of the terms used in defining gear teeth are shown in Fig. 20.2.

Two systems of generating tooth curves are in general use, the involute system and the cycloidal system.   The curve most commonly used for gear-tooth profiles is the involute of a circle.

An involute is the curve generated by a point on a straight-edge as the straight-edge is rolled on a cylinder.   It also may be defined as the curve generated by a point in a taut string as the string is unwrapped from a

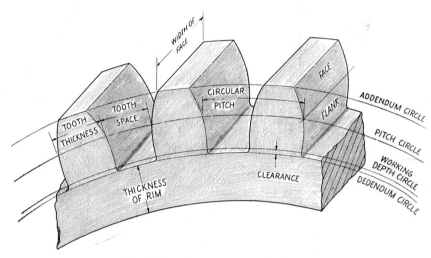

Fig. 20.2.   *Spur gear nomenclature.*

cylinder.   The circle from which the involute is developed is called the *base circle.*

A method of constructing an involute curve is shown in Fig. 20.3. Starting with point 0, on the base circle, divide the base circle into a

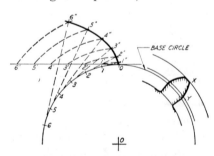

Fig. 20.3.   *Involute tooth.*

convenient number of equal arcs of length 0–1, 1–2, 2–3, and so forth.   (Where the lengths of the divisions on the base circle are not too great, the chord can be taken as the length of the arc.) Draw a tangent to the base circle, at point 0, and divide this line to the left of 0 into equal parts of the same lengths as the arcs.   Next, draw tangents to the circle from points 1, 2, 3, and so on.   With the center of the base circle "0" as a pivot, draw concentric arcs from 1', 2', 3', and so forth, until they intersect the tangent lines drawn from 1, 2, 3, and so forth.   The intersection of the arcs and the tangents are points on the required involute curve, such as $1''$, $2''$, $3''$, and so forth. The illustration at the right in Fig. 20.3 shows the portion XY of the tooth outline as part of the involute curve.

The cycloidal system, as the name implies, has tooth curves of cycloidal form. A cycloid is the curve generated by a point on the circumference of a circle as the circle rolls on a straight line. If the circle rolls on the outside of another circle, the curve generated is called an epicycloid; if it rolls on the inside of another circle, the curve generated is called a hypocycloid. In Fig. 20.4, let R be the radius of the fixed circle and r

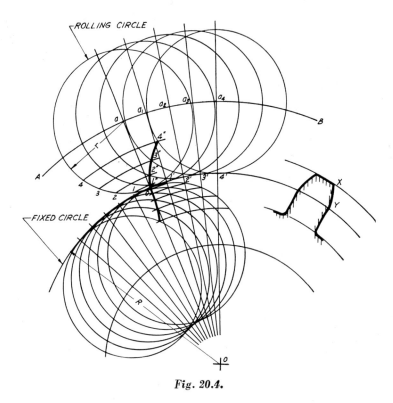

Fig. 20.4.

be the radius of the rolling circle. Draw through a a circle arc, AB, concentric with the fixed circle. Lay off on the rolling circle a convenient number of divisions, such as 0–1, 1–2, 2–3 and so forth; then divide the fixed-circle circumference into divisions of the same length, such as 0–$1'$, $1'$–$2'$, $2'$–$3'$, and so on. Through these points on the fixed circle, draw radii and extend them to intersect the arc AB, thus producing points a_1, a_2, a_3, and so on. These points will be the centers of the successive positions of the rolling circle. Draw the positions of the rolling circle, using the centers a_1, a_2, a_3, and so forth. Next draw, on the rolling circle with the center "0" of the fixed circle as the pivot point, concentric arcs through points 1, 2, 3, and so forth. The intersection of these arcs with the rolling circles about a_1, a_2, a_3, and so forth, determine points, such as $1''$, $2''$, $3''$, and so forth, on the epicyclic curve. The illustration at the right in Fig. 20.4 shows XY of the tooth outline as part of the epicyclic curve.

The hypocyclic curve construction is the same as that for the epicyclic curve. In the construction of the hypocyclic curve, if the rolling circle has a diameter equal to one-half of the diameter of the fixed circle, the hypocyclic curve thus generated will be a radial line of the fixed circle.

GEAR TERMS

1. The addendum circle is drawn with its center at the center of the gear and bounds the ends of the teeth (Fig. 20.2).
2. The dedendum circle, or root circle, is drawn with its center at the center of the gear and bounds the bottoms of the teeth (Fig. 20.2).
3. The pitch circle is a right section of the equivalent cylinder the toothed gear may be considered to replace.
4. Pitch diameter is the diameter of the pitch circle.
5. The addendum is the radial distance from the pitch circle to the outer end of the tooth.
6. The dedendum is the radial distance from the pitch circle to the bottom of the tooth.
7. The clearance is the difference between the dedendum of one gear and the addendum of the mating gear.
8. The face of a tooth is that portion of the tooth surface lying outside the pitch circle.
9. The flank of a tooth is that portion of the tooth surface lying inside the pitch circle.
10. The thickness of a tooth is measured on the arc of the pitch circle. It is the length of an arc and not the length of a straight line.
11. The tooth space is the space between the teeth measured on the pitch circle.
12. Backlash is the difference between the tooth thickness of one gear and the tooth space on the mating gear, measured on the pitch circles.
13. The circular pitch of a gear is the distance between a point on one tooth and the corresponding point on the adjacent tooth, measured along the arc of the pitch circle. The circular pitches of two gears in mesh are equal.
14. The diametral pitch is the number of teeth per inch of pitch diameter. It is obtained by dividing the number of teeth by the pitch diameter.
15. The face of a gear is the width of its rim measured parallel to the axis. It should not be confused with the face of a tooth, for the two are entirely different.
16. The pitch point is on the line joining the centers of the two gears where the pitch circles touch.
17. The common tangent is the line tangent to the pitch circles at the pitch point.
18. The pressure angle is the angle between the line of action and the common tangent.
19. The line of action is a line drawn through the pitch point at an angle (equal to the pressure angle) to the common tangent.
20. The base circle is used in involute gearing to generate the involutes that

form the tooth outlines. It is drawn from the center of each pair of mating gears tangent to the line of action.

21. When two gears mesh with each other, the larger is called the *gear* and the smaller the *pinion*.

It should be noted that *circular pitch* is a linear dimension expressed in inches, whereas *diametral pitch* is a ratio. There must be a whole number of teeth on the circumference of a gear. Thus it is necessary that the circumference of the pitch circle, divided by the circular pitch, be a whole number.

For circular pitch, let P' = circular pitch in inches, D = pitch diameter, and T = number of teeth. Then

$$TP' = \pi D, \qquad T = \frac{\pi D}{P'}, \qquad P' = \frac{\pi D}{T}, \qquad \text{and} \qquad D = \frac{TP'}{\pi}.$$

For diametral pitch, let P = diametral pitch, D = pitch diameter, and T = number of teeth. Then

$$T = PD, \qquad D = \frac{T}{P}, \qquad \text{and} \qquad P = \frac{T}{D}.$$

The Brown and Sharpe $14\frac{1}{2}$-degree involute system has been adopted as one of the American standards and is commonly known as the $14\frac{1}{2}$-Degree Composite System. The tooth proportions of this system are given in terms of the diametral pitch P and circular pitch P'.

Pressure angle $= 14\frac{1}{2}°$.

Addendum (inches) $= \dfrac{1}{\text{diametral pitch}} = \dfrac{1}{P}.$

Dedendum (inches) $=$ addendum plus clearance $= \dfrac{1}{P} + 0.05P'.$

Clearance $= 0.05 \times$ circular pitch $= 0.05P'.$

Whole depth of tooth $= 2 \times$ addendum $+$ clearance $= 2 \times \dfrac{1}{P} + 0.05P'.$

Working depth of tooth $= 2 \times$ addendum $= 2 \times \dfrac{1}{P}.$

Thickness of tooth $= \dfrac{\text{circular pitch}}{2} = \dfrac{P'}{2}.$

Width of tooth space $= \dfrac{\text{circular pitch}}{2} = \dfrac{P'}{2}.$

Minimum radius of fillet $=$ clearance $= 0.05P'.$

In the above calculations the backlash is zero. Actually, however, it is common practice to provide backlash, and this is accomplished by using standard cutters and cutting the teeth slightly deeper than for standard teeth.

20.2. To lay out a pair of standard involute spur gears. The following facts are known regarding the laying out of a pair of standard spur gears: (1) number of teeth on each gear—large gear 24, small gear 16, (2) diametral pitch = 2, (3) pressure angle = $14\frac{1}{2}°$.

To draw a pair of spur gears, determine the pitch diameters, thus:

$$D = \frac{T}{P} = \frac{24}{2} = 12'' \text{ for large gear.}$$

$$D = \frac{T}{P} = \frac{16}{2} = 8'' \text{ for small gear.}$$

In Fig. 20.5 with radii O_1P and O_2P equal to 6″ and 4″ respectively; draw the pitch circles and, through P, draw the common tangent. Draw

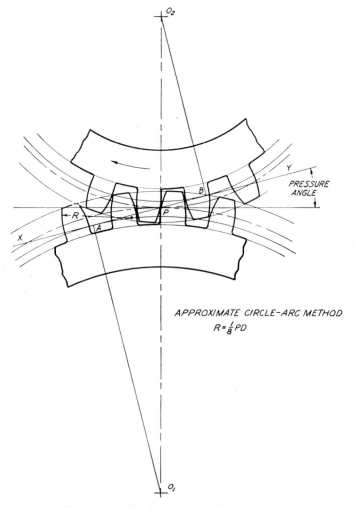

Fig. 20.5. To draw a pair of spur gears.

the line of action XY at an angle of $14\frac{1}{2}°$ to the common tangent. Drop perpendiculars from the centers O_1 and O_2, cutting the line of action at A and B, respectively. O_1A and O_2B are the radii of the base circles that can now be drawn.

From Sec. 20.1 determine the addendum and dedendum of the teeth, and draw in the respective addendum and dedendum circles.

Divide the pitch circle of the smaller gear into 16 equal parts and the pitch circle of the larger gear into 24 equal parts, which will give the circular pitch. Assuming that no allowance is made for backlash, bisect the circular pitch on each of the gears, which will give 32 equal divisions on the small gear and 48 equal divisions on the large gear.

At any point on the base circle of each gear, develop an involute (Fig. 20.3) and draw in the curves between the base and addendum circles through alternate points on the pitch circles. This produces one side of all the teeth in each gear. The curve for the other side of the tooth is the reverse of the side just drawn. The part of the tooth between the base and dedendum circles is part of a radial line drawn from the base circles to the centers of the gears. The tooth is finished by putting in a small fillet between the working depth and dedendum circles.

20.3. Cams. A cam is a plate, cylinder, or any solid having a curved outline or curved groove that, by its oscillating or rotating motion, gives a predetermined motion to another piece, called the follower, in contact with it. The cam plays a very important part in the operation of many classes of machines. Cam mechanisms are commonly used to operate valves in automobiles and stationary and marine internal combustion engines. They also are used in automatic screw machines, clocks, locks, printing machinery, and in nearly all kinds of machinery that we generally regard as "automatic machines." The applications of cams are practically unlimited, and their shapes or outlines are found in wide variety.

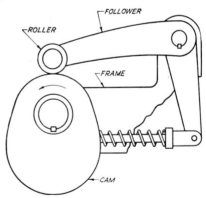

Fig. 20.6.

All cam mechanisms consist of at least three parts: (1) the cam, which has a contact surface either curved or straight; (2) the follower, whose motion is produced by contact with the cam surface; and (3) the frame, which supports the cam and guides the follower.

The most common type of cam is the disc or plate cam. Here the cam takes the form of a revolving disc or plate, the circumference of the disc or plate forming the profile with which the follower makes contact. In Figs. 20.6 and 20.7 two simple examples of a disc cam and follower are shown.   In Fig. 20.6 the cam is given a motion of rotation, thus causing the follower to rise and then return again to its initial position.   In cams of this type it is necessary to use some external force, such as the spring, to keep the follower in contact with the cam at all times.   Contact between the follower and the cam is made through a roller, which serves to reduce friction.   It is sometimes necessary to use a flat-faced follower instead of the roller type, an example of which is shown in Fig. 20.7.   The follower face that comes in contact with the cam usually has a hardened surface to prevent excessive wear.

In another type of cam the follower is constrained to move in a definite path without the application of external forces (Fig. 20.8).   In this type two contact surfaces of the follower bear on the cam at the same time, thus controlling the motion of the follower in two directions.

20.4. Design of a cam.   The design of a cam outline is governed by the requirements with respect to the motion of the follower.   In the layout of a cam, the initial position, displacement, and character of the motion of the follower are generally known.   It is convenient to make first a graphical representation of the follower movement, a procedure which is called *making a displacement diagram*.   This is a linear curve in which the length of the diagram represents the time for one revolution of the cam.   The height of the diagram represents the total displacement of the follower; the length is made to any convenient length and is divided into equal time intervals, the total representing one rotation of the cam.

In Fig. 20.9 is shown a displacement diagram in which the follower rises 2″ during 180° of rotation of the cam, then rests for 30° and returns to its initial position for the remainder of the cam revolution.   Cam outlines should be designed to avoid sudden changes of motion at the beginning and end of the follower stroke.   This can be accomplished by having a uniformly accelerated and decelerated motion at the beginning and end of the constant-velocity curve.   The construction for uniformly accelerated motion is shown in Fig. 20.9.   On a line, OX, making any convenient angle with OA, mark off any unit of length in this figure equal to Oa. The next point, b, is found by marking off, from O, 4 units of length. Point c is found by marking off 9 units of length.   Next, project the intersection (point s) of time unit 3 and the constant-velocity line over to the line OA, thus locating point t.   Connect points c and t with a straight line and draw parallel lines from a and b intersecting the line OA.   From these intersections draw lines parallel to ts, intersecting the time-unit lines 1 and 2, respectively.   These intersections are points on the displacement curve.   With uniformly decelerated motion, the series of points are laid off in the reverse order, such as 9–4–1.   It will be noted that the units are laid off according to the square of the time unit.   Thus, if there were four time units, the acceleration curve would be laid off according to the ratio of 1, 4, 9, 16, and the deceleration, 16, 9, 4, 1.

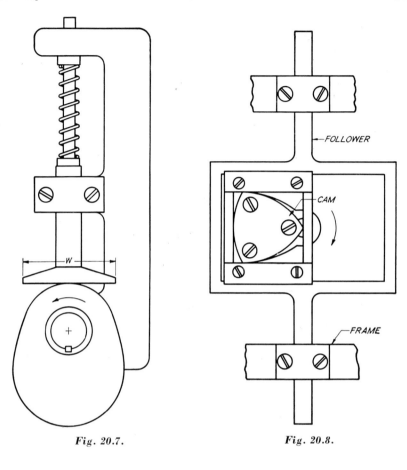

Fig. 20.7.   Fig. 20.8.

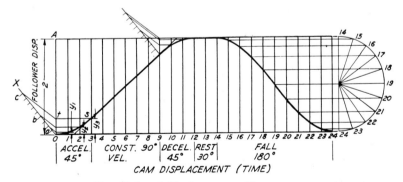

Fig. 20.9.   A displacement diagram.

The construction for the displacement diagram for simple harmonic motion is shown in the same figure.   A semicircle is drawn as shown, the follower diaplacement being used as a diameter, and is then divided into a convenient number of parts equal to the number of cam displacement units.   Horizontal projection lines are drawn from the semicircle, and the intersections of these lines with the cam displacement lines are points

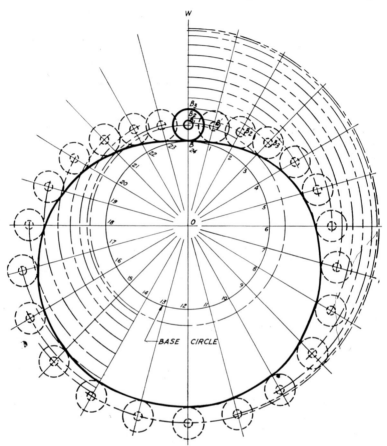

Fig. 20.10.   Construction for cam profile.

on the displacement curve.   Thus, the projection of point 15 on the semicircle to time unit line 15 locates one point on the displacement curve for simple harmonic motion.

The next step is that of finding the cam profile necessary to produce these movements.   The construction is shown in Fig. 20.10.   Select a base circle of convenient size, and on it lay off radial lines according to the number of time units of cam displacement.   Draw line OB extended to W, and on it lay off the distances Y_1, Y_2, Y_3, and so forth, obtained from the displacement diagram, from the center of the roller shown in the starting position, thus locating points B_1, B_2, B_3, and so forth. With O as a center, draw arcs B_1–B_1', B_2–B_2', B_3–B_3', and so forth, and at B_1', B_2', B_3', and so forth draw in the circles representing the diameter of the roller. To complete the cam outline, draw a smooth curve tangent to the positions of the roller.

20.5. Problems. Gears and cams.

GEAR PROBLEMS

1–6. Following the method given in Sec. 20.2, lay out a pair of standard involute spur gears as assigned from the table. The pinion is the driver.

	GEAR				PINION				
Prob. No.	Circular Pitch	Diametral Pitch	Pitch Dia.	No. of Teeth	Cir. cular Pitch	Diametral Pitch	Pitch Dia.	No. of Teeth	Pressure Angle
1	1.31″			24	1.31″			16	$14\frac{1}{2}°$
2		2		20		2		14	$14\frac{1}{2}°$
3		2.5	10			2.5	8		$14\frac{1}{2}°$
4	1.0			30	1.0			20	$14\frac{1}{2}°$
5	2.0			18	2.0			12	$14\frac{1}{2}°$
6		3	8			3	6		$14\frac{1}{2}°$

CAM PROBLEMS

Cam Data:
Diameter of Cam Shaft . . . . $1\frac{1}{4}″$
Diameter of Cam Hub . . . . $2\frac{1}{4}″$
Diameter of Roller . . . . $1″$
Keyway . . . . $\frac{1}{4}″ \times \frac{1}{8}″$
Diameter of Base Circle . . . . $2\frac{3}{4}″$
Follower Displacement . . . . $2″$
Scale: Full size
Cam rotation: As noted
Determine points on the cam profiles at intervals of 15°.

7. Using the above data, design a plate cam to satisfy the following conditions: (a) a rise of 2″ in 180°, with constant velocity, except for uniform acceleration for the first 30° and uniform deceleration for the last 45°; (b) rest 30°; (c) return with simple harmonic motion. Use clockwise cam rotation.

8. Same as problem 7, except that the follower is of the flat-face type and is $2\frac{1}{2}″$ wide.

9. Using the data for problem 7, design a plate cam to satisfy the following conditions: (a) rise of 2″ during 180°, the first 45° of which is uniformly accelerated motion, the next 60° being constant velocity, and the last 75° of rise being uniformly decelerated motion; (*b*) rest 15°; (*c*) return to starting position with simple harmonic motion.   Use counterclockwise cam rotation.

10. Same as problem 9, except that the follower is of the flat-face type and is $2\frac{1}{2}''$ wide.

11. Using the data for problem 7, design a plate cam to satisfy the following conditions: (*a*) rise of $2''$ during 150°, by simple harmonic motion; (*b*) rest 30°; (*c*) return to starting position during remainder of the revolution, with uniformly accelerated and decelerated motion, the value of the deceleration being two times that of the acceleration.   Use clockwise cam rotation.

12. Using the data for problem 7, except that the follower is to be of the flat-face type, $2\frac{1}{2}''$ wide, design a plate cam to satisfy the following conditions: (*a*) rise of $2''$, with simple harmonic motion, in 120°; (*b*) rest 30°; (*c*) return in 150°, with constant velocity, except for uniform acceleration for the first 45° and uniform deceleration for the last 30° of fall; (*d*) rest the balance of the revolution. Use counterclockwise cam rotation.

APPENDIX

AMERICAN STANDARD ELECTRIC POWER
AND WIRING SYMBOLS[1]

	One Line	Complete [2]		One Line	Complete [2]
A-C Generator or Motor— Basic Symbol [4]			Air Circuit Breaker		
D-C Generator or Motor— Basic Symbol			Fuse		
Induction Motor [3]			Resistor [4]		
Synchronous Converter [3]			Rheostat		
Direct Connected Units— Basic Symbols [3]			Reactor		
Single-Phase Two-Winding Transformer—Basic Symbols [3, 4]			Capacitor [4]		
Disconnecting Switch Basic Symbol			Lightning Arrestor Basic Symbol [4]		
Knife Switch, Single-Throw			Indicating Instrument— Basic Symbol [3]	(I)	(6)
			Graphic Instrument Basic Symbol	(○) GRAPH	(6)
Double-Throw Switch			Ampere-Hour Meter	(AH)	(6)
			Ammeter	(A)	(6)
			Frequency Meter	(F)	(6)
Oil Circuit Breaker, Single-Throw			Watthour Meter	(WH)	(6)

AMERICAN STANDARD ELECTRIC POWER
AND WIRING SYMBOLS[1] (Continued)

	One Line	Complete [2]		One Line	Complete [2]
Wattmeter	Ⓦ	(6)	Conductors, Crossing but not Connected		
Voltmeter	Ⓥ	(6)	Conductors, Crossing and Electrically Connected		
Instrument Shunt			Conductors (with Branches)		
Conductors			Bus (with Branches)		
			Ground Connection		

[1] These Symbols for Electric Power and Wiring were extracted from American Standard for Graphical Symbols ASA Z14.2–1935.

[2] The "complete" symbol is intended to illustrate the method of treatment for any desired polyphase combination rather than to show the exact symbol required.

[3] Use symbol (-\/\/\/\/-) for windings of apparatus as required, and connect to suit particular case. It is recognized that no symbol list can show symbols for complete diagrams for all possible methods of connection.

[4] This symbol has not been approved as American Standard because there is still a major difference of opinion concerning the representation of this piece of equipment.

[5] Letter within circle indicates type of instrument if but one is used. If more than one instrument is used, "I" appears within the circle with abbreviation alongside.

(6) For complete symbol show outline approximating that of rear view of actual device and indicate terminals in actual relative location, current terminals by open circles, and potential terminals by solid circles. Scale range and type number may be marked adjacent to symbol, if desired.

GRAPHICAL SYMBOLS FOR PIPE FITTINGS					
	FLANGED	SCREWED	BELL & SPIGOT	WELDED	SOLDERED
1) BUSHING		⟨symbol⟩	⟨symbol⟩	⟨symbol⟩	⟨symbol⟩
2) CAP		⟨symbol⟩	⟨symbol⟩		
3) CROSS-STRAIGHT SIZE	⟨symbol⟩	⟨symbol⟩	⟨symbol⟩	⟨symbol⟩	⟨symbol⟩
4) ELBOW — 45 DEGREE	⟨symbol⟩	⟨symbol⟩	⟨symbol⟩	⟨symbol⟩	⟨symbol⟩
— 90 DEGREE	⟨symbol⟩	⟨symbol⟩	⟨symbol⟩	⟨symbol⟩	⟨symbol⟩
— TURNED DOWN	⟨symbol⟩	⟨symbol⟩	⟨symbol⟩	⟨symbol⟩	⟨symbol⟩
— TURNED UP	⟨symbol⟩	⟨symbol⟩	⟨symbol⟩	⟨symbol⟩	⟨symbol⟩
5) LATERAL	⟨symbol⟩	⟨symbol⟩	⟨symbol⟩		
6) PLUG		⟨symbol⟩	⟨symbol⟩		
7) TEE — STRAIGHT SIZE	⟨symbol⟩	⟨symbol⟩	⟨symbol⟩	⟨symbol⟩	⟨symbol⟩
— OUTLET UP	⟨symbol⟩	⟨symbol⟩	⟨symbol⟩	⟨symbol⟩	⟨symbol⟩
— OUTLET DOWN	⟨symbol⟩	⟨symbol⟩	⟨symbol⟩	⟨symbol⟩	⟨symbol⟩
8) UNION	⟨symbol⟩	⟨symbol⟩		⟨symbol⟩	⟨symbol⟩
9) REDUCER — CONCENTRIC	⟨symbol⟩	⟨symbol⟩	⟨symbol⟩	⟨symbol⟩	⟨symbol⟩
— ECCENTRIC	⟨symbol⟩	⟨symbol⟩	⟨symbol⟩	⟨symbol⟩	⟨symbol⟩
10) CHECK VALVE — STRAIGHT WAY	⟨symbol⟩	⟨symbol⟩	⟨symbol⟩	⟨symbol⟩	⟨symbol⟩
11) GATE VALVE	⟨symbol⟩	⟨symbol⟩	⟨symbol⟩	⟨symbol⟩	⟨symbol⟩
12) GLOBE VALVE	⟨symbol⟩	⟨symbol⟩	⟨symbol⟩	⟨symbol⟩	⟨symbol⟩
13) ANGLE VALVE GLOBE — ELEVATION	⟨symbol⟩	⟨symbol⟩		⟨symbol⟩	⟨symbol⟩
GLOBE — PLAN	⟨symbol⟩	⟨symbol⟩		⟨symbol⟩	⟨symbol⟩

ASA Z 32.2.3 – 1949

TABLE I
Decimal Equivalents of Fractions of an Inch

4ths	8ths	16ths	32nds	64ths	To 4 Places	To 3 Places	To 2 Places
				1/64	.0156	.016	.02
			1/32		.0312	.031	.03
				3/64	.0469	.047	.05
		1/16			.0625	.062	.06
				5/64	.0781	.078	.08
			3/32		.0938	.094	.09
				7/64	.1094	.109	.11
	1/8				.1250	.125	.12
				9/64	.1406	.141	.14
			5/32		.1562	.156	.16
				11/64	.1719	.172	.17
		3/16			.1875	.188	.19
				13/64	.2031	.203	.20
			7/32		.2188	.219	.22
				15/64	.2344	.234	.23
1/4					.2500	.250	.25
				17/64	.2656	.266	.27
			9/32		.2812	.281	.28
				19/64	.2969	.297	.30
		5/16			.3125	.312	.31
				21/64	.3281	.328	.33
			11/32		.3438	.344	.34
				23/64	.3594	.359	.36
	3/8				.3750	.375	.38
				25/64	.3906	.391	.39
			13/32		.4062	.406	.41
				27/64	.4219	.422	.42
		7/16			.4375	.438	.44
				29/64	.4531	.453	.45
			15/32		.4688	.469	.47
				31/64	.4844	.484	.48
					.5000	.500	.50
				33/64	.5156	.516	.52
			17/32		.5312	.531	.53
				35/64	.5469	.547	.55
		9/16			.5625	.562	.56
				37/64	.5781	.578	.58
			19/32		.5938	.594	.59
				39/64	.6094	.609	.61
	5/8				.6250	.625	.62
				41/64	.6406	.641	.64
			21/32		.6562	.656	.66
				43/64	.6719	.672	.67
		11/16			.6875	.688	.69
				45/64	.7031	.703	.70
			23/32		.7188	.719	.72
				47/64	.7344	.734	.73
3/4					.7500	.750	.75
				49/64	.7656	.766	.77
			25/32		.7812	.781	.78
				51/64	.7969	.797	.80
		13/16			.8125	.812	.81
				53/64	.8281	.828	.83
			27/32		.8438	.844	.84
				55/64	.8594	.859	.86
	7/8				.8750	.875	.88
				57/64	.8906	.891	.89
			29/32		.9062	.906	.91
				59/64	.9219	.922	.92
		15/16			.9375	.938	.94
				61/64	.9531	.953	.95
			31/32		.9688	.969	.97
				63/64	.9844	.984	.98
					1.0000	1.000	1.00

TABLE II
Unified and American Thread Series*

NOMINAL DIAMETER	Coarse (NC) (UNC)		Fine (NF) (UNF)		Extra Fine (NEF) (UNEF)	
	Threads per Inch	Tap Drill†	Threads per Inch	Tap Drill†	Threads per Inch	Tap Drill†
0	—	—	80	$\frac{3}{64}$	—	—
1	64	No. 53	72	No. 53	—	—
2	56	No. 50	64	No. 50	—	—
3	48	No. 47	56	No. 45	—	—
4	40	No. 43	48	No. 42	—	—
5	40	No. 38	44	No. 37	—	—
6	32	No. 36	40	No. 33	—	—
8	32	No. 29	36	No. 29	—	—
10	24	No. 25	32	No. 21	—	—
12	24	No. 16	28	No. 14	32	—
1/4	20	No. 7	28	No. 3	32	No. 2
5/16	18	F	24	I	32	K
3/8	16	$\frac{5}{16}$	24	Q	32	S
7/16	14	U	20	$\frac{25}{64}$	28	Y
1/2	13	$\frac{27}{64}$	20	$\frac{29}{64}$	28	$\frac{15}{32}$
9/16	12	$\frac{31}{64}$	18	$\frac{33}{64}$	24	$\frac{17}{32}$
5/8	11	$\frac{17}{32}$	18	$\frac{37}{64}$	24	$\frac{19}{32}$
3/4	10	$\frac{21}{32}$	16	$\frac{11}{16}$	20	$\frac{45}{64}$
7/8	9	$\frac{49}{64}$	14	$\frac{13}{16}$	20	$\frac{53}{64}$
1	8	$\frac{7}{8}$	12	$\frac{59}{64}$	20	$\frac{61}{64}$
1 1/8	7	$\frac{63}{64}$	12	$1\frac{3}{64}$	18	$1\frac{5}{64}$
1 1/4	7	$1\frac{7}{64}$	12	$1\frac{11}{64}$	18	$1\frac{13}{64}$
1 3/8	6	$1\frac{13}{64}$	12	$1\frac{19}{64}$	18	—
1 1/2	6	$1\frac{21}{64}$	12	$1\frac{27}{64}$	18	$1\frac{29}{64}$
1 3/4	5	$1\frac{35}{64}$	—	—	16	$1\frac{11}{16}$
2	4 1/2	$1\frac{25}{32}$	—	—	16	$1\frac{15}{16}$
2 1/4	4 1/2	$2\frac{1}{32}$	—	—	—	—
2 1/2	4	$2\frac{1}{4}$	—	—	—	—
2 3/4	4	$2\frac{1}{2}$	—	—	—	—
3	4	$2\frac{3}{4}$	—	—	—	—
3 1/4	4	3	—	—	—	—
3 1/2	4	$3\frac{1}{4}$	—	—	—	—
3 3/4	4	$3\frac{1}{2}$	—	—	—	—
4	4	$3\frac{3}{4}$	—	—	—	—

* ASA B1.1–1949 (third printing).

Bold type indicates Unified threads.   To be designated UNC or UNF for sizes above $\frac{1}{4}''$.

Unified Standard—Classes 1A, 2A, 3A, 1B, 2B, 3B.

For recommended hole size limits before threading see Table 41, ASA B1.1–1949.

† Tap drill for a 75 per cent thread (not Unified—American Standard).

Bold type sizes smaller than $\frac{1}{4}''$ accepted for limited applications by the British, but the symbols NC or NF, as applicable, are retained.

TABLE III

Unified and American Special Threads*
(8 Pitch, 12 Pitch, and 16 Pitch Series)

Dia.	Threads per Inch			Dia.	Threads per Inch		
1/2	—	**12**	—	2 3/16	—	—	**16**
9/16	—	**12**	—	2 1/4	8	**12**	**16**
5/8	—	**12**	—	2 5/16	—	—	**16**
11/16	—	**12**	—	2 3/8	—	**12**	**16**
3/4	—	**12**	**16**	2 7/16	—	—	**16**
13/16	—	**12**	**16**	2 1/2	8	**12**	**16**
7/8	—	**12**	**16**	2 5/8	—	**12**	**16**
15/16	—	**12**	**16**	2 3/4	8	**12**	**16**
1	8	**12**	**16**	2 7/8	—	**12**	**16**
1 1/16	—	**12**	**16**	3	8	**12**	**16**
1 1/8	8	**12**	**16**	3 1/8	—	**12**	**16**
1 3/16	—	**12**	**16**	3 1/4	8	**12**	**16**
1 1/4	8	**12**	**16**	3 3/8	—	**12**	**16**
1 5/16	—	**12**	**16**	3 1/2	8	**12**	**16**
1 3/8	8	**12**	**16**	3 5/8	—	**12**	**16**
1 7/16	—	**12**	**16**	3 3/4	8	**12**	**16**
1 1/2	8	**12**	**16**	3 7/8	—	**12**	**16**
1 9/16	—	—	**16**	4	8	**12**	**16**
1 5/8	8	**12**	**16**	4 1/4	8	**12**	**16**
1 11/16	—	—	**16**	4 1/2	8	**12**	**16**
1 3/4	8	**12**	**16**	4 3/4	8	**12**	**16**
1 13/16	—	—	**16**	5	8	**12**	**16**
1 7/8	8	**12**	**16**	5 1/4	8	**12**	**16**
1 15/16	—	—	**16**	5 1/2	8	**12**	**16**
2	8	**12**	**16**	5 3/4	8	**12**	**16**
2 1/16	—	—	**16**	6	8	**12**	**16**
2 1/8	8	**12**	**16**				

* ASA B1.1–1949.
For recommended hole size limits before threading see Table 41, ASA B1.1–1949.
Bold type indicates Unified threads (UN).

TABLE IV

Standard Wrench-head Bolts and Nuts—Regular Series*

Bolt Dia. Nominal Size	Bolt Heads				Nuts				
	Width Across Flats	Height of Head			Width Across Flats	Thickness			
						Regular		Jam	
	Unfinished and Semifinished Square and Hex.[1]	Unfinished Square	Unfinished Hexagon	Semifinished Hexagon	Unfinished Hex. Semifinished Hex. and Hex. Jam	Unfinished Square and Hex.	Semifinished Hex. and Hex. Slotted	Unfinished Hexagonal	Semifinished Hexagonal
$\frac{1}{4}$	$\frac{3}{8}$ sq. $\frac{7}{16}$ Hex.	$\frac{11}{64}$	$\frac{11}{64}$	$\frac{5}{32}$	$\frac{7}{16}$	$\frac{7}{32}$	$\frac{13}{64}$	$\frac{7}{32}$	$\frac{13}{64}$
$\frac{5}{16}$	$\frac{1}{2}$	$\frac{13}{64}$	$\frac{7}{32}$	$\frac{13}{64}$	$\frac{9}{16}$	$\frac{17}{64}$	$\frac{1}{4}$	$\frac{17}{64}$	$\frac{1}{4}$
$\frac{3}{8}$	$\frac{9}{16}$	$\frac{1}{4}$	$\frac{1}{4}$	$\frac{15}{64}$	$\frac{5}{8}$	$\frac{21}{64}$	$\frac{5}{16}$	$\frac{21}{64}$	$\frac{5}{16}$
$\frac{7}{16}$	$\frac{5}{8}$	$\frac{19}{64}$	$\frac{19}{64}$	$\frac{9}{32}$	$\frac{3}{4}$	$\frac{3}{8}$	$\frac{23}{64}$	$\frac{3}{8}$	$\frac{23}{64}$
$\frac{1}{2}$	$\frac{3}{4}$	$\frac{21}{64}$	$\frac{11}{32}$	$\frac{5}{16}$	$\frac{13}{16}$	$\frac{7}{16}$	$\frac{27}{64}$	$\frac{7}{16}$	$\frac{27}{64}$
$\frac{9}{16}$	—	—	—	—	$\frac{7}{8}$	$\frac{1}{2}$	$\frac{31}{64}$	$\frac{1}{2}$	$\frac{31}{64}$
$\frac{5}{8}$	$\frac{15}{16}$	$\frac{27}{64}$	$\frac{27}{64}$	$\frac{25}{64}$	1	$\frac{35}{64}$	$\frac{17}{32}$	$\frac{35}{64}$	$\frac{17}{32}$
$\frac{3}{4}$	$1\frac{1}{8}$	$\frac{1}{2}$	$\frac{1}{2}$	$\frac{15}{32}$	$1\frac{1}{8}$	$\frac{21}{32}$	$\frac{41}{64}$	$\frac{21}{32}$	$\frac{41}{64}$
$\frac{7}{8}$	$1\frac{5}{16}$	$\frac{19}{32}$	$\frac{37}{64}$	$\frac{35}{64}$	$1\frac{5}{16}$	$\frac{49}{64}$	$\frac{3}{4}$	$\frac{49}{64}$	$\frac{3}{4}$
1	$1\frac{1}{2}$	$\frac{21}{32}$	$\frac{43}{64}$	$\frac{39}{64}$	$1\frac{1}{2}$	$\frac{7}{8}$	$\frac{55}{64}$	$\frac{7}{8}$	$\frac{55}{64}$
$1\frac{1}{8}$	$1\frac{11}{16}$	$\frac{3}{4}$	$\frac{3}{4}$	$\frac{11}{16}$	$1\frac{11}{16}$	1	$\frac{31}{32}$	1	$\frac{31}{32}$
$1\frac{1}{4}$	$1\frac{7}{8}$	$\frac{27}{32}$	$\frac{27}{32}$	$\frac{25}{32}$	$1\frac{7}{8}$	$1\frac{3}{32}$	$1\frac{1}{16}$	$1\frac{3}{32}$	$1\frac{1}{16}$
$1\frac{3}{8}$	$2\frac{1}{16}$	$\frac{29}{32}$	$\frac{29}{32}$	$\frac{27}{32}$	$2\frac{1}{16}$	$1\frac{13}{64}$	$1\frac{11}{64}$	$1\frac{3}{64}$	$1\frac{11}{64}$
$1\frac{1}{2}$	$2\frac{1}{4}$	1	1	$\frac{15}{16}$	$2\frac{1}{4}$	$1\frac{5}{16}$	$1\frac{9}{32}$	$1\frac{5}{16}$	$1\frac{9}{32}$
$1\frac{5}{8}$	$2\frac{7}{16}$	$1\frac{3}{32}$	—	—	$2\frac{7}{16}$	—	$1\frac{25}{64}$	—	$1\frac{25}{64}$
$1\frac{3}{4}$	$2\frac{5}{8}$	—	$1\frac{5}{32}$	$1\frac{3}{32}$	$2\frac{5}{8}$	—	$1\frac{1}{2}$	—	$1\frac{1}{2}$
$1\frac{7}{8}$	—	—	—	—	$2\frac{13}{16}$	—	$1\frac{39}{64}$	—	$1\frac{39}{64}$
2	3	—	$1\frac{11}{32}$	$1\frac{7}{32}$	3	—	$1\frac{23}{32}$	—	$1\frac{23}{32}$
$2\frac{1}{4}$	$3\frac{3}{8}$	—	$1\frac{1}{2}$	$1\frac{3}{8}$	$3\frac{3}{8}$	—	$1\frac{59}{64}$	—	$1\frac{59}{64}$
$2\frac{1}{2}$	$3\frac{3}{4}$	—	$1\frac{21}{32}$	$1\frac{17}{32}$	$3\frac{3}{4}$	—	$2\frac{9}{64}$	—	$2\frac{9}{64}$
$2\frac{3}{4}$	$4\frac{1}{8}$	—	$1\frac{13}{16}$	$1\frac{11}{16}$	$4\frac{1}{8}$	—	$2\frac{23}{64}$	—	$2\frac{23}{64}$
3	$4\frac{1}{2}$	—	2	$1\frac{7}{8}$	$4\frac{1}{2}$	—	$2\frac{37}{64}$	—	$2\frac{37}{64}$

* ASA B18.2–1955.   All dimensions in inches.

Threads-bolts: course-thread series, class 2A.

Threads-nuts: unfinished; coarse series, class 2B: semifinished; coarse, fine, or 8-pitch series.

TABLE V
Finished Hexagon Castle Nuts*

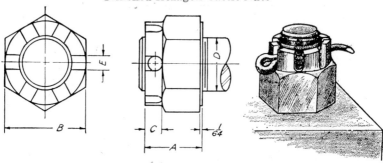

Nominal Size	Threads per Inch		Thickness	Width across Flats	Slot		Dia. of Cylindrical Part Min.
					Depth	Width	
	UNC	UNF					
D			A	B	C	E	
$\frac{1}{4}$	20	28	$\frac{9}{32}$	$\frac{7}{16}$	0.094	0.078	0.371
$\frac{5}{16}$	18	24	$\frac{21}{64}$	$\frac{1}{2}$	0.094	0.094	0.425
$\frac{3}{8}$	16	24	$\frac{13}{32}$	$\frac{9}{16}$	0.125	0.125	0.478
$\frac{7}{16}$	14	20	$\frac{29}{64}$	$\frac{11}{16}$	0.156	0.125	0.582
$\frac{1}{2}$	13	20	$\frac{9}{16}$	$\frac{3}{4}$	0.156	0.156	0.637
$\frac{9}{16}$	12	18	$\frac{39}{64}$	$\frac{7}{8}$	0.188	0.156	0.744
$\frac{5}{8}$	11	18	$\frac{23}{32}$	$\frac{15}{16}$	0.219	0.188	0.797
$\frac{3}{4}$	10	16	$\frac{13}{16}$	$1\frac{1}{8}$	0.250	0.188	0.941
$\frac{7}{8}$	9	14	$\frac{29}{32}$	$1\frac{5}{16}$	0.250	0.188	1.097
1	8	12	1	$1\frac{1}{2}$	0.281	0.250	1.254
$1\frac{1}{8}$	7	12	$1\frac{5}{32}$	$1\frac{11}{16}$	0.344	0.250	1.411

* ASA B18.2–1955.

Thread may be coarse- or fine-thread series, class 2B tolerance; unless otherwise specified fine-thread series shall be furnished.

TABLE VI
American Standard Machine Screws

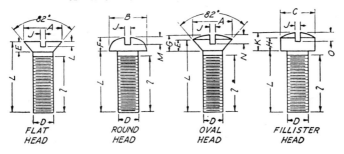

FLAT HEAD   ROUND HEAD   OVAL HEAD   FILLISTER HEAD

Size (Number) and Threads per Inch				American Standard Dimensions (Max.)												
Nominal Size	Diameter D	Thread		Head Diameter			Height Dimensions					Slot Width	Slot Depth			
		Coarse	Fine	A	B	C	E	F	G	H	K	J	L	M	N	O
0	.060	—	80	.119	.113	.096	.035	.053	.056	.045	.059	.023	.015	.039	.030	.025
1	.073	64	72	.146	.138	.118	.043	.061	.068	.053	.071	.026	.019	.044	.038	.031
2	.086	56	64	.172	.162	.140	.051	.069	.080	.062	.083	.031	.023	.048	.045	.037
3	.099	48	56	.199	.187	.161	.059	.078	.092	.070	.095	.035	.027	.053	.052	.043
4	.112	40	48	.225	.211	.183	.067	.086	.104	.079	.107	.039	.030	.058	.059	.048
5	.125	40	44	.252	.236	.205	.075	.095	.116	.088	.120	.043	.034	.063	.067	.054
6	.138	32	40	.279	.260	.226	.083	.103	.128	.096	.132	.048	.038	.068	.074	.060
8	.164	32	36	.332	.309	.270	.100	.120	.152	.113	.156	.054	.045	.077	.088	.071
10	.190	24	32	.385	.359	.313	.116	.137	.176	.130	.180	.060	.053	.087	.103	.083
12	.216	24	28	.438	.408	.357	.132	.153	.200	.148	.205	.067	.060	.096	.117	.094
¼	.250	20	28	.507	.472	.414	.153	.175	.232	.170	.237	.075	.070	.109	.136	.109
5⁄16	.3125	18	24	.635	.590	.518	.191	.216	.290	.211	.295	.084	.088	.132	.171	.137
3⁄8	.375	16	24	.762	.708	.622	.230	.256	.347	.253	.355	.094	.106	.155	.206	.164
7⁄16	.4375	14	20	.812	.750	.625	.223	.328	.345	.265	.368	.094	.103	.196	.210	.170
½	.500	13	20	.875	.813	.750	.223	.355	.354	.297	.412	.106	.103	.211	.216	.190
9⁄16	.5625	12	18	1.000	.938	.812	.260	.410	.410	.336	.466	.118	.120	.242	.250	.214
5⁄8	.625	11	18	1.125	1.000	.875	.298	.438	.467	.375	.521	.133	.137	.258	.285	.240
¾	.750	10	16	1.375	1.250	1.000	.372	.547	.578	.441	.612	.149	.171	.320	.353	.281

ASA B18.6-1947.

TABLE VII
American Standard Cap Screws

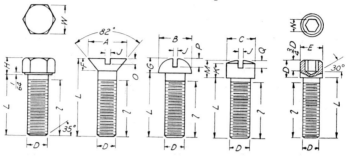

Nominal Size	American Standard Dimensions (Max.)													
	Head Diameter					Height Dimensions					Slot Width	Slot Depth			Socket Width
Dia.	A	B	C	E	W	F Ave.	G	H	K	M	J	O	P	Q	N
$\frac{1}{4}$	.500	.437	.375	$\frac{3}{8}$	$\frac{7}{16}$	.140	.191	$\frac{3}{16}$	.172	.216	.075	.069	.117	.097	$\frac{3}{16}$
$\frac{5}{16}$	.625	.562	.437	$\frac{7}{16}$	$\frac{1}{2}$	.176	.246	$\frac{15}{64}$	.203	.253	.084	.086	.151	.115	$\frac{7}{32}$
$\frac{3}{8}$	.750	.625	.562	$\frac{9}{16}$	$\frac{9}{16}$	.210	.273	$\frac{9}{32}$	.250	.314	.094	.103	.168	.143	$\frac{5}{16}$
$\frac{7}{16}$	.8125	.750	.625	$\frac{5}{8}$	$\frac{5}{8}$	.210	.328	$\frac{21}{64}$	.297	.368	.094	.103	.202	.168	$\frac{5}{16}$
$\frac{1}{2}$	.875	.812	.750	$\frac{3}{4}$	$\frac{3}{4}$	.210	.355	$\frac{3}{8}$	.328	.412	.106	.103	.219	.188	$\frac{3}{8}$
$\frac{9}{16}$	1.000	.937	.812	$\frac{13}{16}$	$\frac{13}{16}$	.245	.410	$\frac{27}{64}$	.375	.466	.118	.120	.253	.214	$\frac{3}{8}$
$\frac{5}{8}$	1.125	1.000	.875	$\frac{7}{8}$	$\frac{7}{8}$	.281	.438	$\frac{15}{32}$	.422	.521	.133	.137	.270	.240	$\frac{1}{2}$
$\frac{3}{4}$	1.375	1.250	1.000	1	1	.352	.547	$\frac{9}{16}$	.500	.612	.149	.171	.337	.283	$\frac{9}{16}$
$\frac{7}{8}$	1.625	—	1.125	$1\frac{1}{8}$	$1\frac{1}{8}$	.423	—	$\frac{21}{32}$	.594	.720	.167	.206	—	.334	$\frac{9}{16}$
1	1.875	—	1.321	$1\frac{5}{16}$	$1\frac{5}{16}$	.494	—	$\frac{3}{4}$	.656	.802	.188	.240	—	.372	$\frac{5}{8}$
$1\frac{1}{8}$	—	—	—	$1\frac{1}{2}$	$1\frac{1}{2}$	—	—	$\frac{27}{32}$	—	—	—	—	—	—	$\frac{3}{4}$
$1\frac{1}{4}$	—	—	—	$1\frac{3}{4}$	$1\frac{11}{16}$	—	—	$\frac{15}{16}$	—	—	—	—	—	—	$\frac{3}{4}$

ASA B18.3–1947.
ASA B18.6–1947.

TABLE VIII
American Standard Washers

 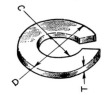

Nominal Size	PLAIN WASHERS[1]					
	LIGHT			MEDIUM		
	A ID	B OD	H Thickness	A ID	B OD	H Thickness
$\frac{1}{4}$	$\frac{9}{32}$	$\frac{5}{8}$	0.065	$\frac{5}{16}$	$\frac{3}{4}$	0.065
$\frac{5}{16}$	$\frac{11}{32}$	$\frac{11}{16}$	0.065	$\frac{3}{8}$	$\frac{3}{4}$	0.065
$\frac{3}{8}$	$\frac{13}{32}$	$\frac{13}{16}$	0.065	$\frac{7}{16}$	$\frac{7}{8}$	0.083
$\frac{7}{16}$	$\frac{15}{32}$	$\frac{59}{64}$	0.065	$\frac{1}{2}$	$1\frac{1}{8}$	0.083
$\frac{1}{2}$	$\frac{17}{32}$	$1\frac{1}{16}$	0.095	$\frac{9}{16}$	$1\frac{1}{4}$	0.109
$\frac{9}{16}$	$\frac{19}{32}$	$1\frac{3}{16}$	0.095	$\frac{5}{8}$	$1\frac{3}{8}$	0.109
$\frac{5}{8}$	$\frac{21}{32}$	$1\frac{5}{16}$	0.095	$\frac{11}{16}$	$1\frac{1}{2}$	0.134
$\frac{3}{4}$	$\frac{13}{16}$	$1\frac{1}{2}$	0.134	$\frac{13}{16}$	$1\frac{3}{4}$	0.148
$\frac{7}{8}$	$\frac{15}{16}$	$1\frac{3}{4}$	0.134	$\frac{15}{16}$	2	0.165
1	$1\frac{1}{16}$	2	0.134	$1\frac{1}{16}$	$2\frac{1}{4}$	0.165
$1\frac{1}{8}$	—	—	—	$1\frac{3}{16}$	$2\frac{1}{2}$	0.165
$1\frac{1}{4}$	—	—	—	$1\frac{5}{16}$	$2\frac{3}{4}$	0.165
$1\frac{3}{8}$	—	—	—	$1\frac{7}{16}$	3	0.180
$1\frac{1}{2}$	—	—	—	$1\frac{9}{16}$	$3\frac{1}{4}$	0.180

Nominal Size	LOCK WASHERS[2]					
	LIGHT			MEDIUM		
	C ID	D OD (Max.)	T Thickness (Min.)	C ID	D OD (Max.)	T Thickness (Min.)
$\frac{1}{4}$	0.255	0.489	0.047		0.493	0.062
$\frac{5}{16}$	0.319	0.575	0.056		0.591	0.078
$\frac{3}{8}$	0.382	0.678	0.070		0.688	0.094
$\frac{7}{16}$	0.446	0.780	0.085		0.784	0.109
$\frac{1}{2}$	0.509	0.877	0.099		0.879	0.125
$\frac{9}{16}$	0.573	0.975	0.113	Same as for Light Lock Washers	0.979	0.141
$\frac{5}{8}$	0.636	1.082	0.126		1.086	0.156
$\frac{11}{16}$	0.700	1.178	0.138		1.184	0.172
$\frac{3}{4}$	0.763	1.277	0.153		1.279	0.188
$\frac{7}{8}$	0.890	1.470	0.179		1.474	0.219
1	1.017	1.656	0.202		1.672	0.250
$1\frac{1}{8}$	1.144	1.837	0.224		1.865	0.281
$1\frac{1}{4}$	1.271	2.012	0.244		2.058	0.312
$1\frac{3}{8}$	1.398	2.183	0.264		2.253	0.344
$1\frac{1}{2}$	1.525	2.352	0.282		2.446	0.375

[1] ASA B27.2–1949. All dimensions in inches.
[2] ASA B27.1–1950. All dimensions in inches.
Dimensions for heavy and extra heavy washers may be found in the standards listed above.

TABLE IX
Cotter Pins

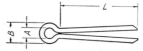

Bolt and Rod Dia. (NC)	Cotter Pins				Length	
	Cotter Dia.	A	B	Drill No.	Short	Long
$\frac{1}{4}$	$\frac{1}{16}$	$\frac{3}{32}$	$\frac{5}{32}$	48	$\frac{1}{2}$	$\frac{5}{8}$
$\frac{5}{16}$	$\frac{1}{16}$	$\frac{3}{32}$	$\frac{5}{32}$	48	$\frac{5}{8}$	$\frac{3}{4}$
$\frac{3}{8}$	$\frac{3}{32}$	$\frac{1}{8}$	$\frac{7}{32}$	36	$\frac{3}{4}$	$\frac{7}{8}$
$\frac{7}{16}$	$\frac{3}{32}$	$\frac{1}{8}$	$\frac{7}{32}$	36	$\frac{3}{4}$	1
$\frac{1}{2}$	$\frac{3}{32}$	$\frac{1}{8}$	$\frac{7}{32}$	36	$\frac{7}{8}$	$1\frac{1}{8}$
$\frac{9}{16}$	$\frac{1}{8}$	$\frac{5}{32}$	$\frac{9}{32}$	28	1	$1\frac{1}{4}$
$\frac{5}{8}$	$\frac{1}{8}$	$\frac{5}{32}$	$\frac{9}{32}$	28	$1\frac{1}{8}$	$1\frac{3}{8}$
$\frac{3}{4}$	$\frac{1}{8}$	$\frac{5}{32}$	$\frac{9}{32}$	28	$1\frac{1}{4}$	$1\frac{1}{2}$
$\frac{7}{8}$	$\frac{1}{8}$	$\frac{5}{32}$	$\frac{9}{32}$	28	$1\frac{3}{8}$	$1\frac{3}{4}$
1	$\frac{1}{8}$	$\frac{5}{32}$	$\frac{9}{32}$	28	$1\frac{5}{8}$	2

TABLE X
Small Rivets

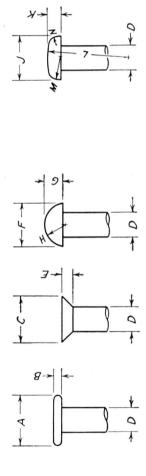

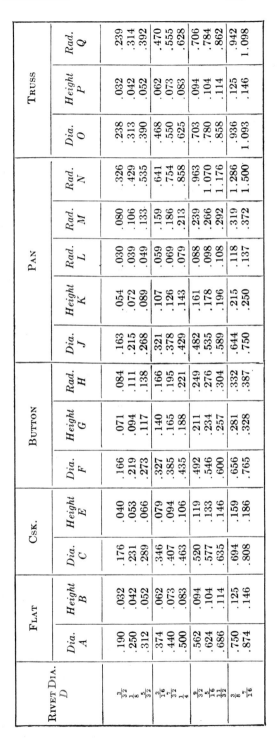

RIVET DIA. D	FLAT Dia. A	FLAT Height B	CSK. Dia. C	CSK. Height E	BUTTON Dia. F	BUTTON Height G	BUTTON Rad. H	PAN Dia. J	PAN Height K	PAN Rad. L	PAN Rad. M	PAN Rad. N	TRUSS Dia. O	TRUSS Height P	TRUSS Rad. Q
$\frac{3}{32}$	.190	.032	.176	.040	.166	.071	.084	.163	.054	.030	.080	.326	.238	.032	.239
$\frac{1}{8}$	.250	.042	.231	.053	.219	.094	.111	.215	.072	.039	.106	.429	.313	.042	.314
$\frac{5}{32}$	.312	.052	.289	.066	.273	.117	.138	.268	.089	.049	.133	.535	.390	.052	.392
$\frac{3}{16}$	.374	.062	.346	.079	.327	.140	.166	.321	.107	.059	.159	.641	.468	.062	.470
$\frac{7}{32}$	.440	.073	.407	.094	.385	.165	.195	.378	.126	.069	.186	.754	.550	.073	.555
$\frac{1}{4}$	.500	.083	.463	.106	.435	.188	.221	.429	.143	.079	.213	.858	.625	.083	.628
$\frac{9}{32}$	.562	.094	.520	.119	.492	.211	.249	.482	.161	.088	.239	.963	.703	.094	.706
$\frac{5}{16}$	.624	.104	.577	.133	.546	.234	.276	.535	.178	.098	.266	1.070	.780	.104	.784
$\frac{11}{32}$	.686	.114	.635	.146	.600	.257	.304	.589	.196	.108	.292	1.176	.858	.114	.862
$\frac{3}{8}$	.750	.125	.694	.159	.656	.281	.332	.644	.215	.118	.319	1.286	.936	.125	.942
$\frac{7}{16}$	.874	.146	.808	.186	.765	.328	.387	.750	.250	.137	.372	1.500	1.093	.146	1.098

TABLE XI
American Standard Square and Flat Keys*

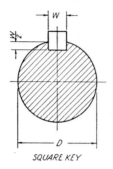

SQUARE KEY

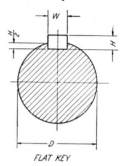

FLAT KEY

Shaft Diameter	Square Stock Key W	Flat Stock Key W × H	Shaft Diameter	Square Stock Key W	Flat Stock Key W × H
$\frac{1}{2}-\frac{9}{16}$	$\frac{1}{8}$	$\frac{1}{8} \times \frac{3}{32}$	$2\frac{5}{16}-2\frac{3}{4}$	$\frac{5}{8}$	$\frac{5}{8} \times \frac{7}{16}$
$\frac{5}{8}-\frac{7}{8}$	$\frac{3}{16}$	$\frac{3}{16} \times \frac{1}{8}$	$2\frac{7}{8}-3\frac{1}{4}$	$\frac{3}{4}$	$\frac{3}{4} \times \frac{1}{2}$
$\frac{15}{16}-1\frac{1}{4}$	$\frac{1}{4}$	$\frac{1}{4} \times \frac{3}{16}$	$3\frac{3}{8}-3\frac{3}{4}$	$\frac{7}{8}$	$\frac{7}{8} \times \frac{5}{8}$
$1\frac{5}{16}-1\frac{3}{8}$	$\frac{5}{16}$	$\frac{5}{16} \times \frac{1}{4}$	$3\frac{7}{8}-4\frac{1}{2}$	1	$1 \times \frac{3}{4}$
$1\frac{7}{16}-1\frac{3}{4}$	$\frac{3}{8}$	$\frac{3}{8} \times \frac{1}{4}$	$4\frac{3}{4}-5\frac{1}{2}$	$1\frac{1}{4}$	$1\frac{1}{4} \times \frac{7}{8}$
$1\frac{13}{16}-2\frac{1}{4}$	$\frac{1}{2}$	$\frac{1}{2} \times \frac{3}{8}$	$5\frac{3}{4}-6$	$1\frac{1}{2}$	$1\frac{1}{2} \times 1$

* ASA B17.1–1943.
All dimensions in inches.

TABLE XII

American Standard Plain Taper and Gib Head Keys*

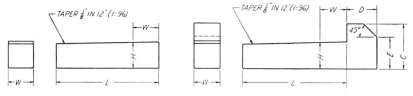

Plain Taper and Gib Head Keys (Square and Flat)			Gib Head					
			Square			Flat		
Diameter of Shaft	Square Type	Flat Type	Height of Head	Length	Height to Chamfer	Height of Head	Length	Height to Chamfer
D	$W = H$	$W \times H$	C	D	E	C	D	E
$\frac{1}{2}-\frac{9}{16}$	$\frac{1}{8}$	$\frac{1}{8} \times \frac{3}{32}$	$\frac{1}{4}$	$\frac{7}{32}$	$\frac{5}{32}$	$\frac{3}{16}$	$\frac{1}{8}$	$\frac{1}{8}$
$\frac{5}{8}-\frac{7}{8}$	$\frac{3}{16}$	$\frac{3}{16} \times \frac{1}{8}$	$\frac{5}{16}$	$\frac{9}{32}$	$\frac{7}{32}$	$\frac{1}{4}$	$\frac{3}{16}$	$\frac{5}{32}$
$\frac{15}{16}-1\frac{1}{4}$	$\frac{1}{4}$	$\frac{1}{4} \times \frac{3}{16}$	$\frac{7}{16}$	$\frac{11}{32}$	$\frac{11}{32}$	$\frac{5}{16}$	$\frac{1}{4}$	$\frac{3}{16}$
$1\frac{5}{16}-1\frac{3}{8}$	$\frac{5}{16}$	$\frac{5}{16} \times \frac{1}{4}$	$\frac{9}{16}$	$\frac{13}{32}$	$\frac{13}{32}$	$\frac{3}{8}$	$\frac{5}{16}$	$\frac{1}{4}$
$1\frac{7}{16}-1\frac{3}{4}$	$\frac{3}{8}$	$\frac{3}{8} \times \frac{1}{4}$	$\frac{11}{16}$	$\frac{15}{32}$	$\frac{15}{32}$	$\frac{7}{16}$	$\frac{3}{8}$	$\frac{5}{16}$
$1\frac{13}{16}-2\frac{1}{4}$	$\frac{1}{2}$	$\frac{1}{2} \times \frac{3}{8}$	$\frac{7}{8}$	$\frac{19}{32}$	$\frac{5}{8}$	$\frac{5}{8}$	$\frac{1}{2}$	$\frac{7}{16}$
$2\frac{5}{16}-2\frac{3}{4}$	$\frac{5}{8}$	$\frac{5}{8} \times \frac{7}{16}$	$1\frac{1}{16}$	$\frac{23}{32}$	$\frac{3}{4}$	$\frac{3}{4}$	$\frac{5}{8}$	$\frac{1}{2}$
$2\frac{7}{8}-3\frac{1}{4}$	$\frac{3}{4}$	$\frac{3}{4} \times \frac{1}{2}$	$1\frac{1}{4}$	$\frac{7}{8}$	$\frac{7}{8}$	$\frac{3}{4}$	$\frac{3}{4}$	$\frac{5}{8}$
$3\frac{3}{8}-3\frac{3}{4}$	$\frac{7}{8}$	$\frac{7}{8} \times \frac{5}{8}$	$1\frac{1}{2}$	1	1	$1\frac{1}{16}$	$\frac{7}{8}$	$\frac{3}{4}$
$3\frac{7}{8}-4\frac{1}{2}$	1	$1 \times \frac{3}{4}$	$1\frac{3}{4}$	$1\frac{3}{16}$	$1\frac{3}{16}$	$1\frac{1}{4}$	1	$\frac{13}{16}$
$4\frac{3}{4}-5\frac{1}{2}$	$1\frac{1}{4}$	$1\frac{1}{4} \times \frac{7}{8}$	2	$1\frac{7}{16}$	$1\frac{7}{16}$	$1\frac{1}{2}$	$1\frac{1}{4}$	1
$5\frac{3}{4}-6$	$1\frac{1}{2}$	$1\frac{1}{2} \times 1$	$2\frac{1}{2}$	$1\frac{3}{4}$	$1\frac{3}{4}$	$1\frac{3}{4}$	$1\frac{1}{2}$	$1\frac{1}{4}$

* ASA B17.1–1943.
All dimensions in inches.   Minimum length $= 4W$.   Maximum length $= 16W$.

Gib head key.

TABLE XIII
American Standard Woodruff Keys*

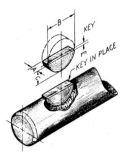
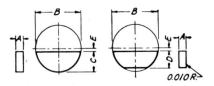

Key[1] Number	Nominal Size $A \times B$	Height of Key		Distance above Center E	Depth of Key Slot in Shaft
		$C_{max.}$	$D_{max.}$		
204	$\frac{1}{16} \times \frac{1}{2}$	0.203	.194	$\frac{3}{64}$	.1718
304	$\frac{3}{32} \times \frac{1}{2}$	.203	.194	$\frac{3}{64}$	.1561
305	$\frac{3}{32} \times \frac{5}{8}$	.250	.240	$\frac{1}{16}$	.2031
404	$\frac{1}{8} \times \frac{1}{2}$	.203	.194	$\frac{3}{64}$	.1405
405	$\frac{1}{8} \times \frac{5}{8}$	.250	.240	$\frac{1}{16}$	.1875
406	$\frac{1}{8} \times \frac{3}{4}$	.313	.303	$\frac{1}{16}$	.2505
505	$\frac{5}{32} \times \frac{5}{8}$	.250	.240	$\frac{1}{16}$	.1719
506	$\frac{5}{32} \times \frac{3}{4}$	.313	.303	$\frac{1}{16}$	.2349
507	$\frac{5}{32} \times \frac{7}{8}$	.375	.365	$\frac{1}{16}$	.2969
606	$\frac{3}{16} \times \frac{3}{4}$	.313	.303	$\frac{1}{16}$	.2193
607	$\frac{3}{16} \times \frac{7}{8}$	.375	.365	$\frac{1}{16}$	.2813
608	$\frac{3}{16} \times 1$	.438	.428	$\frac{1}{16}$	.3443
609	$\frac{3}{16} \times 1\frac{1}{8}$	.484	.475	$\frac{5}{64}$	.3903
807	$\frac{1}{4} \times \frac{7}{8}$	.375	.365	$\frac{1}{16}$	.2500
808	$\frac{1}{4} \times 1$	.438	.428	$\frac{1}{16}$	.3130
809	$\frac{1}{4} \times 1\frac{1}{8}$	.484	.475	$\frac{5}{64}$	.3590
810	$\frac{1}{4} \times 1\frac{1}{4}$	.547	.537	$\frac{5}{64}$	.4220
811	$\frac{1}{4} \times 1\frac{3}{8}$	.594	.584	$\frac{3}{32}$	.4690
812	$\frac{1}{4} \times 1\frac{1}{2}$	.641	.631	$\frac{7}{64}$	.5160
1008	$\frac{5}{16} \times 1$	.438	.428	$\frac{1}{16}$	.2818
1009	$\frac{5}{16} \times 1\frac{1}{8}$	.484	.475	$\frac{5}{64}$	.3278
1010	$\frac{5}{16} \times 1\frac{1}{4}$	.547	.537	$\frac{5}{64}$	.3908
1011	$\frac{5}{16} \times 1\frac{3}{8}$	.594	.584	$\frac{3}{32}$	.4378
1012	$\frac{5}{16} \times 1\frac{1}{2}$	.641	.631	$\frac{7}{64}$	.4848
1210	$\frac{3}{8} \times 1\frac{1}{4}$	.547	.537	$\frac{5}{64}$	.3595
1211	$\frac{3}{8} \times 1\frac{3}{8}$	.594	.584	$\frac{3}{32}$	.4065
1212	$\frac{3}{8} \times 1\frac{1}{2}$	.641	.631	$\frac{7}{64}$	.4535

* ASA B17f–1930.

All dimensions in inches.

[1] Key numbers indicate the nominal key dimensions. The last two digits give the nominal diameter in eighths of an inch and the digits preceding the last two give the nominal width in thirty-seconds of an inch.

TABLE XIV
Pratt and Whitney Keys

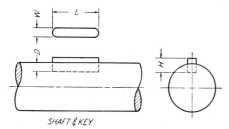

SHAFT & KEY

Key No.	L	W	H	D	Key No.	L	W	H	D
1	$\frac{1}{2}$	$\frac{1}{16}$	$\frac{3}{32}$	$\frac{1}{16}$	22	$1\frac{3}{8}$	$\frac{1}{4}$	$\frac{3}{8}$	$\frac{1}{4}$
2	$\frac{1}{2}$	$\frac{3}{32}$	$\frac{9}{64}$	$\frac{3}{32}$	23	$1\frac{3}{8}$	$\frac{5}{16}$	$\frac{15}{32}$	$\frac{5}{16}$
3	$\frac{1}{2}$	$\frac{1}{8}$	$\frac{3}{16}$	$\frac{1}{8}$	F	$1\frac{3}{8}$	$\frac{3}{8}$	$\frac{9}{16}$	$\frac{3}{8}$
4	$\frac{5}{8}$	$\frac{3}{32}$	$\frac{9}{64}$	$\frac{3}{32}$	24	$1\frac{1}{2}$	$\frac{1}{4}$	$\frac{3}{8}$	$\frac{1}{4}$
5	$\frac{5}{8}$	$\frac{1}{8}$	$\frac{3}{16}$	$\frac{1}{8}$	25	$1\frac{1}{2}$	$\frac{5}{16}$	$\frac{15}{32}$	$\frac{5}{16}$
6	$\frac{5}{8}$	$\frac{5}{32}$	$\frac{15}{64}$	$\frac{5}{32}$	G	$1\frac{1}{2}$	$\frac{3}{8}$	$\frac{9}{16}$	$\frac{3}{8}$
7	$\frac{3}{4}$	$\frac{1}{8}$	$\frac{3}{16}$	$\frac{1}{8}$	51	$1\frac{3}{4}$	$\frac{1}{4}$	$\frac{3}{8}$	$\frac{1}{4}$
8	$\frac{3}{4}$	$\frac{5}{32}$	$\frac{15}{64}$	$\frac{5}{32}$	52	$1\frac{3}{4}$	$\frac{5}{16}$	$\frac{15}{32}$	$\frac{5}{16}$
9	$\frac{3}{4}$	$\frac{3}{16}$	$\frac{9}{32}$	$\frac{3}{16}$	53	$1\frac{3}{4}$	$\frac{3}{8}$	$\frac{9}{16}$	$\frac{3}{8}$
10	$\frac{7}{8}$	$\frac{5}{32}$	$\frac{15}{64}$	$\frac{5}{32}$	26	2	$\frac{3}{16}$	$\frac{9}{32}$	$\frac{3}{16}$
11	$\frac{7}{8}$	$\frac{3}{16}$	$\frac{9}{32}$	$\frac{3}{16}$	27	2	$\frac{1}{4}$	$\frac{3}{8}$	$\frac{1}{4}$
12	$\frac{7}{8}$	$\frac{7}{32}$	$\frac{21}{64}$	$\frac{7}{32}$	28	2	$\frac{5}{16}$	$\frac{15}{32}$	$\frac{5}{16}$
A	$\frac{7}{8}$	$\frac{1}{4}$	$\frac{3}{8}$	$\frac{1}{4}$	29	2	$\frac{3}{8}$	$\frac{9}{16}$	$\frac{3}{8}$
13	1	$\frac{3}{16}$	$\frac{9}{32}$	$\frac{3}{16}$	54	$2\frac{1}{4}$	$\frac{1}{4}$	$\frac{3}{8}$	$\frac{1}{4}$
14	1	$\frac{7}{32}$	$\frac{21}{64}$	$\frac{7}{32}$	55	$2\frac{1}{4}$	$\frac{5}{16}$	$\frac{15}{32}$	$\frac{5}{16}$
15	1	$\frac{1}{4}$	$\frac{3}{8}$	$\frac{1}{4}$	56	$2\frac{1}{4}$	$\frac{3}{8}$	$\frac{9}{16}$	$\frac{3}{8}$
B	1	$\frac{5}{16}$	$\frac{15}{32}$	$\frac{5}{16}$	57	$2\frac{1}{4}$	$\frac{7}{16}$	$\frac{21}{32}$	$\frac{7}{16}$
16	$1\frac{1}{8}$	$\frac{3}{16}$	$\frac{9}{32}$	$\frac{3}{16}$	58	$2\frac{1}{2}$	$\frac{5}{16}$	$\frac{15}{32}$	$\frac{5}{16}$
17	$1\frac{1}{8}$	$\frac{7}{32}$	$\frac{21}{64}$	$\frac{7}{32}$	59	$2\frac{1}{2}$	$\frac{3}{8}$	$\frac{9}{16}$	$\frac{3}{8}$
18	$1\frac{1}{8}$	$\frac{1}{4}$	$\frac{3}{8}$	$\frac{1}{4}$	60	$2\frac{1}{2}$	$\frac{7}{16}$	$\frac{21}{32}$	$\frac{7}{16}$
C	$1\frac{1}{8}$	$\frac{5}{16}$	$\frac{15}{32}$	$\frac{5}{16}$	61	$2\frac{1}{2}$	$\frac{1}{2}$	$\frac{3}{4}$	$\frac{1}{2}$
19	$1\frac{1}{4}$	$\frac{3}{16}$	$\frac{9}{32}$	$\frac{3}{16}$	30	3	$\frac{3}{8}$	$\frac{9}{16}$	$\frac{3}{8}$
20	$1\frac{1}{4}$	$\frac{7}{32}$	$\frac{21}{64}$	$\frac{7}{32}$	31	3	$\frac{7}{16}$	$\frac{21}{32}$	$\frac{7}{16}$
21	$1\frac{1}{4}$	$\frac{1}{4}$	$\frac{3}{8}$	$\frac{1}{4}$	32	3	$\frac{1}{2}$	$\frac{3}{4}$	$\frac{1}{2}$
D	$1\frac{1}{4}$	$\frac{5}{16}$	$\frac{15}{32}$	$\frac{5}{16}$	33	3	$\frac{9}{16}$	$\frac{27}{32}$	$\frac{9}{16}$
E	$1\frac{1}{4}$	$\frac{3}{8}$	$\frac{9}{16}$	$\frac{3}{8}$	34	3	$\frac{5}{8}$	$\frac{15}{16}$	$\frac{5}{8}$

The length L may vary but should always be at least $2W$.

TABLE XV
Standard Taper Pins*

| No. of Pin | DIAMETER AT LARGE END | | MAX. LENGTH |
	D	D	L
00000	.094	$\frac{3}{32}$	$\frac{3}{4}$
0000	.109	$\frac{7}{64}$	$\frac{7}{8}$
000	.125	$\frac{1}{8}$	1
00	.141	$\frac{9}{64}$	$1\frac{1}{8}$
0	.156	$\frac{5}{32}$	$1\frac{1}{4}$
1	.172	$\frac{11}{64}$	$1\frac{1}{4}$
2	.193	$\frac{3}{16}$	$1\frac{1}{2}$
3	.219	$\frac{7}{32}$	$1\frac{3}{4}$
4	.250	$\frac{1}{4}$	2
5	.289	$\frac{19}{64}$	$2\frac{1}{4}$
6	.341	$\frac{11}{32}$	3
7	.409	$\frac{13}{32}$	$3\frac{3}{4}$
8	.492	$\frac{1}{2}$	$4\frac{1}{4}$
9	.591	$\frac{19}{32}$	$5\frac{1}{4}$
10	.706	$\frac{23}{32}$	6
11	.860	$\frac{55}{64}$	$7\frac{1}{4}$
12	1.032	$1\frac{1}{32}$	9
13	1.241	$1\frac{15}{64}$	11
14	1.523	$1\frac{33}{64}$	13

* Taper $\frac{1}{4}''$ per foot.

TABLE XVI
American Standard Wrought Iron and Steel Pipe

Nominal Size	Outside Diameter (All Weights)	Threads per Inch	Tap Drill Sizes[1]	Distance Pipe Enters Fitting	Nominal Wall Thickness		Extra Heavy		Double Extra Heavy[2]	
					Wrought Iron	Steel	Wrought Iron	Steel	Wrought Iron	Steel
$\frac{1}{8}$	.405	27	$\frac{11}{32}$	$\frac{5}{16}$	.070	.068	.098	.095	—	—
$\frac{1}{4}$	.540	18	$\frac{7}{16}$	$\frac{7}{16}$	.090	.088	.122	.119	—	—
$\frac{3}{8}$	.675	18	$\frac{19}{32}$	$\frac{7}{16}$	.093	.091	.129	.126	—	—
$\frac{1}{2}$	.840	14	$\frac{23}{32}$	$\frac{9}{16}$	.111	.109	.151	.147	.307	.294
$\frac{3}{4}$	1.050	14	$\frac{15}{16}$	$\frac{9}{16}$	.115	.113	.157	.154	.318	.308
1	1.315	11½	$1\frac{5}{32}$	$\frac{11}{16}$	.136	.133	.183	.179	.369	.358
1¼	1.660	11½	$1\frac{1}{2}$	$\frac{11}{16}$	.143	.140	.195	.191	.393	.382
1½	1.900	11½	$1\frac{23}{32}$	$\frac{11}{16}$	.148	.145	.204	.200	.411	.400
2	2.375	11½	$2\frac{3}{16}$	$\frac{3}{4}$	.158	.154	.223	.218	.447	.436
2½	2.875	8	$2\frac{5}{8}$	$1\frac{1}{16}$	.208	.203	.282	.276	.565	.552
3	3.500	8	$3\frac{1}{4}$	$1\frac{1}{8}$	.221	.216	.306	.300	.615	.600
3½	4.000	8	$3\frac{3}{4}$	$1\frac{3}{16}$	.231	.226	.325	.318	—	—
4	4.500	8	$4\frac{1}{4}$	$1\frac{3}{16}$	.242	.237	.344	.337	.690	.674
5	5.563	8	$5\frac{5}{16}$	$1\frac{5}{16}$	.263	.258	.383	.375	.768	.750
6	6.625	8	$6\frac{3}{8}$	$1\frac{3}{8}$	.286	.280	.441	.432	.884	.864
8	8.625	8	—	—	.329	.322	.510	.500	.895	.875

ASA B36.10-1939.
ASA B2.1-1945.
All dimensions in inches.
1. Not American Standard.
2. Not American Standard but is commercially available. See ASA B36.10-1939 for sizes larger than 8″.

TABLE XVII-A

Running and Sliding Fits[1]

Limits are in thousandths of an inch.

Limits for hole and shaft are applied algebraically to the basic size to obtain the limits of size for the parts. Symbols H5, g5, etc., are Hole and Shaft designations used in ABC System.[2]

Nominal Size Range Inches Over — To	Class RC 1			Class RC 2			Class RC 3			Class RC 4		
	Limits of Clearance	Hole H5	Shaft g4	Limits of Clearance	Hole H6	Shaft g5	Limits of Clearance	Hole H6	Shaft f6	Limits of Clearance	Hole H7	Shaft f7
0.04–0.12	0.1 / 0.45	+0.2 / 0	-0.1 / -0.25	0.1 / 0.55	+0.25 / 0	-0.1 / -0.3	0.3 / 0.8	+0.25 / 0	-0.3 / -0.55	0.3 / 1.1	+0.4 / 0	-0.3 / -0.7
0.12–0.24	0.15 / 0.5	+0.2 / 0	-0.15 / -0.3	0.15 / 0.65	+0.3 / 0	-0.15 / -0.35	0.4 / 1.0	+0.3 / 0	-0.4 / -0.7	0.4 / 1.4	+0.5 / 0	-0.4 / -0.9
0.24–0.40	0.2 / 0.6	+0.25 / 0	-0.2 / -0.35	0.2 / 0.85	+0.4 / 0	-0.2 / -0.45	0.5 / 1.3	+0.4 / 0	-0.5 / -0.9	0.5 / 1.7	+0.6 / 0	-0.5 / -1.1
0.40–0.71	0.25 / 0.75	+0.3 / 0	-0.25 / -0.45	0.25 / 0.95	+0.4 / 0	-0.25 / -0.55	0.6 / 1.4	+0.4 / 0	-0.6 / -1.0	0.6 / 2.0	+0.7 / 0	-0.6 / -1.3
0.71–1.19	0.3 / 0.95	+0.4 / 0	-0.3 / -0.55	0.3 / 1.2	+0.5 / 0	-0.3 / -0.7	0.8 / 1.8	+0.5 / 0	-0.8 / -1.3	0.8 / 2.4	+0.8 / 0	-0.8 / -1.6
1.19–1.97	0.4 / 1.1	+0.4 / 0	-0.4 / -0.7	0.4 / 1.4	+0.6 / 0	-0.4 / -0.8	1.0 / 2.2	+0.6 / 0	-1.0 / -1.6	1.0 / 3.0	+1.0 / 0	-1.0 / -2.0
1.97–3.15	0.4 / 1.2	+0.5 / 0	-0.4 / -0.7	0.4 / 1.6	+0.7 / 0	-0.4 / -0.9	1.2 / 2.6	+0.7 / 0	-1.2 / -1.9	1.2 / 3.6	+1.2 / 0	-1.2 / -2.4
3.15–4.73	0.5 / 1.5	+0.6 / 0	-0.5 / -0.9	0.5 / 2.0	+0.9 / 0	-0.5 / -1.1	1.4 / 3.2	+0.9 / 0	-1.4 / -2.3	1.4 / 4.2	+1.4 / 0	-1.4 / -2.8
4.73–7.09	0.6 / 1.8	+0.7 / 0	-0.6 / -1.1	0.6 / 2.3	+1.0 / 0	-0.6 / -1.3	1.6 / 3.6	+1.0 / 0	-1.6 / -2.6	1.6 / 4.8	+1.6 / 0	-1.6 / -3.2
7.09–9.85	0.6 / 2.0	+0.8 / 0	-0.6 / -1.2	0.6 / 2.6	+1.2 / 0	-0.6 / -1.4	2.0 / 4.4	+1.2 / 0	-2.0 / -3.2	2.0 / 5.6	+1.8 / 0	-2.0 / -3.8

[1] Extracted from ASA B4.1–1955 (Table 1).
[2] Data are in accordance with ABC agreements.
For diameters greater than 9.85 inches see standard.

TABLE XVII-A

Running and Sliding Fits (Cont.)

Limits are in thousandths of an inch.

Limits for hole and shaft are applied algebraically to the basic size to obtain the limits of size for the parts.

Symbols H7, e7, etc., are Hole and Shaft designations used in ABC System.

Nominal Size Range Inches Over To	Class RC 5			Class RC 6			Class RC 7			Class RC 8			Class RC 9		
	Limits of Clearance	Standard Limits		Limits of Clearance	Standard Limits		Limits of Clearance	Standard Limits		Limits of Clearance	Standard Limits		Limits of Clearance	Standard Limits	
		Hole H7	Shaft e7		Hole H8	Shaft e8		Hole H9	Shaft d8		Hole H10	Shaft c9		Hole H11	Shaft
0.04–0.12	0.6 / 1.4	+0.4 / 0	−0.6 / −1.0	0.6 / 1.8	+0.6 / 0	−0.6 / −1.2	1.0 / 2.6	+1.0 / 0	−1.0 / −1.6	2.5 / 5.1	+1.6 / 0	−2.5 / −3.5	4.0 / 8.1	+2.5 / 0	−4.0 / −5.6
0.12–0.24	0.8 / 1.8	+0.5 / 0	−0.8 / −1.3	0.8 / 2.2	+0.7 / 0	−0.8 / −1.5	1.2 / 3.1	+1.2 / 0	−1.2 / −1.9	2.8 / 5.8	+1.8 / 0	−2.8 / −4.0	4.5 / 9.3	+3.0 / 0	−4.5 / −6.0
0.24–0.40	1.0 / 2.2	+0.6 / 0	−1.0 / −1.6	1.0 / 2.8	+0.9 / 0	−1.0 / −1.9	1.6 / 3.9	+1.4 / 0	−1.6 / −2.5	3.0 / 6.6	+2.2 / 0	−3.0 / −4.4	5.0 / 10.7	+3.5 / 0	−5.0 / −7.2
0.40–0.71	1.2 / 2.6	+0.7 / 0	−1.2 / −1.9	1.2 / 3.2	+1.0 / 0	−1.2 / −2.2	2.0 / 4.6	+1.6 / 0	−2.0 / −3.0	3.5 / 7.9	+2.8 / 0	−3.5 / −5.1	6.0 / 12.8	+4.0 / 0	−6.0 / −8.8
0.71–1.19	1.6 / 3.2	+0.8 / 0	−1.6 / −2.4	1.6 / 4.0	+1.2 / 0	−1.6 / −2.8	2.5 / 5.7	+2.0 / 0	−2.5 / −3.7	4.5 / 10.0	+3.5 / 0	−4.5 / −6.5	7.0 / 15.5	+5.0 / 0	−7.0 / −10.5
1.19–1.97	2.0 / 4.0	+1.0 / 0	−2.0 / −3.0	2.0 / 5.2	+1.6 / 0	−2.0 / −3.6	3.0 / 7.1	+2.5 / 0	−3.0 / −4.6	5.0 / 11.5	+4.0 / 0	−5.0 / −7.5	8.0 / 18.0	+6.0 / 0	−8.0 / −12.0
1.97–3.15	2.5 / 4.9	+1.2 / 0	−2.5 / −3.7	2.5 / 6.1	+1.8 / 0	−2.5 / −4.3	4.0 / 8.8	+3.0 / 0	−4.0 / −5.8	6.0 / 13.5	+4.5 / 0	−6.0 / −9.0	9.0 / 20.5	+7.0 / 0	−9.0 / −13.5
3.15–4.73	3.0 / 5.8	+1.4 / 0	−3.0 / −4.4	3.0 / 7.4	+2.2 / 0	−3.0 / −5.2	5.0 / 10.7	+3.5 / 0	−5.0 / −7.2	7.0 / 15.5	+5.0 / 0	−7.0 / −10.5	10.0 / 24.0	+9.0 / 0	−10.0 / −15.0
4.73–7.09	3.5 / 6.7	+1.6 / 0	−3.5 / −5.1	3.5 / 8.5	+2.5 / 0	−3.5 / −6.0	6.0 / 12.5	+4.0 / 0	−6.0 / −8.5	8.0 / 18.0	+6.0 / 0	−8.0 / −12.0	12.0 / 28.0	+10.0 / 0	−12.0 / −18.0
7.09–9.85	4.0 / 7.6	+1.8 / 0	−4.0 / −5.8	4.0 / 9.6	+2.8 / 0	−4.0 / −6.8	7.0 / 14.3	+4.5 / 0	−7.0 / −9.8	10.0 / 21.5	+7.0 / 0	−10.0 / −14.5	15.0 / 34.0	+12.0 / 0	−15.0 / −22.0

TABLE XVII-B

Clearance Locational Fits[1]

Limits are in thousandths of an inch.

Limits for hole and shaft are applied algebraically to the basic size to obtain the limits of size for the parts.

Symbols H6, h5, etc., are Hole and Shaft designations used in ABC System.[2]

Nominal Size Range Inches (Over – To)	Class LC 1 Limits of Clearance	Class LC 1 Standard Limits Hole H6	Class LC 1 Standard Limits Shaft h5	Class LC 2 Limits of Clearance	Class LC 2 Standard Limits Hole H7	Class LC 2 Standard Limits Shaft h6	Class LC 3 Limits of Clearance	Class LC 3 Standard Limits Hole H8	Class LC 3 Standard Limits Shaft h7	Class LC 4 Limits of Clearance	Class LC 4 Standard Limits Hole H9	Class LC 4 Standard Limits Shaft h9	Class LC 5 Limits of Clearance	Class LC 5 Standard Limits Hole H7	Class LC 5 Standard Limits Shaft g6
0.04–0.12	0 / 0.45	+0.25 / −0	+0 / −0.2	0 / 0.65	+0.4 / −0	+0 / −0.25	0 / 1	+0.6 / −0	+0 / −0.4	0 / 2.0	+1.0 / −0	+0 / −1.0	0.1 / 0.75	+0.4 / −0	−0.1 / −0.35
0.12–0.24	0 / 0.5	+0.3 / −0	+0 / −0.2	0 / 0.8	+0.5 / −0	+0 / −0.3	0 / 1.2	+0.7 / −0	+0 / −0.5	0 / 2.4	+1.2 / −0	+0 / −1.2	0.15 / 0.95	+0.5 / −0	−0.15 / −0.45
0.24–0.40	0 / 0.65	+0.4 / −0	+0 / −0.25	0 / 1.0	+0.6 / −0	+0 / −0.4	0 / 1.5	+0.9 / −0	+0 / −0.6	0 / 2.8	+1.4 / −0	+0 / −1.4	0.2 / 1.2	+0.6 / −0	−0.2 / −0.6
0.40–0.71	0 / 0.7	+0.4 / −0	+0 / −0.3	0 / 1.1	+0.7 / −0	+0 / −0.4	0 / 1.7	+1.0 / −0	+0 / −0.7	0 / 3.2	+1.6 / −0	+0 / −1.6	0.25 / 1.35	+0.7 / −0	−0.25 / −0.65
0.71–1.19	0 / 0.9	+0.5 / −0	+0 / −0.4	0 / 1.3	+0.8 / −0	+0 / −0.5	0 / 2	+1.2 / −0	+0 / −0.8	0 / 4	+2.0 / −0	+0 / −2.0	0.3 / 1.6	+0.8 / −0	−0.3 / −0.8
1.19–1.97	0 / 1.0	+0.6 / −0	+0 / −0.4	0 / 1.6	+1.0 / −0	+0 / −0.6	0 / 2.6	+1.6 / −0	+0 / −1	0 / 5	+2.5 / −0	+0 / −2.5	0.4 / 2.0	+1.0 / −0	−0.4 / −1.0
1.97–3.15	0 / 1.2	+0.7 / −0	+0 / −0.5	0 / 1.9	+1.2 / −0	+0 / −0.7	0 / 3	+1.8 / −0	+0 / −1.2	0 / 6	+3 / −0	+0 / −3	0.4 / 2.3	+1.2 / −0	−0.4 / −1.1
3.15–4.73	0 / 1.5	+0.9 / −0	+0 / −0.6	0 / 2.3	+1.4 / −0	+0 / −0.9	0 / 3.6	+2.2 / −0	+0 / −1.4	0 / 7	+3.5 / −0	+0 / −3.5	0.5 / 2.8	+1.4 / −0	−0.5 / −1.4
4.73–7.09	0 / 1.7	+1.0 / −0	+0 / −0.7	0 / 2.6	+1.6 / −0	+0 / −1.0	0 / 4.1	+2.5 / −0	+0 / −1.6	0 / 8	+4 / −0	+0 / −4	0.6 / 3.2	+1.6 / −0	−0.6 / −1.6
7.09–9.85	0 / 2.0	+1.2 / −0	+0 / −0.8	0 / 3.0	+1.8 / −0	+0 / −1.2	0 / 4.6	+2.8 / −0	+0 / −1.8	0 / 9	+4.5 / −0	+0 / −4.5	0.6 / 3.6	+1.8 / −0	−0.6 / −1.8

[1] Extracted from ASA B4.1–1955 (Table 2).
[2] Data are in accordance with ABC agreements.
For diameters greater than 9.85 inches see standard.

TABLE XVII-B

Clearance Locational Fits (*Cont.*)

Limits are in thousandths of an inch.

Limits for hole and shaft are applied algebraically to the basic size to obtain the limits of size for the parts.

Symbols H8, f8, etc., are Hole and Shaft designations used in ABC System.

Nominal Size Range Inches Over To	Class LC 6 Limits of Clearance	Class LC 6 Standard Limits Hole H8	Class LC 6 Standard Limits Shaft f8	Class LC 7 Limits of Clearance	Class LC 7 Standard Limits Hole H9	Class LC 7 Standard Limits Shaft e9	Class LC 8 Limits of Clearance	Class LC 8 Standard Limits Hole H10	Class LC 8 Standard Limits Shaft d9	Class LC 9 Limits of Clearance	Class LC 9 Standard Limits Hole H11	Class LC 9 Standard Limits Shaft c11	Class LC 10 Limits of Clearance	Class LC 10 Standard Limits Hole H12	Class LC 10 Standard Limits Shaft	Class LC 11 Limits of Clearance	Class LC 11 Standard Limits Hole H13	Class LC 11 Standard Limits Shaft
0.04–0.12	0.3 1.5	+0.6 −0	−0.3 −0.9	0.6 2.6	+1.0 −0	−0.6 −1.6	1.0 2.0	+1.6 −0	−1.0 −2.0	2.5 7.5	+2.5 −0	−2.5 −5.0	4 12	+4 −0	−4 −8	5 17	+6 −0	−5 −11
0.12–0.24	0.4 1.8	+0.7 −0	−0.4 −1.1	0.8 3.2	+1.2 −0	−0.8 −2.0	1.2 4.2	+1.8 −0	−1.2 −2.4	2.8 8.8	+3.0 −0	−2.8 −5.8	4.5 14.5	+5 −0	−4.5 −9.5	6 20	+7 −0	−6 −13
0.24–0.40	0.5 2.3	+0.9 −0	−0.5 −1.4	1.0 3.8	+1.4 −0	−1.0 −2.4	1.6 5.2	+2.2 −0	−1.6 −3.0	3.0 10.0	+3.5 −0	−3.0 −6.5	5 17	+6 −0	−5 −11	7 25	+9 −0	−7 −16
0.40–0.71	0.6 2.6	+1.0 −0	−0.6 −1.6	1.2 4.4	+1.6 −0	−1.2 −2.8	2.0 6.4	+2.8 −0	−2.0 −3.6	3.5 11.5	+4.0 −0	−3.5 −7.5	6 20	+7 −0	−6 −13	8 28	+10 −0	−8 −18
0.71–1.19	0.8 3.2	+1.2 −0	−0.8 −2.0	1.6 5.6	+2.0 −0	−1.6 −3.6	2.5 8.0	+3.5 −0	−2.5 −4.5	4.5 14.5	+5.0 −0	−4.5 −9.5	7 23	+8 −0	−7 −15	10 34	+12 −0	−10 −22
1.19–1.97	1.0 4.2	+1.6 −0	−1.0 −2.6	2.0 7.0	+2.5 −0	−2.0 −4.5	3.6 9.5	+4.0 −0	−3.0 −5.5	5 17	+6 −0	−5 −11	8 28	+10 −0	−8 −18	12 44	+16 −0	−12 −28
1.97–3.15	1.2 4.8	+1.8 −0	−1.0 −3.0	2.5 8.5	+3.0 −0	−2.5 −5.5	4.0 11.5	+4.5 −0	−4.0 −7.0	6 20	+7 −0	−6 −13	10 34	+12 −0	−10 −22	14 50	+18 −0	−14 −32
3.15–4.73	1.4 5.8	+2.2 −0	−1.4 −3.6	3.0 10.0	+3.5 −0	−3.0 −6.5	5.0 13.5	+5.0 −0	−5.0 −8.5	7 25	+9 −0	−7 −16	11 39	+14 −0	−11 −25	16 60	+22 −0	−16 −38
4.73–7.09	1.6 6.6	+2.5 −0	−1.6 −4.1	3.5 11.5	+4.0 −0	−3.5 −7.5	6 16	+6 −0	−6 −10	8 28	+10 −0	−8 −18	12 44	+16 −0	−12 −28	18 68	+25 −0	−18 −43
7.09–9.85	2.0 7.6	+2.8 −0	−2.0 −4.8	4.0 13.0	+4.5 −0	−4.0 −8.5	7 18.5	+7 −0	−7 −11.5	10 34	+12 −0	−10 −22	16 52	+18 −0	−16 −34	22 78	+28 −0	−22 −50

TABLE XVII-C
Transition Locational Fits[1]

Limits are in thousandths of an inch.

Limits for hole and shaft are applied algebraically to the basic size to obtain the limits of size for the mating parts. "Fit" represents the maximum interference (minus values) and the maximum clearance (plus values).

Symbols H8, j6, etc., are Hole and Shaft designations used in ABC System.[2]

Nominal Size Range Inches Over To	Class LT 1			Class LT 2			Class LT 3			Class LT 4			Class LT 6			Class LT 7		
	Fit	Hole H7	Shaft j6	Fit	Hole H8	Shaft j7	Fit	Hole H7	Shaft k6	Fit	Hole H8	Shaft k7	Fit	Hole H8	Shaft m7	Fit	Hole H7	Shaft h6
0.04–0.12	−0.15 +0.5	+0.4 −0	+0.15 −0.1	−0.3 +0.7	+0.6 −0	+0.3 −0.1							−0.55 +0.45	+0.6 −0	+0.55 +0.15	−0.5 +0.15	+0.4 −0	+0.5 +0.25
0.12–0.24	−0.2 +0.6	+0.5 −0	+0.2 −0.1	−0.4 +0.8	+0.7 −0	+0.4 −0.1							−0.7 +0.5	+0.7 −0	+0.7 +0.2	−0.6 +0.2	+0.5 −0	+0.6 +0.3
0.24–0.40	−0.3 +0.7	+0.6 −0	+0.3 −0.1	−0.4 +1.1	+0.9 −0	+0.4 −0.2	−0.5 +0.5	+0.6 −0	+0.5 +0.1	−0.7 +0.8	+0.9 −0	+0.7 +0.1	−0.8 +0.7	+0.9 −0	+0.8 +0.2	−0.8 +0.2	+0.6 −0	+0.8 +0.4
0.40–0.71	−0.3 +0.8	+0.7 −0	+0.3 −0.1	−0.5 +1.2	+1.0 −0	+0.5 −0.2	−0.5 +0.6	+0.7 −0	+0.5 +0.1	−0.8 +0.9	+1.0 −0	+0.8 +0.1	−1.0 +0.7	+1.0 −0	+1.0 +0.3	−0.9 +0.2	+0.7 −0	+0.9 +0.5
0.71–1.19	−0.3 +1.0	+0.8 −0	+0.3 −0.2	−0.5 +1.5	+1.2 −0	+0.5 −0.3	−0.6 +0.7	+0.8 −0	+0.6 +0.1	−0.9 +1.1	+1.2 −0	+0.9 +0.1	−1.1 +0.9	+1.2 −0	+1.1 +0.3	−1.1 +0.2	+0.8 −0	+1.1 +0.6
1.19–1.97	−0.4 +1.2	+1.0 −0	+0.4 −0.2	−0.6 +2.0	+1.6 −0	+0.6 −0.4	−0.7 +0.9	+1.0 −0	+0.7 +0.1	−1.1 +1.5	+1.6 −0	+1.1 +0.1	−1.4 +1.2	+1.6 −0	+1.4 +0.4	−1.3 +0.3	+1.0 −0	+1.3 +0.7
1.97–3.15	−0.4 +1.5	+1.2 −0	+0.4 −0.3	−0.7 +2.3	+1.8 −0	+0.7 −0.5	−0.8 +1.1	+1.2 −0	+0.8 +0.1	−1.3 +1.7	+1.8 −0	+1.3 +0.1	−1.7 +1.3	+1.8 −0	+1.7 +0.5	−1.5 +0.4	+1.2 −0	+1.5 +0.8
3.15–4.73	−0.5 +1.8	+1.4 −0	+0.5 −0.4	−0.8 +2.8	+2.2 −0	+0.8 −0.6	−1.0 +1.3	+1.4 −0	+1.0 +0.1	−1.5 +2.1	+2.2 −0	+1.5 +0.1	−1.9 +1.7	+2.2 −0	+1.9 +0.5	−1.9 +0.4	+1.4 −0	+1.9 +1.0
4.73–7.09	−0.6 +2.0	+1.6 −0	+0.6 −0.4	−0.9 +3.2	+2.5 −0	+0.9 −0.7	−1.1 +1.5	+1.6 −0	+1.1 +0.1	−1.7 +2.4	+2.5 −0	+1.7 +0.1	−2.2 +1.9	+2.5 −0	+2.2 +0.6	−2.2 +0.4	+1.6 −0	+2.2 +1.2
7.09–9.85	−0.7 +2.3	+1.8 −0	+0.7 −0.5	−1.0 +3.6	+2.8 −0	+1.0 −0.8	−1.4 +1.6	+1.8 −0	+1.4 +0.2	−2.0 +2.6	+2.8 −0	+2.0 +0.2	−2.4 +2.2	+2.8 −0	+2.4 +0.6	−2.6 +0.4	+1.8 −0	+2.6 +1.4

[1] Extracted from ASA B4.1–1955 (Table 3).
[2] Data are in accordance with ABC agreements.
For diameters greater than 9.85 inches see standard.

TABLE XVII-D

Interference Locational Fits[1]
Limits are in thousandths of an inch.
Limits for hole and shaft are applied algebraically to the
basic size to obtain the limits of size for the parts.
Symbols H7, p6, etc., are Hole and Shaft designations
used in ABC System.[2]

Nominal Size Range Inches Over To	Class LN 2			Class LN 3		
	Limits of Interference	Standard Limits		Limits of Interference	Standard Limits	
		Hole H7	Shaft p6		Hole H7	Shaft r6
0.04–0.12	0	+0.4	+0.65	0.1	+0.4	+0.75
	0.65	− 0	+0.4	0.75	− 0	+0.5
0.12–0.24	0	+0.5	+0.8	0.1	+0.5	+0.9
	0.8	− 0	+0.5	0.9	− 0	+0.6
0.24–0.40	0	+0.6	+1.0	0.2	+0.6	+1.2
	1.0	− 0	+0.6	1.2	− 0	+0.8
0.40–0.71	0	+0.7	+1.1	0.3	+0.7	+1.4
	1.1	− 0	+0.7	1.4	− 0	+1.0
0.71–1.19	0	+0.8	+1.3	0.4	+0.8	+1.7
	1.3	− 0	+0.8	1.7	− 0	+1.2
1.19–1.97	0	+1.0	+1.6	0.4	+1.0	+2.0
	1.6	− 0	+1.0	2.0	− 0	+1.4
1.97–3.15	0.2	+1.2	+2.1	0.4	+1.2	+2.3
	2.1	− 0	+1.4	2.3	− 0	+1.6
3.15–4.73	0.2	+1.4	+2.5	0.6	+1.4	+2.9
	2.5	− 0	+1.6	2.9	− 0	+2.0
4.73–7.09	0.2	+1.6	+2.8	0.9	+1.6	+3.5
	2.8	− 0	+1.8	3.5	− 0	+2.5
7.09–9.85	0.2	+1.8	+3.2	1.2	+1.8	+4.2
	3.2	− 0	+2.0	4.2	− 0	+3.0

[1] Extracted from ASA B4.1–1955 (Table 4).
[2] Data are in accordance with ABC agreements.
For diameters greater than 9.85 inches see standard.

TABLE XVII-E
Force and Shrink Fits[1]

Limits are in thousandths of an inch.

Limits for hole and shaft are applied algebraically to the basic size to obtain the limits of size for the parts. Symbols H7, s6, etc., are Hole and Shaft designations used in ABC System.[2]

Nominal Size Range Inches Over To	Class FN 1			Class FN 2			Class FN 3			Class FN 4			Class FN 5		
	Limits of Interference	Standard Limits Hole H6	Standard Limits Shaft	Limits of Interference	Standard Limits Hole H7	Standard Limits Shaft s6	Limits of Interference	Standard Limits Hole H7	Standard Limits Shaft t6	Limits of Interference	Standard Limits Hole H7	Standard Limits Shaft u6	Limits of Interference	Standard Limits Hole H7	Standard Limits Shaft x7
0.04–0.12	0.05 / 0.5	+0.25 / −0	+0.5 / +0.3	0.2 / 0.85	+0.4 / −0	+0.85 / +0.6				0.3 / 0.95	+0.4 / −0	+0.95 / +0.7	0.5 / 1.3	+0.4 / −0	+1.3 / +0.9
0.12–0.24	0.1 / 0.6	+0.3 / −0	+0.6 / +0.4	0.2 / 1.0	+0.5 / −0	+1.0 / +0.7				0.4 / 1.2	+0.5 / −0	+1.2 / +0.9	0.7 / 1.7	+0.5 / −0	+1.7 / +1.2
0.24–0.40	0.1 / 0.75	+0.4 / −0	+0.75 / +0.5	0.4 / 1.4	+0.6 / −0	+1.4 / +1.0				0.6 / 1.6	+0.6 / −0	+1.6 / +1.2	0.8 / 2.0	+0.6 / −0	+2.0 / +1.4
0.40–0.56	0.1 / 0.8	+0.4 / −0	+0.8 / +0.5	0.5 / 1.6	+0.7 / −0	+1.6 / +1.2				0.7 / 1.8	+0.7 / −0	+1.8 / +1.4	0.9 / 2.3	+0.7 / −0	+2.3 / +1.6
0.56–0.71	0.2 / 0.9	+0.4 / −0	+0.9 / +0.6	0.5 / 1.6	+0.7 / −0	+1.6 / +1.2				0.7 / 1.8	+0.7 / −0	+1.8 / +1.4	1.1 / 2.5	+0.7 / −0	+2.5 / +1.8
0.71–0.95	0.2 / 1.1	+0.5 / −0	+1.1 / +0.7	0.6 / 1.9	+0.8 / −0	+1.9 / +1.4	0.8 / 2.1	+0.8 / −0	+2.1 / +1.6	0.8 / 2.1	+0.8 / −0	+2.1 / +1.6	1.4 / 3.0	+0.8 / −0	+3.0 / +2.2
0.95–1.19	0.3 / 1.2	+0.5 / −0	+1.2 / +0.8	0.6 / 1.9	+0.8 / −0	+1.9 / +1.4	0.8 / 2.1	+0.8 / −0	+2.1 / +1.6	1.0 / 2.3	+0.8 / −0	+2.3 / +1.8	1.7 / 3.3	+0.8 / −0	+3.3 / +2.5
1.19–1.58	0.3 / 1.3	+0.6 / −0	+1.3 / +0.9	0.8 / 2.4	+1.0 / −0	+2.4 / +1.8	0.8 / 2.4	+1.0 / −0	+2.6 / +2.0	1.5 / 3.1	+1.0 / −0	+3.1 / +2.5	2.0 / 4.0	+1.0 / −0	+4.0 / +3.0
1.58–1.97	0.4 / 1.4	+0.6 / −0	+1.4 / +1.0	0.8 / 2.4	+1.0 / −0	+2.4 / +1.8	1.2 / 2.8	+1.0 / −0	+2.8 / +2.2	1.8 / 3.4	+1.0 / −0	+3.4 / +2.8	3.0 / 5.0	+1.0 / −0	+5.0 / +4.0
1.97–2.56	0.6 / 1.8	+0.7 / −0	+1.8 / +1.3	0.8 / 2.7	+1.2 / −0	+2.7 / +2.0	1.3 / 3.2	+1.2 / −0	+3.2 / +2.5	2.3 / 4.2	+1.2 / −0	+4.2 / +3.5	3.8 / 6.2	+1.2 / −0	+6.2 / +5.0
2.56–3.15	0.7 / 1.9	+0.7 / −0	+1.9 / +1.4	1.0 / 2.9	+1.2 / −0	+2.9 / +2.2	1.8 / 3.7	+1.2 / −0	+3.7 / +3.0	2.8 / 4.7	+1.2 / −0	+4.7 / +4.0	4.8 / 7.2	+1.2 / −0	+7.2 / +6.0

[1] Extracted from ASA B4.1–1955 (Table 5).
[2] Data are in accordance with ABC agreements.
For diameters greater than 3.15 inches see standard.

TABLE XVIII

	Twist Drill Sizes*				
	Number Sizes			Letter Sizes	
No. Size	Decimal Equivalents	No. Size	Decimal Equivalents	Size Letter	Decimal Equivalents
1	.2280	41	.0960	A	.234
2	.2210	42	.0935	B	.238
3	.2130	43	.0890	C	.242
4	.2090	44	.0860	D	.246
5	.2055	45	.0820	E	.250
6	.2040	46	.0810	F	.257
7	.2010	47	.0785	G	.261
8	.1990	48	.0760	H	.266
9	.1960	49	.0730	I	.272
10	.1935	50	.0700	J	.277
11	.1910	51	.0670	K	.281
12	.1890	52	.0635	L	.290
13	.1850	53	.0595	M	.295
14	.1820	54	.0550	N	.302
15	.1800	55	.0520	O	.316
16	.1770	56	.0465	P	.323
17	.1730	57	.0430	Q	.332
18	.1695	58	.0420	R	.339
19	.1660	59	.0410	S	.348
20	.1610	60	.0400	T	.358
21	.1590	61	.0390	U	.368
22	.1570	62	.0380	V	.377
23	.1540	63	.0370	W	.386
24	.1520	64	.0360	X	.397
25	.1495	65	.0350	Y	.404
26	.1470	66	.0330	Z	.413
27	.1440	67	.0320		
28	.1405	68	.0310		
29	.1360	69	.0292		
30	.1285	70	.0280		
31	.1200	71	.0260		
32	.1160	72	.0250		
33	.1130	73	.0240		
34	.1110	74	.0225		
35	.1100	75	.0210		
36	.1065	76	.0200		
37	.1040	77	.0180		
38	.1015	78	.0160		
39	.0995	79	.0145		
40	.0980	80	.0135		

* Fraction size drills range in size from $\frac{1}{16}$–4″ and over in diameter—by 64ths.

TABLE XIX

Gage Number	(A) Brown & Sharpe or American	(B) American Steel & Wire Co.	(C) Piano Wire	(E) U.S. St'd.	Gage Number
0000000	.6513	.4900	....	.5000	0000000
000000	.5800	.4615	.004	.4688	000000
00000	.5165	.4305	.005	.4375	00000
0000	.4600	.3938	.006	.4063	0000
000	.4096	.3625	.007	.3750	000
00	.3648	.3310	.008	.3438	00
0	.3249	.3065	.009	.3125	0
1	.2893	.2830	.010	.2813	1
2	.2576	.2625	.011	.2656	2
3	.2294	.2437	.012	.2500	3
4	.2043	.2253	.013	.2344	4
5	.1819	.2070	.014	.2188	5
6	.1620	.1920	.016	.2031	6
7	.1443	.1770	.018	.1875	7
8	.1285	.1620	.020	.1719	8
9	.1144	.1483	.022	.1563	9
10	.1019	.1350	.024	.1406	10
11	.0907	.1205	.026	.1250	11
12	.0808	.1055	.029	.1094	12
13	.0720	.0915	.031	.0938	13
14	.0641	.0800	.033	.0781	14
15	.0571	.0720	.035	.0703	15
16	.0508	.0625	.037	.0625	16
17	.0453	.0540	.039	.0563	17
18	.0403	.0475	.041	.0500	18
19	.0359	.0410	.043	.0438	19
20	.0320	.0348	.045	.0375	20
21	.0285	.0317	.047	.0344	21
22	.0253	.0286	.049	.0313	22
23	.0226	.0258	.051	.0281	23
24	.0201	.0230	.055	.0250	24
25	.0179	.0204	.059	.0219	25
26	.0159	.0181	.063	.0188	26
27	.0142	.0173	.067	.0172	27
28	.0126	.0162	.071	.0156	28
29	.0113	.0150	.075	.0141	29
30	.0100	.0140	.080	.0125	30
31	.0089	.0132	.085	.0109	31
32	.0080	.0128	.090	.0102	32
33	.0071	.0118	.095	.0094	33
34	.0063	.0104	.100	.0086	34
35	.0056	.0095	.106	.0078	35
36	.0050	.0090	.112	.0070	36
37	.0045	.0085	.118	.0066	37
38	.0040	.0080	.124	.0063	38
39	.0035	.0075	.130	....	39
40	.0031	.0070	.138	....	40

(A) Standard in U.S. for sheet metal and wire (except steel & iron).
(B) Standard for iron and steel wire (U.S. Steel Wire Gage).
(C) American Steel and Wire Company's music (or piano) wire gage sizes. Recognized by U.S. Bureau of Standards.
(E) U.S. Standard for iron and steel plate. However, plate is now generally specified by its thickness in decimals of an inch.

TABLE XX
Trigonometric Functions

Angle	Sine	Cosine	Tan	Co-Tan	Angle
0°	0.0000	1.0000	0.0000	*Infin.*	90°
1°	0.0175	0.9998	0.0175	57.290	89°
2°	.0349	.9994	.0349	28.636	88°
3°	.0523	.9986	.0524	19.081	87°
4°	.0698	.9976	.0699	14.301	86°
5°	.0872	.9962	.0875	11.430	85°
6°	.1045	.9945	.1051	9.5144	84°
7°	.1219	.9925	.1228	8.1443	83°
8°	.1392	.9903	.1405	7.1154	82°
9°	.1564	.9877	.1584	6.3138	81°
10°	.1736	.9848	.1763	5.6713	80°
11°	.1908	.9816	.1944	5.1446	79°
12°	.2079	.9781	.2126	4.7046	78°
13°	.2250	.9744	.2309	4.3315	77°
14°	.2419	.9703	.2493	4.0108	76°
15°	.2588	.9659	.2679	3.7321	75°
16°	.2756	.9613	.2867	3.4874	74°
17°	.2924	.9563	.3057	3.2709	73°
18°	.3090	.9511	.3249	3.0777	72°
19°	.3256	.9455	.3443	2.9042	71°
20°	.3420	.9397	.3640	2.7475	70°
21°	.3584	.9336	.3839	2.6051	69°
22°	.3746	.9272	.4040	2.4751	68°
23°	.3907	.9205	.4245	2.3559	67°
24°	.4067	.9135	.4452	2.2460	66
25°	.4226	.9063	.4663	2.1445	65°
26°	.4384	.8988	.4877	2.0503	64°
27°	.4540	.8910	.5095	1.9626	63°
28°	.4695	.8829	.5317	1.8807	62°
29°	.4848	.8746	.5543	1.8040	61°
30°	.5000	.8660	.5774	1.7321	60°
31°	.5150	.8572	.6009	1.6643	59°
32°	.5299	.8480	.6249	1.6003	58°
33°	.5446	.8387	.6494	1.5399	57°
34°	.5592	.8290	.6745	1.4826	56°
35°	.5736	.8192	.7002	1.4281	55°
36°	.5878	.8090	.7265	1.3764	54°
37°	.6018	.7986	.7536	1.3270	53°
38°	.6157	.7880	.7813	1.2799	52°
39°	.6293	.7771	.8098	1.2349	51°
40°	.6428	.7660	.8391	1.1918	50°
41°	.6561	.7547	.8693	1.1504	49°
42°	.6691	.7431	.9004	1.1106	48°
43°	.6820	.7314	.9325	1.0724	47°
44°	.6947	.7193	.9657	1.0355	46°
45°	.7071	.7071	1.0000	1.0000	45°
Angle	Cosine	Sine	Co-Tan	Tan	Angle

TABLE XXI
Abbreviations and Symbols

Alternating current	a-c	Lateral	lat.
Aluminum	Al.	Long	lg.
American Standard	Am. Std.	Longitudinal	long.
Approved	App.	Linear foot	lin. ft.
Average	avg.	Machine	mach.
Ball bearing	bb	Malleable iron	Mal. I.
Brown & Sharpe	B & S	Material	mat.
Babbitt	Bab.	Maximum	max.
Brass	Br.	Meter	m.
Bronze	Bro.	Mile	mile
Brinell hardness number	Bhn.	Millimeter	mm.
Cast iron	C.I.	Miles per hour	mph
Center line	CL or ₵	Minimum	min.
Center to center	c to c.	Minute (angular measure)	'
Centimeter	cm.	Minute (time)	min.
Chemical	chem.	Outside diameter	O.D.
Circular	cir.	Pattern	patt.
Circular pitch	CP	Phosphor bronze	Phos. Bro.
Copper	Cop.	Piece	pc.
Cold rolled steel	C.R.S.	Pitch	P
Counterbore	c'bore	Pitch diameter	P.D.
Countersink	c's'k	Plate	pl.
Cubic	cu.	Pound	# or lb.
Cubic inch	cu.in.	Pounds per square foot	lb.per.sq.ft.
Cubic foot	cu.ft.	Pounds per square inch	lb.per.sq.in.
Cubic yard	cu.yd.	Pratt & Whitney	P & W.
Cylinder	cyl.	Quantity	quan.
Degree	deg. or °	Radius	R or Rad.
Diameter	D., Dia., or Diam.	Required	req. or req'd.
Direct current	d-c	Revolution per minute	rpm
Diagonal	diag.	Right hand	R.H.
Diametral pitch	DP	Round	rd.
Drawing	Dwg.	Round bar	ϕ
Drawn	Dr.	Screw	sc.
Detail drawing	Dtl.dwg.	Second (time)	sec.
Efficiency	eff.	Second (angular measure)	"
Electric	elec.	Section	sec.
Engineer	engr.	Society of Automotive Engineers	SAE
External	ext.	Square	sq.
Fabricate	fab.	Square inch	sq.in.
Fillister	fil.	Square foot	sq.ft.
Finish	fin.	Standard	std.
Foot	ft. or '	Steel	Stl.
Gallon	gal.	Steel casting	Stl.C.
Galvanized iron	G.I.	Thousand	M
Grind	G or gr.	Ton	ton
Harden	hdn.	Thread	thd.
Hexagonal	hex.	Traced	Tr.
Horsepower	hp.	Volt	v
Hour	hr.	Watt	w
Impregnate	impreg.	Weight	wt.
Inch	in. or "	Woodruff key	Wdrf. key
Inside Diameter	I. D.	Wrought iron	W. I.
Internal	int.	Yard	yd.
Left hand	L.H.	Year	yr.

ASA STANDARDS

A few of the more than 500 standards approved by the American Standards Association are listed below. Copies may be obtained from the Association's offices at 29 West 39th Street, New York, N. Y.

A13–1928	Identification of Piping Systems, Scheme for
B1.1–1949	Unified and American Screw Threads for Screws, Bolts, Nuts, and Other Threaded Parts
B1.2–1951	Screw Thread Gages and Gaging
B1.5–1952	Acme Screw Threads
B2.1–1945	Pipe Threads
B4.1–1955	Preferred Limits and Fits for Cylindrical Parts
B5.6-1941	Jig Bushings
B5.10–1953	Machine Tapers, Self-holding and Steep Taper Series
B5.15–1950	Involute Splines, Side Bearing
B5.20–1954	Machine Pins
B6.1–1932	Spur Gear Tooth Form
B16.1–1948	Cast-Iron Pipe Flanges and Flanged Fittings, Class 125
B16b–1944	Cast-Iron Pipe Flanges and Flanged Fittings for Maximum WSP of 250 lb
B16b2–1931	Cast-Iron Pipe Flanges and Flanged Fittings for Maximum WSP of 25 lb
B16.3–1951	Malleable-Iron Screwed Fittings, 150 lb
B16.4–1949	Cast-Iron Screwed Fittings for Maximum WSP of 125 and 250 lb
B16.5–1953	Steel Pipe Flanges and Flanged Fittings
B16.9–1951	Steel Butt-Welding Fittings
B16.10–1939	Face-to-Face Dimensions of Ferrous Flanged and Welding End Valves
B17c–1927	Transmission Shafting, Code for Design of
B17f–1930	Woodruff Keys, Keyslots, and Cutters
B17.1–1943	Shafting and Stock Keys
B18.1–1953	Small Solid Rivets
B18.2–1955	Square and Hexagon Bolts and Nuts
B18.3-1954	Socket Set Screws and Socket Head Cap Screws
B18.4–1950	Large Rivets
B18.5-1952	Round Head Bolts
B18.6–1947	Slotted and Recessed Head Screws, Machine, Cap, Wood, Tapping, and Slotted Headless Type
B36.1–1950	Welded and Seamless Steel Pipe (ASTM A53-44)
B36.2–1950	Welded Wrought-Iron Pipe
B36.10–1950	Wrought-Iron and Wrought-Steel Pipe
B45.1–1932	Foundry Patterns of Wood (CS 19-32)
B48.1–1933	Inch-Millimeter Conversion for Industrial Use
Z10.1–1941	Abbreviations for Scientific and Engineering Terms*
Z10.5–1949	Electrical Quantities, Letter Symbols for*
Z14.1–1946	Drawings and Drafting Room Practice (Under revision)*
Z15.1–1932	Engineering and Scientific Charts for Lantern Slides*
Z15.2–1938	Time-Series Charts, Manual of Design and Construction*
Z15.3–1943	Engineering and Scientific Graphs for Publications*
Z32.2.1–1949	Welding Symbols and Instructions for Their Use R 1953*
Y32.2–1954	Graphical Symbols for Electrical Diagrams
Z32.3–1946	Graphical Symbols for Power Control and Measurement*
Z32.5–1944	Symbols for Telephone, Telegraph, and Radio Use*

* Y is the new letter assigned to standards for abbreviations, charts and graphs, drawings, graphical symbols, and letter symbols. The Z will be changed to Y as the standards are revised and reaffirmed.

GLOSSARY OF COMMON SHOP TERMS

Anneal (*v*). To heat a piece of metal to a particular temperature and then allow it to cool slowly to remove internal stresses.

Bore (*v*). To enlarge a hole using a boring bar in order to make it smooth, round, and co-axial. Boring is usually done on a lathe or boring mill.

Boss (*n*). A circular projection that is raised above a principal surface of a casting or forging.

Braze (*v*). To join two pieces of metal by the use of hard solder. The solder is usually a copper-zinc alloy.

Broach (*v*). To machine a hole to a desired shape, usually other than round. The cutting tool, known as a broach, is pushed or pulled through the rough finished hole. It has transverse cutting edges.

Burnish (*v*). To smooth or apply a brilliant finish.

Bushing (*n*). A removable cylindrical sleeve which is used to provide a bearing surface.

Carburize (*v*). To harden the surface of a piece of low grade steel by heating in a carbonizing material to increase the carbon content and then quenching.

Caseharden (*v*). To harden a surface as described above or through the use of potassium cyanide.

Chamfer (*v*). To bevel an external edge or corner.

Chase (*v*). To cut screw threads on a lathe using a chaser, a tool shaped to the profile of a thread.

Chill (*v*). To cool the surface of a casting suddenly so that the surface will be white and hard.

Chip (*v*). To cut away or remove surface defects with a chisel.

Color-harden (*v*). See caseharden. A piece is color-hardened mainly for the sake of appearance.

Core (*v*). To form a hole or hollow cavity in a casting through the use of a core.

Counterbore (*v*). To enlarge the end of a cylindrical hole to a certain depth, as is often done to accommodate the head of a fillister head screw. (*n*) The name of the tool used to produce the enlargement.

Countersink (*v*). To form a conical enlargement at the end of a cylindrical hole to accommodate the head of a screw or rivet. (*n*) The name of the tool used to form a conical shaped enlargement.

Crown (*n*). The angular or curved contour of the outer surface of a part such as on a pulley.

Die (*n*). A metal block used for forming or stamping operations. A thread-cutting tool for producing external threads.

Die Casting (*n*). A casting which has been produced by forcing a molten alloy having an aluminum, copper, zinc, tin, or lead base into a metal mold composed of two halves.

Die Stamping (*n*). A piece which has been cut or formed from sheet metal through the use of a die.

Draw (*v*). To form metal, which may be either cold or hot, by a distorting or stretching process. To temper steel by gradual or intermittent quenching.

Drill (*v*). To form a cylindrical hole in metal. (*n*) A revolving cutting tool designed for cutting at the point.

Drop Forging (*n*). A piece formed while hot between two dies under a drop hammer.

Face (*v*). To machine on a lathe a flat face which is perpendicular to the axis of rotation of the piece.

Feather (*n*). A rectangular sliding key which permits a pulley to move along the shaft parallel to its axis.

File (*v*). To shape, finish, or trim with a fine-toothed metal cutting tool that is used with the hands.

Fillet (*n*). A rounded filling which increases the strength at the junction of two surfaces which form an internal angle.

Fit (*n*). The tightness of adjustment between the contacting surfaces of mating parts.

Flange (*n*). The top and bottom member of a beam. A projecting rim added on the end of a pipe or fitting for making a connection.

Forge (*v*). To shape hot metals by hammering, using a hand-hammer or machine.

Galvanize (*v*). To coat steel or iron by immersion in a bath of zinc.

Graduate (*v*). To mark off or divide a scale into intervals.

Grind (*v*). To finish a surface through the action of a revolving abrasive wheel.

Key (*n*). A piece used between a shaft and a hub to prevent the movement of one relative to the other.

Keyway or Keyseat (*n*). A longitudinal groove cut in a shaft or a hub to receive a key. A key rests in a keyseat and slides in a keyway.

Knurl (*v*). To roughen a cylindrical surface to produce a better grip for the fingers.

Lap (*v*). To finish or polish with a piece of soft metal, wood, or leather impregnated with an abrasive.

Lug (*n*). A projection or ear which has been cast or forged as a portion of a piece to provide a support or to allow the attachment of another part.

Malleable Casting (*n*). A casting which has been annealed to toughen it.

Mill (*v*). To machine a piece on a milling machine by means of a rotating toothed cutter.

Neck (*v*). To cut a circumferential groove around a shaft.

Pack-harden (*v*). To case-carburize and harden.

Peen (*v*). To stretch or bend over metal using the peen end (ball end) of a hammer.

Pickle (*v*). To remove scale and rust from a casting or forging by immersing it in an acid bath.

Plane (*v*). To machine a flat surface on a planer, a machine having a fixed tool and a reciprocating bed.

Polish (*v*). To make a surface smooth and lustrous through the use of a fine abrasive.

Punch (*v*). To perforate a thin piece of metal by shearing out a circular wad with a non-rotating tool under pressure.

Ream (*v*). To finish a hole to an exact size using a rotating fluted cutting tool known as a reamer.

Rivet (*n*). A headed shank which more or less permanently unites two pieces. (*v*) To fasten steel plates with rivets.

Round (*n*). A rounded external corner on a casting.

Sandblast (*v*). To clean the surface of castings or forgings by means of sand forced from a nozzle at a high velocity.

Shear (*v*). To cut off sheet or bar metal through the shearing action of two blades.

Shim (*n*). A thin metal plate which is inserted between two surfaces for the purpose of adjustment.

Spline (*n*). A keyway, usually for a feather key. See feather.

Spotface (*v*). To finish a round spot on the rough surface of a casting at a drilled hole for the purpose of providing a smooth seat for a bolt or screw head.

Spot Weld (*v*). To weld two overlapping metal sheets in spots by means of the heat of resistance to an electric current between a pair of electrodes.

Steel Casting (*n*). A casting made of cast iron to which scrap steel has been added.

Swage (*v*). To form metal with a "swage block," a tool so constructed that through hammering or pressure the work may be made to take a desired shape.

Sweat (*v*). To solder together by clamping the pieces in contact with soft solder between and then heating.

Tack weld (*n*). A weld of short intermittent sections.

Tap (*v*). To cut an internal thread, by hand or with power, by screwing into the hole a fluted tapered tool having thread-cutting edges.

Temper (*v*). To reduce the hardness of a piece of hardened steel through reheating and sudden quenching.

Template (*n*). A pattern cut to a desired shape which is used in layout work to establish shearing lines, to locate holes, etc.

Tumble (*v*). To clean and smooth castings and forgings through contact in a revolving barrel. To further the results, small pieces of scrap are added.

Turn (*v*). To turn-down or machine a cylindrical surface on a lathe.

Upset (*v*). To increase the diameter or form a shoulder on a piece during forging.

Weld (*v*). To join two pieces of metal by pressure or hammering after heating to the fusion point.

BIBLIOGRAPHY OF ENGINEERING DRAWING AND
ALLIED SUBJECTS

Aeronautical Drafting and Engineering

Anderson, N. H., *Aircraft Layout and Detail Design.* McGraw-Hill.

Apalategui, J. J., *Aircraft Analytic Geometry with Applications to Aircraft.* Macmillan.

Faulconer, T. P., *Introduction to Aircraft Design.* McGraw-Hill.

Katz, H. H., *Aircraft Drafting.* Macmillan.

Leavell, S. and Bungay, S., *Aircraft Production Standards.* McGraw-Hill.

LeMaster, C. A., *Aircraft Sheet Metal Work.* American Technical Society.

Meadowcroft, N., *Aircraft Detail Drafting.* McGraw-Hill.

Nelson, W., *Airplane Lofting.* McGraw-Hill.

Svensen, C. L., *A Manual of Aircraft Drafting.* Van Nostrand.

Tharratt, G., *Aircraft Production Illustration.* McGraw-Hill.

Castings

Campbell, H. I., *Metal Castings.* Wiley.

Descriptive Geometry

Bradley, H. C. and Uhler, E. H., *Descriptive Geometry for Engineers.* International.

Grant, H. E., *Practical Descriptive Geometry.* McGraw-Hill.

Hood, G. J., *Geometry of Engineering Drawing.* McGraw-Hill.

Larkins, J. T., Jr., *Descriptive Geometry.* Prentice-Hall.

Levens, A. S. and Eggers, H., *Descriptive Geometry.* Harper.

Street, W. E., *Technical Descriptive Geometry.* Van Nostrand.

Warner, F. M., *Applied Descriptive Geometry.* McGraw-Hill.

Watts, E. F. and Rule, J. T., *Descriptive Geometry.* Prentice-Hall.

Wellman, B. L., *Technical Descriptive Geometry.* McGraw-Hill.

Die Casting

Chase, H., *Die Castings.* Wiley.

Engineering Drawing

French, T. E. and Vierck, C. J., *Engineering Drawing.* McGraw-Hill.

Giesecke, F. E., Mitchell, A., and Spencer, H. C., *Technical Drawing.* Macmillan.

Hesse, H. C., *A Manual in Engineering Drawing.* Macmillan.

Hobart, D. E., *Engineering Drawing.* Heath.

Hoelscher, R. P. and others, *Industrial Production Illustration.* McGraw-Hill.

Hoelscher, R. P. and Springer, C. H., *Engineering Drawing and Geometry.* Wiley.

Luzadder, W. J., *Fundamentals of Engineering Drawing*, 3rd ed. Prentice-Hall.

———, *Technical Drafting Essentials*, 2nd ed. Prentice-Hall.

Orth, H. D., Worsencroft, R. R., and Doke, H. B., *Basic Engineering Drawing.* Ronald.

Radzinsky, H., *Making Patent Drawings*. Macmillan.

Sahag, L. M., *Engineering Drawing*. Ronald.

Schumann, C. H., *Technical Drafting*. Harper.

Svensen, C. L., *Drafting for Engineers*. Van Nostrand.

————, *Essentials of Drafting*, 3rd ed. Van Nostrand.

Thayer, H. R., *Industrial Drawing*. McGraw-Hill.

Turner, W. W. and others, *Basic Engineering Drawing*. Ronald.

Zozzoro, F., *Engineering Drawing*. McGraw-Hill.

Graphical Representation and Computation

Adams, D. P., *Index of Nomograms*. Wiley.

Davis, D. S., *Empirical Equations and Nomography*. McGraw-Hill.

Douglass, R. D. and Adams, D. P., *Elements of Nomography*. McGraw-Hill.

Hoelscher, R. P., Arnold, J. N., and Pierce, S. H., *Graphic Aids in Engineering Computations*. McGraw-Hill.

Karsten, K. G., *Charts and Graphs*. Prentice-Hall.

Levens, A. S., *Nomography*. Wiley.

————, *Graphics in Engineering and Science*. Wiley.

Lipka, J., *Graphical and Mechanical Computation*. Wiley.

Mackey, C. O., *Graphic Solutions*. Wiley.

Malcolm, C. W., *Graphic Statics*. McGraw-Hill.

Mavis, F. T., *The Construction of Nomographic Charts*. International.

Handbooks

Colvin, F. H., *Aircraft Handbook*. McGraw-Hill.

————, and Stanley, F. A., *American Machinists Handbook and Dictionary of Shop Terms*. McGraw-Hill.

Kent, W., *Mechanical Engineers Handbook*. Wiley.

Lawle, F. F., *Standard Handbook for Electrical Engineers*. McGraw-Hill.

Machinery Handbook. Industrial Press.

Marks, L. S., *Mechanical Engineers Handbook*. McGraw-Hill.

Merriman, T., *American Civil Engineers Handbook*. Wiley.

O'Rourke, C. E., *General Engineering Handbook*. McGraw-Hill.

Perry, J. H., *Chemical Engineers Handbook*. McGraw-Hill.

Steel Construction. American Institute of Steel Construction.

Tool Engineers Handbook. Am. Soc. of Tool Engineers.

Walker, J. H., Crocker, S., and Allen, J. R., *Piping Handbook*. McGraw-Hill.

Jig and Fixture Design

Bryant, L. A. and Dickinson, T. A., *Jigs and Fixtures*. Pitman.

Colvin, F. H. and Haas, L. L., *Jigs and Fixtures*. McGraw-Hill.

Hinman, C. W., *Die Engineering Layouts and Formulas*. McGraw-Hill.

Jones, F. D., *Jig and Fixture Design*. Industrial Press.

Lettering

De Garmo, E. P. and Jonassen, F., *Technical Lettering.* Macmillan.

French, T. E. and Turnbill, W. D., *Lessons in Lettering*, Vols. 1 and 2. McGraw-Hill.

Machine Design

Faires, V. M., *Design of Machine Elements.* Macmillan.

Maleev, V. L., *Machine Design.* International.

Norman, C. A., Ault, E. S., and Zarobsky, I. F., *Fundamentals of Machine Design.* Macmillan.

Sahag, L. M., *Kinematics of Machines.* Ronald.

Spotts, M. F., *Design of Machine Elements*, 2nd ed. Prentice-Hall.

Machine Drawing

Lent, D., *Machine Drawing.* Prentice-Hall.

Svensen, C. L., *Machine Drawing.* Van Nostrand.

Map and Topographic Drawing

Deetz, C. H., *Cartography.* U. S. Printing Office.

Greitzer, S. L., *Elementary Topography and Map Reading.* McGraw-Hill.

Hinks, A. R., *Maps and Surveys.* Cambridge, (Macmillan).

Sloane, R. C. and Montz, I. M., *Elements of Topographic Drawing.* McGraw-Hill.

Pattern Design

Hall, B. R. and Kiley, H. E., *Pattern Design.* International.

Perspective

Brahdy, J., *Perspective Drawing.* Macmillan.

Everett, H. E. and Lawrence, W. H., *Freehand and Perspective Drawing.* American Technical Society.

Lawson, P. J., *Practical Perspective Drawing.* McGraw-Hill.

Lubschez, B. J., *Perspective.* Van Nostrand.

Turner, W. W., *Simplified Perspective.* Ronald.

Pipe

Crocker, S., *Piping Hand Book.* McGraw-Hill.

Day, L. J., *Standard Plumbing Details.* Wiley.

Svensen, C. L., *A Handbook on Piping.* Van Nostrand.

Sheet-metal Work

Atkins, E. A., *Practical Sheet and Plate Metal Work.* Pitman.

Frazer, R. H. and Berthiaume, O., *Practical Aircraft Sheet-metal Work.* McGraw-Hill.

Norcross, C. and Quinn, J. D., *How to Do Aircraft Sheet-metal Work.* McGraw-Hill.

O'Rourke, F. J., *Sheet-metal Pattern Drafting.* McGraw-Hill.

Shop Practice

Begeman, M. L., *Manufacturing Processes*. Wiley.

Boston, O. W., *Engineering Shop Practice*, Vol. 1. Wiley.

————, *Metal Processing*. Wiley.

Campbell, H. L., *The Working, Heating, Treating, and Welding of Steel*. Wiley.

Marek, C. T., *The Production and Design of Castings*. Wiley.

Wendt, R. E., *Foundry Work*. McGraw-Hill.

Young, J. F., *Materials and Processes*. Wiley.

Sketching

Katz, H., *Technical Sketching*. Macmillan.

Turner, W. W., *Freehand Sketching for Engineers*. Ronald.

Zipprich, A. E., *Freehand Drafting*. Van Nostrand.

Structural Drafting

Bishop, C. T., *Structural Drafting*. Wiley.

Technical Dictionary

Tweney, C. F. and Hughes, L. E. C., *Chambers Technical Dictionary*. Macmillan.

Tool Design

Cole, C. B., *Tool Design*. American Technical Society.

Donaldson, C. and LeCain, G. H., *Tool Design*. Harper.

Doyle, L. E., *Tool Engineering*. Prentice-Hall.

Welding

Churchill, H. D. and Austin, J. B., *Weld Design*. Prentice-Hall.

Elzea, L. S., *Aircraft Welding*. McGraw-Hill.

Lincoln Electric Co., *Simple Blueprint Reading*. Cleveland.

Lincoln Electric Co., *Procedure Handbook of Arc Welding Design and Practice*. Cleveland.

Index